FOUNDATIONS
OF MATHEMATICS

10

SECOND EDITION

THE McGRAW-HILL RYERSON MATHEMATICS PROGRAM

MATH 1 SOURCE BOOK
MATH 2 SOURCE BOOK
MATH 3
MATH 4
MATH 5
MATH 6

LIFE MATH 1
LIFE MATH 2
LIFE MATH 3

INTERMEDIATE MATHEMATICS 1
INTERMEDIATE MATHEMATICS 2
INTERMEDIATE MATHEMATICS 3

APPLIED MATHEMATICS 9
APPLIED MATHEMATICS 10
APPLIED MATHEMATICS 11
APPLIED MATHEMATICS 12

FOUNDATIONS OF MATHEMATICS 9
FOUNDATIONS OF MATHEMATICS 10
FOUNDATIONS OF MATHEMATICS 11
FOUNDATIONS OF MATHEMATICS 12

TEACHER'S EDITIONS FOR:
MATH 3
MATH 4
MATH 5
MATH 6
INTERMEDIATE MATHEMATICS 1
INTERMEDIATE MATHEMATICS 2
INTERMEDIATE MATHEMATICS 3
APPLIED MATHEMATICS 9
FOUNDATIONS OF MATHEMATICS 9

TEACHER'S GUIDES FOR:
AM 10
AM 11
AM 12
FM 10
FM 11
FM 12

FOUNDATIONS
OF MATHEMATICS

SECOND EDITION

Dino Dottori, B.Sc., M.S.Ed.
George Knill, B.Sc., M.S.Ed.
James Stewart, Ph.D.
Gerry Gadoury, B.A., B.Ed.

Consultant
Dennis Braun, B.A., B.Ed.

McGRAW-HILL RYERSON LIMITED

TORONTO MONTREAL NEW YORK AUCKLAND BOGOTÁ CAIRO CARACAS HAMBURG
LISBON LONDON MADRID MEXICO MILAN NEW DELHI PANAMA PARIS
SAN JUAN SÃO PAULO SINGAPORE SYDNEY TOKYO

FOUNDATIONS OF MATHEMATICS 10
SECOND EDITION

Copyright © McGraw-Hill Ryerson Limited, 1987, 1977. All rights
reserved. No part of this publication may be reproduced, stored in a
retrieval system, or transmitted, in any form, or by any means,
mechanical, electronic, photocopying, recording, or otherwise, without
the prior written permission of McGraw-Hill Ryerson Limited.

ISBN 0-07-548728-4

8 9 10 11 12 13 14   BG   0 9 8 7 6 5 4

Cover Art Direction/Display Headings by Dan Kewley
Cover Design by Marc Mireault
Cover Photography by Imtek Imagineering
Technical Illustrations by Frank Zsigo

A complete list of notes and photo credits appears on page 562.

Printed and bound in Canada

Canadian Cataloguing in Publication Data
Main entry under title:
Foundations of mathematics 10

(McGraw-Hill Ryerson mathematics program)
ISBN 0-07-548728-4

1. Mathematics — 1961-   . I. Dottori, Dino, date — . II. Series.
QA39.2.F68 1987   512.14   C87-093163-6

Communications Branch, Consumer and Corporate Affairs has granted
permission for the use of the National Symbol for Metric Conversion.

Care has been taken to trace ownership of copyright material
contained in this text. The publishers will gladly take any information
that will enable them to rectify any reference or credit in
subsequent editions.

TABLE OF CONTENTS

REAL NUMBERS

CHAPTER

God made the integers, all the rest is the work of man or mankind.

L. Kronecker

REVIEW AND PREVIEW TO CHAPTER 1

DECIMALS
ROUNDING

The following table shows how we use the rules for rounding off.

Rules	Numbers	Required Place	Key Digit	Rounded Number
If the key digit is less than 5, we round down.	26 632	nearest 100	26 6$\overset{3}{}$2	26 600
	5278	nearest 1000	5$\overset{2}{}$78	5000
	27.51	nearest tenth	27.5$\overset{1}{}$	27.5
If the key digit is greater than 5, we round up.	7368	nearest 10	736$\overset{8}{}$	7370
	31 493	nearest 100	31 4$\overset{9}{}$3	31 500
	241.86	nearest tenth	241.8$\overset{6}{}$	241.9
If the key digit is 5 followed by nonzero digits, we round up.	7523	nearest 1000	7$\overset{5}{}$23	8000
	36 251	nearest 100	36 2$\overset{5}{}$1	36 300
	9.254	nearest tenth	9.2$\overset{5}{}$4	9.3
	0.0856	nearest hundredth	0.08$\overset{5}{}$6	0.09
If the key digit is 5 followed only by zeros, we round to the nearest even digit.	4500	nearest 1000	4$\overset{5}{}$00	4000
	3500	nearest 1000	3$\overset{5}{}$00	4000
	65 000	nearest 10 000	6$\overset{5}{}$000	60 000
	42.15	nearest tenth	42.1$\overset{5}{}$	42.2
	9.365	nearest hundredth	9.36$\overset{5}{}$	9.36

EXERCISE

1. Round to the nearest ten.
   (a) 32.75   (b) 127.9
   (c) 3276.09   (d) 176.91

2. Round to the nearest tenth.
   (a) 14.17   (b) 213.15
   (c) 147.525   (d) 0.314

3. Round to the nearest hundredth.
   (a) 3.125   (b) 5.144
   (c) 63.2151   (d) 143.189

4. Calculate and round to the nearest tenth.
   (a) 3.125 + 42.53 + 0.65 + 5.2701
   (b) 13.21 + 2.793 + 20.7 + 0.02
   (c) 31.375 − 28.5
   (d) 142.7 − 44.36
   (e) 4.6 × 19.93
   (f) 0.3825 × 5.25
   (g) 135.45 ÷ 45.5
   (h) 347.19 ÷ 2.1

5. Express as decimals.
   (a) $\frac{1}{2}$ (b) $\frac{1}{4}$ (c) $\frac{3}{4}$ (d) $\frac{1}{5}$ (e) $\frac{3}{5}$
   (f) $\frac{3}{8}$ (g) $\frac{5}{8}$ (h) $2\frac{1}{8}$ (i) $3\frac{4}{5}$ (j) $4\frac{7}{8}$

6. Express as common fractions.
   (a) 0.35   (b) 0.75
   (c) 0.42   (d) 0.611
   (e) 0.525   (f) 0.037

LE SYSTÈME INTERNATIONAL D'UNITÉS: SI

SI is the international system of units of measurement.

The metre (m) is an SI unit for length.

The square metre (m²) is an SI unit for area.

The cubic metre (m³) and the litre (L) are SI units for volume or capacity.

The gram (g) is an SI unit for mass.

We can attach a system of prefixes to SI units. Most of our everyday experiences with SI units will involve some of the following prefixes.

Name	Symbol	Meaning	Multiplier
mega	M	one million	1 000 000
kilo	k	one thousand	1000
hecto	h	one hundred	100
deca	da	ten	10
no prefix		one	1
deci	d	one tenth of a	0.1
centi	c	one hundredth of a	0.01
milli	m	one thousandth of a	0.001
micro	μ	one millionth of a	0.000 001

EXERCISE

1. Express each of the following in terms of m, L, or g.

(a) 3 dm

(b) 4000 mL

(c) $\frac{1}{10}$ kg

(d) 0.75 km

(e) 500 mm

(f) 150 hm

(g) 0.3 kL

(h) 70 000 mg

(i) 2.1 dm

(j) 500 mL

(k) 0.25 kg

(l) 2.3 km

(m) 4200 mm

(n) 3.25 hm

(o) 1.2 kL

(p) 6500 mg

2. Place the following in increasing order.

(a) 15 km, 150 m, 2000 cm

(b) 112.3 g, 1.1 kg, 9990 mg

(c) 25.8 L, 2 kL, 5000 mL

(d) 0.01 km, 7 dm, 0.5 m

(e) $\frac{1}{100}$ kg, 1 g, 100 mg

3. Based on the cost per unit, which of the following products are more economical?

(a) Laundry soap: 6 L for $5.75 or 750 mL for 79¢

(b) Vinegar: 2 L for $1.80 or 500 mL for $0.44

(c) Lemonade crystals: 850 g for $2.99 or 1 kg for $3.29

(d) Shortening: 454 g for $1.49 or 1 kg for $2.99

KNOW YOUR CALCULATOR

ORDER OF OPERATIONS

Brackets
Exponents
Division
Multiplication
Addition
Subtraction

Using the rules for the order of operations, we calculate that

$$2 + 3 \times 7 = 2 + 21$$
$$= 23$$

Does your calculator respect the order of operations?

Press `C` `2` `+` `3` `×` `7` `=`

If your calculator did not display 23 as the result, then you will have to input the expressions in such a way that certain operations are executed before others.

The `C` key clears the calculator for a new input.

Display

$2 + 3 \times 7$ would be input as `C` `3` `×` `7` `+` `2` `=`   `23`

$35 \div (2 + 3)$ would be input in 2 steps   `C` `2` `+` `3` `=`   `5`

`3` `5` `÷` `5` `=`   `7`

THE CONSTANT FEATURE

Calculators with the constant feature will store in their memory a number and an operation entered prior to the `=` key. The following examples show how some calculators handle constants.

Multiplication

1. Press `C` `2` `×` `=`
   The automatic constant multiplier is 2.
   Now press   Display

   `3` `=`   `6` 2×3
   `7` `=`   `14` 2×7
   `5` `=`   `10` 2×5

2. Press `C` `5` `×` `3` `=`
   Now press   Display

   `2` `=`   `10` 5×2
   `3` `=`   `15` 5×3
   `6` `=`   `30` 5×6

From the display, we observe that this calculator stored 5 as the constant multiplier.

Division

1. Press   `C` `6` `÷` `2` `=`

   Now press   Display

               `8` `=`   4   8 ÷ 2

           `5` `0` `=`   25   50 ÷ 2

           `1` `2` `=`   6   12 ÷ 2

From the display, we observe that this calculator stored 2 as the constant divisor.

EXERCISE

Complete the following tables to determine whether your calculator has a constant for multiplication, division, addition, and subtraction.

1.

Press	Display
`C` `5` `×` `=`	
`2` `=`	
`7` `=`	
`1` `5` `=`	

2.

Press	Display
`C` `1` `0` `×` `4` `=`	
`2` `=`	
`3` `3` `=`	
`1` `·` `5` `=`	

3.

Press	Display
`C` `9` `÷` `3` `=`	
`6` `=`	
`1` `2` `=`	
`3` `0` `=`	

4.

Press	Display
`C` `3` `+` `5` `=`	
`2` `=`	
`3` `=`	
`7` `=`	

5.

Press	Display
`C` `1` `0` `−` `2` `=`	
`8` `=`	
`5` `=`	
`4` `=`	

6. Determine if your calculator uses a constant in the following calculation.

Press   

              `3` `=`

              `7` `=`

7. The constant can be used for repeated operations such as

$$3 \times 3 \times 3 \times 3 \times 3$$

Press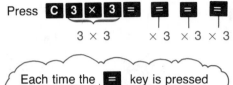

Each time the [=] key is pressed after the first time means [× 3]

(a) Evaluate.
  (i) $4 \times 4 \times 4 \times 4$
  (ii) $5 \times 5 \times 5 \times 5 \times 5$
  (iii) $7 \times 7 \times 7 \times 7$
(b) How many times must 2 be multiplied to give the following results?
  (i) 256
  (ii) 1024
  (iii) 65 536

8. Use your calculator to evaluate the following.
(a) $4 + 3 \times 5$
(b) $(2 + 3) \times 6$
(c) $88 - 12 \times 3$
(d) $(76 + 16) \div 23$
(e) $35 - 14 \div 7$
(f) $(2 + 3) \times (72 - 36)$
(g) $4.75^2 - 16.5$
(h) $(4.27 + 0.43)^2$

9. To find 7% of a number we multiply by 0.07. Find 7% of each of the following using a constant if possible. Round off to the nearest cent.
(a) $23.00
(b) $4.55
(c) $18.92
(d) $126.95
(e) $29.85
(f) $4392.63
(g) $0.49
(h) $23 805.72

SETS

A set is a well-defined collection of objects.

The symbol $\in$ means "belongs to," "is a member of," or "is an element of."	$x \in A$
If every member of set A is also a member of set B, then we write $A \subset B$ and say that "A is a subset of B."	$A \subset B$
The intersection of sets A and B, denoted by $A \cap B$, is the set consisting of all elements common to A and B.	$A \cap B$
The union of sets A and B, denoted by $A \cup B$, is the set consisting of all elements of A, B, or both.	$A \cup B$

Some sets of numbers are

The natural numbers $N = \{1, 2, 3, ...\}$

The whole numbers $W = \{0, 1, 2, 3, ...\}$

The integers $I = \{..., -3, -2, -1, 0, 1, 2, 3, ...\}$

The empty set contains no elements and is denoted by $\{\ \}$ or ϕ.

EXERCISE

1. True or false?

(a) $\{1, 2\} \subset \{1, 2, 3\}$
(b) $\{a, b, c\} \subset \{a, b, c, d\}$
(c) $a \in \{a, b, c\}$
(d) $0 \in W$
(e) $3 \in \phi$
(f) $-\frac{5}{9} \in I$
(g) $N \subset W$
(h) $N \cap W = N$

2. If $A = \{1, 2, 3\}$, $B = \{3, 5, 7\}$, and $C = \{1, 2, 5, 6\}$, list the elements of the following sets.

(a) $A \cup B$ (b) $A \cup C$ (c) $B \cup C$
(d) $A \cap B$ (e) $A \cap C$ (f) $B \cap C$

3. Which of the following diagrams best represents the given sets A and B?

(a)

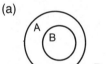

$B \subset A$

(b)

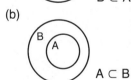

$A \subset B$

(c)

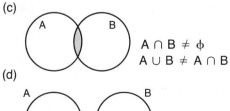

$A \cap B \neq \phi$
$A \cup B \neq A \cap B$

(d)

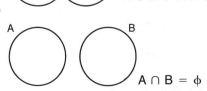

$A \cap B = \phi$

(i) $A = \{d, e, f, g\}$
     $B = \{e, g\}$
(ii) $A = \{2, 4, 6\}$
     $B = \{1, 3, 5\}$
(iii) $A = \{1, 2, 3, 4\}$
     $B = \{0, 1, 2, 3, 4\}$
(iv) $A = \{0, 5, 10\}$
     $B = \{5, 10, 15\}$
(v) $A = \{-1, 0, 1\}$
     $B = \{-1, -\frac{1}{2}, 0, \frac{1}{2}, 1\}$

(vi) A is the set of odd natural numbers; B is the set of natural numbers that are multiples of 3

(vii) A is the set of natural numbers that are multiples of 5; B is the set of natural numbers that are multiples of 10

(viii) A is the set of natural numbers from 1 to 25 inclusive; $B = \{1^2, 2^2, 3^2, 4^2, 5^2\}$

CALCULATOR MATH

CONVERTING FRACTIONS TO DECIMALS

Fraction	Press	Display
$\frac{3}{10}$	[C] [3] [÷] [1] [0] [=]	0.3
$2\frac{1}{4}$	[C] [1] [÷] [4] [+] [2] [=]	2.25

1.1 RATIONAL AND IRRATIONAL NUMBERS — PART I

We have used the following sets of numbers.

Natural numbers $N = \{1, 2, 3, ...\}$
Whole numbers $W = \{0, 1, 2, 3, ...\}$
Integers $I = \{..., -3, -2, -1, 0, 1, 2, 3, ...\}$

Any number that can be expressed as the quotient of two integers (the divisor not being zero) is a rational number

$$Q = \left\{ \frac{a}{b} \,\middle|\, a, b \in I, b \neq 0 \right\}$$

$\frac{3}{5}$ is a rational number in the form $\frac{a}{b}$, where $a = 3$, $b = 5$, $a \in I$, $b \in I$, and $b \neq 0$.

5 is a rational number in the form $\frac{a}{b}$, where $a = 5$, $b = 1$, $a \in I$, $b \in I$, and $b \neq 0$.

Rational numbers can also be expressed in decimal form. Decimal equivalents such as

$$\frac{1}{2} = 0.5$$

$$\frac{3}{4} = 0.75$$

$$\frac{5}{8} = 0.625$$

are called terminating decimals because the division process terminates. Decimal equivalents such as

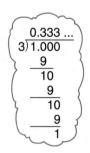

$$\frac{1}{3} = 0.333\,...$$
$$= 0.\overline{3}$$

$$\frac{1}{6} = 0.166\,6\,...$$
$$= 0.1\overline{6}$$

$$\frac{1}{7} = 0.142\,857\,142\,...$$
$$= 0.\overline{142\,857}$$

are called periodic decimals because the division process does not terminate and a portion of the decimal repeats. The repeating portion is called the period

EXAMPLE 1. For each of the following, find the decimal equivalent. State the period and length of period in each case.

(a) $\frac{5}{8}$ (b) $\frac{5}{11}$ (c) $\frac{10}{3}$ (d) $\frac{3}{13}$

SOLUTION:

For convenience we present the solution in a table.

> Note that the terminating decimal 0.625 can be considered a periodic decimal with period 0.

	Common Fraction	Decimal Equivalent	Periodic Form	Period	Length of Period
(a)	$\frac{5}{8}$	0.625 000 ...	0.625	0	1
(b)	$\frac{5}{11}$	0.454 545 ...	$0.\overline{45}$	45	2
(c)	$\frac{10}{3}$	3.333 3 ...	$3.\overline{3}$	3	1
(d)	$\frac{3}{13}$	0.230 769 230 7 ...	$0.\overline{230\ 769}$	230 769	6

Any periodic decimal can be expressed as a fraction.

EXAMPLE 2. Express $0.\overline{36}$ as a fraction.

SOLUTION:

By multiplying by a power of 10, relocate the decimal point after the first period at $\triangle$ and before the first period at $\triangle\!\!\!2$.

Let x = 0.363 636 ...

$$\quad\quad\quad \triangle\!\!\!2\ \triangle$$

① $\quad\quad\quad\quad 100x = 36.363\ 6\ ...$
② $\quad\quad\quad\quad\quad\quad x = \ \ 0.363\ 6\ ...$

Subtract ① – ②. $\quad 99x = 36$

$$x = \frac{36}{99}$$

$$x = \frac{4}{11}$$

EXAMPLE 3. Express 2.145 345 3 ... as a common fraction.

SOLUTION:

Let x = 2.145 345 3 ...

$$\quad\quad\quad \triangle\!\!\!2 \quad \triangle$$

① $\quad\quad\quad 10\ 000x = 21\ 453.453\ ...$
② $\quad\quad\quad\quad\ \ 10x = \ \ \ \ \ 21.453\ ...$

Subtract ① – ②. $\quad 9\ 990x = 21\ 432$

$$x = \frac{21\ 432}{9\ 990}$$

$$= 2\frac{242}{1665}$$

> Every rational number can be expressed as a terminating or periodic decimal.

> Every terminating or periodic decimal represents a rational number.

We combine these two statements as follows.

> A number is rational, if and only if, it can be expressed as a terminating or periodic decimal.

This last statement supports the fact that natural numbers, whole numbers, and integers are rational numbers, since all of these are terminating decimals.

$$21 = 21.0$$
$$-5 = -5.0$$

They can also be considered as periodic decimals with period 0.

$$21 = 21.000\,000\,...$$
$$= 21.\overline{0}$$
$$-5 = -5.000\,000\,...$$
$$= -5.\overline{0}$$

Not all numbers are periodic decimals. The following are some examples of non-periodic decimals.

$$0.215\,793\,286\,...$$
$$\pi = 3.141\,519\,265\,...$$
$$\sqrt{2} = 1.414\,213\,56\,...$$

Some numbers can have patterns without being periodic.

$$0.251\,251\,125\,111\,251\,111\,...$$
$$0.253\,253\,325\,333\,253\,333\,...$$
$$0.101\,001\,000\,100\,001\,...$$

We can continue to manufacture many other non-periodic decimals. These non-periodic decimals are called irrational numbers.

An irrational number is a number that is not a rational number; it cannot be expressed as a ratio of integers. We designate the set of irrational numbers as $\overline{Q}$.

> $\overline{Q}$ is the set of non-periodic decimals.

The relationship between various sets of numbers is shown in the diagram below.

N is the set of natural numbers;
W is the set of whole numbers;
I is the set of integers;
Q is the set of rational numbers;
and $N \subset W \subset I \subset Q$.

EXERCISE 1.1

A 1. Identify each of the following as rational or irrational.
(a) 0.225 225 225 ...   (b) 0.252 255 222 ...
(c) 3.125 125 ...   (d) 4.317 327 337 ...
(e) 2.141 516 ...   (f) 0.230 530 530 5 ...

2. State the period and length of the period for each of the following rational numbers.
(a) $4.\overline{205}$ (b) $6.0\overline{204}$
(c) $3.1\overline{542}$ (d) $0.\overline{3427}$
(e) 4.012 22 ...   (f) 0.725 25 ...
(g) 0.363 6 ...   (h) 122.122 122
(i) 4.012 012 ...   (j) 4.012 12 ...
(k) $6.543\ 2\overline{1}$ (l) $18.650\ \overline{247\ 3}$

B 3. Express each rational number in decimal form.
(a) $\frac{3}{4}$ (b) $\frac{5}{8}$ (c) $\frac{9}{16}$ (d) $\frac{7}{4}$ (e) $\frac{11}{8}$
(f) $\frac{5}{32}$ (g) $\frac{41}{50}$ (h) $\frac{3}{11}$ (i) $\frac{15}{11}$ (j) $\frac{11}{15}$
(k) $\frac{53}{100}$ (l) $\frac{53}{99}$ (m) $\frac{1}{9}$ (n) $\frac{4}{9}$ (o) $\frac{12}{11}$

4. Express each of the following rational numbers in the form $\frac{a}{b}$.
(a) 0.625   (b) 0.732   (c) 3.21   (d) 4.65
(e) $0.\overline{72}$ (f) $0.\overline{7}$ (g) $0.\overline{215}$ (h) $0.3\overline{014}$
(i) $0.3\overline{7}$ (j) $0.2\overline{45}$ (k) $0.30\overline{25}$ (l) $0.72\overline{1}$
(m) $3.\overline{25}$ (n) $4.0\overline{75}$ (o) $7.0\overline{375}$ (p) 7.0375

C 5. Evaluate and express your final answer in the form $\frac{a}{b}$.
(a) $(0.\overline{6})(0.5)$ (b) $(0.\overline{3})(0.25)$
(c) $(0.\overline{3})^2$ (d) $(0.\overline{18})(0.5)$
(e) $(0.\overline{5})(0.2)$ (f) $(0.\overline{6})(0.2)$

6. Express in the form $\frac{a}{b}$.
(a) $0.4\overline{9}$ (b) $0.2\overline{9}$ (c) $0.5\overline{9}$ (d) $0.\overline{9}$

7. Determine which of the following pairs of numbers are equal.
(a) $3.\overline{25}, 3.2\overline{52}$ (b) $4.\overline{36}, 4.3\overline{63}$

8. The decimal equivalent of a rational number $\frac{a}{b}$ is periodic and the maximum length of the period is $(b - 1)$. What is the maximum length of the period of the decimal equivalent of each of the following?
(a) $\frac{1}{5}$ (b) $\frac{5}{6}$ (c) $\frac{3}{7}$ (d) $\frac{2}{13}$
(e) $\frac{5}{17}$ (f) $\frac{11}{31}$ (g) $\frac{11}{43}$ (h) $\frac{19}{71}$

9. Express the following sums in the form $\frac{a}{b}$.
(a) 0.1 + 0.01 + 0.001 + ...
(b) 0.2 + 0.02 + 0.002 + ...

EXTRA

The following decimals can be expressed as fractions with the same denominator. Determine the cyclic pattern and find the fractions.

1. $0.\overline{142\ 857}$ 2. $0.\overline{428\ 571}$
3. $0.\overline{285\ 714}$ 4. $0.\overline{857\ 142}$
5. $0.\overline{571\ 428}$ 6. $0.\overline{714\ 285}$

CALCULATOR MATH

Some people use $\frac{22}{7}$ as a rational approximation for π.

Use your calculator to investigate the difference between $\frac{22}{7}$ and π.

Press `C` `2` `2` `÷` `7` `=` `-` `π` `=`

If your calculator does not have a

`π` key, press `C` `2` `2` `÷` `7` `=`
`-` `3` `.` `1` `4` `1` `5` `9` `2` `7` `=`

An approximation for π.

1.2 RATIONAL AND IRRATIONAL NUMBERS — PART II

Squaring a number means multiplying the number by itself.

$$2^2 = 2 \times 2$$
$$= 4$$

$$1.5^2 = 1.5 \times 1.5$$
$$= 2.25$$

$$\left(\frac{1}{3}\right)^2 = \frac{1}{3} \times \frac{1}{3}$$
$$= \frac{1}{9}$$

squaring

finding the
square root

Finding the square root is the inverse operation to squaring a number. It is represented by the symbol $\sqrt{}$. Numbers such as $\sqrt{2}, \sqrt{3}, \sqrt{5},$ and $\sqrt{8}$ are called radicals. Although 9 has two square roots, $+3$ and -3, when we write $\sqrt{9}$ we mean the principal (positive) square root, $+3$.

$$\sqrt{4} = 2$$
$$\sqrt{2.25} = 1.5$$
$$\sqrt{\frac{4}{9}} = \frac{2}{3}$$
$$= 0.\overline{6}$$

Using a calculator, press

C **2** **.** **2** **5** **√**

The square roots in the examples above were expressed as either terminating or periodic decimals. For this reason, they are rational numbers.

Other examples of roots are $\sqrt[3]{27}$ the cube root of 27
                                     $\sqrt[4]{16}$ the fourth root of 16

EXAMPLE 1. Evaluate.

(a) $\sqrt[3]{8}$
(b) $\sqrt[3]{0.027}$

(c) $\sqrt[3]{\dfrac{8}{125}}$

SOLUTION:
(a) $\sqrt[3]{8} = 2$,   since $2^3 = 8$

(b) $\sqrt[3]{0.027} = 0.3$, since $(0.3)^3 = 0.027$

(c) $\sqrt[3]{\dfrac{8}{125}} = \dfrac{2}{5}$,   since $\left(\dfrac{2}{5}\right)^3 = \dfrac{8}{125}$

EXAMPLE 2. Evaluate.

(a) $\sqrt[4]{16}$

(b) $\sqrt[4]{49}$ to the nearest thousandth

SOLUTION:

(a) $\sqrt[4]{16} = 2$, since $2^4 = 16$

(b) $\sqrt[4]{49} = \sqrt{\sqrt{49}}$

$= \sqrt{7}$

$= 2.645\ 751\ 3\ ...$

$\doteq 2.646$

Using a calculator, press

C 4 9 √ √

Some roots cannot be represented by a periodic decimal.

$$\sqrt{7} = 2.645\ 751\ 3\ ...$$

$$\sqrt{3} = 1.732\ 050\ 8\ ...$$

$$\sqrt{2} = 1.414\ 213\ 5\ ...$$

These are irrational. That is,

$$\sqrt{7} \in \overline{Q}$$

$$\sqrt{3} \in \overline{Q}$$

$$\sqrt{2} \in \overline{Q}$$

EXAMPLE 3. Identify each of the following as rational or irrational.

(a) $\sqrt{64}$

(b) $\sqrt{2.5}$

(c) $\sqrt{\dfrac{1}{9}}$

(d) $\sqrt{0.25}$

SOLUTION:

For convenience we present the solution in a table.

	Root	Calculator Display	Classification	Type
(a)	$\sqrt{64}$	8	terminating	rational
(b)	$\sqrt{2.5}$	1.5811388	non-terminating, non-periodic	irrational
(c)	$\sqrt{\dfrac{1}{9}}$	0.3333333	non-terminating, periodic	rational
(d)	$\sqrt{0.25}$	0.5	terminating	rational

EXERCISE 1.2

A 1. Identify each of the following roots as rational or irrational.

(a) $\sqrt{100} = 10$
(b) $\sqrt{81} = 9$
(c) $\sqrt{15} = 3.872\,983\,34\,...$
(d) $\sqrt{1.21} = 1.1$
(e) $\sqrt{\frac{9}{25}} = \frac{3}{5}$
(f) $\sqrt{\frac{1}{4}} = \frac{1}{2}$
(g) $\sqrt[3]{8} = 2$
(h) $\sqrt[4]{625} = 5$
(i) $\sqrt[3]{\frac{1}{27}} = \frac{1}{3}$
(j) $\sqrt[4]{0.0001} = 0.1$

B 2. Identify the rational numbers among the following roots.

(a) $\sqrt{225}$ (b) $\sqrt{35}$
(c) $\sqrt{0.39}$ (d) $\sqrt{1.44}$
(e) $\sqrt{\frac{16}{49}}$ (f) $\sqrt{10}$
(g) $\sqrt[3]{9}$ (h) $\sqrt[4]{8}$
(i) $\sqrt[3]{0.001}$ (j) $\sqrt[4]{\frac{16}{81}}$
(k) $\sqrt{\sqrt{81}}$ (l) $\sqrt[3]{0.1}$

 3. Using a calculator, approximate the following

(a) to the nearest integer.
    (i) $\sqrt{145}$
    (ii) $\sqrt{4093.8}$
    (iii) $\sqrt{394.76}$
    (iv) $\sqrt[4]{82}$

(b) to the nearest tenth.
    (i) $\sqrt{11}$
    (ii) $\sqrt{73.5}$
    (iii) $\sqrt{98.63}$
    (iv) $\sqrt[4]{20.7}$

(c) to the nearest hundredth.
    (i) $\sqrt{55}$
    (ii) $\sqrt{6.479}$
    (iii) $\sqrt{192.16}$
    (iv) $\sqrt[4]{62.446}$

4. Place each of the following within the appropriate set in the diagram.

(a) $\sqrt{49}$ (b) $\sqrt{\frac{25}{81}}$
(c) $\sqrt{0}$ (d) $\sqrt{0.0049}$
(e) $\sqrt{2}$ (f) $\sqrt{2.25}$
(g) $\sqrt[3]{-1}$ (h) $\sqrt[4]{1}$
(i) $2.131\,313\,13\,...$ (j) $1.921\,476\,159\,...$

EXTRA

The word radical comes from the Latin word radix. At one time, it was represented by *r*. Through the years it changed to **r** then to $\sqrt{}$, and finally to $\sqrt{}$. Mathematicians of the sixteenth century used four different symbols to represent a square root. For example, the square root of 4 could have been written as

$$\mathbb{R}4, \quad \ell 4, \quad \mathscr{L}4, \quad \text{or} \quad 4^{\frac{1}{2}}.$$

Even more confusing were the symbols representing other roots, such as the cube root and fourth root, which were quite different. In fact, by the end of the third century, there were well over twenty different symbols for radicals.

THE EXPONENT KEY

If your calculator has an exponent key y^x , you can calculate a root of a positive number using the special property

$$\sqrt[n]{y} = y^{\frac{1}{n}}$$

EXAMPLE 1. Calculate. $\sqrt[4]{23}$

SOLUTION:

Press [C] [2] [3] [y^x] [·] [2] [5] [=]

The display is 2.1899387

Checking, we press [x^2] [x^2]

and the display is 23

EXAMPLE 2. Calculate. $\sqrt[3]{5}$

SOLUTION:

Press [C] [5] [y^x] [(] [1] [÷] [3] [)] [=]

The display is 1.7099759

Checking, we press [×] [=] [=]

$(\sqrt[3]{5})^2$ $(\sqrt[3]{5})^3$

The display is 4.9999997

which rounds to 5.

$\sqrt{2}$ IS NOT RATIONAL: PROOF

To prove that $\sqrt{2}$ is not rational, we can use the method of indirect proof, sometimes called proof by contradiction This method involves assuming that the opposite is true, and then showing that this assumption leads to a contradiction of facts.

To prove that $\sqrt{2}$ is not rational, we begin by assuming that it is rational. Based on this assumption, suppose that $\sqrt{2} = \frac{a}{b}$ where $\frac{a}{b}$ is in simplest form. Squaring both sides,

$$2 = \frac{a^2}{b^2}$$
$$2b^2 = a^2$$

Because the value of $2b^2$ is even, then a^2 is even so that a is also even. If we now let $a = 2c$, then $a^2 = 4c^2$.

$$2b^2 = 4c^2$$
$$b^2 = 2c^2$$

Continuing the same reasoning, we have now shown that b is also even. If a and b are both even as shown, then the fraction $\frac{a}{b}$ is not in simplest form because both a and b have 2 as a factor. This contradicts the original assumption that $\frac{a}{b}$ was in simplest form.

We then must conclude that the assumption that $\sqrt{2}$ is a rational number is false so that $\sqrt{2}$ is not rational.

EXERCISE

1. Use the method of indirect proof to prove that the following are not rational numbers.

(a) $\sqrt{3}$ (b) $\sqrt{5}$ (c) $\sqrt{7}$

1.3 REAL NUMBERS

The set of real numbers, R, is the set of all periodic and non-periodic decimals. We can also define R as the union of the set of rational numbers, Q, and the set of irrational numbers, $\overline{Q}$.

$$R = Q \cup \overline{Q}$$

Examples of real numbers are $-2, \frac{2}{3}, \sqrt{2}, \sqrt{5}$, and $\pi = 3.141\,59\,...$, where $\sqrt{2}, \sqrt{5}$, and π are irrational.

Each real number can be associated with a position on a number line called the real number line

EXAMPLE 1. Graph each set on a number line.
(a) $\{x \in R \mid x < 2\}$
(b) $\{x \in R \mid x \geqslant -2\}$
(c) $\{x \in R \mid -3 \leqslant x \leqslant 2\}$

SOLUTION:

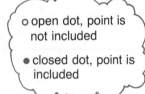
(a) $\{x \in R \mid x < 2\}$

(b) $\{x \in R \mid x \geqslant -2\}$

(c) $\{x \in R \mid -3 \leqslant x \leqslant 2\}$

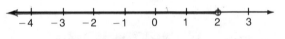

EXAMPLE 2. Given A = $\{x \in R \mid x > -3\}$
B = $\{x \in R \mid x \leqslant 0\}$
C = $\{x \in R \mid x \geqslant 2\}$
graph each of the following on a number line.
(a) A ∩ B
(b) B ∪ C

SOLUTION:
A

B

C

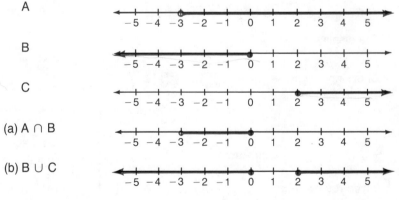

(a) A ∩ B

(b) B ∪ C

In set-builder notation, A ∩ B can be written $\{x \in R \mid -3 < x \leqslant 0\}$.

EXERCISE 1.3

A 1. Identify as members of N, Q, or $\overline{Q}$.

(a) $\frac{3}{4}$ (b) $\sqrt{25}$ (c) $\sqrt{7}$ (d) -2 (e) 0.36

(f) $\sqrt{3}$ (g) $0.\overline{3}$ (h) $\frac{2}{3}$ (i) π (j) $\sqrt{16}$

(k) $1.\overline{25}$ (l) 0.7   (m) $0.\overline{7}$ (n) $3\frac{1}{7}$ (o) $-\sqrt{3}$

2. Describe each of the following in set-builder notation.

(a)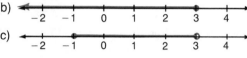

(b)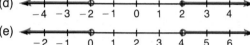

(c)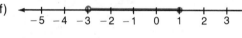

(d)
```
  -4 -3 -2 -1  0  1  2  3  4
```

(e)
```
  -2 -1  0  1  2  3  4  5  6
```

(f)
```
  -5 -4 -3 -2 -1  0  1  2  3
```

> The symbol $\neq$ is read "is not equal to." What meaning do the following symbols have?
>
> $\nless$ $\ngtr$

B 3. Graph the following sets where $x \in R$.

(a) $\{x \mid x > 1\}$ (b) $\{x \mid x \geq -2\}$
(c) $\{x \mid x \leq 3\}$ (d) $\{x \mid x \neq 0\}$
(e) $\{x \mid x > -2\}$ (f) $\{x \mid x \leq 0\}$

4. Graph the following on a number line where $x \in R$.

(a) $\{x \mid x > -1\} \cap \{x \mid x \leq 3\}$
(b) $\{x \mid x \leq 0\} \cup \{x \mid x \geq 3\}$
(c) $\{x \mid x \leq -2\} \cup \{x \mid x > 0\}$
(d) $\{x \mid x \leq 0\} \cap \{x \mid x \geq 0\}$

5. Graph on a number line where $x \in R$.

(a) $\{x \mid -2 \leq x \leq 1\{ \cap \{x \mid 0 < x \leq 3\}$
(b) $\{x \mid -3 \leq x < 0\} \cup \{x \mid 0 \leq x \leq 2\}$
(c) $\{x \mid -2 \leq x \leq 3\} \cap \{x \mid x \neq 3\}$
(d) $\{x \mid -1 < x \leq 2\} \cup \{x \mid x + 1 = 0\}$

C 6. Graph on a number line.

(a) $\{x \in R \mid x^2 > 4\}$ (b) $\{x \in R \mid x^2 < 4\}$
(c) $\{x \in R \mid x \leq 2 \text{ and } x \geq -3\}$
(d) $\{x \in R \mid x \leq -2 \text{ or } x \geq 1\}$

7. Continue the pattern established in the diagram below to locate the irrational numbers $-\sqrt{6}$, $-\sqrt{5}$, $\sqrt{5}$, and $\sqrt{6}$ on the real number line. We calculate the length of 0A using the Pythagorean Theorem.

$$c = \sqrt{a^2 + b^2}$$
$$0A = \sqrt{1^2 + 1^2}$$
$$= \sqrt{2}$$

$$c = \sqrt{a^2 + b^2}$$

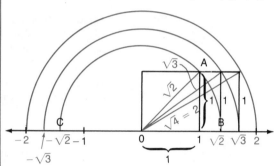

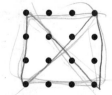

> Cross all the dots with six straight lines without lifting your pencil.

1.4 ORDER AND DENSITY

In 1876, Richard Dedekind, a German mathematician, showed that there is a one-to-one correspondence between the real numbers and all the points on a number line. Because of this property, we note that there are no "holes" or "gaps" in the real number line and we say that the real number system is complete.

This property helps us to determine whether one number is less than, equal to, or greater than another number according to their positions on a number line. When comparing two numbers, a and b, only one of

(i) $a < b$
(ii) $a = b$
(iii) $a > b$

is true. This is called the trichotomy property of order

The following examples illustrate the transitive property of inequality in R.

Since $3 < 5$ and $5 < 7$, then $3 < 7$	If $a < b$ and $b < c$, then $a < c$
Since $9 > 6$ and $6 > 4$, then $9 > 4$	If $a > b$ and $b > c$, then $a > c$
Since $3 = 3$ and $3 = 3$, then $3 = 3$	If $a = b$ and $b = c$, then $a = c$

Another interesting property is that it is possible to find a rational and an irrational number between any two rational or irrational numbers.

EXAMPLE 1.   Given two irrational numbers
$$a = 2.152\ 636\ 295\ ...$$
$$b = 2.152\ 753\ 124\ ...$$
find a rational and an irrational number between them.

SOLUTION:
Rational : $a < 2.1527 < b$

Irrational : $a < 2.152\ 643\ 216\ ... < b$
(Provided that 2.152 643 216 ... continues without repetition.)

EXAMPLE 2.   Given two rational numbers
$$a = 2.152\ 626\ 262\ ...$$
$$b = 2.152\ 783$$
find a rational and an irrational number between them.

SOLUTION:
Rational : $a < 2.152\ 7 < b$

Irrational : $a < 2.152\ 643\ 216\ ... < b$
(Provided that 2.152 643 216 ... continues without repetition.)

Examples 1 and 2 suggest that between any two real numbers we can find both a rational number and an irrational number. We express that fact by saying that both Q and $\overline{Q}$ are dense in the real numbers.

> Find where the numbers a and b begin to differ 2.152 ...

EXERCISE 1.4

B 1. Arrange the elements of each set in increasing order.

(a) {0.5, 0.45, 0.65}   (b) {−2, 4, −1, 3, 0}

(c) $\{\frac{1}{2}, -\frac{1}{2}, 1, \frac{2}{3}\}$ (d) {−5, 0, −2, −4, 1}

2. Arrange the following in decreasing order.

(a) {0.75, 0.33, 0.28, 0.2}

(b) {−3, 5, −2, 1, 0}

(c) $\{\frac{2}{3}, -\frac{1}{3}, -2, 3, 0\}$

(d) {−2, 0, 2, −3, 1}

3. Find simpler inequalities.

(a) $x + 3 > 7$ (b) $x - 2 < 3$ (c) $x + 4 < 4$

(d) $x + 3 < 0$ (e) $2x > 8$ (f) $3x < 9$

(g) $-x > 2$ (h) $-x < 2$ (i) $-2x > 6$

(j) $\frac{1}{2}x < 3$ (k) $-\frac{1}{3}x > 2$ (l) $-\frac{x}{4} < 1$

4. Find a real number between each of the following pairs of real numbers.

(a) 3, 4   (b) −2, 1   (c) −3, −5

(d) 42, 43   (e) 2.5, 2.6   (f) −2.6, −2.7

(g) −3.4, −3.5 (h) 2.75, 2.83 (i) $\frac{1}{2}, \frac{1}{3}$

(j) $-\frac{1}{3}, -\frac{1}{4}$ (k) $\frac{3}{4}, \frac{11}{16}$ (l) $-\frac{1}{5}, -\frac{3}{10}$

5. Find a rational number and irrational number between each of the following.

(a) a = 7.217 46 ...
   b = 7.223 45 ...

(b) c = −0.271 55 ...
   d = −0.271 45 ...

(c) e = 4.275 ...
   f = 4.273 ...

EXTRA

BETWEENNESS

We can prove that between any two real numbers there exists another real number. The proof is based on the following properties of inequality.

Property   If $a < b$, then $a - b < 0$ Example. $3 < 7$, then $3 - 7 < 0$

If $a > b$, then $a - b > 0$ $5 > 2$, then $5 - 2 > 0$

If $a = b$, then $a - b = 0$ $4 = 4$, then $4 - 4 = 0$

GIVEN: $a, b \in R, a < b$

PROVE: $a < \dfrac{a + b}{2} < b, \dfrac{a + b}{2} \in R$

Part 1.   We prove that $a < \dfrac{a + b}{2}$.

PROOF: $\dfrac{a + b}{2} - a = \dfrac{a + b - 2a}{2}$

$= \dfrac{b - a}{2}$

> 0, because $a < b$

$\therefore a < \dfrac{a + b}{2}$

Part 2.   We prove that $\dfrac{a + b}{2} < b$.

PROOF: $b - \dfrac{a + b}{2} = \dfrac{2b - a - b}{2}$

$= \dfrac{b - a}{2}$

> 0, because $a < b$

$\therefore \dfrac{a + b}{2} < b$

Combining parts 1 and 2, $a < \frac{a + b}{2} < b$.

1.5 RADICALS

A radical represents the principal (positive) square root of a number. Remember that even though 25 has two square roots, 5 and -5, $\sqrt{25}$ equals 5.

We know that

$$10 = 5 \times 2$$
$$= \sqrt{25} \times \sqrt{4}$$

and that

$$10 = \sqrt{100}$$
$$= \sqrt{25 \times 4}$$

It follows that $\sqrt{25} \times \sqrt{4} = \sqrt{25 \times 4}$.

We generalize this result in the following rule.

$$\sqrt{a} \times \sqrt{b} = \sqrt{ab} \quad \text{where a, b} \geq 0$$

EXAMPLE 1. Evaluate $\sqrt{2} \times \sqrt{3}$ to the nearest hundredth.

SOLUTION:

METHOD I.

$$\sqrt{2} \times \sqrt{3} \doteq 1.414 \times 1.732$$
$$= 2.449\ 048$$
$$\doteq 2.45$$

METHOD II.

$$\sqrt{2} \times \sqrt{3} = \sqrt{6}$$
$$\doteq 2.45$$

Note that the first method required multiplying 1.414×1.732, while the second method required multiplying 2 by 3 which is much easier.

Radicals such as $\sqrt{2}$, $\sqrt{3}$, $\sqrt{12}$, and $\sqrt{18}$ are called entire radicals. Other radicals such as $2\sqrt{3}$, $3\sqrt{2}$, and $5\sqrt{7}$ are called mixed radicals. It is sometimes possible to express one radical in both forms.

$$2\sqrt{3} = \sqrt{12}$$
$$3\sqrt{2} = \sqrt{18}$$

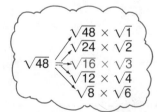

Using a calculator to check

C 2 × 3 √ =
3.4641016
C 1 2 √ =
3.4641016

EXAMPLE 2. Express as entire radicals.
(a) $5\sqrt{2}$ (b) $4\sqrt{5}$

SOLUTION:

(a) $5\sqrt{2} = \sqrt{25} \times \sqrt{2}$
$\quad\quad\ = \sqrt{25 \times 2}$
$\quad\quad\ = \sqrt{50}$

(b) $4\sqrt{5} = \sqrt{16} \times \sqrt{5}$
$\quad\quad\ = \sqrt{16 \times 5}$
$\quad\quad\ = \sqrt{80}$

EXAMPLE 3. Express as mixed radicals in simplest form.
(a) $\sqrt{48}$ (b) $\sqrt{27}$

SOLUTION:

A radical is in simplest form when it has the smallest possible number under the radical sign.

(a) $\sqrt{48} = \sqrt{16 \times 3}$
$\quad\quad\ = \sqrt{16} \times \sqrt{3}$
$\quad\quad\ = 4\sqrt{3}$

(b) $\sqrt{27} = \sqrt{9 \times 3}$
$\quad\quad\ = \sqrt{9} \times \sqrt{3}$
$\quad\quad\ = 3\sqrt{3}$

$\sqrt{48} \Big\langle$
$\sqrt{48} \times \sqrt{1}$
$\sqrt{24} \times \sqrt{2}$
$\sqrt{16} \times \sqrt{3}$
$\sqrt{12} \times \sqrt{4}$
$\sqrt{8} \times \sqrt{6}$

EXAMPLE 4. Simplify.

(a) $3\sqrt{2} \times 2\sqrt{7}$

(b) $2\sqrt{5} \times 3\sqrt{15}$

SOLUTION:

(a) $3\sqrt{2} \times 2\sqrt{7} = 3 \times 2 \times \sqrt{2} \times \sqrt{7}$
$= 6\sqrt{14}$

(b) $2\sqrt{5} \times 3\sqrt{15} = 6\sqrt{75}$
$= 6 \times \sqrt{25} \times \sqrt{3}$
$= 6 \times 5 \times \sqrt{3}$
$= 30\sqrt{3}$

EXERCISE 1.5

A 1. Evaluate.

(a) $\sqrt{16}$　　(b) $\sqrt{49}$　　(c) $\sqrt{81}$

(d) $\sqrt{100}$　　(e) $\sqrt{121}$　　(f) $\sqrt{\frac{4}{9}}$

(g) $\sqrt{\frac{36}{25}}$　　(h) $\sqrt{\frac{64}{81}}$　　(i) $\sqrt{\frac{36}{49}}$

2. Simplify.

(a) $\sqrt{3} \times \sqrt{2}$　　(b) $\sqrt{6} \times \sqrt{11}$
(c) $\sqrt{3} \times \sqrt{5}$　　(d) $\sqrt{5} \times \sqrt{7}$
(e) $\sqrt{11} \times \sqrt{7}$　　(f) $\sqrt{5} \times \sqrt{6}$
(g) $\sqrt{6} \times \sqrt{7}$　　(h) $\sqrt{2} \times \sqrt{11}$
(i) $\sqrt{11} \times \sqrt{13}$　　(j) $\sqrt{5} \times \sqrt{17}$

3. Simplify.

(a) $3\sqrt{2} \times 2\sqrt{5}$　　(b) $5\sqrt{7} \times \sqrt{3}$
(c) $2\sqrt{5} \times 2\sqrt{3}$　　(d) $6\sqrt{5} \times 7\sqrt{2}$
(e) $2\sqrt{5} \times 3\sqrt{6}$　　(f) $4\sqrt{7} \times 2\sqrt{5}$
(g) $6\sqrt{2} \times 2\sqrt{5}$　　(h) $2\sqrt{2} \times 3\sqrt{3}$
(i) $3\sqrt{2} \times 5\sqrt{3}$　　(j) $4\sqrt{3} \times 2\sqrt{7}$

B 4. Change to mixed radicals in simplest form.

(a) $\sqrt{12}$　　(b) $\sqrt{18}$　　(c) $\sqrt{20}$
(d) $\sqrt{32}$　　(e) $\sqrt{45}$　　(f) $\sqrt{75}$
(g) $\sqrt{50}$　　(h) $\sqrt{1024}$　　(i) $\sqrt{72}$
(j) $\sqrt{68}$　　(k) $\sqrt{200}$　　(l) $\sqrt{24}$

5. Using $\sqrt{2} \doteq 1.414$, $\sqrt{3} \doteq 1.732$, and $\sqrt{5} \doteq 2.236$, approximate the following to the nearest hundredth by first expressing as a mixed radical.

(a) $\sqrt{8}$　　(b) $\sqrt{32}$　　(c) $\sqrt{24}$
(d) $\sqrt{50}$　　(e) $\sqrt{40}$　　(f) $\sqrt{27}$

6. Change to entire radicals.

(a) $2\sqrt{3}$　　(b) $5\sqrt{2}$　　(c) $3\sqrt{5}$
(d) $5\sqrt{3}$　　(e) $3\sqrt{11}$　　(f) $5\sqrt{10}$
(g) $10\sqrt{3}$　　(h) $2\sqrt{7}$　　(i) $5\sqrt{8}$
(j) $3\sqrt{14}$　　(k) $6\sqrt{7}$　　(l) $11\sqrt{2}$

7. Simplify.

(a) $\sqrt{2} \times \sqrt{6}$　　(b) $\sqrt{10} \times \sqrt{6}$
(c) $\sqrt{7} \times \sqrt{14}$　　(d) $\sqrt{3} \times \sqrt{6}$
(e) $\sqrt{15} \times \sqrt{5}$　　(f) $\sqrt{5} \times \sqrt{50}$
(g) $\sqrt{5} \times 2\sqrt{3}$　　(h) $5\sqrt{2} \times 3\sqrt{3}$
(i) $2\sqrt{10} \times 5\sqrt{3}$　　(j) $5\sqrt{7} \times 2\sqrt{14}$
(k) $5\sqrt{3} \times 2\sqrt{15}$　　(l) $3\sqrt{3} \times 2\sqrt{12}$
(m) $\sqrt{6} \times \sqrt{3} \times \sqrt{2}$　　(n) $\sqrt{5} \times \sqrt{2} \times \sqrt{15}$
(o) $\sqrt{10} \times \sqrt{15} \times \sqrt{6}$
(p) $3\sqrt{2} \times 2\sqrt{6} \times \sqrt{3}$
(q) $3\sqrt{5} \times 2\sqrt{3} \times 3\sqrt{5}$
(r) $3\sqrt{6} \times 2\sqrt{3} \times 4\sqrt{2}$

MICRO MATH

The following BASIC program will change an entire radical to a mixed radical. The expression under the radical is called the radicand. The radical sign will be printed as RAD(　).

NEW

```
100 REM CHANGING AN ENTIRE RADICAL
101 REM TO A MIXED RADICAL
110 PRINT "WHAT IS THE RADICAND";
120 INPUT N
130 FOR I = INT(SQR(N)) TO 1 STEP -1
140 IF INT(N/(I*I))<>N/(I*I) THEN 180
150 A=I
160 B=N/(I*I)
170 I=1
180 NEXT I
190 IF A=1 THEN PRINT "NO MIXED
    RADICAL" : GOTO 210
200 PRINT "RAD("; N; ") =["; A;
    "RAD("; B; ")"
210 END
```

RUN

1.6 ADDING AND SUBTRACTING RADICALS

Like terms such as 2a and 5a can be added using the distributive law.

$$2a + 5a = (2 + 5)a$$
$$= 7a$$

Radicals such as $5\sqrt{2}$ and $3\sqrt{2}$ are called like radicals and can be added in the same way.

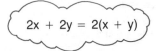

$$5\sqrt{2} + 3\sqrt{2} = (5 + 3)\sqrt{2}$$
$$= 8\sqrt{2}$$

EXAMPLE 1. Simplify. $5\sqrt{7} + 4\sqrt{7} - 3\sqrt{7}$

SOLUTION:
$$5\sqrt{7} + 4\sqrt{7} - 3\sqrt{7} = (5 + 4 - 3)\sqrt{7}$$
$$= 6\sqrt{7}$$

EXAMPLE 2. Simplify. $4\sqrt{5} + 7\sqrt{13} + 3\sqrt{5} - 2\sqrt{13}$

SOLUTION:
$$4\sqrt{5} + 7\sqrt{13} + 3\sqrt{5} - 2\sqrt{13} = 4\sqrt{5} + 3\sqrt{5} + 7\sqrt{13} - 2\sqrt{13}$$
$$= 7\sqrt{5} + 5\sqrt{13}$$

Note that $\sqrt{5}$ and $\sqrt{13}$ are not added because they are not like radicals.

EXAMPLE 3. Simplify. $\sqrt{5} + \sqrt{45} - \sqrt{20}$

SOLUTION:
$$\sqrt{5} + \sqrt{45} - \sqrt{20} = \sqrt{5} + 3\sqrt{5} - 2\sqrt{5}$$
$$= 2\sqrt{5}$$

It is necessary to change all radicals to mixed radicals in simplest form before adding and subtracting, since unlike radicals cannot be added or subtracted.

EXAMPLE 4. Simplify. $5\sqrt{x} + 3\sqrt{x}, x \geq 0$

SOLUTION:
$$5\sqrt{x} + 3\sqrt{x} = (5 + 3)\sqrt{x}$$
$$= 8\sqrt{x}$$

EXAMPLE 5. Simplify. $3\sqrt{4a} + 5\sqrt{9a}, a \geq 0$

SOLUTION:
$$3\sqrt{4a} + 5\sqrt{9a} = 3 \times 2\sqrt{a} + 5 \times 3\sqrt{a}$$
$$= 6\sqrt{a} + 15\sqrt{a}$$
$$= 21\sqrt{a}$$

EXERCISE 1.6

A 1. Simplify.
(a) $3\sqrt{2} + 5\sqrt{2}$ (b) $7\sqrt{3} - 4\sqrt{3}$
(c) $6\sqrt{11} + 7\sqrt{11}$ (d) $3\sqrt{5} + 4\sqrt{5}$
(e) $2\sqrt{13} + 7\sqrt{13}$ (f) $12\sqrt{5} - 7\sqrt{5}$
(g) $5\sqrt{2} + \sqrt{2}$ (h) $\sqrt{3} + 6\sqrt{3}$
(i) $7\sqrt{2} - \sqrt{2}$ (j) $8\sqrt{3} + 10\sqrt{3}$
(k) $\sqrt{7} + \sqrt{7}$ (l) $2\sqrt{2} - \sqrt{2}$
(m) $\sqrt{2} + 7\sqrt{2} + 3\sqrt{2}$
(n) $5\sqrt{3} + 7\sqrt{3} - 4\sqrt{3}$

2. Simplify.
(a) $5\sqrt{2} - 3\sqrt{2} + 7\sqrt{11} + 2\sqrt{11}$
(b) $3\sqrt{13} + 2\sqrt{7} + 11\sqrt{13} - 5\sqrt{7}$
(c) $6\sqrt{3} + 4\sqrt{3} - 5\sqrt{2} + 7\sqrt{2}$
(d) $5\sqrt{7} + 2\sqrt{11} - 3\sqrt{11} - \sqrt{7}$
(e) $4\sqrt{5} - 2\sqrt{7} + 3\sqrt{7} - \sqrt{5}$
(f) $5\sqrt{6} + 2\sqrt{3} - 5\sqrt{6} + 4\sqrt{3}$
(g) $3\sqrt{10} + 5\sqrt{10} - 7$
(h) $12 - 6\sqrt{11} - 5\sqrt{11} + 4$

B 3. Simplify.
(a) $\sqrt{3} + 5 + 3\sqrt{3} - 2$
(b) $6\sqrt{3} - 2 + 4\sqrt{3} + 7$
(c) $7 + 3\sqrt{5} - 2\sqrt{5} + 4$
(d) $3\sqrt{5} + 2\sqrt{3} + 3\sqrt{3} + 4\sqrt{5}$
(e) $3\sqrt{7} + 3 - 2\sqrt{7} - 3$
(f) $5\sqrt{2} - 4 - 7 - 3\sqrt{2}$

4. Simplify.
(a) $\sqrt{12} + \sqrt{27}$
(b) $\sqrt{18} - \sqrt{8}$
(c) $\sqrt{32} + \sqrt{50}$
(d) $\sqrt{50} - \sqrt{18}$
(e) $\sqrt{98} - \sqrt{8}$
(f) $\sqrt{75} - \sqrt{48}$
(g) $2\sqrt{8} + \sqrt{18} + 4\sqrt{2}$
(h) $5\sqrt{12} - 3\sqrt{12} - 2\sqrt{3}$
(i) $\sqrt{8} - 6\sqrt{2} + \sqrt{24}$
(j) $\sqrt{50} + 3\sqrt{18} - 10\sqrt{2}$

C 5. Simplify, where a, x $\geq$ 0.
(a) $5\sqrt{x} + 2\sqrt{x} - 4\sqrt{x}$
(b) $7\sqrt{a} + 3\sqrt{a} - 6\sqrt{a}$
(c) $5\sqrt{9x} + 3\sqrt{4x}$
(d) $2\sqrt{36a} - 5\sqrt{4a}$
(e) $4\sqrt{2x} - \sqrt{8x}$
(f) $2\sqrt{3a} - \sqrt{12a}$

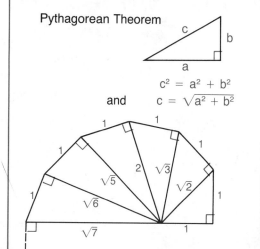

1.7 MULTIPLICATION OF RADICAL EXPRESSIONS

Radicals can be multiplied by applying the distributive property.

EXAMPLE 1.   Simplify. $\sqrt{3}(\sqrt{2} - 4)$

SOLUTION:

$\sqrt{3} \times \sqrt{2} = \sqrt{6}$
$\sqrt{3} \times (-4) = -4\sqrt{3}$

$a(b + c) = ab + ac$

$\sqrt{3}(\sqrt{2} - 4) = \sqrt{3}(\sqrt{2} - 4)$
$\qquad\qquad = \sqrt{6} - 4\sqrt{3}$

EXAMPLE 2.   Simplify. $3\sqrt{5}(\sqrt{2} + 3\sqrt{10})$

SOLUTION:

$9\sqrt{50} = 9\sqrt{25 \times 2}$
$\qquad = 9 \times 5\sqrt{2}$
$\qquad = 45\sqrt{2}$

$3\sqrt{5}(\sqrt{2} + 3\sqrt{10}) = 3\sqrt{10} + 9\sqrt{50}$
$\qquad\qquad\qquad\qquad = 3\sqrt{10} + 45\sqrt{2}$

EXERCISE 1.7

A 1. Simplify.
  (a) $2(\sqrt{3} + 5)$
  (b) $7(6 - 4\sqrt{3})$
  (c) $5(\sqrt{2} + \sqrt{6})$
  (d) $\sqrt{2}(3 - 2\sqrt{11})$
  (e) $\sqrt{7}(3\sqrt{4} + 1)$
  (f) $\sqrt{3}(2 + 3\sqrt{2})$
  (g) $2\sqrt{5}(\sqrt{2} + 1)$
  (h) $3\sqrt{3}(\sqrt{11} + 2)$

B 2. Simplify.
  (a) $2\sqrt{5}(\sqrt{2} - 4\sqrt{3})$
  (b) $3\sqrt{2}(\sqrt{5} - 2\sqrt{6})$
  (c) $5\sqrt{5}(2\sqrt{3} + 6\sqrt{2})$
  (d) $9\sqrt{3}(3\sqrt{15} + 2\sqrt{2})$
  (e) $3\sqrt{13}(2\sqrt{2} - 5\sqrt{3})$

  3. Simplify.
  (a) $\sqrt{2}(1 + 2\sqrt{3} + \sqrt{5})$
  (b) $2\sqrt{3}(\sqrt{2} + \sqrt{5} + \sqrt{11})$
  (c) $3\sqrt{5}(2\sqrt{2} + 3\sqrt{3} + 4\sqrt{7})$

MICRO MATH

This program will print the squares and square roots of the natural numbers from 1 to 10.

NEW

```
10 REM SQUARES AND SQUARE ROOTS
20 FOR I = 1 TO 10
30 PRINT I, I*I, SQR(I)
40 NEXT I
50 END
```

RUN

```
1      1      1
2      4      1.4142135623731
3      9      1.73205080756888
4      16     2
5      25     2.23606797749979
6      36     2.44948974278318
7      49     2.64575131106459
8   .  64     2.82842712474619
9      81     3
10     100    3.16227766016838
```

1.8 DIVISION OF RADICAL EXPRESSIONS

Division is the inverse operation of multiplication.

If $\sqrt{3} \times \sqrt{5} = \sqrt{15}$, then $\dfrac{\sqrt{15}}{\sqrt{5}} = \sqrt{3}$.   But we also know that

$\sqrt{\dfrac{15}{5}} = \sqrt{3}$.   It follows that $\dfrac{\sqrt{15}}{\sqrt{5}} = \sqrt{\dfrac{15}{5}} = \sqrt{3}$.

This can be generalized as follows.

$$\dfrac{\sqrt{ab}}{\sqrt{b}} = \sqrt{\dfrac{ab}{b}} = \sqrt{a}, \quad b \neq 0$$

$$\dfrac{\sqrt{ab}}{\sqrt{b}} = \dfrac{\sqrt{a}\sqrt{b}}{\sqrt{b}}$$
$$= \sqrt{a}, \quad b \neq 0$$

EXAMPLE 1.   Simplify.

(a) $\dfrac{\sqrt{14}}{\sqrt{2}}$

(b) $\dfrac{24\sqrt{21}}{6\sqrt{3}}$

SOLUTION:

(a) $\dfrac{\sqrt{14}}{\sqrt{2}} = \sqrt{\dfrac{14}{2}}$
$$= \sqrt{7}$$

(b) $\dfrac{24\sqrt{21}}{6\sqrt{3}} = \dfrac{24}{6}\sqrt{\dfrac{21}{3}}$
$$= 4\sqrt{7}$$

We can also simplify quotients involving radicals by using the principle of equivalent fractions and expressing the denominator as a rational number.

EXAMPLE 2.   Simplify by expressing the denominator as a rational number.

(a) $\dfrac{\sqrt{5}}{\sqrt{2}}$

(b) $\dfrac{15\sqrt{7}}{2\sqrt{3}}$

SOLUTION:

$$\dfrac{a}{b} = \dfrac{ax}{bx}$$

(a) Multiply the numerator and the denominator by $\sqrt{2}$.
$$\dfrac{\sqrt{5}}{\sqrt{2}} = \dfrac{\sqrt{5}}{\sqrt{2}} \times \dfrac{\sqrt{2}}{\sqrt{2}}$$
$$= \dfrac{\sqrt{10}}{2}$$

(b) Multiply the numerator and the denominator by $\sqrt{3}$.
$$\dfrac{15\sqrt{7}}{2\sqrt{3}} = \dfrac{15\sqrt{7}}{2\sqrt{3}} \times \dfrac{\sqrt{3}}{\sqrt{3}}$$
$$= \dfrac{15\sqrt{21}}{2(3)}$$
$$= \dfrac{5\sqrt{21}}{2}$$

EXERCISE 1.8

A 1. Simplify.

(a) $\dfrac{\sqrt{14}}{\sqrt{7}}$ (b) $\dfrac{\sqrt{18}}{\sqrt{3}}$ (c) $\dfrac{27\sqrt{15}}{3\sqrt{5}}$ (d) $\dfrac{\sqrt{28}}{\sqrt{7}}$

(e) $\dfrac{\sqrt{72}}{\sqrt{24}}$ (f) $\dfrac{3\sqrt{8}}{\sqrt{2}}$ (g) $\dfrac{\sqrt{50}}{\sqrt{2}}$ (h) $\dfrac{3\sqrt{75}}{\sqrt{3}}$

B 2. Simplify by expressing the denominator as a rational number.

(a) $\dfrac{\sqrt{5}}{\sqrt{3}}$ (b) $\dfrac{2}{\sqrt{2}}$ (c) $\dfrac{3\sqrt{5}}{2\sqrt{6}}$ (d) $\dfrac{4\sqrt{7}}{5\sqrt{2}}$

(e) $\dfrac{3\sqrt{7}}{2\sqrt{3}}$ (f) $\dfrac{\sqrt{3}}{\sqrt{5}}$ (g) $\dfrac{3\sqrt{7}}{4\sqrt{2}}$ (h) $\dfrac{2\sqrt{3}}{\sqrt{6}}$

1.9 APPROXIMATING RADICALS

USING A CALCULATOR WITH A √ KEY

Find an approximation for $\sqrt{23.15}$.

| C | 2 | 3 | · | 1 | 5 | √ |

USING A CALCULATOR WITH A yˣ KEY

Find an approximation for $\sqrt{149.7}$.

| C | 1 | 4 | 9 | · | 7 | yˣ | · | 5 | = |

BY SUCCESSIVE APPROXIMATION

Find an approximation for $\sqrt{39}$.

Trial Number	Calculator	Display	Observation
6	6 × 6 =	36	too small
6.1	6 · 1 × 6 · 1 =	37.21	too small
6.2	6 · 2 × 6 · 2 =	38.44	too small
6.3	6 · 3 × 6 · 3 =	39.69	too large
6.25	6 · 2 5 × 6 · 2 5 =	39.0625	too large
6.24	6 · 2 4 × 6 · 2 4 =	38.9376	too small

$\sqrt{39}$ is between 6.2 and 6.3.

$\sqrt{39}$ is between 6.24 and 6.25.

We can continue this method to find that 6.245 is even closer.

6.24^2 gives a result closer to 39.

$\therefore \sqrt{39} \doteq 6.24$

USING A COMPUTER WITH BASIC

Find an approximation for $\sqrt{117.3}$.

Type   PRINT SQR(117.3)

or   PRINT 117.3↑0.5

Press the ⟨RETURN⟩ or ⟨ENTER⟩ key after each line.

USING A COMPUTER WITH LOGO

Find an approximation for $\sqrt{73.96}$.

Type   PRINT SQRT 73.96

To find a square root by Newton's method

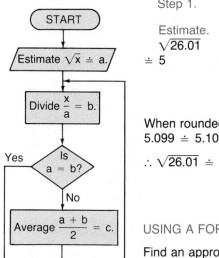

USING NEWTON'S METHOD

Find an approximation for $\sqrt{26.01}$ to the nearest hundredth.

Step 1.	Step 2.	Step 3.	Step 4.
Estimate.	Divide.	Average.	Divide.
$\sqrt{26.01}$	$\dfrac{26.01}{5}$	$\dfrac{5 + 5.202}{2}$	$\dfrac{26.01}{5.101}$
$\doteq 5$	$\doteq 5.202$	$\doteq \dfrac{10.202}{2}$	$\doteq 5.099$
		$= 5.101$	

When rounded off to the nearest hundredth $5.101 \doteq 5.10$ and $5.099 \doteq 5.10$.

$\therefore \sqrt{26.01} \doteq 5.10$ to the nearest hundredth.

USING A FORMAL METHOD

Find an approximation for $\sqrt{2.197}$ to the nearest hundredth.

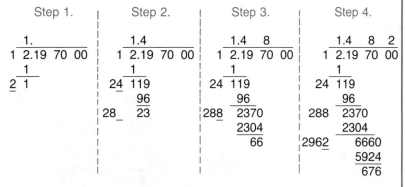

$\therefore \sqrt{2.197} \doteq 1.48$ to the nearest hundredth.

n	$\sqrt{n}$
1	1.000
2	1.414
3	1.732
4	2.000
5	2.236
6	2.449
7	2.645

BY CHANGING TO A MIXED RADICAL AND USING A TABLE

Find an approximation for $\sqrt{162}$ to the nearest tenth.

Step 1.

Change to a mixed radical

$$\sqrt{162} = \sqrt{81 \times 2}$$
$$= 9\sqrt{2}$$

Step 2.

Using a table for square roots we see that $\sqrt{2} \doteq 1.414$.

$$\sqrt{162} = 9\sqrt{2}$$
$$\doteq 9(1.414)$$
$$= 12.726$$
$$\doteq 12.7 \text{ to the nearest tenth}$$

1.10 APPROXIMATION OF RADICALS

n	√n	n	√n
1	1.000	51	7.141
2	1.414	52	7.211
3	1.732	53	7.280
4	2.000	54	7.349
5	2.236	55	7.416
6	2.450	56	7.483
7	2.646	57	7.550
8	2.828	58	7.616
9	3.000	59	7.681
10	3.162	60	7.746
11	3.317	61	7.810
12	3.464	62	7.874
13	3.606	63	7.937
14	3.742	64	8.000
15	3.873	65	8.062
16	4.000	66	8.124
17	4.123	67	8.185
18	4.243	68	8.246
19	4.359	69	8.307
20	4.472	70	8.367
21	4.583	71	8.426
22	4.690	72	8.485
23	4.796	73	8.544
24	4.899	74	8.602
25	5.000	75	8.660
26	5.099	76	8.718
27	5.196	77	8.775
28	5.292	78	8.832
29	5.385	79	8.888
30	5.477	80	8.944
31	5.568	81	9.000
32	5.657	82	9.055
33	5.745	83	9.110
34	5.831	84	9.165
35	5.916	85	9.220
36	6.000	86	9.274
37	6.083	87	9.327
38	6.164	88	9.381
39	6.245	89	9.434
40	6.325	90	9.487
41	6.403	91	9.539
42	6.481	92	9.592
43	6.557	93	9.644
44	6.633	94	9.695
45	6.708	95	9.747
46	6.782	96	9.798
47	6.856	97	9.849
48	6.928	98	9.900
49	7.000	99	9.950
50	7.071	100	10.000

When radicals appear in practical problems it is often necessary to convert them to decimal approximations so that they can be used.

EXAMPLE 1. Evaluate the following to the nearest hundredth.

(a) $\dfrac{\sqrt{92}}{\sqrt{46}}$

(b) $\dfrac{3\sqrt{60}}{\sqrt{27}}$

SOLUTION:

(a) $\dfrac{\sqrt{92}}{\sqrt{46}} = \sqrt{\dfrac{92}{46}}$

$= \sqrt{2}$

$\doteq 1.41$

(b) $\dfrac{3\sqrt{60}}{\sqrt{27}} = \dfrac{3\sqrt{4 \times 15}}{\sqrt{9 \times 3}}$

$= \dfrac{3 \times 2\sqrt{15}}{3\sqrt{3}}$

$= 2\sqrt{5}$

$\doteq 2(2.236)$

$\doteq 4.47$

> Change to mixed radicals.

EXAMPLE 2. Evaluate $\dfrac{2\sqrt{5}}{3\sqrt{2}}$ to the nearest hundredth by first expressing the denominator as a rational number.

SOLUTION:

$$\dfrac{2\sqrt{5}}{3\sqrt{2}} = \dfrac{2\sqrt{5}}{3\sqrt{2}} \times \dfrac{\sqrt{2}}{\sqrt{2}}$$

$$= \dfrac{2\sqrt{10}}{3 \times 2}$$

$$\doteq \dfrac{3.162}{3}$$

$$= 1.05 \quad \text{to the nearest hundredth}$$

EXAMPLE 3. A ladder 6 m long leans against a wall with the foot of the ladder 2 m from the wall. Calculate how high up the wall the ladder will reach to the nearest tenth of a metre.

SOLUTION:

Applying the Pythagorean relation,

$$a^2 + b^2 = c^2$$
$$h^2 + 2^2 = 6^2$$
$$h^2 + 4 = 36$$
$$h^2 = 32$$
$$h = \sqrt{32}$$
$$\doteq 5.657$$

The ladder will reach 5.7 m up the wall.

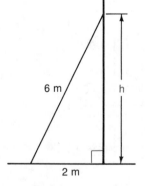

6 m

h

2 m

EXERCISE 1.10

Unless otherwise stated, all answers should be to the nearest tenth.

B 1. Evaluate by any method.
- (a) $\sqrt{45}$
- (b) $\sqrt{128}$
- (c) $\sqrt{29}$
- (d) $\sqrt{140}$
- (e) $\sqrt{345}$
- (f) $\sqrt{61.25}$
- (g) $\sqrt{0.0345}$
- (h) $\sqrt{0.002\,745}$

2. Evaluate.
- (a) $\dfrac{\sqrt{42}}{\sqrt{6}}$
- (b) $\dfrac{\sqrt{12}}{\sqrt{6}}$
- (c) $\dfrac{\sqrt{42}}{\sqrt{7}}$
- (d) $\dfrac{15\sqrt{20}}{\sqrt{2}}$
- (e) $\dfrac{20\sqrt{15}}{\sqrt{3}}$
- (f) $\dfrac{\sqrt{36}}{\sqrt{3}}$
- (g) $\dfrac{\sqrt{26}}{\sqrt{2}}$
- (h) $\dfrac{3\sqrt{50}}{\sqrt{10}}$
- (i) $\dfrac{2\sqrt{75}}{\sqrt{15}}$
- (j) $\dfrac{\sqrt{18} + \sqrt{12}}{\sqrt{3}}$
- (k) $\dfrac{15 - \sqrt{75}}{5}$
- (l) $\dfrac{9 - \sqrt{45}}{3}$

3. Evaluate by first expressing the denominator as a rational number.
- (a) $\dfrac{2}{\sqrt{3}}$
- (b) $\dfrac{5}{\sqrt{7}}$
- (c) $\dfrac{\sqrt{6}}{\sqrt{5}}$
- (d) $\dfrac{2\sqrt{3}}{\sqrt{7}}$
- (e) $\dfrac{\sqrt{3}}{2\sqrt{5}}$
- (f) $\dfrac{3\sqrt{5}}{4\sqrt{2}}$
- (g) $\dfrac{3\sqrt{6}}{2\sqrt{7}}$
- (h) $\dfrac{5\sqrt{3}}{3\sqrt{7}}$
- (i) $\dfrac{3\sqrt{21}}{\sqrt{5}}$
- (j) $\dfrac{7\sqrt{2}}{2\sqrt{11}}$
- (k) $\dfrac{5\sqrt{3}}{4\sqrt{7}}$
- (l) $\dfrac{7\sqrt{7}}{2\sqrt{2}}$

4. Determine the value of x to the nearest tenth in each of the following using the Pythagorean relationship.

(a)

(b)

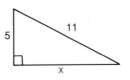

(c)

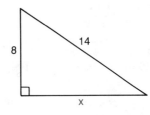

5. A 5 m ladder leans against a wall and the foot of the ladder is 2 m from the wall. Find the distance the ladder reaches up the wall.

6. Find the dimensions of a square whose area is 60 cm².

7. Find the length of the sides of a square having the same area as a rectangle with dimensions 4 cm by 7 cm.

8. The perimeter of a square can be found using the formula

$$P = 4\sqrt{A}$$

where A is the area and P the perimeter. Find the perimeter of a square having an area of 136 cm².

9. The period of a pendulum is given by the formula

$$T = 2\pi \sqrt{\dfrac{\ell}{9.8}}$$

where T is the period in seconds and ℓ is the length of the pendulum in metres. Calculate the period to the nearest second when the length is
- (a) 19.6 m
- (b) 0.98 m

10. The time t (in seconds) it takes an object to reach the ground when dropped from a height h (in metres) is determined by

$$t = \sqrt{\frac{h}{4.9}}$$

Determine to the nearest second the time it takes an object to hit the ground when dropped from a height of
(a) 20 m   (b) 100 m   (c) 42.7 m

11. Police can use the length of a skid mark to approximate the speed of a car. The formula is

$$S = 13\sqrt{\ell}$$

where S is the speed in km/h and ℓ is the length of the skid mark in metres. Determine, to the nearest tenth of a kilometre, the speed of the car if the length of the skid mark was
(a) 30 m   (b) 25.5 m   (c) 15.2 m

12. Two cars leave an intersection at the same time. One travels 4.8 km south and the other travels 3.2 km east. How far apart are they?

13. Two speed boats leave a dock at the same time. One travels north at 32 km/h and the other travels west at 28 km/h. How far apart are they after 45 min?

14. A square has sides 7 cm long. Use the Pythagorean relation to find the length of a diagonal.

15. A rectangle is 5 cm by 7 cm. Find the length of a diagonal.

16. Find the diameter of a circle that will circumscribe a square with sides 3 cm.

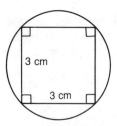

17. Find the length of a guy wire required to secure a 20 m tower 14 m from the base if you must add 4 m for fastening.

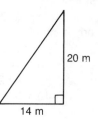

18. Three towns A, B, and C are situated so that A is 10 km east of B and C is 7 km north of B. Find the distance from A to C.

19. The greatest distance from which an object of height h can be seen from the same level is given by the formula

$$d = \sqrt{0.8h}$$

where d is in kilometres and h is in metres. From what distance can you see the light at the 300 m mark of the CN Tower in Toronto?

20. A ladder 3.2 m from the foot of a wall reaches 8.4 m up the wall. How long is the ladder?

C 21. The area of a triangle can be found using Heron's formula

$$A = \sqrt{s(s - a)(s - b)(s - c)}$$

where a, b, and c are the lengths of the sides of the triangle and

$$s = \tfrac{1}{2}(a + b + c)$$

Calculate the area of the following triangles to the nearest square metre.
(a)

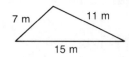

(b)

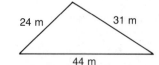

(c)

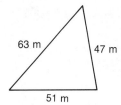

(d)

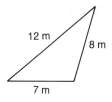

22. Find the altitude of an equilateral triangle with sides 8 cm.

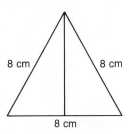

23. Find the altitude to the shortest side of an isosceles triangle with sides 10 cm, 10 cm, and 6 cm.

24.

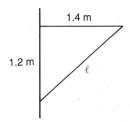

Find the length of the brace ℓ to the nearest tenth of a metre.

25.

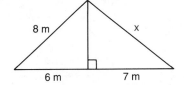

Find the value of the dimension x to the nearest tenth of a metre.

In the following computer program, the user inputs a positive number, then the computer calculates and prints the square root, cube root, and fourth root of the number. Note that the program makes use of the special property that

$$\sqrt[n]{x} = x^{\frac{1}{n}}$$

NEW

```
10 REM ROOT CALCULATOR
20 PRINT "WHAT IS YOUR NUMBER";
30 INPUT N
40 PRINT "THE SQUARE ROOT IS"; N↑0.5
50 PRINT "THE CUBE ROOT IS  "; N↑(1/3)
60 PRINT "THE FOURTH ROOT IS"; N↑0.25
70 END
```

RUN

```
WHAT IS YOUR NUMBER? 19
THE SQUARE ROOT IS 4.35889894354067
THE CUBE ROOT IS   2.66840164872194
THE FOURTH ROOT IS 2.08779762992984
```

Alter the program to calculate the fifth, eighth, and tenth roots of a number.

MIND BENDER

Find the missing digits in this division.

1.11 POWERS WITH INTEGRAL BASES

In an addition question, the terms to be added are called addends. A repeated addition of equal addends can be expressed as a product.

$$3 + 3 + 3 + 3 = 4 \times 3$$

In a multiplication question, the terms to be multiplied are called factors. A repeated multiplication of equal factors can be expressed as a power.

$$3 \times 3 \times 3 \times 3 = 3^4$$

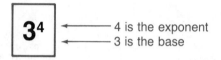

3⁴ is a power (of 3)

The expression is read "3 to the fourth power," "3 raised to the fourth power," or "3 to the fourth." Since 3^4 is a power and $3^4 = 81$, then 81 is also a power. It is the fourth power of 3. Similarly, 16 is the fourth power of 2, 1000 is the third power of 10, and 125 is the third power of 5.

EXAMPLE 1. Express the following as powers of integral bases.
(a) 25
(b) 27
(c) 81

SOLUTION:
(a) $25 = 5 \times 5$
  $= 5^2$
(b) $27 = 3 \times 3 \times 3$
  $= 3^3$
(c) $81 = 3 \times 3 \times 3 \times 3$ or $81 = 9 \times 9$
  $= 3^4$ $= 9^2$

A negative base must be enclosed in brackets. Notice the pattern when a negative base is raised to odd and even natural exponents.

$$
\begin{aligned}
(-2)^2 &= (-2)(-2) & &= 4 \\
(-2)^3 &= (-2)(-2)(-2) & &= -8 \\
(-2)^4 &= (-2)(-2)(-2)(-2) & &= 16 \\
(-2)^5 &= (-2)(-2)(-2)(-2)(-2) & &= -32 \\
(-2)^6 &= (-2)(-2)(-2)(-2)(-2)(-2) & &= 64 \\
(-2)^7 &= (-2)(-2)(-2)(-2)(-2)(-2)(-2) &&= -128
\end{aligned}
$$

> A power with a negative base gives a positive result when the exponent is even, and a negative result when the exponent is odd.

EXAMPLE 2. Simplify.

(a) $(-3)^4$

(b) $(-3)^5$

SOLUTION:

(a) $(-3)^4 = (-3)(-3)(-3)(-3)$
$= 81$

(b) $(-3)^5 = (-3)(-3)(-3)(-3)(-3)$
$= -243$

$$\left(\begin{array}{l} (-1)^{even} = 1 \\ (-1)^{odd} = -1 \end{array} \right)$$

EXAMPLE 3. Simplify.

(a) $(-1)^2$

(b) $(-1)^3$

(c) $(-1)^{100}$

(d) $(-1)^{207}$

SOLUTION:

(a) $(-1)^2 = (-1)(-1)$
$= 1$

(b) $(-1)^3 = (-1)(-1)(-1)$
$= -1$

(c) $(-1)^{100} = 1$

(d) $(-1)^{207} = -1$

EXAMPLE 4. If $x = -2$ and $y = 3$, evaluate.

(a) x^3

(b) $3x^2y$

Brackets
Exponents
Division
Multiplication
Addition
Subtraction

SOLUTION:

(a) $x^3 = (-2)^3$
$= (-2)(-2)(-2)$
$= -8$

(b) $3x^2y = 3(-2)^2(3)$
$= 3(-2)(-2)(3)$
$= 36$

EXAMPLE 5. If $x = -4$, evaluate.

(a) $2x^3$

(b) $(2x)^3$

SOLUTION:

(a) $2x^3 = 2(-4)^3$
$= 2(-64)$
$= -128$

(b) $(2x)^3 = [2(-4)]^3$
$= [-8]^3$
$= -512$

EXAMPLE 6. If $x = -2$ and $y = 3$, evaluate $(x^2 - y^2)^2$.

SOLUTION:
$$\begin{aligned}
(x^2 - y^2)^2 &= [(-2)^2 - (3)^2]^2 \\
&= [(-2)(-2) - (3)(3)]^2 \\
&= [4 - 9]^2 \\
&= [-5]^2 \\
&= 25
\end{aligned}$$

Many of the formulas used to calculate area and volume involve exponents.

EXAMPLE 7. The area of the annulus is calculated using the formula

$$A = \pi(R^2 - r^2)$$

where R is the measure of the outer radius and r is the measure of the inner radius.

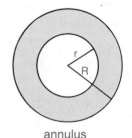

annulus

Find the area to the nearest tenth of a square centimetre of an annulus whose outer radius is 5 cm and whose inner radius is 3 cm.

SOLUTION:
Area of annulus,
$$\begin{aligned}
A &= \pi(R^2 - r^2) \\
A &= (3.14)(5^2 - 3^2) \longleftarrow \text{Use } \pi \doteq 3.14. \\
&= (3.14)(25 - 9) \\
&= (3.14)(16) \\
&= 50.24
\end{aligned}$$

To the nearest tenth of a square centimetre, the area of the annulus is 50.2 cm².

The metric system is based on the powers of 10. From a unit such as the metre (m) or the gram (g), larger units can be obtained using such prefixes as deca (da), hecto (h), kilo (k), and mega (M). These prefixes magnify the unit by powers of 10.

Prefix	Magnification of Unit	Using Base Unit (m)
deca (da)	$10^1 = 10$	1 dam = 10 m
hecto (h)	$10^2 = 100$	1 hm = 100 m
kilo (k)	$10^3 = 1000$	1 km = 1000 m
mega (M)	$10^6 = 1\ 000\ 000$	1 Mm = 1 000 000 m

EXAMPLE 8. Express
(a) 30 hm in metres.
(b) 400 kg in grams.

SOLUTION:

> 1 hm = 10^2 m
>
> 1 kg = 10^3 g

(a) 30 hm = 30×10^2 m
    $= 3 \times 10 \times 10^2$ m
    $= 3 \times 10^3$ m
    or $= 3000$ m

(b) 400 kg = 400×10^3 g
    $= 4 \times 10^2 \times 10^3$ g
    $= 4 \times 10^5$ g
    or $= 400\ 000$ g

EXAMPLE 9. Find the volume of a rectangular cement slab whose dimensions are 1 m × 1 m × 10 cm. Express your answer as a power of 10 in cubic centimetres.

SOLUTION:

The dimensions are   1 m ×   1 m × 10 cm
or   100 cm × 100 cm × 10 cm

$V = \ell wh$
$V = 100 \times 100 \times 10$
$\quad = 10^2 \times 10^2 \times 10$
$\quad = 10^5$

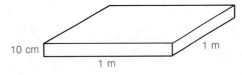

The volume of the cement slab is 10^5 cm^3.

EXERCISE 1.11

A 1. Express the following as powers of integral bases.

(a) 8   (b) −27
(c) 49   (d) 100
(e) 36   (f) −125
(g) 144   (h) 289
(i) 216   (j) 400

2. Simplify.

(a) $(-2)^2$ (b) $(-1)^{27}$
(c) $(-3)^2$ (d) $(-5)^3$
(e) $(-1)^{16}$ (f) $(-3)^3$

3. Fill the squares.

(a) 30 km = ■ hm = ■ dam = ■ m
(b) 200 kg = ■ hg = ■ dag = ■ g

B 4. Express each of the following as powers of two different integral bases.

(a) 16   (b) 625
(c) 64   (d) 1296
(e) 256   (f) 512

5. If $x = 2$ and $y = -3$, evaluate.

(a) x^3 (b) y^2
(c) $2x^2y$ (d) $-3xy^2$
(e) $(-y)^3$ (f) $x^2 + 2xy + y^2$
(g) $(x + y)^2$ (h) $(2x - y)(2x + y)$
(i) $(x^3 - 8)$ (j) $(x - 2)(x^2 + 2x + 4)$

6. Find the area of each of the following two-dimensional figures to the nearest tenth.

(a) a square with sides 4 m
(b) a circle with a radius of 3 m
(c) an annulus whose outer radius is 6 cm and whose inner radius is 3 cm

7. Find the total surface area and volume of each of the following three-dimensional figures to the nearest integer.

(a) a cube with sides 8 cm
(b) a beach ball with a radius of 20 cm
(c) a can of peas whose height is 10 cm and whose circular top and bottom have a radius of 4 cm
(d) a cone whose height is 15 cm and whose circular base has a radius of 6 cm

8. The radius of the moon is 1730 km. Find the area to the nearest hundred thousand square kilometres.

C 9. Find the area of the shaded region to the nearest tenth.

(a)

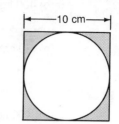

├──10 cm──┤

(b)

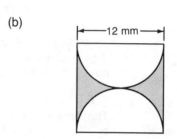

├──12 mm──┤

Use the following formulas to solve questions 7 and 8.

Two-dimensional Figures	Diagram	Area
square	☐	$A = s^2$
circle	◯	$A = \pi r^2$
annulus	◎	$A = \pi(R^2 - r^2)$

Three-dimensional Figures	Diagram	Total Surface Area	Volume
cube		$S = 6s^2$	$V = s^3$
sphere		$S = 4\pi r^2$	$V = \frac{4}{3}\pi r^3$
cylinder		$S = 2\pi r(r + h)$	$V = \pi r^2 h$
cone		$S = \pi r(r + \sqrt{r^2 + h^2})$	$V = \frac{1}{3}\pi r^2 h$

(c)

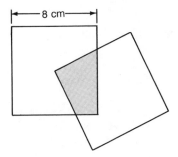

10. Find the volume of the pencil to the nearest tenth of a cubic centimetre.

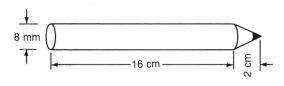

11. A solid rubber sphere with a radius of 5 cm is sliced by a horizontal plane 3 cm above its centre. Find the area of the circular cross-section to the nearest tenth.

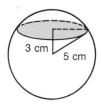

MIND BENDER

Put the numbers 1 to 9 in the spaces to make the statements true.

$$■ × ■ - ■ = 2$$
$$■ + ■ ÷ ■ = 2$$
$$■ - ■ + ■ = 2$$

ACCURACY AND PRECISION

In most problems, unless otherwise stated, the accuracy of the answers should reflect the precision of the numbers given.

EXAMPLE 1. Find the area of a square 2.1 cm by 2.1 cm.

SOLUTION:
The area is
$$A = s^2$$
$$A = (2.1)^2$$
$$= 4.41$$

The area of the square is approximately 4.4 cm^2.

When the original data are assumed to be exact, we round the answer to what is reasonable and qualify the accuracy of the answer.

EXAMPLE 2. A cable is 13 m long. It is to be divided into 8 equal lengths. How long is each part?

SOLUTION:
$$13 ÷ 8 = 1.625$$

Each part is 1.6 m long to the nearest tenth of a metre.

MICRO MATH

This program will determine if a given natural number is a perfect square.

NEW

```
10 REM PERFECT SQUARE?
20 PRINT "WHAT IS YOUR NATURAL NUMBER";
30 INPUT NUM
40 SROOT = SQR(NUM)
50 IF INT(SROOT) = SROOT THEN PRINT
   NUM; "IS A PERFECT SQUARE."
60 IF INT(SROOT) <> SROOT THEN PRINT
   NUM; "IS NOT A PERFECT SQUARE."
70 END
```

RUN

```
WHAT IS YOUR NATURAL NUMBER? 3136
3136 IS A PERFECT SQUARE.
```

1.12 EXPONENT LAWS

Expressions involving exponents can often be simplified using the laws for exponents which we shall establish in this section.

MULTIPLICATION

	$3^4 \times 3^2 = 3 \times 3 \times 3 \times 3 \times 3 \times 3$ $= 3^6$	$x^4 \times x^2 = x \times x \times x \times x \times x \times x$ $= x^6$
Observation	$3^4 \times 3^2 = 3^{4+2}$ $= 3^6$	$x^4 \times x^2 = x^{4+2}$ $= x^6$
Generalization	The exponent law for multiplication: $$x^a \times x^b = x^{a+b}$$ When multiplying two powers of the same base, add the exponents.	

DIVISION

	$2^5 \div 2^3 = \dfrac{2 \times 2 \times 2 \times 2 \times 2}{2 \times 2 \times 2}$ $= 2^2$	$x^5 \div x^3 = \dfrac{x \times x \times x \times x \times x}{x \times x \times x}$ $= x^2$
Observation	$2^5 \div 2^3 = 2^{5-3}$ $= 2^2$	$x^5 \div x^3 = x^{5-3}$ $= x^2$
Generalization	The exponent law for division: $$\text{If } x \neq 0, \ x^a \div x^b = x^{a-b}$$ When dividing two powers of the same base, subtract the exponents.	

POWERS

We use the exponent law for multiplication.

	$(5^2)^3 = 5^2 \times 5^2 \times 5^2$ $= 5^{2+2+2}$ $= 5^6$	$(x^2)^3 = x^2 \times x^2 \times x^2$ $= x^{2+2+2}$ $= x^6$
Observation	$(5^2)^3 = 5^{2 \times 3}$ $= 5^6$	$(x^2)^3 = x^{2 \times 3}$ $= x^6$
Generalization	The exponent law for powers: $$(x^a)^b = x^{ab}$$ For the power of a power, multiply the exponents.	

POWER OF A PRODUCT

We use the exponent law for multiplication.

$(5^3 \times 7^4)^2 = (5^3 \times 7^4) \times (5^3 \times 7^4)$ $= 5^3 \times 5^3 \times 7^4 \times 7^4$ $= 5^6 \times 7^8$	$(x^3y^4)^2 = (x^3y^4)(x^3y^4)$ $= x^3 \times x^3 \times y^4 \times y^4$ $= x^6y^8$

Observation

$(5^3 \times 7^4)^2 = 5^{3 \times 2} \times 7^{4 \times 2}$ $= 5^6 \times 7^8$	$(x^3y^4)^2 = x^{3 \times 2}y^{4 \times 2}$ $= x^6y^8$

Generalization

The exponent law for the power of a product:

$$(x^ay^b)^c = x^{ac}y^{bc}$$

POWER OF A QUOTIENT

$\left(\dfrac{7^5}{5^3}\right)^2 = \left(\dfrac{7^5}{5^3}\right)\left(\dfrac{7^5}{5^3}\right)$ $= \dfrac{7^5 \times 7^5}{5^3 \times 5^3}$ $= \dfrac{7^{10}}{5^6}$	$\left(\dfrac{x^5}{y^3}\right)^2 = \left(\dfrac{x^5}{y^3}\right)\left(\dfrac{x^5}{y^3}\right)$ $= \dfrac{x^5 \times x^5}{y^3 \times y^3}$ $= \dfrac{x^{10}}{y^6}$

Observation

$\left(\dfrac{7^5}{5^3}\right)^2 = \dfrac{7^{5 \times 2}}{5^{3 \times 2}}$ $= \dfrac{7^{10}}{5^6}$	$\left(\dfrac{x^5}{y^3}\right)^2 = \dfrac{x^{5 \times 2}}{y^{3 \times 2}}$ $= \dfrac{x^{10}}{y^6}$

Generalization

The exponent law for the power of a quotient:

$$\text{If } y \neq 0, \ \left(\frac{x^a}{y^b}\right)^c = \frac{x^{ac}}{y^{bc}}$$

EXAMPLE 1. Simplify.

(a) $(2x)(3x^2)$

(b) $(x^2y)(x^4y^3)$

(c) $\dfrac{14x^5}{7x^3}$

SOLUTION:

(a) $(2x)(3x^2) = 2 \times 3 \times x \times x^2$
$= 6x^3$

$x^ax^b = x^{a+b}$

(b) $(x^2y)(x^4y^3) = x^2 \times x^4 \times y \times y^3$
$= x^6y^4$

$$\frac{x^a}{x^b} = x^{a-b}$$

(c) $\dfrac{14x^5}{7x^3} = \dfrac{14}{7} \times \dfrac{x^5}{x^3}$

$\qquad\quad = \dfrac{14}{7} x^{5-3}$

$\qquad\quad = 2x^2$

EXAMPLE 2. Simplify.

(a) $(2x^2y)(3x^3y^4)$

(b) $\dfrac{18a^4b^5}{12a^2b}$

(c) $\dfrac{(3x^2)^4}{x^3}$

SOLUTION:

$$x^a x^b = x^{a+b}$$

(a) $(2x^2y)(3x^3y^4) = 2 \times 3 \times x^2 \times x^3 \times y \times y^4$

$\qquad\qquad\qquad\quad = 6x^5y^5$

$$\frac{x^a}{x^b} = x^{a-b}$$

(b) $\dfrac{18a^4b^5}{12a^2b} = \dfrac{18}{12} \times \dfrac{a^4}{a^2} \times \dfrac{b^5}{b}$

$\qquad\qquad\quad = \dfrac{18}{12} \times a^{4-2}b^{5-1}$

$\qquad\qquad\quad = \dfrac{3}{2}a^2b^4$

$$(x^ay^b)^c = x^{ac}y^{bc}$$

$$\frac{x^a}{x^b} = x^{a-b}$$

(c) $\dfrac{(3x^2)^4}{x^3} = \dfrac{(3^1x^2)^4}{x^3}$

$\qquad\qquad = \dfrac{3^4x^8}{x^3}$

$\qquad\qquad = 3^4x^{8-3}$

$\qquad\qquad = 81x^5$

EXAMPLE 3. Simplify. $\quad\dfrac{(6a^2b^3)(2a^3b^5)}{(2ab)^2}$

SOLUTION:

$$\frac{(6a^2b^3)(2a^3b^5)}{(2ab)^2} = \frac{6 \times 2\, a^{2+3}b^{3+5}}{2^2\, a^2\, b^2}$$

$$= \frac{12\, a^5b^8}{4\, a^2b^2}$$

$$= \frac{12}{4} a^{5-2}b^{8-2}$$

$$= 3a^3b^6$$

EXERCISE 1.12

A 1. Simplify.

(a) $(x^3)(x^5)$ (b) $(a^2)(a^{10})$
(c) $(b)(b)(b)$ (d) $(m^2)(m^3)(m)$
(e) $(a^2)(a^3)(b)(b^4)$ (f) $(a)(b)(a^2)(b^3)$

2. Simplify.

(a) $a^7 \div a^3$ (b) $b^3 \div b^2$ (c) $n^{12} \div n^3$
(d) $x^8 \div x^5$ (e) $a^5 \div a$ (f) $x^{10} \div x^9$

3. Simplify.

(a) $(x^4)^2$ (b) $(a^3)^3$ (c) $(a^2b)^3$
(d) $(xy^3)^5$ (e) $(abc)^5$ (f) $(b^8)^3$
(g) $(2x^3)^3$ (h) $(a^5b^2)^3$ (i) $(3a^5)^2$
(j) $(3xy^2)^3$ (k) $(5a^8)^3$ (l) $(4x^2yz)^3$

4. Simplify.

(a) $\left(\dfrac{x}{y}\right)^5$ (b) $\left(\dfrac{a^2}{3}\right)^2$ (c) $\left(\dfrac{x^2}{y}\right)^3$ (d) $\left(\dfrac{a}{b^5}\right)^4$

(e) $\left(\dfrac{3x}{y}\right)^2$ (f) $\left(\dfrac{2x^2}{w}\right)^3$ (g) $\left(\dfrac{5a^2}{2b^3}\right)^2$ (h) $\left(\dfrac{3a}{b^3}\right)^2$

B 5. Simplify.

(a) $(5a^3)(3a^6)$ (b) $(4x^2)(-2x^3)$
(c) $(3a^2b^3)(2ab^2)$ (d) $(2x)(5x^3)$
(e) $(5mn)(3m)$ (f) $(-4x^3)(-3x^2)$
(g) $(3y)(5y)(2y^2)$ (h) $(a)(2a^2)(-3a^5)$
(i) $(-7x^3)(-2x^3)(-x^2)$

6. Simplify.

(a) $12a^5 \div 3a^3$ (b) $21x^2y^5 \div 7xy$
(c) $8a^2 \div 8a$ (d) $48m^2n \div 6mn$
(e) $30m^2 \div (-6m^2)$
(f) $(-18ab^3) \div (-2ab)$
(g) $56pqr \div 8pr$
(h) $(-24a^2b^2) \div (8a^2b^2)$
(i) $(15x^{10}y^2) \div (-5xy)$

7. Simplify.

(a) $(-2a^3)^3$ (b) $[(3x)(x^2)]^2$

(c) $\left(\dfrac{12x^5}{4x^3}\right)^2$ (d) $[(2a^3b)(3a^4)]^2$

(e) $\left(\dfrac{a^5b}{c^4}\right)^3$ (f) $\left(\dfrac{-32a^5b}{-16ab}\right)^3$

(g) $\left(\dfrac{48x^3y^7}{-12xy}\right)^3$ (h) $\left(\dfrac{5a^2x}{15a^2}\right)^3$

8. Simplify.

(a) $(2x^2)^3(2x^5)$ (b) $\dfrac{(8ab^2)(3a^2b)}{12a^3}$

(c) $\dfrac{(3x^2y^5)^3}{9xy^2}$ (d) $\dfrac{(12m^2n^5)(-5mn^3)}{15m^3n^2}$

(e) $\dfrac{(-12x^2)(-4x^2y)}{(-6x^3)}$ (f) $\dfrac{-32m^{10}n^3}{(8m^5)(mn)}$

MICRO MATH

Pythagoras discovered that the square of a number can be obtained by adding a corresponding number of consecutive odd numbers.

$1^2 = 1$ $= 1$

$2^2 = 1 + 3$ $= 4$

$3^2 = 1 + 3 + 5$ $= 9$

$4^2 = 1 + 3 + 5 + 7$ $= 16$

$5^2 = 1 + 3 + 5 + 7 + 9 = 25$

The following BASIC program illustrates this fact.

NEW

```
100 REM PERFECT SQUARES BY ADDING
101 REM CONSECUTIVE ODD NUMBERS
110 PRINT "HOW MANY ODD NUMBERS";
120 INPUT N
130 PRINT N; "↑2 =";
140 FOR I= 1 TO 2*N-1 STEP 2
150 S = S + I
160 PRINT I;
170 IF I < 2*N-1 THEN PRINT "+";
180 NEXT I
190 PRINT "="; S
200 END
```

RUN

1.13 INTEGRAL EXPONENTS

ZERO EXPONENT

$\dfrac{x^2}{x^2} = x^{2-2}$ $= x^0$	$\dfrac{x^2}{x^2} = \dfrac{\cancel{x} \times \cancel{x}}{\cancel{x} \times \cancel{x}}$ $= 1$

Observation	$\dfrac{x^2}{x^2} = x^0$ $= 1$
Generalization	If $x \neq 0$, $x^0 = 1$

NEGATIVE EXPONENT

$\dfrac{x^2}{x^5} = x^{2-5}$ $= x^{-3}$	$\dfrac{x^2}{x^5} = \dfrac{\cancel{x} \times \cancel{x}}{\cancel{x} \times \cancel{x} \times x \times x \times x}$ $= \dfrac{1}{x^3}$

Observation	$\dfrac{x^2}{x^5} = x^{-3}$ $= \dfrac{1}{x^3}$
Generalization	If $x \neq 0$, $x^{-n} = \dfrac{1}{x^n}$

EXAMPLE 1. Simplify to an expression which does not involve exponents.

(a) 2^0 (b) $(-3)^0$
(c) 4^{-1} (d) 2^{-3}

SOLUTION:

$x^0 = 1$

$x^{-1} = \dfrac{1}{x}$

(a) $2^0 = 1$ (b) $(-3)^0 = 1$

(c) $4^{-1} = \dfrac{1}{4^1}$ (d) $2^{-3} = \dfrac{1}{2^3}$

          $= \dfrac{1}{4}$ $= \dfrac{1}{8}$

EXAMPLE 2. Simplify.

(a) $\left(\dfrac{-2}{3}\right)^0$ 　　　(b) $\left(\dfrac{3}{5}\right)^{-2}$ 　　　(c) $3^{-1} + 2^{-2}$

SOLUTION:

(a) $\left(-\dfrac{2}{3}\right)^0 = 1$

(b) $\left(\dfrac{3}{5}\right)^{-2} = \dfrac{1}{\left(\dfrac{3}{5}\right)^2}$

$= \dfrac{1}{\dfrac{9}{25}}$

$= \dfrac{25}{9}$

(c) $3^{-1} + 2^{-2} = \dfrac{1}{3} + \dfrac{1}{2^2}$

$= \dfrac{1}{3} + \dfrac{1}{4}$

$= \dfrac{4 + 3}{12}$

$= \dfrac{7}{12}$

EXAMPLE 3. Simplify. 　$\dfrac{(x^2y^3)^2}{(xy^2)(x^3y^6)}$

SOLUTION:

$\dfrac{(x^2y^3)^2}{(xy^2)(x^3y^6)} = \dfrac{x^4y^6}{x^4y^8}$

$= x^0y^{-2}$

$= y^{-2}$ 　or 　$\dfrac{1}{y^2}$

EXERCISE 1.13

A **1. Simplify.**

(a) $(x^3)(x^{-5})$ 　　　(b) $(a^{-1})(a^8)$
(c) $(y^0)(y^4)$ 　　　(d) $(b^{-1})(b^{-3})$
(e) $(a^{10})(a^3)(a^{-5})$ 　(f) $(x)(x^0)$
(g) $(b^{-5})(b^5)$ 　　　(h) $(m)(m^{-1})(m^0)$

2. Simplify.

(a) $x^{10} \div x^5$ 　　　(b) $b^9 \div b^{12}$
(c) $a^0 \div a^3$ 　　　(d) $x^{-3} \div x^2$
(e) $m^{-5} \div m^0$ 　　(f) $n^4 \div n^{-3}$
(g) $0 \div y^5$ 　　　(h) $m^{-8} \div m^{-4}$

3. Evaluate.

(a) 4^0 　　　(b) 2^{-1}
(c) $(-3)^0$ 　　(d) 10^{-1}
(e) 3^{-2} 　　(f) 10^0
(g) 4^{-2} 　　(h) 2^{-3}

B **4. Simplify.**

(a) $(3x^5)(5x^{-2})$ 　　(b) $(a^2b^5)(a^3b^{-8})$
(c) $(2y^5)(3y^{-5})$ 　　(d) $(x^{10})(x^{-3})(x^{-5})$
(e) $(3m^{-1})^2$ 　　　(f) $(3a^2)(5a^{-8})$

(g) $(m^2n)(m^5n^{-1})$ 　(h) $(2a^5b^{-3})^3$
(i) $(x^{-5}y^{-2})^{-1}$ 　　(j) $(5xy^{-1})(7x^3y^{-1})$
(k) $(7m^3)(m^{-5}n^{-2})$ 　(l) $(5a^{-3})(3a^3)$

5. Simplify.

(a) $(a^{-3}) \div (a^{-5})$ 　　(b) $(12x^5) \div (4x^{10})$
(c) $(24b^{-5}) \div (6b^5)$ 　(d) $(m^2n) \div (m^5n^0)$
(e) $(a^{12}) \div (a^{15}) \times (a^3)$ 　(f) $(15a^4b^5) \div (5a^2b^7)$
(g) $(b^0) \div (b^{-4})$ 　　(h) $(y^4y^2) \div y^{10}$
(i) $(4x^{-2})^2$ 　　　(j) $(3x^{-5})^{-1}(3x^2)$
(k) $\dfrac{(12b^2)(8b^{-4})}{6b^{-10}}$ 　(l) $(2a^3)^{-3}(4a^{-5})$

6. Evaluate.

(a) $5^0 + 5^{-1}$ 　　(b) $3^{-1} + 4^{-1}$
(c) $(5^{-1})^2$ 　　　(d) $[(4^{-3})(4^2)]^2$
(e) $(2^{-1})^{-1}$ 　　(f) $\left(\dfrac{1}{4}\right)^{-1}$
(g) $\left(\dfrac{2}{3}\right)^0$ 　　　(h) $5^{-1} + 2^{-2}$
(i) $\left(\dfrac{1}{10}\right)^{-1}$ 　　(j) 10^{-2}
(k) $\left(\dfrac{1}{3}\right)^{-2}$ 　　(l) $(10^3)(10^{-5})$

1.14 PRINCIPLES OF PROBLEM SOLVING

A problem is a situation that requires a solution. The word itself implies that the solution is not obvious and requires a conscientious effort.

The question "What is $2 + 3$?" can hardly be called a problem because in fact it poses no problem. However, the question "How many FM 10 textbooks placed end-to-end would span the distance from Halifax to Vancouver?" would at first be considered a problem, since its solution requires a conscientious approach. If you were to solve many problems similar to this one, their solutions would eventually become so methodical and routine that they would be considered drill exercises rather than problems.

Though there are no hard and fast rules for solving problems, most mathematical problems can be solved using the following four-step approach: READ — PLAN — SOLVE — ANSWER.

Whether it be in everyday situations or in a mathematics class, common sense and confidence are the key ingredients to problem solving. The READ — PLAN — SOLVE — ANSWER model presented in this section and used throughout the book will help you to develop both.

READ

Read the problem carefully and devote sufficient time to understanding the problem before trying to solve it. Note key words. Put the problem in your own words. Know what you are asked to find. Be aware of what is given.

PLAN

Think of a plan. Find a connection between the given information and the unknown which will enable you to calculate the unknown.

1. Classify information. Study the information carefully to determine what is needed to solve the problem. Identify the relevant and irrelevant information. Some information may be extraneous or redundant.

You may find it helpful to summarize the information or make lists.

2. Search for a pattern. Try to recognize patterns. Some problems are solved by recognizing that some kind of pattern is occurring. The pattern could be geometric, numerical, or algebraic. If you can see there is some sort of regularity or repetition in a problem, then you might be able to guess what the continuing pattern is, and then prove it.

3. Draw a diagram or flow chart. For many problems it is useful to draw a diagram and identify the given and required quantities on the diagram. A flow chart can be used to organize a series of steps that must be performed in a definite order.

4. Estimate, guess, and check. This is a valid method to solve a problem where a direct method is not apparent. You may find it necessary to improve your guess and "zero in" on the correct answer.

5. Sequence operations. To solve some problems, several operations performed in a definite order are needed.

6. Work backwards. Sometimes it is useful to imagine that your problem is solved and work backwards step by step until you arrive at the given data. Then, you may be able to reverse your steps to solve the original problem.

7. Use a formula or an equation. In some problems, after analyzing the data, the problem can be written as an equation, or the data can be substituted into a formula.

8. Solve a simpler problem. A problem can sometimes be broken into smaller problems that can be solved more easily.

9. Account for all possibilities. List all of the cases. Your solution must account for all of these cases. You may sometimes be able to solve your problem using a process of elimination.

10. Make a table. In some problems, it is helpful to organize the data in a table, chart, or grid.

11. Check for hidden assumptions. In some problems, the information concerning what is given is presented in a subtle manner that may not attract your attention. Re-read the problem carefully and look for the implied information.

12. Conclude from assumptions. In some problems, it will be necessary to make assumptions. The conclusions that you draw from these assumptions should be those that you have made in the past, from the same types of information.

13. Introduce something extra. Sometimes it may be necessary to introduce something new, an auxiliary aid, to help make the connection between the given and the unknown. For instance in geometry, the auxiliary could be a new line drawn in the diagram. In algebra, it could be a new unknown which is related to the original unknown.

SOLVE

Before solving the problem, look at the reasons for selecting your strategy. If you have more than one strategy available, you should consider familiarity, efficiency, and ease, in making your choice. In carrying out your strategy, work with care and check each step as you proceed. Remember to present your ideas clearly.

ANSWER

State the answer in a clear and concise manner. Check your answer in the original problem and use estimation to decide if your answer is reasonable. In checking your answer, you may discover an easier way to solve the problem. You may wish to generalize your method of solution so that it can be applied to similar problems.

The following examples illustrate how various strategies can be combined to solve a problem.

EXAMPLE 1. Twenty-two students reserved seats for graduation dinner together at a restaurant. The small square tables at the restaurant will seat only one person on each side. If the tables are placed side by side so as to form one long table, how many are necessary to seat all 22 students?

PLAN

SOLUTION:

What are we asked to find?

The number of tables.

What are we given?

22 people
square tables
one person per side
tables placed side by side

We can draw a diagram showing the seating plan for 1, 2, 3, and 4 tables.

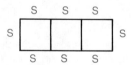   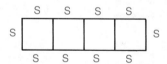

     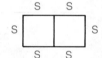

We can make a chart that summarizes our findings.

Number of Tables	Number of People
1	4
2	6
3	8
4	10

We can search for a pattern.

Number of Tables	Number of People
1	$4 = 2 \times 2$
2	$6 = 2 \times 3$
3	$8 = 2 \times 4$
4	$10 = 2 \times 5$

⎣————— compare —————⎦

It would appear that

$$\text{Number of People} = 2 \times (\text{Number of Tables} + 1)$$

At this point, we can guess the solution. By trial and error, we see that if there are 10 tables,

$$\text{Number of People} = 2 \times (10 + 1)$$
$$= 22$$

We now try to prove our guess.

Two people will automatically sit at the ends.
The remaining 20 people must sit 2 per table, facing each other.

Hence 10 tables are required.
We can use an equation to solve the problem.
Let t represent the number of tables.

SOLVE

$$2 + 2t = 22$$
$$2t = 20$$
$$t = 10$$

ANSWER

With this seating arrangement, 10 tables are required.

We can generalize that for n people the number of tables required is

$$t = \frac{n - 2}{2}$$

READ

EXAMPLE 2. In how many ways can 8 coins be divided into 4 groups so that there is at least 1 coin in each group?

PLAN

SOLUTION:

1	1	1	5
1	1	2	4
1	1	3	3
1	2	2	3
2	2	2	2

SOLVE

ANSWER

There are 5 ways to divide the coins.

EXERCISE 1.14

A 1. In each of the following, identify
(a) what you are required to find;
(b) what is given;
(c) what additional information is needed to solve the problem.

(i) How many CN Towers placed one on top of the other would equal the height of Mount Everest?
(ii) How many litres of paint would it take to paint a gymnasium wall?
(iii) Find a three digit number abc equal to the sum of the cubes of its digits.
(iv) Terry can wash a floor in 1 h and Pat can wash it in 2 h. Working together, how long would it take them to wash the floor?

2. What strategy was used to solve the following problems?

(a) When asked to find the cube root of 53 to the nearest tenth without tables or a calculator, a student first tried the number 3. She multiplied $3 \times 3 \times 3$ and found it too small. She then tried 4 and found it too large. The student tried a number in between and continued this process until she realized that 3.8 was the best approximation.
(b) In order to determine how much soft ice cream a cone will hold when levelled at the top, a store owner measured the height and the radius of the circular top of the cone. The data were then substituted into

$$V = \frac{\pi r^2 h}{3}.$$

(c) An architect who designed her own home was worried that the two-storey structure might look too tall for its width. Before starting to build, she built a scale model to see how it looked.
(d) In order to determine the number of edges of a regular octahedron (8 faces), John cut out a cardboard model, put it together and counted the vertices. Mary was able to calculate mentally the number of edges. Together, they used Euler's formula

$$E = F + V - 2$$

to calculate the number of edges.

(e) When asked to determine the number of Ford LTD's which placed bumper to bumper would span the distance from Vancouver to Halifax, Sally decided that it was best to divide the distance between cities (in metres) by the length of a Ford LTD (in metres).
(f) Tom is a short order cook. He was asked to determine the maximum number of pieces of apple that can be obtained from exactly 8 chops of the cleaver. He tried one chop, then recorded his answer. He rearranged the pieces and recorded his answer. After a few more tries he was able to predict the solution by analysing the results that he had recorded.

B 3. A sheet of paper is folded in half, then folded in half again and again until 6 folds have been made. How many layers thick is the final bundle?

4. A red disk is placed on a table. Without overlapping disks, how many white ones of the same size can be placed tangent to the red one?

5. In an experiment, it was found that a single cell will divide into two distinct cells every 24 h. How many cells were there after one week if the experiment began when there were 8 cells?

6. Maggie was asked to paint the faces of 27 identical cubes red so that they could be stacked in such a way as to form a large red cube. Paint is expensive and she was asked not to paint a face that would not show. How many cubes will have

(a) at least one painted face?
(b) exactly one painted face?
(c) exactly two painted faces?
(d) exactly three painted faces?
(e) exactly four painted faces?

7. A square is traced on a piece of paper. With one corner fixed, the square is rotated 45°, then traced again. The same procedure is repeated, always rotating about the same point, until the square is returned to its original position.
(a) How many triangles can you find in the diagram that is produced?
(b) How many squares are there?

8. A drawer contains 6 identical blue and 10 identical white socks. In total darkness, Tony reaches in and picks one sock after another. How many must he pick to be sure that he has
(a) a pair of blue socks?
(b) a pair of white socks?
(c) any matching pair?
(d) one sock of each colour?
(e) If 5 black socks are added, how many should he pick to be sure of a match of any colour?

9. Mike says: "The building where I work is in the shape of a perfect cube and its dimensions (measured in metres) are natural numbers."
Karen says: "The building where I work is 25 m long and 16 m wide. It is not as tall as it is long, but its height (measured in metres) is also a natural number. Its volume is the same as yours."
What is the height of Karen's building?

10. A frog wishes to jump off the end of a 9.9 m incline. It starts at the bottom of the incline. How many jumps will it take if every jump is 1 m long and if it slides back 0.5 m after each jump?

11. At 12:00 a turtle is 10 m away from its lunch. With each minute the turtle halves the distance between itself and the food. If a chime sounds at each minute starting at 12:01, how many chimes will have been heard by the time the turtle is within 1 cm of its target?

MICRO MATH

If you have access to a computer with LOGO, use the following program to help solve question 7.

```
TO SQUARE
REPEAT 4 [FD 80 RT 90]
END
CS
REPEAT 8 [SQUARE LT 45]
```

CALCULATOR MATH

A calculator can only display a certain number of digits.

To divide 2 by 11, we press

C 2 ÷ 1 1 =

A calculator that displays up to 8 digits will display the result 0.1818181

In this case, by realizing that the length of the period is 2, and that the period is 18, we can continue the decimal equivalent to read
0.181 818 181 818 181 818 ...

Most calculators will not display enough digits for us to establish the period of a fraction.

To convert $\frac{9}{53}$, we press

C 9 ÷ 5 3 =

The display 0.1698113 does not provide any hint for determining the period which happens to be 1698113207547 and whose length is 13.

Determine a method for converting a common fraction such as $\frac{13}{17}$ to as many decimal places as desired using a calculator.

1.15 REVIEW EXERCISE

1. Find the decimal equivalents of each of the following.

(a) $\frac{7}{8}$ (b) $\frac{5}{13}$ (c) $\frac{2}{9}$

(d) $\frac{8}{11}$ (e) $\frac{3}{13}$ (f) $\frac{7}{9}$

2. Express in the form $\frac{a}{b}$.

(a) $0.\overline{81}$ (b) $0.1\overline{3}$
(c) $0.\overline{235}$ (d) $0.1\overline{35}$

3. Draw the graph of each of the following.
(a) $\{x \in R \mid x \geqslant -2\}$
(b) $\{x \in R \mid -2 \leqslant x < 3\}$
(c) $\{x \in R \mid x \neq 2\}$

4. Graph the following.
(a) $\{x \in R \mid x \leqslant 3\} \cap \{x \in R \mid x > -1\}$
(b) $\{x \in R \mid -2 \leqslant x \leqslant 3\} \cup \{x \in R \mid 0 \leqslant x < 4\}$
(c) $\{x \in R \mid -3 < x \leqslant 0\} \cap \{x \in R \mid x = 2\}$

5. Arrange the elements of
$\{0.3, -0.25, 0, 1.3, 0.54\}$ in

(a) increasing order.
(b) decreasing order.

6. Find a rational and an irrational number between each of the following.
(a) 3, 4
(b) $2.\overline{5}$, $2.\overline{6}$
(c) 3.125 125 ..., 3.121 2 ...

7. Express as entire radicals.
(a) $3\sqrt{2}$ (b) $5\sqrt{7}$
(c) $2\sqrt{11}$ (d) $7\sqrt{2}$
(e) $5\sqrt{5}$ (f) $2\sqrt{13}$

8. Express as mixed radicals.
(a) $\sqrt{32}$ (b) $\sqrt{75}$
(c) $\sqrt{288}$ (d) $\sqrt{242}$
(e) $\sqrt{147}$ (f) $\sqrt{108}$

9. Simplify.
(a) $3\sqrt{5} \times 2\sqrt{10}$ (b) $6\sqrt{3} \times 2\sqrt{6}$
(c) $5\sqrt{2} \times 4\sqrt{6}$ (d) $2\sqrt{7} \times 3\sqrt{14}$
(e) $4\sqrt{6} \times 2\sqrt{12}$ (f) $3\sqrt{15} \times 2\sqrt{6}$

(g) $\frac{1}{2}\sqrt{\frac{2}{3}} \times \frac{1}{3}\sqrt{\frac{3}{4}}$ (h) $2\sqrt{\frac{14}{3}} \times 3\sqrt{\frac{3}{2}}$

(i) $3\sqrt{\frac{3}{8}} \times 2\sqrt{\frac{4}{9}}$ (j) $2\sqrt{\frac{5}{14}} \times 3\sqrt{\frac{7}{10}}$

10. Expand.
(a) $\sqrt{3}(\sqrt{2} - 5)$ (b) $2\sqrt{2}(3\sqrt{3} - 5)$
(c) $\sqrt{5}(2\sqrt{3} - \sqrt{2})$ (d) $2\sqrt{2}(\sqrt{2} + 1)$
(e) $5\sqrt{3}(\sqrt{6} - \sqrt{2})$ (f) $2\sqrt{3}(\sqrt{3} + \sqrt{6})$

11. Simplify.
(a) $\frac{\sqrt{18}}{\sqrt{3}}$ (b) $\frac{\sqrt{40}}{\sqrt{8}}$

(c) $\frac{3\sqrt{20}}{6\sqrt{5}}$ (d) $\frac{\sqrt{21}}{\sqrt{3}}$

(e) $\frac{\sqrt{200}}{\sqrt{2}}$ (f) $\frac{\sqrt{28}}{\sqrt{63}}$

12. Simplify.
(a) $\sqrt{18} + \sqrt{32} - \sqrt{50}$
(b) $\sqrt{12} + \sqrt{27} + \sqrt{48} - \sqrt{75}$
(c) $3\sqrt{8} + 2\sqrt{18} - \sqrt{32}$
(d) $3\sqrt{40} + 2\sqrt{90} - \sqrt{1000}$
(e) $3\sqrt{150} + 2\sqrt{24} - \sqrt{96}$
(f) $2\sqrt{20} - 3\sqrt{125} + 3\sqrt{80}$
(g) $3\sqrt{28} - 2\sqrt{112} + 4\sqrt{63}$

13. Simplify.
(a) $2\sqrt{12} + 5\sqrt{2} + \sqrt{18}$
(b) $6\sqrt{27} - 3\sqrt{12} + \sqrt{72}$
(c) $3\sqrt{8} + 2\sqrt{27} - 5\sqrt{12} + 2\sqrt{32}$
(d) $3\sqrt{500} - 10\sqrt{20} + 4\sqrt{125}$
(e) $2\sqrt{2} + 4\sqrt{4} + 8\sqrt{8}$

14. Simplify by expressing the denominator as a rational number.

(a) $\frac{3}{\sqrt{2}}$ (b) $\frac{2\sqrt{5}}{\sqrt{2}}$

(c) $\frac{3\sqrt{7}}{\sqrt{3}}$ (d) $\frac{4}{\sqrt{6}}$

(e) $\frac{3\sqrt{5}}{\sqrt{10}}$ (f) $\frac{2\sqrt{7}}{\sqrt{14}}$

(g) $\frac{2\sqrt{3}}{\sqrt{5}}$ (h) $\frac{4\sqrt{3}}{\sqrt{8}}$

15. Evaluate correct to the nearest tenth using a square root table, by first expressing the denominator as a rational number.

(a) $\dfrac{3}{\sqrt{5}}$

(b) $\dfrac{2\sqrt{7}}{\sqrt{3}}$

(c) $\dfrac{3\sqrt{5}}{\sqrt{15}}$

(d) $\dfrac{2\sqrt{7}}{\sqrt{2}}$

(e) $\dfrac{5}{\sqrt{10}}$

(f) $\dfrac{14\sqrt{11}}{2\sqrt{7}}$

16. A 12 m ladder leads against a wall and reaches 10 m up the wall. How far is the foot of the ladder from the wall to the nearest tenth of a metre?

17. A boat sails 30 km north then 21 km east. How far is the boat from the starting point to the nearest tenth of a kilometre?

18. Find to the nearest tenth of a centimetre the diameter of the circle that will circumscribe a square 2 cm by 2 cm.

19. Simplify.

(a) $(3a^2)(5a^5)$

(b) $(4y^2)(7y)$

(c) $(a^2b^3)(a^5b)$

(d) $(6x^3)(-2x^5)$

(e) $(-7a^3)(-5a^5)$

(f) $(3a)(-5a)$

(g) $(a^7)(7ab)$

(h) $(3a^2b)(-5ab^4)$

(i) $(15a^5)(3a^{-3})$

(j) $(4xy)(-5xy^2)$

(k) $(5a^{-7})(3a^{-2})$

(l) $(6ab^{-2})(-3a^4b^3)$

20. Simplify.

(a) $(12b^3) \div (4b)$

(b) $(45x^7) \div (9x)$

(c) $(18a^2b^5) \div (2a^2)$

(d) $(24x^3y^3) \div (8x^3y)$

(e) $(12x^5) \div (3x^{-2})$

(f) $(-14a^2) \div (7a)$

(g) $(54ab^3) \div (6ab)$

(h) $(12x^3) \div (2x^{-2})$

(i) $(-35a^5) \div (-7a^3)$

(j) $(51xy^5) \div (3xy)$

(k) $(56w^3) \div (-7w^{-2})$

(l) $(a^{-3}b^{-5}) \div (a^2b^{-8})$

21. Simplify.

(a) $\dfrac{(15x^3)(3x^5)}{9x^4}$

(b) $\dfrac{(12a^2)(5a^3)}{4a}$

(c) $(x^3y^5)^2$

(d) $\dfrac{(3x^2)^3}{9x^4}$

(e) $(8x^{-3})(2x^7) \div 4x$

(f) $(3x^5)^2(2x^{-1})^3$

(g) $\left(\dfrac{15a^2b}{3ab}\right)^2$

(h) $(5m^5n)(m^2n)^{-2}$

22. Evaluate.

(a) 5^3

(b) 3^4

(c) 2^5

(d) 15^0

(e) 2^{-1}

(f) 3^{-1}

(g) $(-7)^0$

(h) 10^{-1}

(i) $\left(\dfrac{1}{2}\right)^2$

(j) $\left(\dfrac{2}{3}\right)^3$

(k) $3^8 \div 3^6$

(l) $5^{-3} \times 5^4$

(m) $7^{-5} \times 7^5$

(n) $2^0 \div 2$

(o) 3^{-2}

(p) $\left(\dfrac{1}{4}\right)^{-1}$

(q) $\left(\dfrac{3}{4}\right)^{-1}$

(r) $4^0 + 2^{-1}$

MICRO MATH

The following BASIC program converts a common fraction to decimal form. The user determines the number of decimal places.

NEW

```
100 REM CONVERTING A COMMON FRACTION
110 PRINT "ENTER A COMMON FRACTION"
120 PRINT "NUMERATOR";
130 INPUT N
140 PRINT "DENOMINATOR";
150 INPUT D
160 IF D > N THEN 200
170 PRINT N; "/"; D; "IS NOT A"
180 PRINT "COMMON FRACTION."
190 GOTO 110
200 PRINT "HOW MANY DECIMAL PLACES";
210 INPUT P
220 PRINT N; "/"; D
230 PRINT "= 0 . ";
240 N = N*10
250 Q = INT(N/D)
260 PRINT Q;
270 R = N-Q*D
280 N = 10*R
290 I = I+1
300 IF I < P THEN 250
310 END
```

RUN

```
ENTER A COMMON FRACTION
NUMERATOR? 89
DENOMINATOR? 349
HOW MANY DECIMAL PLACES? 100
  89 / 349
= 0 . 2 5 5 0 1 4 3 2 6 6 4
  7 5 6 4 4 6 9 9 1 4 0 4 0
  1 1 4 6 1 3 1 8 0 5 1 5 7
  5 9 3 1 2 3 2 0 9 1 6 9 0
  5 4 4 4 1 2 6 0 7 4 4 9 8
  5 6 7 3 3 5 2 4 3 5 5 3 0
  0 8 5 9 5 9 8 8 5 3 8 6 8
  1 9 4 8 4 2 4 0 6 8 7
```

1. Find the period of the following fractions.

(a) $\dfrac{7}{23}$

(b) $\dfrac{1}{19}$

(c) $\dfrac{2}{29}$

(d) $\dfrac{89}{147\,211}$

1.16 CHAPTER 1 TEST

1. (a) Find the decimal equivalent, the period, and the length of the period for the following.

   (i) $\frac{1}{9}$ (ii) $\frac{2}{7}$

   (b) Express $0.\overline{23}$ as a common fraction.

2. Graph each set on a number line.

   (a) $\{x \in R \mid -2 \leqslant x \leqslant 3\}$

   (b) $\{x \in R \mid x < -1\} \cup \{x \in R \mid x > 2\}$

3. Find a rational and an irrational number between the irrational numbers

           3.125 716 32 ... and
           3.125 647 17 ... .

4. (a) Change $\sqrt{125}$ to a mixed radical.

   (b) Change $3\sqrt{7}$ to an entire radical.

5. Simplify.

   (a) $2\sqrt{5} \times 3\sqrt{7}$ (b) $2\sqrt{3} \times 3\sqrt{2} \times 4\sqrt{6}$

   (c) $5\sqrt{2}(3\sqrt{3} - 4)$ (d) $\frac{2\sqrt{27}}{\sqrt{12}}$

6. Simplify.

   (a) $2\sqrt{7} - 4\sqrt{2} + \sqrt{7} - 3\sqrt{2}$

   (b) $3\sqrt{48} - \sqrt{75}$

7. A guy wire is fastened to the top of a post that stands 7 m high. The guy wire is anchored 5 m from the base of the post on level ground. Find the length of the guy wire to the nearest tenth of a metre.

7 m

5 m

8. Simplify.

   (a) $(2xy^2)(3xy^3)$ (b) $(-3a^2b^3)(7ab)$

   (c) $\frac{24a^4c^3}{18a^2c}$ (d) $\frac{(2x^2)^3}{2x^4}$

   (e) $\left(\frac{8x^3y^2}{4xy^4}\right)^2$ (f) $\frac{(3a^3bc)(-12a^3b^2c)}{(6a^2b^2c)^2}$

9. Evaluate.

   (a) $3^{-2} \times 3^2$ (b) $\left(\frac{2}{3}\right)^{-2}$

   (c) $3^{-1} + 5^{-1}$ (d) $4^0 - \left(\frac{1}{2}\right)^{-2}$

ALGEBRA

CHAPTER

2

Algebra is the intellectual instrument for rendering clear the
quantitative aspects of the world.

Alfred North Whitehead

REVIEW AND PREVIEW TO CHAPTER 2

OPERATIONS WITH INTEGERS

EXERCISE

1. Simplify.

(a) $2 - 5$ (b) $-2 + 7$
(c) $-4 - 5 + 1$ (d) $-3 + 12 - 8$
(e) $7 + 3 - 5 - 6$
(f) $3 - 4 + 2 - 5$
(g) $-1 - 2 - 3 - 4$
(h) $4 - 5 + 6 - 7$

2. Simplify.

(a) $(-1)(2)$ (b) $(-3)(-4)$
(c) $(-3)(5)$ (d) $(-2)(-9)$
(e) $(24) \div (-6)$ (f) $(-36) \div (18)$
(g) $\dfrac{-48}{-24}$ (h) $\dfrac{16}{-4}$

ORDER OF OPERATIONS

There is a definite order of operations when simplifying numerical expressions.
  Many numerical expressions contain powers. The acronym BEDMAS is used to remember the order of operations.

B	Do the computations in brackets first.
E	Simplify numbers with exponents and "of."
D M	Divide or multiply in the order in which $\div$ and $\times$ appear from left to right.
A S	Add or subtract in the order in which $+$ and $-$ appear from left to right.

EXERCISE

1. Simplify.

(a) $6 \times 5 - (12 - 4) \div 2$
(b) $2 \times 4^2 - (5 \times 2) + 15$
(c) $3(6 - 1) \div 5 + 4 - 1$
(d) $(4^3 - 5 \times 2) \div 2 + 10$
(e) $6^2 \div (9 + 3^2) - 1$
(f) $4[10 - (4 \times 1)] \div 3$
(g) $\dfrac{8^2 - 4 \times 3}{2^4 - 3}$
(h) $\dfrac{2^4 - 3 + 12 \div 4}{64 \div 2^3}$
(i) $\dfrac{17 \times 4 - 2^3}{3^2 + 1}$
(j) $\dfrac{8^2 - 14}{(3 + 2) \times 10}$
(k) $(-8 + 1)(3 - 10)$

SUBSTITUTION

Order of operations is also used to simplify an expression after substitution.

EXERCISE

1. If $w = 3$, $x = 2$, and $y = 4$, evaluate.

(a) $2xy$ (b) $3wxy$
(c) $3x + 4w + 5y$ (d) $3x - 2y$
(e) $w^2 + x^2 + y^2$ (f) $w - x - y$
(g) $2x^2 - 3x - 4$ (h) $wx - xy - 2wy$
(i) $3x^2 - 2xy - y^2$ (j) $4(3x - 2y)$
(k) $2w^2x - 3xy^2$ (l) $w^3 - x^4 - y^2$
(m) $3x(w - x - y)$ (n) $3w^2 - 2w - 4$
(o) $-x^2(x - 2)$ (p) $(wxy)^2$

2. If $w = -1$, $x = -2$, and $y = 3$, evaluate.

(a) $3w + 2x + 4y$ (b) $5x - 3y$
(c) $3wxy$ (d) $-4wxy$
(e) $w - x - y$ (f) $w^2 + x^2 + y^2$
(g) $x^2 - w^2 - y^2$ (h) $3wx - xy + y$
(i) $3w^2x^2 - 4xy^2$ (j) $w^5 - 2x^3 - 7$
(k) $-2(w^3 - 3w^2)$ (l) $4w(x - y - w)$
(m) $w^2x^2 - 3wxy$ (n) $w^7 - w^6 + w^5$
(o) $-7 - 4w - 5x - 3y$
(p) $(x + y)(x - y)$

THE RULE OF THREE

EXAMPLE. If a car can travel 121 km on 9 L of gasoline, how far can it travel on 50 L of gasoline?

PLAN

SOLUTION:

The statement of the problem can be represented by the following chart.

Gasoline (L)	Distance (km)
9	121
50	?

SOLVE

To solve, we first find the distance the car travels on 1 L of gasoline.

> Divide by 9 to find the distance travelled on 1 L. Multiply by 50 to find the distance travelled on 50 L.

Gasoline (L)	Distance (km)
9	121
1	$\frac{121}{9}$
50	$\frac{121}{9} \times 50 \doteq 672.2$

> Using a calculator, press
>
> C 1 2 1 ÷ 9
> = × 5 0 =
>
> or
>
> C 1 2 1 × 5
> 0 = ÷ 9 =

ANSWER

The car can travel approximately 672 km on 50 L of gasoline.

EXERCISE

1. How far will a car travel on 25 L of gasoline if it goes 300 km on 40 L?

2. If you can earn $87.64 for seven hours' work, how much can you earn in a 40 h week?

3. The Norseman 1 satellite revolves about the moon 6 times in 4 h. How many times does it revolve in 22 h?

4. It takes about 1680 kJ to melt 5 g of ice. How much ice can be melted with 10 000 kJ?

5. It takes 2.478 MJ to vaporize 10 g of chloroform. How much energy is required to vaporize 5000 g of chloroform?

6. A pendulum completes 17 vibrations in 13 s. How many vibrations does it make in 25 s?

7. The price of copper pipe is $72.00 for 20 m. What is the cost of 9 m of pipe?

8. It takes a radio wave about 1.3 s to go from earth to the moon, a distance of 383 000 km. How far will the radio wave travel in 25 s?

9. In electroplating, 42 g of copper are deposited in 18 min. How much copper is deposited in 2 h 10 min?

10. Sound travels approximately 1360 m in 4.0 s. How far will sound travel in 9 s?

CALCULATOR MATH

THE MEMORY KEY

The **M** key allows you to store an answer in the calculator's memory. You can recall it later using the **MR** or **RCL** key.

> **MR** stands for Memory Recall
> **RCL** stands for Recall

EXAMPLE 1. Use a calculator with a **M** key to evaluate $(2 + 7) \times (3 + 5)$.

SOLUTION:

Evaluate the bracket $(2 + 7)$. | **C** **2** **+** **7** **=**

Store the display in the memory. | **M**

Evaluate the second bracket. | **C** **3** **+** **5** **=**

Multiply the display by the number stored in the memory. | **×** **MR** **=**

The display is **12**

EXAMPLE 2. Use a calculator with a **M** key to evaluate $\dfrac{7 \times 5 - 7}{12 \div 6 + 5}$.

SOLUTION:

Evaluate the divisor. | **C** **1** **2** **÷** **6** **=** **+** **5** **=**

Store the result in memory. | **M**

Evaluate the numerator. | **C** **7** **×** **5** **=** **−** **7** **=**

Divide the result of the numerator by the result of the divisor which is stored in the memory. | **÷** **MR** **=**

The display is **4**

Some calculators may have **M+** and **M−** keys without having a **M** key. When **M+** is pressed the value of the display is added to the value in the memory and stored. Similarly, when **M−** is pressed, the display is subtracted from the value in the memory and the result is stored.

In the above solutions, the **M** can be replaced by **M+** provided the memory is cleared before starting. To do this, press **CA** "Clear All" or **CM** "Clear Memory."

EXERCISE

1. Use a calculator with a memory key to evaluate the following.

(a) $(72 + 35) \times (49 - 26)$
(b) $147 - (37 \times 3)$
(c) $343 \div (98 \div 14)$
(d) $132 \div (47 + 16 - 39)$
(e) $(14 + 96) \div 22$
(f) $5.2^2 + 2.1^2$
(g) $\dfrac{43 + 78}{86 - 75}$
(h) $\dfrac{17 \times 4 + 30}{32 \times 3 - 82}$

FLOW CHARTS

A flow chart is a diagram that shows the order in which steps are performed.

The following symbols are used in flow charting.

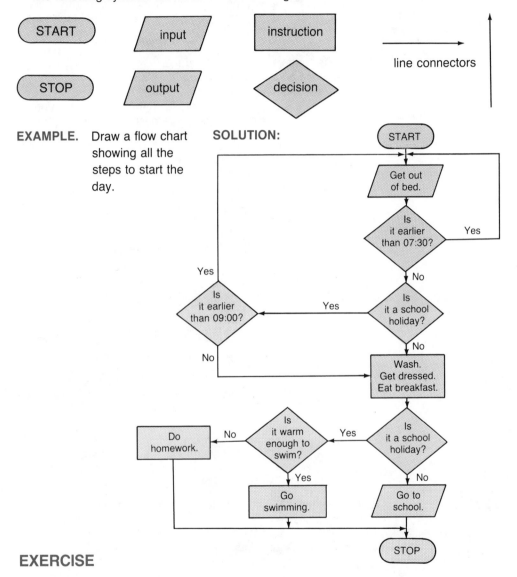

EXAMPLE. Draw a flow chart showing all the steps to start the day.

SOLUTION:

EXERCISE

1. Draw a flow chart showing all the steps to

(a) make a telephone call.
(b) wash a car.
(c) buy a CD.

2. Draw a flow chart showing all the steps to buy a sandwich for $1.35 from a machine.

2.1 ADDING AND SUBTRACTING POLYNOMIALS

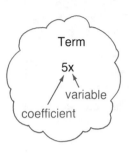

Before examining the product of polynomials, we shall review some of the terminology of algebra.

A term is a mathematical expression using numbers or variables combined to form a product or a quotient. Examples of terms are:

$$5x, \quad 7, \quad -4y^2 \quad \text{and} \quad 3xy.$$

The number part of a term is called the numerical coefficient. A term may also have a variable part. A variable is a symbol which may represent any member of a particular set.

A polynomial is an algebraic expression formed by adding or subtracting terms whose variables have positive integral exponents. We classify polynomials by the number of terms they contain.

$$5x : \text{one term:} \quad \text{monomial}$$
$$2x + 3y : \text{two terms:} \quad \text{binomial}$$
$$4x^2 - 3x + 7 : \text{three terms:} \quad \text{trinomial}$$

The degree of a term is the sum of the exponents of its variables.

$$3y^4 \text{ is a term of degree 4.}$$
$$-5x^2y^3 \text{ is a term of degree 5.}$$

Terms that have the same variable factors, such as $5xy$ and $9xy$, are called like terms. Using the distributive property to collect like terms we see that

$$5xy + 9xy = (5 + 9)xy$$
$$= 14xy$$

$$2x + 3x + 7x = (2 + 3 + 7)x$$
$$= 12x$$

$$2a + 3b + 4a - 5b = (2 + 4)a + (3 - 5)b$$
$$= 6a - 2b$$

> To add polynomials, collect like terms.

Remember that polynomials are in simplest form when like terms have been collected.

EXAMPLE 1. Add.
$$2x^2 + 3x - 1$$
$$x^2 + 2x + 4$$
$$3x^2 - x + 3$$

SOLUTION:
Collect like terms.
$$2x^2 + 3x - 1$$
$$x^2 + 2x + 4$$
$$\underline{3x^2 - x + 3}$$
$$6x^2 + 4x + 6$$

EXAMPLE 2. Simplify. $(x^2 - 3xy + 2y^2) + (2x^2 - xy - y^2)$

SOLUTION:

$$(x^2 - 3xy + 2y^2) + (2x^2 - xy - y^2)$$
$$= x^2 - 3xy + 2y^2 + 2x^2 - xy - y^2$$
$$= x^2 + 2x^2 - 3xy - xy + 2y^2 - y^2$$
$$= 3x^2 - 4xy + y^2$$

Subtracting polynomials is similar to subtracting integers.

To subtract a polynomial, determine its opposite and add.

To determine the opposite we multiply each term of the polynomial by -1 using the distributive property.

EXAMPLE 3. Subtract. $4x^2 - 3x + 1$
$\underline{x^2 + 2x - 3}$

SOLUTION:
Determine the opposite and add.

$$4x^2 - 3x + 1$$
$$\underline{-x^2 - 2x + 3}$$
$$3x^2 - 5x + 4$$

EXAMPLE 4. Simplify. $(9y^2 + y - 3) - (6y^2 + 2y + 4)$

SOLUTION:
$$(9y^2 + y - 3) - (6y^2 + 2y + 4) = (9y^2 + y - 3) - 1(6y^2 + 2y + 4)$$
$$= 9y^2 + y - 3 - 6y^2 - 2y - 4$$
$$= 3y^2 - y - 7$$

EXERCISE 2.1

B 1. Add.

(a) $3x + 4y$
$\underline{2y + 5y}$

(b) $4x^2 + 3x$
$\underline{7x^2 + 10x}$

(c) $7xy + 5w$
$\underline{20xy - 2w}$

(d) $5x - 6y$
$\underline{2x + 5y}$

2. Add the following polynomials.
(a) $3w - 7x + 4y$; $6w - 5x - 8y$
(b) $2m^2 - 3m - 9$; $m^2 - m + 6$; $2m^2 + 6m - 3$
(c) $6x^2 - 5 + 4x$; $6x - x^2 + 7$; $10 - 3x^2 + 9x$

3. Subtract.

(a) $5x + 3y$
$\underline{2x + 2y}$

(b) $3x^2 + 3x - 7$
$\underline{x^2 - x + 2}$

(c) $5x^2 - 2x + 3$
$\underline{2x^2 + 4x - 2}$

(d) $4y^2 - 2y + 3$
$\underline{5y^2 + 3y + 1}$

4. Subtract the first polynomial from the second.
(a) $2x + 3y$; $5x + 6y$
(b) $3w + 2x + 5y$; $7w + 11x + 9y$
(c) $6x - 5x^2 + 8$; $4 - 3x + 2x^2$

5. Simplify.
(a) $(x^3 + 6) + (x + 3)$
(b) $(x^2 + 2x) + (-7x + 2)$
(c) $(y^3 + 2y^2 + 3) + (4y^2 - 3y - 1)$

6. Simplify.
(a) $(6x - 3) - (7x + y)$
(b) $(7y^2 - xy) - (8x^2 + xy)$
(c) $(13x^3 - 3x^2 - xy) - (13y^3 - 3y^2 - xy)$

7. Simplify.
(a) $(3x^2 - 2y) - (2y + 3x^2) + (x^2 - 2y)$
(b) $(-3xy + 2y^2) - (x^2 - y^2) + (3x^2 - xy)$

2.2 MULTIPLYING A POLYNOMIAL BY A MONOMIAL

Multiplying monomials involves multiplying the coefficients, and then multiplying the variables.

$$x^a x^b = x^{a+b}$$

$$(2x)(3x^2) = (2)(3)(x)(x^2)$$
$$= 6x^3$$

$$(2x)(5y^2) = (2)(5)(x)(y^2)$$
$$= 10xy^2$$

Using the distributive property, the product of a polynomial and a monomial is treated as successive products of monomials.

EXAMPLE 1. Expand. $2x(3x^2 + 5y^2)$

SOLUTION:
We multiply the monomials $2x$ and $3x^2$, and then we multiply the monomials $2x$ and $5y^2$.

$$2x(3x^2 + 5y^2) = 2x(3x^2 + 5y^2)$$
$$= (2x)(3x^2) + (2x)(5y^2)$$
$$= 6x^3 + 10xy^2$$

EXAMPLE 2. Expand. $2a^2b(3a + 2b - 5ab)$

The problem is treated as three products of monomials:
$(2a^2b)(3a)$
$(2a^2b)(2b)$
$(2a^2b)(-5ab)$

SOLUTION:
$$2a^2b(3a + 2b - 5ab) = 2a^2b(3a + 2b - 5ab)$$
$$= (2a^2b)(3a) + (2a^2b)(2b) + (2a^2b)(-5ab)$$
$$= 6a^3b + 4a^2b^2 - 10a^3b^2$$

EXAMPLE 3. Expand and simplify. $5x(x - 4) - 3(x^2 - 5)$

SOLUTION:
$$5x(x - 4) - 3(x^2 - 5) = 5x(x - 4) - 3(x^2 - 5)$$
$$= 5x^2 - 20x - 3x^2 + 15$$
$$= 2x^2 - 20x + 15$$

Collect like terms.

EXERCISE 2.2

A 1. Expand.
(a) $2(a + b)$
(b) $3(x - y)$
(c) $3(2a - 5b)$
(d) $5(2x + 3y)$
(e) $7(p + q - r)$
(f) $-3(2c - d)$
(g) $-(a + b)$
(h) $-2(2a - b + c)$

B 2. Expand.
(a) $2x(x - 5y)$
(b) $3a(2a - 5b)$
(c) $-4a(5p + 3q)$
(d) $2x^2(5x - 2y)$
(e) $3c^3(2c - 4d)$
(f) $2xy(x + 2y)$.
(g) $3x^2y(2x + 5y)$
(h) $5xy^2(4x - 2y^2)$

3. Expand.
(a) $2x^2(3x + 2y + 5)$
(b) $xy(x - 2y + 5)$

(c) $3ab(2a - 7b - 9)$
(d) $3x^2y(x - 2y + 3)$
(e) $abc(2a - 3b + c)$
(f) $3ab^2(9a - 2b + 4ab)$

4. Expand and simplify.
(a) $2(x + 5) + 3(x + 4)$
(b) $3(m - 4) + 5(m + 6)$
(c) $4(3x - 5) - 6(2x - 1)$
(d) $2(3y - 4) - 2(2y - 1)$
(e) $3(2x - 5) - (x - 4)$
(f) $2(m - 3) - 4 + 2(m - 5)$
(g) $5(x - 6) - 4(y + 3)$
(h) $3x - 2(x + 5) - (x - 4)$
(i) $3(x^2 - 5x + 2) - 4(x - 6)$
(j) $4(x^2 - x - 1) - 2(x^2 + 6x - 5)$

2.3 MULTIPLYING BINOMIALS

The distributive property is also used to multiply two binomials.

EXAMPLE 1. Multiply. $(x + 5)(x + 3)$

SOLUTION:

$a(b + c) = ab + ac$
$(b + c)a = ab + ac$

$$(x + 5)(x + 3) = (x + 5)(x + 3)$$
$$= (x + 5)x + (x + 5)3$$
$$= x^2 + 5x + 3x + 15$$
$$= x^2 + 8x + 15$$

The same result is obtained by multiplying each term of one binomial by each term of the other binomial.

First
Outer
Inner
Last

$$(x + 5)(x + 3) = (x + 5)(x + 3)$$
$$= x^2 + 3x + 5x + 15$$
$$= x^2 + 8x + 15$$

The product $(x + 5)(x + 3)$ can be interpreted geometrically as the area of a rectangle with sides $(x + 3)$ and $(x + 5)$.

Area of rectangle $= (x + 5)(x + 3)$

Area of rectangle $= A_1 + A_2 + A_3 + A_4$
$$= x^2 + 3x + 5x + 15$$
$$= x^2 + 8x + 15$$

$(x + 3)(x + 5) = x^2 + 8x + 15$

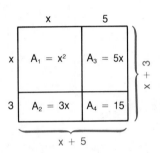

EXAMPLE 2. Expand and simplify. $(2x - 3)(5x + 7)$

SOLUTION:
$$(2x - 3)(5x + 7) = (2x - 3)(5x + 7)$$
$$= 10x^2 + 14x - 15x - 21$$
$$= 10x^2 - x - 21$$

EXAMPLE 3. Expand and simplify.
$$2(2x + 1)(x - 3) - 4(x + 5)$$

SOLUTION:
$$2(2x + 1)(x - 3) - 4(x + 5)$$
$$= 2(2x + 1)(x - 3) - 4(x + 5)$$
$$= 2(2x^2 - 6x + x - 3) - 4(x + 5)$$
$$= 2(2x^2 - 5x - 3) - 4(x + 5)$$
$$= 4x^2 - 10x - 6 - 4x - 20$$
$$= 4x^2 - 14x - 26$$

The same procedure is used to multiply binomials involving radicals.

EXAMPLE 4. Simplify. $(5\sqrt{2} - 4\sqrt{3})(3\sqrt{2} + 2\sqrt{3})$

SOLUTION:
$$(5\sqrt{2} - 4\sqrt{3})(3\sqrt{2} + 2\sqrt{3})$$

$$= (5\sqrt{2} - 4\sqrt{3})(3\sqrt{2} + 2\sqrt{3})$$

$$= 15(2) + 10\sqrt{6} - 12\sqrt{6} - 8(3)$$
$$= 30 - 2\sqrt{6} - 24$$
$$= 6 - 2\sqrt{6}$$

EXERCISE 2.3

A 1. (a) Determine the area of each of the smaller rectangles, then add them together.

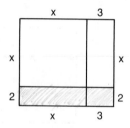

(b) Determine the area of the rectangle by expanding the binomials.

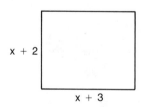

B 2. Expand.

(a) $(x + 1)(x + 2)$ (b) $(x + 2)(x + 3)$
(c) $(x + 4)(x + 2)$ (d) $(x - 1)(x - 3)$
(e) $(x - 3)(x + 5)$ (f) $(x + 2)(x - 1)$
(g) $(y - 5)(y - 4)$ (h) $(t + 7)(t + 8)$
(i) $(m - 4)(m + 9)$ (j) $(n - 2)(n - 9)$
(k) $(x + 8)(x - 7)$ (l) $(y + 1)(y - 7)$
(m) $(x + 7)(x + 6)$ (n) $(t - 5)(t - 9)$
(o) $(m - 6)(m - 11)$ (p) $(w - 4)(w + 4)$

3. Expand and simplify.

(a) $(2x + 3)(x + 5)$
(b) $(3x + 4)(2x + 7)$
(c) $(7y - 2)(2y + 5)$
(d) $(2m - 5)(3m - 1)$
(e) $(4m - 3)^2$
(f) $(3x + 5)^2$
(g) $(2x - 5)(2x + 5)$
(h) $(4t + 7)(2t + 3)$
(i) $(5t - 6)^2$
(j) $(7t + 4)^2$
(k) $(3x - 2y)(4x - 3y)$
(l) $(5m + 2n)(4m - n)$
(m) $(3x + 5y)^2$
(n) $(3x + 7y)(4y - x)$
(o) $(7 - 8t)(7 + 8t)$
(p) $(4x - 9y)(2y + 7x)$
(q) $(9x + 10y)(8x + 3y)$
(r) $(7m - 5n)(8m + 3n)$
(s) $(3x^2 - 2x)(4x^2 - x)$
(t) $(4xy - x^2)(x^2 - xy)$
(u) $(2t^2 - 7)^2$
(v) $(x^4 - 3)(5x^4 - 6)$
(w) $(-2x + 3y)(4x - 7y)$

4. Expand and simplify.

(a) $2(x + 3)(x + 4) + 3(2x + 3)$
(b) $3(x + 1)(x + 2) + 2(x + 4)(x + 5)-$
(c) $3(m - 2)(m - 3) - 4(m + 1)(m - 1)$
(d) $5(t - 3)(t + 4) - 5(t - 6)(t - 5)$
(e) $2(m + 3)^2 + 3(m - 1)^2 - 2(m - 4)$
(f) $4(2x + 1)(x + 5) - 3(3x - 2)(2x - 3)$
(g) $5(2m + 3)(4m + 1) + 2(5m + 6)(3m - 4)$
(h) $2(2x - 3)^2 - (3x + 5)(3x + 7) - 4x^2$

(i) $2(1 - 3t) - (2t - 1)^2 - 3(3t - 5)(4t + 1)$
(j) $5x^2 - (4x + 7)(x + 6) - (2x + 5)^2 + 3x$
(k) $4 - 2(6w - 7)(6w + 7) - 3(2w + 1)^2$

5. Express the area of the rectangle in terms of x.

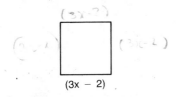

$(x - 4)$

$(2x + 3)$

6. Express the area of the square in terms of x.

$(3x - 2)$

C 7. Multiply the following binomial radicals.
(a) $(\sqrt{3} + 2)(\sqrt{3} + 4)$
(b) $(2\sqrt{3} + \sqrt{5})(\sqrt{3} + \sqrt{5})$
(c) $(\sqrt{3} + \sqrt{2})(2\sqrt{3} - \sqrt{2})$
(d) $(3\sqrt{5} + 2)(2\sqrt{5} - 3)$
(e) $(5\sqrt{7} - \sqrt{2})(\sqrt{7} - \sqrt{2})$
(f) $(3\sqrt{2} + \sqrt{5})(\sqrt{2} - 3\sqrt{5})$
(g) $(5\sqrt{3} + \sqrt{7})(2\sqrt{3} - 2\sqrt{7})$
(h) $(3\sqrt{5} + 4)(2\sqrt{5} - 3)$

8. Expand and simplify.
(a) $(x + 2)(x^2 + x + 1)$
(b) $(2x + 3)(x^2 - 2x - 4)$
(c) $(2x^2 - x - 5)(3x + 1)$
(d) $(3m - 4)(m^2 - 3m - 2)$
(e) $(x^2 + 2x - 1)(x^2 - x - 5)$
(f) $(2m^2 - 3m + 1)(3m^2 + 2m + 2)$
(g) $(x + 6)(x^3 + 3x^2 - 5x - 4)$
(h) $(2w - 3x + 4y)(w + 5x - 3y)$

9. Expand and simplify.
(a) $(2x - 3)(x - 4)(2x + 5)$
(b) $(x^2 - 3x - 1)^2$
(c) $\left(x + \dfrac{1}{x} \right)\left(x - \dfrac{1}{x} \right)$
(d) $\left(1 + x - \dfrac{1}{x} \right)\left(2 - x + \dfrac{2}{x} \right)$
(e) $(w + x + y + z)^2$

EXTRA

USING THE ALGORITHM FOR LONG MULTIPLICATION

To multiply polynomials, we can use a procedure that is similar to the one we use to multiply numbers. This procedure is called the algorithm for long multiplication

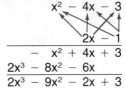

Multiply by 1. $1\ 3$
Multiply by 2. $2\ 6$
Add. $2\ 7\ 3$

Multiply by 1. $x + 3$
Multiply by 2x. $2x^2 + 6x$
Add like terms. $2x^2 + 7x + 3$

This procedure is especially useful for multiplying larger polynomials such as $(2x - 1)(x^2 - 4x - 3)$.

EXAMPLE. Expand and simplify.
$(2x - 1)(x^2 - 4x - 3)$

SOLUTION:
METHOD I.
Using the distributive property,
$(2x - 1)(x^2 - 4x - 3)$

$= (2x - 1)(x^2 - 4x - 3)$

$= 2x(x^2 - 4x - 3) - 1(x^2 - 4x - 3)$
$= 2x^3 - 8x^2 - 6x - x^2 + 4x + 3$
$= 2x^3 - 9x^2 - 2x + 3$

METHOD II.
Using the algorithm for long multiplication,
$x^2 - 4x - 3$
$2x - 1$
$- x^2 + 4x + 3$
$2x^3 - 8x^2 - 6x$
$2x^3 - 9x^2 - 2x + 3$

2.4 SPECIAL PRODUCTS OF BINOMIALS

The following examples suggest a pattern for squaring binomials.

$$\begin{aligned}(x + 3)^2 &= (x + 3)(x + 3) \\ &= x^2 + 3x + 3x + 9 \\ &= x^2 + 2(3x) + 9 \\ &= x^2 + 6x + 9\end{aligned}$$ $$\begin{aligned}(3x - 5)^2 &= (3x - 5)(3x - 5) \\ &= 9x^2 - 15x - 15x + 25 \\ &= 9x^2 - 2(15x) + 25 \\ &= 9x^2 - 30x + 25\end{aligned}$$

For the special products $(a + b)^2$ and $(a - b)^2$,

$$\begin{aligned}(a + b)^2 &= (a + b)(a + b) \\ &= a^2 + ab + ab + b^2 \\ &= a^2 + 2ab + b^2\end{aligned}$$ $$\begin{aligned}(a - b)^2 &= (a - b)(a - b) \\ &= a^2 - ab - ab + b^2 \\ &= a^2 - 2ab + b^2\end{aligned}$$

To square a binomial, add the square of the first term, the square of the last, and twice the product of both terms.

EXAMPLE 1. Use the pattern established above to simplify $(2x + 3y)^2$.

SOLUTION:

$$\begin{aligned}(a + b)^2 &= a^2 \; + \; 2ab \; + \; b^2 \\ (2x + 3y)^2 &= (2x)^2 + 2(2x)(3y) + (3y)^2 \\ &= 4x^2 + 12xy + 9y^2\end{aligned}$$

The following product of binomials suggests another special pattern.

$$\begin{aligned}(2x + 5)(2x - 5) &= (2x + 5)(2x - 5) \\ &= 4x^2 - 10x + 10x - 25 \\ &= 4x^2 - 25\end{aligned}$$

For the special product $(a + b)(a - b)$,

$$\begin{aligned}(a + b)(a - b) &= a^2 - ab + ab - b^2 \\ &= a^2 - b^2\end{aligned}$$

The product $(a + b)(a - b)$ gives a difference of squares.

EXAMPLE 2. Use the pattern established for the product $(a + b)(a - b)$ to simplify $(3x - 4y)(3x + 4y)$.

$$\begin{aligned}(a + b)(a - b) \\ = (a - b)(a + b) \\ = a^2 - b^2\end{aligned}$$

SOLUTION:

$$\begin{aligned}(a - b)(a + b) &= a^2 - b^2 \\ (3x - 4y)(3x + 4y) &= (3x)^2 - (4y)^2 \\ &= 9x^2 - 16y^2\end{aligned}$$

EXAMPLE 3.   Expand and simplify. $(5x + 2)(5x - 2) - (3x - 4)^2$

SOLUTION:
Using the special products $(a + b)^2 = a^2 + 2ab + b^2$ and
$(a + b)(a - b) = a^2 - b^2$,

$$(5x + 2)(5x - 2) - (3x - 4)^2$$
$$= (25x^2 - 4) - (9x^2 - 24x + 16)$$
$$= 25x^2 - 4 - 9x^2 + 24x - 16$$
$$= 16x^2 + 24x - 20$$

The special products $(a + b)^2$ and $(a - b)^2$ can often be used to simplify numerical computations.

EXAMPLE 4.   Evaluate.
(a) 54^2 (b) 97^2

SOLUTION:
We first express the base as a sum or difference of two numbers, the first being a multiple of 10, and then we use the pattern for squaring a binomial.

> Try this method to evaluate 61^2 mentally.

(a) $54^2 = (50 + 4)^2$
$$= 2500 + 400 + 16$$
$$= 2916$$

(b) $97^2 = (100 - 3)^2$
$$= 10\ 000 - 600 + 9$$
$$= 9409$$

The special products can also be used to simplify binomials involving radicals.

EXAMPLE 5.   Simplify.
(a) $(\sqrt{3} + \sqrt{5})^2$ (b) $(2\sqrt{7} - 5)(2\sqrt{7} + 5)$

SOLUTION:

> $(\sqrt{3})^2 = 3$
> $(\sqrt{5})^2 = 5$

(a) $(\sqrt{3} + \sqrt{5})^2$
$$= (\sqrt{3})^2 + 2(\sqrt{3})(\sqrt{5}) + (\sqrt{5})^2$$
$$= \sqrt{9} + 2\sqrt{15} + \sqrt{25}$$
$$= 3 + 2\sqrt{15} + 5$$
$$= 8 + 2\sqrt{15}$$

(b) $(2\sqrt{7} - 5)(2\sqrt{7} + 5)$
$$= (2\sqrt{7})^2 - (5)^2$$
$$= 4\sqrt{49} - 25$$
$$= 4(7) - 25$$
$$= 28 - 25$$
$$= 3$$

> A rational number.

EXERCISE 2.4

B 1. Expand.

(a) $(x + 3)^2$ (b) $(x - 2)^2$
(c) $(x + 5)^2$ (d) $(x - 4)(x + 4)$
(e) $(y + 2)^2$ (f) $(m - 7)^2$
(g) $(t + 5)(t - 5)$ (h) $(x + 6)(x - 6)$
(i) $(y + 1)^2$ (j) $(x - 9)^2$
(k) $(x + 10)^2$ (l) $(x - 7)(x + 7)$
(m) $(x + 12)^2$ (n) $(x - 6)^2$
(o) $(y - 1)(y + 1)$ (p) $(a + b)(a - b)$

2. Expand and simplify.

(a) $(3x - 5)(3x + 5)$ (b) $(2x + 7)^2$
(c) $(4x + 5)^2$ (d) $(2x - 3y)^2$
(e) $(5x - y)(5x + y)$
(f) $(a + 2b)^2$
(g) $(ab + 2)(ab - 2)$
(h) $(x^2 - 4)^2$
(i) $(4 - 3m)(4 + 3m)$
(j) $(6 + 7x)^2$

3. Evaluate the following using one of the special products $(a + b)^2$, $(a - b)^2$, or $(a + b)(a - b)$.

(a) 52^2
(b) $(40 - 5)(40 + 5)$
(c) 95^2
(d) 71^2
(e) 101^2
(f) $(30 + 3)(30 - 3)$
(g) 83^2
(h) $(4 + 50)(4 - 50)$

4. Expand and simplify.

(a) $2x + (x + 4)^2$
(b) $x^2 - (2x - 1)^2$
(c) $3ab + (2a - 7b)^2$
(d) $-4x^2 + (3x - y)(3x + y)$
(e) $(2a - 3b)^2 - (a^2 + 4ab)$
(f) $(ab - 2c)(ab + 2c) - (ab)^2$

5. Expand and simplify.

(a) $(x + 2)^2 + (x - 5)^2$
(b) $2(x - 4)(x + 4) - x^2$
(c) $(x + 5)(x - 3) + (x + 4)^2$
(d) $7 - (x - 6)^2$
(e) $(3 + 2x)(3 - 2x) - (3 + 2x)^2$
(f) $4(5x - 1)^2 - 2(3x + 1)(3x - 1)$

C 6. Simplify.

(a) $(\sqrt{3} + \sqrt{2})^2$
(b) $(\sqrt{5} - \sqrt{2})^2$
(c) $(\sqrt{6} - \sqrt{3})^2$
(d) $(\sqrt{7} - \sqrt{6})^2$
(e) $(3\sqrt{2} + 2)^2$
(f) $(8\sqrt{2} - 5\sqrt{6})^2$
(g) $(\sqrt{3} - \sqrt{2})(\sqrt{3} + \sqrt{2})$
(h) $(\sqrt{3} - 2)(\sqrt{3} + 2)$
(i) $(2\sqrt{5} + \sqrt{2})(2\sqrt{5} - \sqrt{2})$
(j) $(2\sqrt{3} + 2)(2\sqrt{3} - 2)$
(k) $(\sqrt{7} + 2\sqrt{3})(\sqrt{7} - 2\sqrt{3})$
(l) $(4\sqrt{5} - \sqrt{2})(4\sqrt{5} + \sqrt{2})$

7. Evaluate the following using the special product $(a + b)(a - b)$.

(a) 87×93
(b) 105×95
(c) 48×52
(d) 29×51

PASCAL'S TRIANGLE

We know that $(a + b)^2 = a^2 + 2ab + b^2$

Using the algorithm for long multiplication of polynomials, we can obtain the following expansions for the powers of $(a + b)$.

$(a + b)^3 = (a + b)^2(a + b)$
$ = a^3 + 3a^2b + 3ab^2 + b^3$

$(a + b)^4 = (a + b)^3(a + b)$
$ = a^4 + 4a^3b + 6a^2b^2 + 4ab^3 + b^4$

The coefficients obtained in the various expansions of $(a + b)^n$ where $n = 0, 1, 2, 3,$ and 4, can be arranged in a triangular form called Pascal's triangle.

$$
\begin{array}{ccccccccc}
 & & & & 1 & & & & \\
 & & & 1 & & 1 & & & \\
 & & 1 & & 2 & & 1 & & \\
 & 1 & & 3 & & 3 & & 1 & \\
1 & & 4 & & 6 & & 4 & & 1
\end{array}
$$

$\leftarrow (a + b)^0 = 1$
$\leftarrow (a + b)^1 = a + b$
$\leftarrow (a + b)^2 = a^2 + 2ab + b^2$
$\leftarrow (a + b)^3 = a^3 + 3a^2b + 3ab^2 + b^3$
$\leftarrow (a + b)^4 = a^4 + 4a^3b + 6a^2b^2 + 4ab^3 + b^4$

EXERCISE

1. Determine a pattern within Pascal's triangle. Use this pattern to determine the coefficients obtained in the expansions of $(a + b)^5$, $(a + b)^6$, $(a + b)^7$, ...

2. Use Pascal's triangle to evaluate 11^5 by first expressing it as $(10 + 1)^5$.

2.5 SIMPLIFYING RADICAL EXPRESSIONS INVOLVING BINOMIAL DENOMINATORS

In a previous example we noticed that multiplying two binomial expressions involving radicals will sometimes give a rational result.

$$(\sqrt{3} + \sqrt{2})(\sqrt{3} - \sqrt{2}) = (\sqrt{3})^2 - (\sqrt{2})^2$$
$$= 3 - 2$$
$$= 1 \quad \text{A rational number.}$$

$(a + b)(a - b) = a^2 - b^2$

This occurs when the factors are in the form $(a + b)$ and $(a - b)$. We say that $(\sqrt{3} + \sqrt{2})$ and $(\sqrt{3} - \sqrt{2})$ are conjugate radicals

EXAMPLE 1. Multiply $(2 - \sqrt{7})$ by its conjugate radical.

SOLUTION:
The conjugate of $(2 - \sqrt{7})$ is $(2 + \sqrt{7})$.

$$(2 - \sqrt{7})(2 + \sqrt{7}) = 2^2 - (\sqrt{7})^2$$
$$= 4 - 7$$
$$= -3$$

We can simplify radical expressions with a binomial denominator by multiplying the numerator and the denominator by the conjugate of the denominator.

EXAMPLE 2. Simplify. $\dfrac{5}{3 + \sqrt{2}}$

SOLUTION:
The conjugate of the denominator is $3 - \sqrt{2}$.

$$\frac{5}{3 + \sqrt{2}}$$

$\dfrac{a}{b} = \dfrac{ac}{bc}$

$$= \frac{5}{(3 + \sqrt{2})} \times \frac{(3 - \sqrt{2})}{(3 - \sqrt{2})} \qquad a(b + c)$$
$$\qquad\qquad\qquad\qquad\qquad (a + b)(a - b) = a^2 - b^2$$
$$= \frac{15 - 5\sqrt{2}}{3^2 - (\sqrt{2})^2}$$
$$= \frac{15 - 5\sqrt{2}}{9 - 2}$$
$$= \frac{15 - 5\sqrt{2}}{7} \qquad \text{A rational denominator.}$$

EXERCISE 2.5

B Simplify to an expression involving a rational denominator.

1. (a) $\dfrac{1}{2 + \sqrt{3}}$ (b) $\dfrac{1}{\sqrt{5} + 2}$

(c) $\dfrac{1}{\sqrt{15} - 4}$ (d) $\dfrac{3}{\sqrt{2} - 1}$

(e) $\dfrac{5}{2 - \sqrt{3}}$ (f) $\dfrac{2}{\sqrt{26} + 5}$

2. (a) $\dfrac{1}{3 + 2\sqrt{2}}$ (b) $\dfrac{1}{5 - 2\sqrt{6}}$

(c) $\dfrac{1}{7 + 4\sqrt{3}}$ (d) $\dfrac{2}{9 - 4\sqrt{5}}$

3. (a) $\dfrac{1}{\sqrt{3} + \sqrt{2}}$ (b) $\dfrac{1}{\sqrt{6} - \sqrt{5}}$

(c) $\dfrac{1}{\sqrt{5} - \sqrt{3}}$ (d) $\dfrac{3}{\sqrt{5} + \sqrt{2}}$

2.6 COMMON FACTORS

Expressing a given polynomial as a product of two or more polynomials is called factoring. The distributive property, which is used to find products, is also used to factor.

$$\xrightarrow{\quad\text{EXPANDING}\quad}$$
$$3x(2x - 1) = 6x^2 - 3x$$
$$\xleftarrow{\quad\text{FACTORING}\quad}$$

When a factor is contained in every term of an algebraic expression, it is called a common factor. We can determine common factors by inspection.

EXAMPLE 1. Factor completely.
(a) $5xy + 10y$
(b) $6x^3 - 3x^2 + 9x$

5y is the greatest common factor (GCF) of 5xy and 10y.

3x is the GCF of $6x^3$, $-3x^2$, and 9x.

SOLUTION:
(a) $5xy + 10y = 5y(x) + 5y(2)$
$$= 5y(x + 2)$$
(b) $6x^3 - 3x^2 + 9x = 3x(2x^2) - 3x(x) + 3x(3)$
$$= 3x(2x^2 - x + 3)$$

We shall agree that a polynomial is completely factored when no more variable factors can be removed and no more integer factors other than 1 or -1 can be removed.

EXAMPLE 2. Factor completely. $2x(y + 3) + 5w(y + 3)$

SOLUTION:
The greatest common factor is $(y + 3)$.
Think of $(y + 3)$ as one number.
$$2x(y + 3) + 5w(y + 3) = (y + 3)(2x) + (y + 3)(5w)$$
$$= (y + 3)(2x + 5w)$$

EXERCISE 2.6

A 1. Factor completely, where possible.
(a) $2x + 6$ (b) $5y - 10$
(c) $3x + 6y$ (d) $7w - 7$
(e) $3x + 11$ (f) $2x^2 - 82$
(g) $2tw + 4tx - 6ty$ (h) $3abx - aby - 2abz$

B 2. Factor completely, where possible.
(a) $25x^3 + 10x^2 + 15x$
(b) $y^5 - y^4 + y^3 - y^2$
(c) $36x^5 - 9y^3$
(d) $12xy + 4wx - 8xz$
(e) $9m^3 - 6m^2t + 3mt^2$
(f) $7xyz - 14xy + 21txy$
(g) $7pqr - 5xy + 8t$
(h) $22xy - 11y^2 + 33wy$

(i) $36mn^2 - 24m^2n + 28mn$
(j) $7rst - 14r^2s^2t$
(k) $18r^2s^3 - 9rs^2 - 27r^3s^2$
(l) $20m^6n^4 - 30m^5n^5 + 40m^7n^3 - 10m^5n^3$
(m) $14rst + 17xy - 3w$
(n) $40x^5y^7 - 32x^7y^6 - 28x^8y^4 - 36x^7y^5$

3. Factor.
(a) $3m(x + y) + 2(x + y)$
(b) $3x(y - 1) + 2(y - 1)$
(c) $9x(m + 3) - 2(m + 3)$
(d) $5y(m + n) + t(m + n)$
(e) $5w(x - 2) - 3t(x - 2)$
(f) $2t(x + 5) + (x + 5)$
(g) $4mn(t - 4) - (t - 4)$

2.7 FACTORING $x^2 + bx + c$

Many polynomials, such as $x^2 + 7x + 12$, can be written as the product of two binomials of the form $(x + r)$ and $(x + s)$.

$$\xrightarrow{\hspace{1cm}\text{FACTORING}\hspace{1cm}}$$
$$x^2 + 7x + 12 = (x + 3)(x + 4)$$
$$\xleftarrow{\hspace{1cm}\text{EXPANDING}\hspace{1cm}}$$

An analysis of a general expansion of two linear polynomials will simplify factoring.

$$(x + r)(x + s) = x^2 + sx + rx + rs$$
$$= x^2 + (s + r)x + rs$$
$$= x^2 + bx + c$$

Here, $b = (s + r)$ and $c = rs$.
To write $x^2 + 8x + 15$ in the form $(x + r)(x + s)$,

$$b = r + s \quad \text{and} \quad c = rs$$
$$= 8 \quad\quad\quad\quad = 15$$

Find two numbers whose sum is 8 and whose product is 15.

Hence $r = 3$ and $s = 5$, and the factors of $x^2 + 8x + 15$ are $(x + 3)$, $(x + 5)$.

EXAMPLE. Factor. $x^2 - 3x - 10$

SOLUTION:
For $x^2 - 3x - 10$,
$r + s = -3$
and $rs = -10$.
The two integers that add to give -3 and multiply to give -10 are -5 and 2.

$$x^2 - 3x - 10 = (x - 5)(x + 2)$$

EXERCISE 2.7

A 1. Complete the factoring.
(a) $x^2 + 9x + 20 = (x + 5)(\blacksquare)$
(b) $x^2 + 5x + 6 = (x + 3)(\blacksquare)$
(c) $x^2 - 7x + 12 = (x - 4)(\blacksquare)$
(d) $m^2 - 3m - 18 = (\blacksquare)(m - 6)$
(e) $y^2 + 5y - 14 = (\blacksquare)(y + 7)$
(f) $t^2 - 2t - 24 = (t - 6)(\blacksquare)$
(g) $s^2 - 8s + 16 = (\blacksquare)(s - 4)$
(h) $w^2 + 10w + 25 = (w + 5)(\blacksquare)$
(i) $n^2 + 3n - 40 = (\blacksquare)(n + 8)$
(j) $x^2 - x - 42 = (x + 6)(\blacksquare)$

(i) $n^2 + 11n + 18$
(j) $x^2 + 12x + 20$
(k) $w^2 + 2w - 18$
(l) $s^2 + 6x - 16$
(m) $y^2 - 2y - 35$
(n) $x^2 + 3x - 40$
(o) $t^2 + 17t + 72$
(p) $w^2 + 18w + 90$
(q) $r^2 - 18r + 80$
(r) $m^2 - 6m + 9$
(s) $y^2 + 10y + 25$
(t) $x^2 + 2x - 63$
(u) $w^2 + 3w + 5$
(v) $x^2 - 20x + 100$
(w) $m^2 - 8x - 20$
(x) $n^2 + 10n - 24$

3. Factor completely.
(a) $2x^2 + 4x + 2$
(b) $3w^2 + 12w + 9$
(c) $m^2 - 4m - 77$
(d) $5x^2 - 35x + 50$
(e) $n^2 + 16x + 55$
(f) $w^2 - 13w + 30$
(g) $3x^2 + 3x + 3$
(h) $2x^2 - 28x + 90$
(i) $2w^2 + 28w + 98$
(j) $35 - 12m + m^2$
(k) $16 + 6x - x^2$
(l) $2x^2 - 6x + 10$
(m) $4x^2 - 48x + 144$
(n) $m^2 + 11m - 42$

B 2. Factor, if possible.
(a) $x^2 + 7x + 10$
(b) $m^2 + 8m + 12$
(c) $n^2 + 6n + 8$
(d) $w^2 - 7w + 10$
(e) $x^2 - 9x + 20$
(f) $x^2 - 6x - 14$
(g) $r^2 - r - 30$
(h) $m^2 + m - 42$

2.8 FACTORING $ax^2 + bx + c, a \neq 1$

Factoring trinomials of this type, such as $6x^2 + 17x + 12$, is simplified if we break up the middle term into two parts.

$$6x^2 + 17x + 12 = 6x^2 + 9x + 8x + 12$$
$$= (6x^2 + 9x) + (8x + 12)$$
$$= 3x(2x + 3) + 4(2x + 3)$$
$$= (2x + 3)(3x + 4)$$

In the previous example we replaced $17x$ by $9x + 8x$. We might have used other sums such as $10x + 7x$ or $20x - 3x$. However, $9x + 8x$ is the required sum. The decision as to what two terms must be used will be clarified if we analyze the general expansion.

$$(px + r)(qx + s) = pqx^2 + psx + qrx + rs$$
$$= pqx^2 + (ps + qr)x + rs$$
$$= ax^2 + bx + c$$

If we break up the middle term bx into two terms, say mx and nx, then it is clear that

$$m + n = ps + qr \quad \text{and} \quad mn = pqrs$$
$$= b \qquad\qquad\qquad = ac$$

EXAMPLE. Factor. $6x^2 + 7x + 2$

SOLUTION:
For $6x^2 + 7x + 2$, $\quad a = 6, \quad b = 7, \quad$ and $\quad c = 2$.

In order to replace $7x$ by $mx + nx$, we must determine m and n.

$$m + n = b = 7$$
$$mn = ac = 12$$

Therefore, m and n are 3 and 4.

$$6x^2 + 7x + 2 = 6x^2 + 3x + 4x + 2$$
$$= (6x^2 + 3x) + (4x + 2)$$
$$= 3x(2x + 1) + 2(2x + 1)$$
$$= (2x + 1)(3x + 2)$$

EXERCISE 2.8

A 1. If possible, determine integer values for m and n.

(a) $m + n = 7, mn = 10$
(b) $m + n = 5, mn = 6$
(c) $m + n = -7, mn = 12$
(d) $m + n = -3, mn = -15$
(e) $m + n = -2, mn = 5$
(f) $m + n = 9, mn = 18$
(g) $m + n = 7, mn = -30$
(h) $m + n = -8, mn = 16$
(i) $m + n = -1, mn = -20$
(j) $m + n = 5, mn = -14$

B 2. Factor.

(a) $6x^2 + 13x + 5$
(b) $2w^2 + 5w + 3$
(c) $6x^2 - 7x + 2$
(d) $4m^2 + 27m + 18$
(e) $3w^2 - 10w + 8$
(f) $15t^2 - t - 2$
(g) $2m^2 - m - 10$
(h) $4x^2 + 25x + 6$
(i) $6n^2 - 13n + 6$
(j) $3x^2 - 23x + 14$

3. Factor.

(a) $4t^2 + 31t + 21$
(b) $6m^2 + 5m - 4$
(c) $2x^2 + 17x + 30$
(d) $9x^2 + 6x + 1$
(e) $4m^2 + 21m - 18$
(f) $6x^2 - 19x + 10$
(g) $10x^2 + 29x + 10$
(h) $6t^2 - 17t - 14$

2.9 FACTORING SPECIAL QUADRATICS

We can use the following identities to factor special quadratics.

$$a^2 + 2ab + b^2 = (a + b)(a + b) = (a + b)^2$$
$$a^2 - 2ab + b^2 = (a - b)(a - b) = (a - b)^2$$
}Perfect Squares

$$a^2 - b^2 = (a - b)(a + b)$$
}Difference of Squares

EXAMPLE 1. Factor. $9x^2 + 30x + 25$

SOLUTION:

$9x^2 + 30x + 25$ is a perfect square trinomial.

$$9x^2 + 30x + 25 = (3x)^2 + 2(3x)(5) - (5)^2$$
$$= (3x + 5)(3x + 5)$$
$$= (3x + 5)^2$$

EXAMPLE 2. Factor. $4x^2 - 12x + 9$

SOLUTION:

$16x^2 - 49$ is a difference of squares.

$$4x^2 - 12x + 9 = (2x)^2 - 2(2x)(3) + (3)^2$$
$$= (2x - 3)(2x - 3)$$
$$= (2x - 3)^2$$

EXAMPLE 3. Factor. $16x^2 - 49$

SOLUTION:

$$16x^2 - 49 = (4x)^2 - (7)^2$$
$$= (4x - 7)(4x + 7)$$

EXERCISE 2.9

A 1. Factor.

(a) $x^2 - 16$
(b) $m^2 + 6m + 9$
(c) $r^2 - 10r + 25$
(d) $m^2 - 49$
(e) $t^2 - 8t + 16$
(f) $x^2 - 36$
(g) $x^2 + 14x + 49$
(h) $m^2 - 4m + 4$
(i) $w^2 + 20w + 100$
(j) $y^2 - 2y + 1$
(k) $x^2 - 64$
(l) $n^2 + 18n + 81$
(m) $s^2 + 16s + 64$
(n) $r^2 - 6r + 9$
(o) $x^2 - 144$
(p) $9 - y^2$

B 2. Factor, if possible.

(a) $4x^2 - 25$
(b) $4x^2 + 4x + 1$
(c) $9x^2 - 6x + 1$
(d) $9x^2 + 16$
(e) $16m^2 - 8m + 1$
(f) $100t^2 - 49$
(g) $4w^2 - 12w + 9$
(h) $25s^2 + 40s + 16$
(i) $9 - 49y^2$
(j) $4 - 20x + 25x^2$
(k) $49y^2 + 42y + 9$
(l) $1 - 14m + 49m^2$
(m) $1 + 4x^2$
(n) $4r^2 + 28r + 49$

3. Factor.

(a) $9x^2 - 36$
(b) $x^2 - 2x - 8$
(c) $6x^2 - 11x - 10$
(d) $3mnt - 6m^2t - 9nt$
(e) $16x^2 + 8x + 1$
(f) $2x^2 - 2x - 24$
(g) $5m(x - 2) - 4(x - 2)$

4. Factor.

(a) $4m^2 + 8m - 60$
(b) $8 - 18x^2$
(c) $mn^2 + 9mn + 18m$
(d) $15y^2 - 22y + 8$
(e) $36x^2 + 60x + 25$
(f) $2(x + y)^2 - m(x + y)$
(g) $49m^2n^5 - 28m^3n^6 - 14m^6n^7$
(h) $8x^2 + 34x + 35$

2.10 DIVIDING A POLYNOMIAL BY A MONOMIAL

The rule for exponents in division is

> Division by zero is not defined.
> Replacements for variables which make the denominator zero are not allowed.

$$\frac{x^m}{x^n} = x^{m-n}$$

$$\therefore \quad \frac{x^7}{x^3} = x^{7-3}$$

$$= x^4, \qquad x \neq 0$$

EXAMPLE 1. Simplify. $\dfrac{18x^4y^5}{6x^3y^2}$

SOLUTION:

$$\frac{18x^4y^5}{6x^3y^2} = \frac{18}{6} \times \frac{x^4}{x^3} \times \frac{y^5}{y^2}$$

$$= 3xy^3, \qquad x, y \neq 0$$

The distributive property applies to division as well as multiplication.

$$\frac{a + b}{c} = \frac{1}{c}(a + b)$$

$$= \frac{a}{c} + \frac{b}{c}$$

To divide a polynomial by a monomial, each term of the polynomial is divided by the monomial.

EXAMPLE 2. Simplify. $\dfrac{20x^7 - 15x^6 + 25x^5}{5x^3}$

SOLUTION:

$$\frac{20x^7 - 15x^6 + 25x^5}{5x^3} = \frac{20x^7}{5x^3} - \frac{15x^6}{5x^3} + \frac{25x^5}{5x^3}$$

$$= 4x^4 - 3x^3 + 5x^2, \qquad x \neq 0$$

EXERCISE 2.10

A 1. Divide and state restrictions on the variables.

(a) $\dfrac{10xy}{5x}$

(b) $\dfrac{20mn}{10mn}$

(c) $\dfrac{14x^2}{2x}$

(d) $\dfrac{25m^2n^2}{5m^2}$

(e) $\dfrac{-30x^2y}{6x}$

(f) $\dfrac{24x^6}{-4x^2}$

(g) $\dfrac{27x^3y^2z^4}{-3xyz}$

(h) $\dfrac{-75r^2s^3}{-25r^2s^2}$

(i) $\dfrac{100x^7y^6}{-20x^3y^6}$

(j) $\dfrac{-36m^{10}n^8}{6m^7n^3}$

(k) $\dfrac{-60x^4y^5z^3}{-5x^2y^2z^3}$

(l) $\dfrac{50r^3s^3t^2}{50r^3s^3t}$

B 2. Simplify and state restrictions on the variables.

(a) $\dfrac{2x + 4y}{2}$

(b) $\dfrac{5x - 15y}{5}$

(c) $\dfrac{20x^2 - 30x}{5x}$

(d) $\dfrac{-8x^5 + 12x^3}{4x^2}$

(e) $\dfrac{15x^4y^2 - 20x^2y^3 - 5xy}{5xy}$

(f) $\dfrac{32x^5y^3 - 8x^3y^5 + 16x^4y^4}{8x^3}$

2.11 SIMPLIFYING RATIONAL EXPRESSIONS

We simplify rational expressions the same way we simplify rational numbers. Recall that

$$\frac{6}{8} = \frac{\overset{1}{\cancel{2}} \times 3}{\underset{}{\cancel{2}} \times 4} = \frac{3}{4}$$

EXAMPLE 1. Simplify. $\dfrac{12abc}{18ac}$, $a, c \neq 0$

SOLUTION:

$$\frac{12abc}{18ac} = \frac{\overset{2 \ 1 \ 1}{\cancel{12abc}}}{\underset{3 \ 1 \ 1}{\cancel{18ac}}}$$

$$= \frac{2b}{3}$$

In order to simplify a rational expression, it is sometimes necessary to factor both the numerator and the denominator, if possible, and then to divide by any common factors.

EXAMPLE 2. Simplify. $\dfrac{3x^2}{3x^2 - 6x}$

The greatest common factor is 3x.

$$\frac{x^a}{x^b} = x^{a-b}$$

SOLUTION:

$$\frac{3x^2}{3x^2 - 6x} = \frac{\overset{1}{\cancel{3x^2}}}{\underset{1}{\cancel{3x}}(x - 2)}$$

$$= \frac{x}{x - 2}, \qquad x \neq 0, 2$$

We state the restrictions $x \neq 0$ and $x \neq 2$ because division by zero is not defined in the real numbers.

EXERCISE 2.11

A 1. Simplify and state the restrictions on the variables.

(a) $\dfrac{4x}{xy}$

(b) $\dfrac{18}{24x}$

(c) $\dfrac{6x}{x^2}$

(d) $\dfrac{2a^2}{4ab}$

(e) $\dfrac{16abc}{36c^2}$

(f) $\dfrac{2x}{x(x + 1)}$

(g) $\dfrac{(x + 3)}{(x + 1)(x + 3)}$

(h) $\dfrac{x^2}{x(x - 7)}$

(i) $\dfrac{8x(x - 9)}{4x}$

(j) $\dfrac{x(x - 4)}{x(x + 2)}$

(k) $\dfrac{2(x - 1)}{(x - 1)^2}$

(l) $\dfrac{4abc(a + 1)}{4ac(a + 1)}$

B 2. Simplify and state the restrictions on the variables.

(a) $\dfrac{2x}{4x^2 - 2x}$

(b) $\dfrac{x^2}{x^2 + 3x}$

(c) $\dfrac{5x - 10}{15x}$

(d) $\dfrac{x^2 - 2x}{x^2 + 3x}$

(e) $\dfrac{4x - 12}{9x - 27}$

(f) $\dfrac{6x + 36}{x + 6}$

3. Simplify and state the restrictions on the variables.

(a) $\dfrac{4x + 6y}{2x^2 + 8x}$

(b) $\dfrac{x + 3}{x^2 - 9}$

(c) $\dfrac{x - 2}{x^2 - 4x + 4}$

(d) $\dfrac{x^2 + 7x + 12}{x^2 + 8x + 15}$

2.12 MULTIPLYING AND DIVIDING RATIONAL EXPRESSIONS

We multiply rational expressions the same way we multiply rational numbers. Recall that

$$\frac{2}{3} \times \frac{5}{9} = \frac{2 \times 5}{3 \times 9}$$

$$= \frac{10}{27}$$

EXAMPLE 1. Simplify. $\dfrac{4x}{3y} \times \dfrac{6y}{x}$, $x, y \neq 0$

SOLUTION:

$$\frac{4x}{3y} \times \frac{6y}{x} = \frac{\overset{1}{\cancel{4x}}}{\underset{1\,1}{\cancel{3y}}} \times \frac{\overset{2\,1}{\cancel{6y}}}{\underset{1}{\cancel{x}}}$$

$$= 8$$

When multiplying rational expressions, it is sometimes necessary to first factor the numerators and denominators, and divide by any common factors. We then express the product as a rational expression.

EXAMPLE 2. Multiply $\dfrac{x^2 - x - 20}{x + 3}$ by $\dfrac{1}{x^2 + 6x + 8}$.

SOLUTION:

$$\frac{x^2 - x - 20}{x + 3} \times \frac{1}{x^2 + 6x + 8}$$

$$= \frac{(x - 5)(x + 4)}{(x + 3)} \times \frac{1}{(x + 4)(x + 2)}$$

$$= \frac{x - 5}{(x + 3)(x + 2)}, \qquad x \neq -3, -4, -2$$

Rational expressions are divided the same way as we divide rational numbers. Recall that

$$\frac{3}{5} \div \frac{7}{2} = \frac{3}{5} \times \frac{2}{7}$$

$$= \frac{6}{35}$$

EXAMPLE 3. Divide $\dfrac{3x - 3}{x^2 - x - 6}$ by $\dfrac{x - 1}{x + 2}$.

SOLUTION:

$$\frac{3x - 3}{x^2 - x - 6} \div \frac{x - 1}{x + 2} = \frac{3x - 3}{x^2 - x - 6} \times \frac{x + 2}{x - 1}$$

$$= \frac{3(x - 1)}{(x + 2)(x - 3)} \times \frac{(x + 2)}{(x - 1)}$$

$$= \frac{3}{x - 3}, \qquad x \neq 1, 3, -2$$

EXERCISE 2.12

A Express each of the following as rational expressions in lowest terms. Assume that all variables are restricted so that no denominator or divisor is equal to zero.

1. (a) $\dfrac{4}{x} \times \dfrac{x}{2}$ (b) $\dfrac{3}{m} \times \dfrac{m}{4}$

(c) $\dfrac{1}{3} \times \dfrac{5}{6}$ (d) $\dfrac{mn}{5} \times \dfrac{7}{mnt}$

(e) $2 \times \dfrac{x}{y}$ (f) $7 \div \dfrac{1}{4}$

(g) $\dfrac{x}{y} \div \dfrac{y}{x}$ (h) $\dfrac{x}{y} \div \dfrac{1}{5}$

(i) $\dfrac{5}{(x-1)} \times \dfrac{(x-1)}{7}$ (j) $\dfrac{1}{x-7} \div \dfrac{7}{x-7}$

(k) $y \div \dfrac{1}{y}$ (l) $\dfrac{x^3}{y^2} \times \dfrac{y^3}{x^4}$

(m) $\dfrac{(x-1)(x+3)}{(x+2)(x-1)} \times \dfrac{(x+2)}{(x-5)}$

(n) $\dfrac{m(x+y)}{n(x-y)} \div \dfrac{m}{n}$

(o) $\dfrac{x+y}{x-y}$

(p) $\dfrac{x+3}{x+4} \div \dfrac{x+1}{x+4}$

B 2. (a) $\dfrac{6x^2y^2}{xy} \times \dfrac{5x^2y}{10xy^2}$ (b) $\dfrac{4x^5y^4}{9x^2y} \times \dfrac{3xy^2}{8x^2y}$

(c) $\dfrac{5mn}{6m^2n} \div \dfrac{10mn^2}{9m^3n^2}$ (d) $\dfrac{6r^2s}{5xy^3} \div \dfrac{9rs}{10xy^4}$

(e) $\dfrac{27x^6y^4}{8m^2n^2} \times \dfrac{16mn}{9x^5y^2}$ (f) $\dfrac{3x^2}{7x^3y} \div \dfrac{1}{14x}$

3. (a) $\dfrac{x-7}{5x} \times \dfrac{10x^2}{x-7}$

(b) $\dfrac{14x^2}{y-3} \times \dfrac{3y-9}{7x}$

(c) $\dfrac{x^2-9}{4t^2} \div \dfrac{2x+6}{16t^3}$

(d) $\dfrac{6x^2}{3x+3} \div \dfrac{5x}{x^2+3x+2}$

(e) $\dfrac{3mn}{mn+2m} \times \dfrac{n^2+2n}{6m}$

(f) $\dfrac{4x+4}{8x^2} \div (x+1)$

C 4. (a) $\dfrac{x^2+3x+2}{x^2+4x+3} \times \dfrac{x^2+x-6}{x^2-4}$

(b) $\dfrac{t^2-7t+12}{t^2+2t-15} \div \dfrac{t^2-3t-4}{t^2+5t}$

(c) $\dfrac{w^2+8w+15}{w^2-13w+42} \times \dfrac{w^2-3w-28}{w^2+7w+12}$

(d) $\dfrac{4x+12}{x^2+2x-3} \times \dfrac{x^2-8x+7}{x^2-14x+49}$

(e) $\dfrac{x^2-9}{x^2-2x-24} \times \dfrac{x^2+3x-4}{x^2+8x+15}$

$\div \dfrac{x^2-4x+3}{10x+50}$

Which of the following nets can you draw without lifting your pencil or retracing any lines?

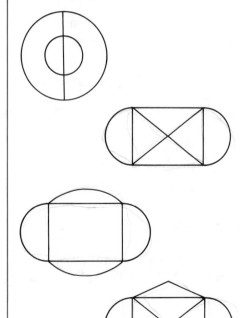

2.13 LEAST COMMON MULTIPLE

In order to add or subtract rational expressions it is necessary to know how to determine the least common multiple (LCM) of two or more polynomials.

The LCM for 20 and 24 is the smallest number that has 20 and 24 as factors. To determine the LCM for 20 and 24 we first factor 20 and 24.

$$20 = 2 \times 2 \times 5$$
$$24 = 2 \times 2 \times 2 \times 3$$

The LCM for 20 and 24 must include all the separate factors that make up 20 and 24.

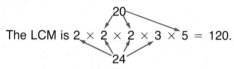

The LCM is $2 \times 2 \times 2 \times 3 \times 5 = 120$.

EXAMPLE 1.   Find the LCM for $4xy^2$ and $6x^2$.

SOLUTION:
Factor each term.

$$4xy^2 = 2 \times 2 \times x \times x \times y \times y$$
$$6x^2 = 2 \times 3 \times x \times x \times x$$

The LCM is $2 \times 2 \times 3 \times x \times x \times x \times y \times y$.

EXAMPLE 2.   Find the LCM for each of the following.
(a) $4x - 8$ and $x^2 + x - 6$ (b) $x^2 - 6x + 5$ and $x^2 + x - 30$

SOLUTION:
Factor each polynomial.

(a) $4x - 8 = 4(x - 2)$
            $x^2 + x - 6 = (x - 2)(x + 3)$

$$4x - 8$$

The LCM is $4(x - 2)(x + 3)$.

$$x^2 + x - 6$$

(b) $x^2 - 6x + 5 = (x - 1)(x - 5)$
      $x^2 + x - 30 = (x - 5)(x + 6)$

$$x^2 - 6x + 5$$

The LCM is $(x - 1)(x - 5)(x + 6)$.

$$x^2 + x - 30$$

EXERCISE 2.13

B Find the LCM for each of the following. Answers may be left in factored form.

1. (a) 8, 20   (b) 8, 10, 25
(c) 12, 18, 30   (d) 25, 30, 35
(e) 20, 30, 45   (f) 20, 28, 35

2. (a) $10x^3$, $15x^4$, $20x^2$ (b) $2x^2$, $4xy$, $6y^2$
(c) $3m^2n$, $6mn^2$, $2mn$ (d) $10x^3$, $25x^2y$, $15xy^2$
(e) $3ab$, $6bc$, $9ac$ (f) $6a^2b$, $15ab^2$, $24ab$

3. (a) $x - 1$, $x - 4$
(b) $x + 1$, $x + 2$, $x - 3$
(c) $x^2 + 7x + 12$, $x^2 + 9x + 20$
(d) $x^2 + x$, $x^2 - 1$
(e) $2x - 6$, $6x - 18$
(f) $x^2 - 2x - 3$, $x^2 + 2x - 15$
(g) $m^2 - m - 2$, $m^2 - 5m + 6$,
    $m^2 - 8m + 15$
(h) $3x + 12$, $x^2 + 11x + 28$, $x^2 - x - 56$
(i) $x^2 - 5x$, $x^2 - 25$, $x^2 + x - 20$

2.14 ADDING AND SUBTRACTING RATIONAL EXPRESSIONS

To add or subtract rational expressions with equal denominators we use the distributive property.

$$\frac{a}{b} + \frac{c}{b} = a\left(\frac{1}{b}\right) + c\left(\frac{1}{b}\right)$$
$$= \left(\frac{1}{b}\right)(a + c)$$
$$= \frac{a + c}{b}$$

EXAMPLE 1. Simplify. $\dfrac{2x + 3}{5} - \dfrac{3x - 2}{5}$

SOLUTION:

$$\frac{2x + 3}{5} - \frac{3x - 2}{5} = \frac{(2x + 3) - (3x - 2)}{5}$$
$$= \frac{2x + 3 - 3x + 2}{5}$$
$$= \frac{-x + 5}{5}$$

EXAMPLE 2. Simplify. $\dfrac{2}{x} + \dfrac{7}{x} - \dfrac{4}{x}$

SOLUTION:

$$\frac{2}{x} + \frac{7}{x} - \frac{4}{x} = \frac{2 + 7 - 4}{x}$$
$$= \frac{5}{x}$$

To add or subtract rational expressions with different denominators, equivalent fractions with a common denominator are found.

> The lowest common denominator (LCD) is the least common multiple (LCM) of the denominators.

The least common multiple (LCM) and greatest common divisor (GCD) can be illustrated in a diagram.

Find the LCM and the GCD of $3x^2y$ and $6xy^2$.

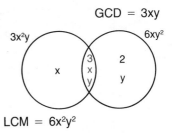

GCD = 3xy

LCM = $6x^2y^2$

EXAMPLE 3. Simplify. $\dfrac{2x-3}{3}+\dfrac{x+2}{2}-\dfrac{x-1}{4}$

SOLUTION:
The LCD is 12.

$$\dfrac{2x-3}{3}+\dfrac{x+2}{2}-\dfrac{x-1}{4}=\dfrac{4(2x-3)}{4(3)}+\dfrac{6(x+2)}{6(2)}-\dfrac{3(x-1)}{3(4)}$$

$$=\dfrac{4(2x-3)}{12}+\dfrac{6(x+2)}{12}-\dfrac{3(x-1)}{12}$$

$$=\dfrac{4(2x-3)+6(x+2)-3(x-1)}{12}$$

$$=\dfrac{8x-12+6x+12-3x+3}{12}$$

$$=\dfrac{11x+3}{12}$$

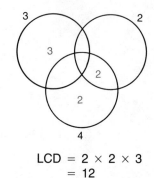

LCD $= 2 \times 2 \times 3$
$\quad\ = 12$

EXAMPLE 4. Simplify. $\dfrac{3}{2x^2}-\dfrac{1}{3x}+\dfrac{7}{5x^3}$

SOLUTION:
The LCD is $30x^3$.

$$\dfrac{3}{2x^2}-\dfrac{1}{3x}+\dfrac{7}{5x^3}=\dfrac{15x(3)}{15x(2x^2)}-\dfrac{10x^2(1)}{10x^2(3x)}+\dfrac{6(7)}{6(5x^3)}$$

$$=\dfrac{45x}{30x^3}-\dfrac{10x^2}{30x^3}+\dfrac{42}{30x^3}$$

$$=\dfrac{-10x^2+45x+42}{30x^3},\quad x\neq 0$$

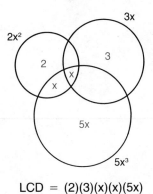

LCD $= (2)(3)(x)(x)(5x)$
$\quad\ = 30x^3$

In the following examples, the binomial denominators are treated as one term.

EXAMPLE 5. Simplify. $\dfrac{3}{x+1}-\dfrac{2}{x+1}+\dfrac{5}{x+1}$

SOLUTION:

$$\dfrac{3}{x+1}-\dfrac{2}{x+1}+\dfrac{5}{x+1}=\dfrac{3-2+5}{x+1}$$

$$=\dfrac{6}{x+1},\quad x\neq 1$$

EXAMPLE 6. Simplify. $\dfrac{2x+1}{x-5}+\dfrac{3x-5}{x-5}$

SOLUTION:

$$\dfrac{2x+1}{x-5}+\dfrac{3x-5}{x-5}=\dfrac{(2x+1)+(3x-5)}{x-5}$$

$$=\dfrac{5x-4}{x-5},\quad x\neq 5$$

EXAMPLE 7. Simplify. $\dfrac{x}{x + 1} + \dfrac{2}{x + 3}$

SOLUTION:

The LCD is $(x + 1)(x + 3)$.

$$\frac{x}{x + 1} + \frac{2}{x + 3} = \frac{(x + 3)(x)}{(x + 3)(x + 1)} + \frac{(x + 1)(2)}{(x + 1)(x + 3)}$$

$$= \frac{x^2 + 3x}{(x + 3)(x + 1)} + \frac{2x + 2}{(x + 1)(x + 3)}$$

$$= \frac{x^2 + 3x + 2x + 2}{(x + 1)(x + 3)}$$

$$= \frac{x^2 + 5x + 2}{(x + 1)(x + 3)}, \quad x \neq -1, -3$$

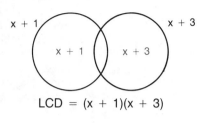

$$LCD = (x + 1)(x + 3)$$

EXERCISE 2.14

A Perform the indicated operations and simplify. Assume that all variables are restricted so that no denominator is equal to zero.

1. (a) $\dfrac{5}{7} - \dfrac{1}{7} + \dfrac{3}{7}$

(b) $\dfrac{3}{11} + \dfrac{5}{11} - \dfrac{2}{11}$

(c) $\dfrac{6}{x} + \dfrac{5}{x}$

(d) $\dfrac{7}{m} - \dfrac{3}{m} + \dfrac{4}{m}$

(e) $\dfrac{x}{2} + \dfrac{y}{2}$

(f) $\dfrac{4x}{5} - \dfrac{1}{5}$

(g) $\dfrac{2}{x + 1} + \dfrac{3}{x + 1}$

(h) $\dfrac{m}{x - 3} - \dfrac{n}{x - 3}$

B 2. (a) $\dfrac{1}{2} + \dfrac{3}{5} - \dfrac{1}{4}$

(b) $\dfrac{7}{6} - \dfrac{3}{8} + 1\dfrac{1}{2}$

(c) $\dfrac{3x}{4} - \dfrac{x}{2} + \dfrac{x}{6}$

(d) $\dfrac{2x + y}{3} + \dfrac{4x + 3y}{2}$

(e) $\dfrac{3m - 7}{4} - \dfrac{2m - 1}{3}$

(f) $\dfrac{x - 2y}{6} + 1 - \dfrac{x + 3y}{4}$

(g) $3x + \dfrac{x - 4}{7} - \dfrac{x - 1}{2}$

(h) $\dfrac{5t - 1}{6} - \dfrac{4t + 3}{8}$

3. (a) $\dfrac{3}{2x} + \dfrac{4}{3x} - \dfrac{1}{x}$

(b) $\dfrac{4}{5x} - \dfrac{3}{4x} - \dfrac{1}{10x}$

(c) $\dfrac{5}{2x} - \dfrac{3}{4x^2} - \dfrac{1}{3x}$

(d) $\dfrac{2}{s^2} - \dfrac{3}{st} + \dfrac{4}{t^2}$

(e) $\dfrac{2x + 3}{xy} - \dfrac{1}{x} + 4$

(f) $x - \dfrac{1}{x} + 4$

(g) $3 - \dfrac{2}{y} + y$

(h) $1 + \dfrac{1}{x} + y$

4. (a) $\dfrac{2}{x + 1} + \dfrac{3}{x + 2}$

(b) $\dfrac{3}{m - 4} + \dfrac{2}{m + 1}$

(c) $\dfrac{5}{x - 3} - \dfrac{4}{x + 2}$

(d) $\dfrac{1}{2} - \dfrac{3}{x + 1}$

(e) $4 - \dfrac{1}{x + 1} + \dfrac{3}{5}$

(f) $\dfrac{x + 1}{x} + \dfrac{x - 1}{x - 2}$

(g) $3 - \dfrac{1}{x - 2} + \dfrac{x + 1}{x + 3}$

(h) $4 + \dfrac{1}{x + 1} - \dfrac{1}{x - 1}$

2.15 EQUATIONS IN ONE VARIABLE

An equation is a statement that two expressions are equal.
The equation $2x + 3 = 7$ states that the value of the left side, $2x + 3$, equals the value of the right side, 7. Of course, this statement of equality holds true only if $x = 2$.

To solve an equation means to find a value of the variable that makes the statement true. This value is called a root. The set consisting of all possible roots of an equation is called a solution set.

We shall now review the rules for solving equations.

Rules for Solving Equations		
Since 8 = 8, then	If a = b, then	
$8 + 2 = 8 + 2$	$a + c = b + c$	Addition Rule
$8 - 2 = 8 - 2$	$a - c = b - c$	Subtraction Rule
$8 \times 2 = 8 \times 2$	$a \times c = b \times c$	Multiplication Rule
$\dfrac{8}{2} = \dfrac{8}{2}$	$\dfrac{a}{c} = \dfrac{b}{c}, c \neq 0$	Division Rule

EXAMPLE 1. Solve. $3x - 4 = 2x + 6, x \in R$

SOLUTION:

$$3x - 4 = 2x + 6$$
$$3x - 4 + 4 = 2x + 6 + 4 \longleftarrow \text{Addition Rule}$$
$$3x = 2x + 10$$
$$3x - 2x = 2x + 10 - 2x \longleftarrow \text{Subtraction Rule}$$
$$x = 10$$

The root is 10.

EXAMPLE 2. Solve $2(2a + 5) - 3 = 5a - 17 - 7a, a \in R$. Check your answer.

SOLUTION:

$$2(2a + 5) - 3 = 5a - 17 - 7a$$
$$4a + 10 - 3 = 5a - 17 - 7a$$
$$4a + 7 = -2a - 17$$
$$4a + 7 - 7 = -2a - 17 - 7 \longleftarrow \text{Subtraction Rule}$$
$$4a = -2a - 24$$
$$4a + 2a = -2a - 24 + 2a \longleftarrow \text{Addition Rule}$$
$$6a = -24$$
$$\frac{6a}{6} = -\frac{24}{6} \longleftarrow \text{Division Rule}$$
$$a = -4$$

Check.

L.S. $= 2[2(-4) + 5] - 3$
$= 2[-8 + 5] - 3$
$= 2[-3] - 3$
$= -9$

R.S. $= 5(-4) - 17 - 7(-4)$
$= -20 - 17 + 28$
$= -9$

The root is -4.

EXAMPLE 3. Solve. $2.5x - 4.7 = 3.2 + 2.6, x \in R$

SOLUTION:
We can proceed in two ways:

METHOD I.

We clear the decimal fractions by multiplying both sides by 10.

$10[2.5x - 4.7] = 10[3.2 + 2.6]$
$25x - 47 = 32 + 26$
$25x - 47 = 58$
$25x = 105$
$x = 4.2$

METHOD II.

Keeping the decimals,

$2.5x - 4.7 = 3.2 + 2.6$
$2.5x - 4.7 = 5.8$
$2.5x = 10.5$
$x = 4.2$

The root is 4.2.

EXERCISE 2.15

In this exercise variables have domain R.

A 1. Solve for each variable.

(a) $3a + 2 = 17$
(b) $6a + 6 = 18$
(c) $5a + 24 = -6$
(d) $4a + 16 = 20$
(e) $6x - 3 = 5x + 2$
(f) $5x + 2 = 4x + 5$
(g) $4x + 7 = 3x + 3$
(h) $7x + 2 = 4 + 6x$

B 2. Solve and check.

(a) $2(b - 1) = 4$
(b) $3(b + 1) = 6$
(c) $5(b + 2) = 20$
(d) $4(b - 3) = 0$

3. Solve and check.

(a) $0.5x = 3.2$
(b) $2.5a = 12.5$
(c) $10x = 42.4$
(d) $b + 3.5 = 8.5$
(e) $y - 2.3 = 3.1$
(f) $2x + 4.3 = 8.3$

4. Solve.

(a) $3a + 6 - 2a = 4 - 8$
(b) $5a + 2 - 2a = 7a - 5a + 6$
(c) $5 + 6a + 3a = 12 - 2a + 10a$
(d) $-3 - 2a + 6a = 11 + a + 2a$
(e) $-3 + 4(a - 1) = 3(a + 5)$
(f) $6(a - 3) = 5(a + 2) - 8$

(g) $3b - 8 = 5b - 4$
(h) $3 - 6b + 6 = 2b - 7$
(i) $3b + 6 - 7b = 12 - 8b + 2$
(j) $-4b + 4 + 2b = 3b - 16$
(k) $2(b - 6) + 8 = 4(b + 7)$
(l) $2(2a - 1) + 4 = 5(a + 1)$
(m) $4(x - 5) - 2(x + 1) = 3(1 - x)$
(n) $(x + 1) - 2(x + 3) - 3(x - 2) = 13$
(o) $2(x - 2) + 3(x + 1) = 4x + 1$
(p) $4(x - 2) - 3(x + 1) = 1 - 3x$
(q) $2(x - 5) = 4(x - 7) - (x - 9)$

5. Solve.

(a) $9.8x - 3.7 = 6.1$
(b) $4.2 - 3.5x = 2.1$
(c) $3.0(x - 2.5) = 7.5$
(d) $3.5 = 5.2 - 6.3(x + 1.4)$
(e) $3.5x - 2.4(x + 3.5) = 0$
(f) $5.5x - 2.3 = 3.2(2.5x - 4.6)$

C 6. Solve.

(a) $\quad 3.1(2.5x - 4.3) - 3.8x$
$\quad = 4.3(1.4 - 2.3x)$
(b) $\quad 6.2(1.1x - 2.5) + 3.7(2.4x - 3.7)$
$\quad = 8.4x - 5.2$

2.16 EQUATIONS INVOLVING RATIONAL EXPRESSIONS

To solve equations involving rational expressions, we first find the lowest common denominator (LCD). To clear the fractions, we then multiply both sides of the equation by the lowest common denominator.

EXAMPLE 1. Solve. $\frac{2}{3}x - \frac{1}{2}(x - 3) = \frac{2x - 3}{4}$, $x \in R$

SOLUTION:

The lowest common denominator (LCD) is 12.

Multiply both sides of the equation by 12.

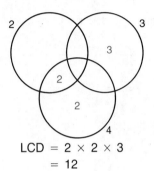

LCD = 2 × 2 × 3
   = 12

$$12\left[\frac{2}{3}x - \frac{1}{2}(x - 3)\right] = 12\left[\frac{2x - 3}{4}\right]$$
$$8x - 6(x - 3) = (2x - 3)3$$
$$8x - 6x + 18 = 6x - 9$$
$$-4x = -27$$
$$x = \frac{-27}{-4}$$
$$x = 6\frac{3}{4}$$

The root is $6\frac{3}{4}$.

EXAMPLE 2. Solve. $\frac{3}{2x} + 2 = \frac{1}{x}$, $x \in R$, $x \neq 0$

SOLUTION:

The LCD is 2x.

Multiply both sides by the LCD.

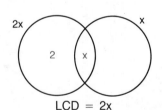

LCD = 2x

$$2x\left[\frac{3}{2x} + 2\right] = 2x\left[\frac{1}{x}\right]$$
$$3 + 4x = 2$$
$$4x = -1$$
$$x = -\frac{1}{4}$$

The root is $-\frac{1}{4}$.

EXAMPLE 3. Solve. $\dfrac{3}{4x} = \dfrac{1}{x+1}$, $x \in R$, $x \neq 0$, $x \neq -1$

SOLUTION:

The LCD is $4x(x+1)$.

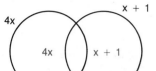

LCD $= 4x(x+1)$

Multiply both sides by the LCD.

$$4x(x+1)\left[\dfrac{3}{4x}\right] = 4x(x+1)\left[\dfrac{1}{x+1}\right]$$

$$\overset{1}{4x}(x+1)\left[\dfrac{3}{\underset{1}{4x}}\right] = 4x\overset{1}{(x+1)}\left[\dfrac{1}{\underset{1}{(x+1)}}\right]$$

$$3(x+1) = 4x(1)$$
$$3x + 3 = 4x$$
$$3 = x$$

The root is 3.

EXERCISE 2.16

A Solve the following equations whose variables have domain R.

1. (a) $\frac{1}{4}x = 2$

(b) $\dfrac{x}{3} = 5$

(c) $\frac{3}{5}x = 1$

(d) $\dfrac{3x}{4} = 8$

2. (a) $a - \frac{1}{2} = \frac{3}{2}$

(b) $2b + \frac{3}{4} = 1$

(c) $a - \frac{1}{3} = \frac{1}{2}$

(d) $2(x - \frac{1}{4}) = \frac{1}{2}$

B 3. (a) $\dfrac{b-1}{3} = 6$

(b) $\dfrac{b+2}{8} = \dfrac{1}{4}$

(c) $\dfrac{c}{3} - \dfrac{1}{2} = \dfrac{1}{4}$

(d) $\dfrac{2c}{3} + 2 = \dfrac{1}{2}$

(e) $\dfrac{2c+1}{3} = 6$

(f) $\dfrac{c-7}{2} = \dfrac{1}{4}$

(g) $\dfrac{2-3c}{4} = \dfrac{6-2c}{5}$

(h) $\dfrac{3c+7}{4} - \dfrac{c}{3} = -\dfrac{1}{3}$

(i) $\frac{1}{2}x - \frac{1}{3}(x+2) = \frac{5}{6}$

(j) $\dfrac{3x}{2} - \dfrac{5x}{4} = \dfrac{3x+1}{2}$

4. (a) $\dfrac{2}{x} + 3 = \dfrac{1}{x}$, $x \neq 0$

(b) $\dfrac{3}{5x} - 4 = \dfrac{-7}{2}$, $x \neq 0$

(c) $\dfrac{6}{x} + 7 = \dfrac{20}{x}$, $x \neq 0$

(d) $\dfrac{9}{x} - 1 = \dfrac{6}{x}$, $x \neq 0$

5. (a) $\dfrac{1}{3} + \dfrac{1}{x} = \dfrac{17}{6}$, $x \neq 0$

(b) $\dfrac{4}{x} - \dfrac{3}{4} = \dfrac{1}{4}$, $x \neq 0$

(c) $\dfrac{3}{2x} + \dfrac{1}{3} = \dfrac{5}{6}$, $x \neq 0$

(d) $\dfrac{2}{5x} - \dfrac{1}{4} = \dfrac{1}{x}$, $x \neq 0$

C 6. Solve.

(a) $\dfrac{4}{x-1} + 1 = \dfrac{1}{2}$, $x \neq 1$

(b) $\dfrac{3x+2}{x-4} = \dfrac{2}{3}$, $x \neq 4$

(c) $\dfrac{2}{x} = \dfrac{1}{x+1}$, $x \neq 0, -1$

(d) $\dfrac{5}{2x} = \dfrac{3}{x-2}$, $x \neq 0, 2$

7. Solve.

(a) $\dfrac{4}{x+3} = \dfrac{6}{2x-1}$, $x \neq -3, \frac{1}{2}$

(b) $\dfrac{3}{x-4} + \dfrac{2}{x-4} = \dfrac{5}{3}$, $x \neq 4$

(c) $\dfrac{x+1}{x^2-4} - \dfrac{1}{x} = 0$, $x \neq 0, 2, -2$

2.17 PROBLEM SOLVING WITH EQUATIONS

We shall now use the problem solving techniques of Chapter 1 to solve problems algebraically. The PLAN involves translating the problem into a single equation with one variable.

READ

EXAMPLE 1. The boat slips in a marina are numbered consecutively. The sum of three consecutive boat slip numbers is 63. Find the numbers.

PLAN

SOLUTION:
We first express each unknown in terms of one variable.

Since the numbers are consecutive, they differ by 1. Therefore, if x represents the first number, then x + 1 represents the second number, and x + 2 represents the third number.

$$x + (x + 1) + (x + 2) = 63$$
$$x + x + 1 + x + 2 = 63$$
$$3x + 3 = 63$$
$$3x = 60$$
$$x = 20$$

SOLVE

ANSWER

The three boat slip numbers are 20, 21, and 22.

Check.

20 + 21 + 22 = 63, and 20, 21, and 22 are consecutive numbers.

READ

EXAMPLE 2. Sam is twice Jennie's age. Three years ago, the sum of their ages was 45. How old is Jennie today?

PLAN

$E=mc^2$

SOLUTION:
Let x represent Jennie's age in years.

Since Sam is twice as old, then let 2x represent Sam's age in years.

Three years ago, Jennie's age was x − 3 and Sam's age was 2x − 3.

$$(x - 3) + (2x - 3) = 45$$
$$x - 3 + 2x - 3 = 45$$
$$3x - 6 = 45$$
$$3x = 51$$
$$x = 17$$

SOLVE

ANSWER

Jennie is 17 years old and Sam is 34 years old.

Check.

Three years ago,
Jennie: 14
Sam: <u>31</u>
Sum of their ages: 45

READ

EXAMPLE 3. The cash box for the school play contains $233 in $2 bills and $5 bills. How many bills of each denomination are there if the total number of bills is 61?

PLAN

SOLUTION:

Let x represent the number of $2 bills.

Since the total number of bills is 61, then let (61 − x) represent the number of $5 bills.

The value of the $2 bills is 2x and the value of the $5 bills is 5(61 − x).

$$2x + 5(61 - x) = 233$$
$$2x + 305 - 5x = 233$$
$$-3x + 305 = 233$$
$$-3x = -72$$
$$x = 24$$
$$61 - x = 37$$

SOLVE

ANSWER

There are 24 $2 bills and 37 $5 bills.

Check.

The total number of bills is 24 + 37 = 61.
The value of the bills is

$$\$2(24) + \$5(37) = \$48 + \$185$$
$$= \$233$$

READ

EXAMPLE 4. How many millilitres of 50% acid solution must be mixed with 30% solution to produce 100 mL of 45% solution?

PLAN

$E=mc^2$

SOLUTION:

Let x represent the amount of 50% solution in millilitres.
Since 100 mL of solution are required, let (100 − x) represent the amount of 30% solution in millilitres.

$$0.5x + 0.3(100 - x) = 0.45(100)$$
$$0.5x + 30 - 0.3x = 45$$
$$0.2x + 30 = 45$$
$$0.2x = 15$$
$$x = 75$$

SOLVE

ANSWER

75 mL of 50% solution are required.

Check.

50% of 75 mL contains 37.5 mL of acid.
30% of 25 mL contains 7.5 mL of acid.
            Total acid: 45.0 mL

READ

EXAMPLE 5. Carla drove from Ajax to Devon at 50 km/h and returned at 60 km/h. Find the distance between Ajax and Devon if the total travelling time was 11 h.

PLAN

SOLUTION:

Let x represent the distance between Ajax and Devon in kilometres.

D(km)	R(km/h)	T(h)
x	50	$\dfrac{x}{50}$
x	60	$\dfrac{x}{60}$

$E=mc^2$

SOLVE

$$\frac{x}{50} + \frac{x}{60} = 11$$
$$300\left(\frac{x}{50} + \frac{x}{60}\right) = (11)300$$
$$6x + 5x = 3300$$
$$11x = 3300$$
$$x = 300$$

ANSWER

The distance between Ajax and Devon is 300 km.

Check.

300 km at 50 km/h takes   6 h
300 km at 60 km/h takes   5 h
Total time is   11 h

EXERCISE 2.17

A 1. Express each of the following as an algebraic expression.

(a) a number increased by three
(b) twice Pat's age
(c) 5 less than x
(d) the length is three times the width
(e) twice a number increased by three
(f) three consecutive numbers
(g) three consecutive even numbers
(h) Mary's age in five years.

B Solve the following problems using one variable.

2. The sum of three consecutive numbers is 66. Find the numbers.

3. The sum of three consecutive even numbers is 48. Find the numbers.

4. The sum of three consecutive odd numbers is 75. Find the numbers.

5. A department store employs 119 people. The full-time staff outnumbers the part-time staff by 13. How many people work part-time?

6. A boutique sold 3 more sweaters than skirts. Three times the number of skirts sold plus four times the number of sweaters is 96. How many sweaters were sold?

7. Linda is twice as old as Susan. In four years, the sum of their ages will be 32. How old are they today?

8. A box contains 25 small flashlights, some worth $1.00 each and the remainder $2.00 each. How many of each are there if the total value of the flashlights is $35.00?

9. Steve paid a library fine of $1.60 using nickels, dimes, and quarters. The number of nickels was two more than the number of dimes, and the number of quarters was two fewer than the number of dimes. How many nickels, dimes, and quarters were there?

10. How many millilitres of 50% acid solution must be mixed with 10% solution to produce 200 mL of 25% solution?

11. Kasmir travelled 3 h by car and 4 h by bus. The speed of the car was 10 km/h faster than the bus. Find the speed of the bus if the total distance travelled was 660 km.

12. Shirley walked a certain distance, then returned along the same route. She walked 10 km/h going and returned at 8 km/h. How far did she walk if the round trip took 9 h?

13. A plane flew from Toronto to Ottawa at an average speed of 700 km/h. Had the plane flown at an average speed of 500 km/h, then the trip would have taken 0.2 h longer. How far is it from Toronto to Ottawa?

14. A car travelled a certain distance in 3 h. Had the driver increased the speed by 10 km/h, the trip would have taken 2.5 h. How fast should the driver have gone to cover the distance in 2.5 h?

15. The Appleton family left for vacation by car. On the first day they averaged 70 km/h. On the second day they averaged 90 km/h and drove for 1 h longer than the first day. How long did they travel on the first day if the total distance for two days was 890 km?

16. A printed page is 8 cm longer than it is wide. If the length is increased by 10 cm and the width is increased by 9 cm, the area is increased by 580 cm^2. What are the original dimensions of the page?

Find the missing digits in this multiplication.

$$
\begin{array}{r}
\blacksquare\blacksquare 3 \\
\times\ \blacksquare\blacksquare 3 \\
\hline
3\,\blacksquare\blacksquare \\
\blacksquare 3\,\blacksquare \\
\blacksquare\blacksquare 3 \\
\hline
\blacksquare\blacksquare\blacksquare\blacksquare\blacksquare
\end{array}
$$

2.18 EQUATIONS WITH LITERAL COEFFICIENTS

To solve an equation with literal coefficients, we isolate the specified variable. In the case where the solution involves a rational expression, we state the restrictions.

EXAMPLE 1. Solve for x. $ax = bx + c$, $x \in R$

SOLUTION:

$$ax = bx + c$$
$$ax - bx = c$$
$$x(a - b) = c \longleftarrow \text{Common factor.}$$
$$x = \frac{c}{a - b}, \quad a \neq b$$

Note that $a \neq b$ since, in the real numbers, the denominator cannot be zero.

EXAMPLE 2. Solve for x. $\frac{a}{3}x = \frac{b}{2}x + c$, $x \in R$

SOLUTION:
The LCD is 6.
Multiply both sides of the equation by the LCD.

$$\overset{2}{\cancel{6}}\left[\frac{a}{\cancel{3}}x\right] = \left[\frac{b}{2}x + c\right]6$$

$$2ax = 3bx + 6c$$
$$2ax - 3bx = 6c$$
$$x(2a - 3b) = 6c \longleftarrow \text{Common factor.}$$
$$x = \frac{6c}{2a - 3b}, \quad a \neq \frac{3b}{2}$$

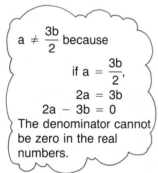

$a \neq \dfrac{3b}{2}$ because

if $a = \dfrac{3b}{2}$,

$2a = 3b$

$2a - 3b = 0$

The denominator cannot be zero in the real numbers.

When working with formulas, it is often necessary to solve for one of the variables.

EXAMPLE 3. The formula for calculating the perimeter of a square is $P = 4s$
(a) Solve for s.
(b) Determine the length of the sides of a square whose perimeter is 24 cm.

SOLUTION:
(a) $P = 4s$
Divide by 4.

$$\frac{P}{4} = s \quad \text{or} \quad s = \frac{P}{4}$$

(b) Substitute P $= 24$ into the result obtained in (a).

$$s = \frac{P}{4}$$
$$= \frac{24}{4}$$
$$= 6$$

The length of each side is 6 cm.

EXAMPLE 4. The formula for calculating the area of a trapezoid is $A = \frac{h}{2}(a + b)$. Solve for h.

SOLUTION:

$$A = \frac{h}{2}(a + b)$$
$$2[A] = 2\left[\frac{h}{2}(a + b)\right]$$
$$2A = h(a + b)$$

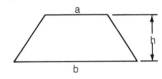

> In a trapezoid, a, b > 0
> hence $a + b \neq 0$.

$$\frac{2A}{a + b} = h \quad \text{or} \quad h = \frac{2A}{a + b}$$

EXERCISE 2.18

A 1. Solve for x where a, b, c, and d > 0.

(a) $ax = b$

(b) $2cx = d$

(c) $(a + b)x = 2$

(d) $ax = b - 2$

(e) $2ax = 4b$

(f) $x(3 + a) = 5$

B 2. Solve for x and state the restrictions.

(a) $4 = b(x - a)$

(b) $a = 4bx + 2$

(c) $10 = 3(x - a)$

(d) $2x = 5 + ax$

(e) $ax + bx + cx = 5$

(f) $\frac{1}{x + b} = \frac{1}{c}$

(g) $\frac{a}{x} + \frac{b}{x} = c$

(h) $c = \frac{x}{2}(a + b)$

For the following problems assume that all variables are positive.

3. Solve the following formulas for the variables indicated.

(a) $A = \ell w$; ℓ and w

(b) $P = 2(\ell + w)$; ℓ and w

(c) $C = 2\pi r$; r

(d) $V = \pi r^2 h$; h

(e) $V = \ell w h$; ℓ, w, and h

(f) $v = u + at$; u, a, and t

(g) $s = \frac{1}{2}at^2$; a

(h) $I = prt$; p, r, and t

C 4. Solve the following formulas for the variable indicated.

(a) $A = \frac{h}{2}(a + b)$, a, b, h, A > 0; a

(b) $t = a + (n - 1)d$, d $\neq 0$; n

(c) $S = \frac{a}{1 - r}$, r $\neq 1$, S $\neq 0$; r

2.19 INEQUALITIES IN ONE VARIABLE

Inequalities are expressions involving symbols such as $>$, $<$, $\geq$, $\leq$, and $\neq$. We shall now review the rules for solving inequalities.

Rules		
Since 8 > 6, then	If a > b, then	
$8 + 2 > 6 + 2$	$a + c > b + c$	Addition Rule
$8 - 2 > 6 - 2$	$a - c > b - c$	Subtraction Rule
$8 \times 2 > 6 \times 2$ $8 \times (-2) < 6 \times (-2)$	$ac > bc$ for $c > 0$ $ac < bc$ for $c < 0$	Multiplication Rule
$\dfrac{8}{2} > \dfrac{6}{2}$ $\dfrac{8}{-2} < \dfrac{6}{-2}$	$\dfrac{a}{c} > \dfrac{b}{c}$ for $c > 0$ $\dfrac{a}{c} < \dfrac{b}{c}$ for $c < 0$	Division Rule

Similar rules apply to inequalities involving $<$, $\geq$, and $\leq$.

EXAMPLE 1. Solve. $3 + 5x > 4x + 6, x \in R$

SOLUTION:

$$3 + 5x > 4x + 6$$
$$3 - 3 + 5x > 4x + 6 - 3 \longleftarrow \text{Subtraction Rule}$$
$$5x > 4x + 3$$
$$5x - 4x > 4x - 4x + 3 \longleftarrow \text{Subtraction Rule}$$
$$x > 3$$

The solution set is $\{x \in R \mid x > 3\}$.

EXAMPLE 2. Graph the solution set of
$3(x - 5) + 2x \leq 5 - 2(x + 3), x \in R$.

SOLUTION:

$$3(x - 5) + 2x \leq 5 - 2(x + 3)$$
$$3x - 15 + 2x \leq 5 - 2x - 6$$
$$5x - 15 \leq -2x - 1$$
$$5x + 2x - 15 + 15 \leq -2x + 2x - 1 + 15 \longleftarrow \text{Addition Rule}$$
$$7x \leq 14$$
$$x \leq 2 \longleftarrow \text{Division Rule}$$

The solution set is $\{x \in R \mid x \leq 2\}$.

Check the direction of the arrow by substituting
$x = 0$.
L.S. $= 3(x - 5) + 2x$
$= -15$
R.S. $= 5 - 2(x + 3)$
$= -1$
L.S. $\leq$ R.S.
0 is in the solution.

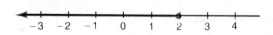

EXAMPLE 3. Graph the solution set of $\frac{x}{3} + \frac{1}{2} < \frac{2x}{3} - \frac{5}{2}$, $x \in R$.

SOLUTION:

$$\frac{x}{3} + \frac{1}{2} < \frac{2x}{3} - \frac{5}{2} \longleftarrow \text{The LCD is 6}$$

$$6\left[\frac{x}{3} + \frac{1}{2}\right] < \left[\frac{2x}{3} - \frac{5}{2}\right]6 \longleftarrow \text{Multiplication Rule}$$

$$2x + 3 < 4x - 15$$

$$2x + 3 - 3 < 4x - 15 - 3 \longleftarrow \text{Subtraction Rule}$$

$$2x < 4x - 18$$

$$2x - 4x < 4x - 18 - 4x \longleftarrow \text{Subtraction Rule}$$

$$-2x < -18$$

$$\frac{-2x}{-2} > \frac{-18}{-2} \longleftarrow \text{Division Rule}$$

$$x > 9$$

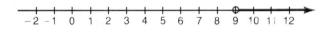

EXERCISE 2.19

A Solve the following inequalities. Variables have domain R.

1. (a) $x + 5 > 7$ (b) $a - 4 < 7$
(c) $3x < 2x + 4$ (d) $5x - 3 \geqslant 4x + 2$
(e) $3x \leqslant 12$ (f) $5x + 1 \leqslant 21$
(g) $-3x > 6$ (h) $2x \leqslant 3x + 2$

2. (a) $\frac{1}{2}x < 3$ (b) $\frac{2}{3}x \leqslant 6$
(c) $-\frac{1}{3}x \geqslant 2$ (d) $-\frac{3}{4}x < -6$
(e) $0.5a > 3.5$ (f) $0.25m \geqslant 10$
(g) $-2.5b \leqslant 10$ (h) $x + 2.4 \leqslant 3.5$

All variables have domain R.

B 3. Solve.
(a) $6x + 8 < 5x + 5$
(b) $4x - 2 \geqslant 3x + 5$
(c) $3 + 5m + 1 \leqslant 1 + 4m$
(d) $3x + 1 + 2x > 4x - 6$
(e) $3a - 2a + 5 \leqslant -6$
(f) $8x + 4 - 6 \leqslant 7x$
(g) $7x - 5 \geqslant 2x + 20$

4. Solve and graph the solution.
(a) $3(c - 5) \leqslant 4 - (c - 5)$
(b) $2(x + 3) < 3x + 5$
(c) $3a - 7 \geqslant 2(a + 2) + 1$
(d) $3b - 2 + 2(b + 1) \geqslant 2(2b + 3)$

(e) $3(2x - 1) - 4 \leqslant 5(1 + x) - 1$
(f) $-3 + 4(3 + a) < 5 + 3a$
(g) $3(2x - 3) > 2(1 - 3x) + 4$
(h) $2x + 3(x - 7) \leqslant 9(x - 1)$

5. Solve.
(a) $a - 3.1 \leqslant 3.15 - 1.5a$
(b) $0.8(x + 4) > 0.2 - 0.7x$
(c) $x - 0.75 \leqslant 0.5(x + 1)$
(d) $2(x - 1) > 5(1 - 0.3x)$
(e) $7(0.5x - 0.3) \leqslant 2.5x + 2.4$
(f) $1.5(x - 3) \geqslant 0.5(x - 9) - 2.5$

6. Solve and graph the solution.
(a) $1.5(3x - 5) \leqslant 3.5(x - 1) - 1.5$
(b) $5x - 2 > 1.5(x - 1) + 3$
(c) $1.3(5x + 2) - 3.1 \leqslant 5.5(x + 1) - 2$
(d) $8(0.4x + 1) \geqslant 5(x + 1) - 2.8x$

7. Solve and graph the solution.
(a) $\frac{a + 1}{3} > \frac{a - 2}{4}$

(b) $\frac{b - 3}{5} + 1 \leqslant \frac{b + 4}{3}$

(c) $\frac{2x - 3}{6} + \frac{1}{8} > \frac{3x + 1}{4}$

(d) $3 + \frac{x - 3}{6} \geqslant x$

2.20 PROBLEM SOLVING WITH FORMULAS

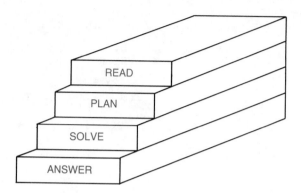

The problem solving model in Chapter 1 suggested that your PLAN might include the use of a formula or an equation.

READ

EXAMPLE. Find the area of the largest square playing surface that can be marked on a circular field with a radius of 50 m.

PLAN

SOLUTION:

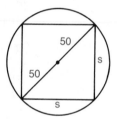

$E=mc^2$

Let s represent the length of each side of the square in metres.

The area of the square will be

$$A = s^2$$

By the Pythagorean Theorem,

$$c^2 = a^2 + b^2$$
$$100^2 = s^2 + s^2$$
$$10\ 000 = 2s^2$$
$$5000 = s^2$$

SOLVE

ANSWER

Since $A = s^2$ and $s^2 = 5000$, then the maximum area A is 5000 m².

EXERCISE 2.20

The answers to each of the following problems should be expressed to the nearest whole number unless otherwise specified.

1. The six rectangular figures can be arranged to form a large square. What will be the perimeter of the square?

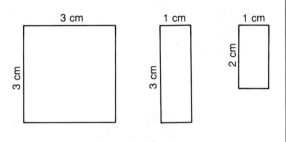

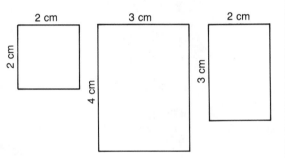

2. An open box (no top) is made by cutting out a 5 cm by 5 cm square from each corner of a rectangular piece of cardboard and folding up the sides.

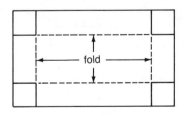

Find the volume of the box to the nearest cubic centimetre if the original piece of cardboard measures 20 cm by 35 cm.

3. Find the area of a square having the same perimeter as the given rectangle.

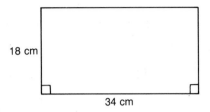

4. Find the perimeter in metres of the field whose dimensions are shown in the diagram below.

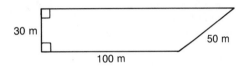

5. A couple wishes to subdivide their farm in such a way that their son and daughter receive equal areas. The son receives a lot in the form of an isosceles triangle whose dimensions are shown below. The daughter is given a square lot of equal area.

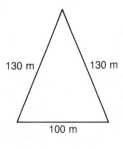

What are the dimensions of the daughter's lot to the nearest tenth of a metre?

6. A steel cylindrical drum has a height of 1 m and a radius of 30 cm. If one can of spray enamel covers 2 m², how many cans should Jerry buy to paint the exterior of the drum, including the top and bottom?

7. Two cylindrical drums are tied together by two metal straps.

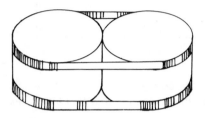

If the radius of each drum is 40 cm, what is the length of each strap to the nearest centimetre?

8. Find the area of the largest square platform that can be placed on a semi-circular stage with a radius of 10 m.

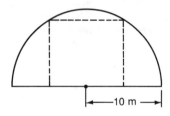

—10 m—

9. How much longer than the earth's circumference would a metal band placed around the earth's equator one metre above the ground be? (Assume that the cross-section of the earth at the equator is a circle of radius 6371 km.)

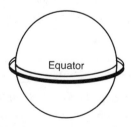

Equator

10. A church has 12 windows in the form of rectangles surmounted by semi-circles. The width of a window is 1.6 m and the height of its rectangular part is 2 m. The custodian wishes to draft-proof the windows for the winter by applying a bead of caulking around the perimeter. If one tube of caulking will make a bead 10 m long, how many tubes should the custodian order?

11. A cyclist rigged a special counting mechanism on the back wheel of a bicycle that counted the number of revolutions of the wheel. On a cross-country excursion, the wheel registered 10 455 turns.

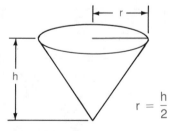

If the diameter of the rear wheel is 70 cm, what was the total distance of the round-trip excursion in kilometres?

C 12. A large storage tank in the shape of a cone is such that the radius of any circular cross-section equals one half of the depth to the vertex of the cone. It is being filled with grain at the rate of 1.09 m³/s.

$r = \dfrac{h}{2}$

How deep is the grain after 4 min? (Answer to the nearest metre.)

13. In a contest to guess the capacity of a large cylindrical storage tank, Charles and Sharon teamed up to solve the problem using a mathematical approach. Charles measured the circumference of the tank and found it to be 30.2 m. Sharon noticed that the tank cast a shadow of 12 m while a nearby 2 m post cast a shadow of 1.5 m. Find the capacity of the tank to the nearest ten.

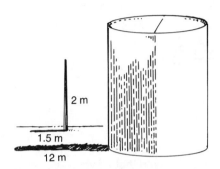

14. A dog's leash is 5 m long. One end is tied to a ring that slides freely along a clothesline which is 3 m above the ground and 10 m long.

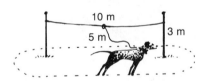

How much ground area to the nearest integer, does the dog have to roam?

Use the given BASIC programs to help solve the following problems.

EXERCISE

1. Find to the nearest tenth of a centimetre, the dimensions of a square having an area equal to that of a circle with a radius of 5 cm.

NEW

```
10 REM SQUARE WITH SAME AREA AS CIRCLE
20 PRINT "WHAT IS THE RADIUS";
30 INPUT R
40 A = 3.14159*R*R
50 L = SQR(A)
60 PRINT "AREA OF CIRCLE IS"; A
70 PRINT "A SQUARE OF SIDE";
   INT(L*10+.5)/10;"HAS THE SAME AREA."
80 END
```

RUN

2. Find to the nearest tenth of a centimetre, the radius of a circle having the same area as a square whose sides are 7 cm.

NEW

```
10 REM CIRCLE WITH SAME AREA AS SQUARE
20 PRINT "WHAT IS THE LENGTH OF ONE
   SIDE OF YOUR SQUARE";
30 INPUT L
40 A = L*L
50 R = SQR(A/3.14159)
60 PRINT "AREA OF SQUARE IS"; A
70 PRINT "A CIRCLE OF RADIUS";
   INT(R*10+.5)/10;"HAS THE SAME AREA."
80 END
```

RUN

Find unequal rational numbers such that

$$x^y = y^x.$$

2.21 REVIEW EXERCISE

1. Simplify.
(a) $(x + 3xy - y) + (2x - xy - 3y)$
(b) $(-3x^2 + 5x - 4) + (-4x^2 - 7x + 3)$
(c) $(3x^2 - 2x + 4) - (5x^2 - 7x + 3)$
(d) $(-2 + 3x - 6x^2) - (3 - 4x - 5x^2)$
(e) $(x^2y + 3x^3) + (x^3 - 2xy^2) - (2x^2y + 3xy^2)$
(f) $(2x^3 - 3x^2 + 7x - 2) - (x^3 - 7x)$
$+ (4x^2 - 3)$

2. Expand and simplify.
(a) $2(x - 5) - 3(x + 2)$
(b) $(x + 3)(2x - 4)$
(c) $(x + 2)^2 - 3$
(d) $(x - 2y)(x + 2y) + 3y^2$
(e) $2(x - 3) + 3(x - 5) - 4(x + 2)$
(f) $(x - 4)(x - 7) - 2(x - 6)$
(g) $(m + 2)^2 + (m - 7)(m + 7) + (m - 3)^2$
(h) $2(w - 3)(w + 4) - (w - 7)(w - 6) - 16$
(i) $(2x - 3)(3x - 1) - (x - 4)(2x - 5)$
(j) $5(3x + 2)(x + 4) - (2x - 1)^2 + 3(3x - 5)$
(k) $5(2t - 1)(t + 3) - (t - 7)(2t + 7) - 6$
(l) $6 - (5x - 1)(4x - 3) - 2(3x - 5)^2$

3. Factor.
(a) $3mn - 9m^2n - 12mn^2$
(b) $x^2 - x - 30$
(c) $x^2 - 81$
(d) $x^2 + 8x + 16$
(e) $36t^2 - 49$
(f) $5x(m - 7) - 3(m - 7)$
(g) $2x^2 + 8x - 120$
(h) $x^2 - 14x + 49$
(i) $9x^2y - 3x + 12xy^2$
(j) $100m^2 - 121$
(k) $4m^2 + 28m + 49$
(l) $25x^2 - 20x + 4$
(m) $5x^2(m - n) - 2x(m - n)$
(n) $3x^2 - 48$

4. Simplify the following rational expressions and state the restrictions on the variables.
(a) $\dfrac{3x}{6x^2 - 9x}$
(b) $\dfrac{5xy - 25y}{15y}$
(c) $\dfrac{6x - 30}{x - 5}$
(d) $\dfrac{x - 7}{x^2 - 49}$
(e) $\dfrac{x + 3}{x^2 + 5x + 6}$
(f) $\dfrac{x^2 - 25}{x^2 + 10x + 25}$

5. Express each of the following as rational expressions in lowest terms. Assume that all variables are restricted so that no denominator or divisor is equal to zero.
(a) $\dfrac{25m^3n^2}{16xy} \times \dfrac{32x^3y^2}{5m^2n}$
(b) $\dfrac{21t^4w^2}{8xy} \div \dfrac{14tw}{12x^2y^3}$
(c) $\dfrac{x + 4}{4x^2} \times \dfrac{16x}{x + 4}$
(d) $\dfrac{x^2 - 4}{x + 1} \div \dfrac{x + 2}{x + 1}$
(e) $\dfrac{x^2 + 2x}{x + 3} \times \dfrac{x^2 - 9}{x^2 - x - 6}$
(f) $\dfrac{2x + 4}{x - 3} \div (x^2 - 4)$

6. Perform the indicated operations and simplify. Assume that all variables are restricted so that no denominator is equal to zero.
(a) $\dfrac{2}{7} + \dfrac{1}{3} - \dfrac{4}{21}$
(b) $\dfrac{3x}{5} - \dfrac{x}{6} + \dfrac{7x}{10}$
(c) $\dfrac{3x + 1}{2} - \dfrac{x + 1}{3} + \dfrac{x}{4}$
(d) $\dfrac{m - 3}{9} - \dfrac{m + 4}{2} - \dfrac{m - 7}{6}$
(e) $\dfrac{5}{2x^2} - \dfrac{1}{3x} + \dfrac{5}{6x^3}$
(f) $\dfrac{3}{x + 1} + \dfrac{4}{x - 1}$

7. Solve the following equations whose variables have domain R.
(a) $3x - 5(x + 2) = 4$
(b) $3(a + 2) - 2(a + 1) = 5$
(c) $3(a - 1) + 2a + 3 = 25$
(d) $\frac{1}{2}x + 2 = 3$
(e) $\frac{2}{3}x + \frac{3}{4} = \frac{1}{2}$
(f) $3.5(x - 1) = 1.5x - 1$
(g) $7(1 - 0.6x) = 1 - 5.2x$
(h) $\dfrac{3x - 4}{2} = \dfrac{7x - 12}{5}$
(i) $\dfrac{2}{3x} = \dfrac{1}{x + 1}$, $x \neq 0, -1$

8. Solve the following for the variables indicated. All variables are positive.

(a) $A = \ell w$; ℓ
(b) $I = prt$; r
(c) $V = IR$; I
(d) $V = \frac{1}{3}\pi r^2 h$; h
(e) $d = vt$; t
(f) $A = \frac{h}{2}(a + b)$; h

9. The sum of three consecutive integers is 96. Find the integers.

10. There are 36 more pages in one textbook than another. There are 960 pages in all. How many pages are there in each textbook?

11. A parking meter contained only quarters and dimes. There were twice as many dimes as quarters. How many quarters were there if the meter contained $9.45 in all?

12. Dan drove a certain distance at 60 km/h, then returned along the same route at 80 km/h. The whole trip took 7 h. How far did he drive?

13. Solve the following inequalities. Variables have domain R.

(a) $3 + x < 5$
(b) $2x + 3 \geq x + 2$
(c) $2(x + 3) \leq x + 2$
(d) $3x + 4 \geq 2(x + 1) + 3$
(e) $\frac{x + 2}{3} \leq 1$
(f) $\frac{x + 1}{5} > \frac{2x + 1}{3}$
(g) $2.5(3x + 1) > 5(1.3x + 1)$
(h) $6(x + 1) - 7.5 \leq 1.5(x + 2)$

14. A cube has dimensions 40 cm by 40 cm by 40 cm. A rectangular solid with the same volume has a base whose dimensions are 35 cm by 50 cm.

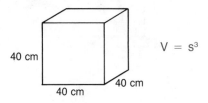

$V = s^3$

40 cm
40 cm
40 cm

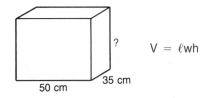

? $V = \ell wh$

50 cm   35 cm

What is the height of the second solid to the nearest tenth of a centimetre?

15. Three cylindrical drums are stacked as shown in the diagram below. Each drum has a radius of 30 cm.

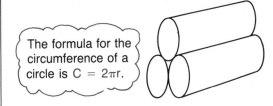

The formula for the circumference of a circle is $C = 2\pi r$.

What is the total height of the pile to the nearest centimetre?

16. A metal strap is used to secure the three drums in question 15.

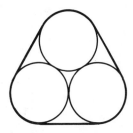

What is the length of the strap to the nearest centimetre?

2.22 CHAPTER 2 TEST

1. Simplify.
(a) $(x^2 + 3x - 7) - (2x^2 - x + 3)$
(b) $(2xy - x^2 + y^2) - (3xy - x^2) + y^2$

2. Expand and simplify.
(a) $2(x - 3y) - 3(2x - y)$
(b) $(c + 3d)(2c + 5d) + (c + 2d)^2$

3. Factor, if possible.
(a) $4a^2b - 2ab + 8ab^3$ (b) $4x^2 - 9$
(c) $x^2 + 4x - 25$ (d) $4x^2 - 20x + 25$
(e) $2x^2 - 242$ (f) $2x(x + 3) - 3(x + 3)$

4. Simplify the following and state the restrictions on the variables.
(a) $\dfrac{5x}{15x - 20x^2}$ (b) $\dfrac{2x^2 - 16x}{x^2 - 10x + 16}$
(c) $\dfrac{42a^3b^2}{7ab} \times \dfrac{a^4b^3}{3a^2b}$ (d) $\dfrac{3x - 15}{2x - 3} \div \dfrac{x^2 - 25}{x + 5}$

5. Simplify.
(a) $\dfrac{2x}{3} + \dfrac{4x - 1}{2} - \dfrac{x}{5}$ (b) $\dfrac{3}{4x} + \dfrac{4}{3x^2} + \dfrac{1}{x}$, $x \neq 0$

6. Solve the following where $x \in R$.
(a) $2x + 3(2x - 4) = 4$ (b) $\frac{2}{3}x + 4 = 10$
(c) $3.2(x + 1) = 4x$ (d) $\dfrac{3}{x} + \dfrac{4}{5} = \dfrac{2}{3x}$, $x \neq 0$

7. Solve the following inequalities where $x \in R$.
(a) $x - 4(x + 3) \leq 3$ (b) $\dfrac{x - 2}{3} > \dfrac{2x - 5}{5}$
(c) $2.5(x + 2) \leq 12.5$ (d) $-2x + \frac{3}{2} \geq \frac{1}{2}$

8. A circle has a radius of 4 cm. Find, to the nearest tenth of a centimetre, the dimensions of a square having the same area.

4 cm

$A = \pi r^2$

?

?

$A = s^2$

RELATIONS

CHAPTER

3

Anyone who understands algebraic notation, reads at a glance in an equation results reached arithmetically only with great labour and pains.

A. Cournot

POINTS ON A GRID — BATTLESHIP

I. The game is played between two people.

II. Each player has two grids as shown in the diagram below. One grid is used to record a player's shots. The other is used to record the positions of his own ships.

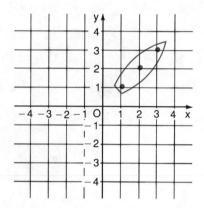 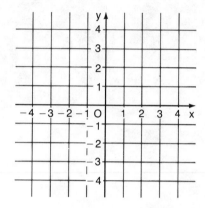

III. Ships may be entered in the grid horizontally, vertically, or diagonally, but always in a straight line.

IV. Each player enters

     1 battleship (5 points)

     1 aircraft carrier (4 points)

     1 cruiser (3 points)

     1 destroyer (2 points)

V. Players call shots alternately as ordered pairs, for example, $(2, -3)$. The opponent says "hit" or "miss" according to the result of the shot.

VI. The opponent need not say what has been hit after a "hit" is called.

VII. To sink a ship you must hit all points of the ship. Once a ship has been sunk, the opponent must say what ship has been sunk.

VIII. The winner is the first player to sink all of the opponent's ships.

TABLES OF VALUES

EXERCISE

1. Given the following equations, complete the tables of values.

(a) x + y = 7

x	y
5	
	3.3
	−6
	−1.6

(b) x − y = 4

x	y
9	
	1.4
	−3
	−2.3

(c) m + n = −3

m	n
8	
	5.6
−5	
	−0.5

(d) m − n = −4

m	n
2	
	8.9
−7	
	−0.9

(e) y = 3x + 7

x	y
3	
−6.3	
−12	
2.2	
−6.5	

(f) y = −2x − 1

x	y
8	
15.4	
−9	
3.7	
−11.8	

(g) y = ½x + 3

x	y
8	
7	
12	
24	

(h) y = −⅔x + 4

x	y
12	
24	
30	
63	

SUBSTITUTION

EXERCISE

Given the equation and one of the variables, find the value of the other variable.

1. If xy = 36,
(a) find x if y = 9
(b) find y if x = −4
(c) find x if y = 0.02
(d) find y if x = −0.12

2. If $\frac{s}{t}$ = 7.2,

(a) find s if t = 13
(b) find t if s = 8
(c) find s if t = −7.3
(d) find t if s = −3.6

3. If $\frac{m}{n}$ = 0.63,

(a) find m if n = 1000
(b) find n if m = 0.07
(c) find m if n = 3.5
(d) find n if m = 90

4. If xy = 1.44,
(a) find x if y = −0.4
(b) find y if x = 24
(c) find x if y = −6
(d) find y if x = −0.036

5. If $\frac{c}{d}$ = −2.88,

(a) find c if d = 350
(b) find d if c = 1.2
(c) find c if d = −11.2
(d) find d if c = −0.24

6. If ab = 25.2
(a) find a if b = 2.4
(b) find b if a = 1.5
(c) find a if b = 6.3
(d) find b if a = 4.2

3.1 SCATTER DIAGRAMS AND CURVE OF BEST FIT

A scatter diagram is used to show whether or not there is a relationship between two variables.

The table below gives the number of chin-ups by age for the participants at a fitness camp.

Age (a)	Chin-ups	Age (a)	Chin-ups
10	8	13	10
11	8	14	12
12	8	16	14
13	11	17	16
15	13	11	7
14	11	16	15
12	7	10	7
13	8	15	14
17	14	12	6

To make a scatter diagram we select and mark a scale on a pair of axes. In this example we use the horizontal axis for the age and the vertical axis for the number of chin-ups.

Using the data in the table, we plot the points to make a scatter diagram of chin-ups versus age.

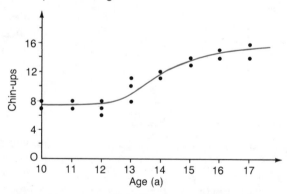

From the graph it appears that there is a relationship between age and the number of chin-ups. As the age increases, so does the number of chin-ups.

Sometimes a smooth curve or line can be used to show the trend in a scatter diagram.

> This curve is often called the curve of best fit.

EXERCISE 3.1

B 1. A cell divides in half every minute. If you start with one cell, after 1 min you will have 2 cells. After 2 min you will have 4 cells.

(a) Complete the table.

Time (min)	Number of Cells
0	1
1	2
2	4
3	8
4	
5	
6	
7	
8	

(b) Plot the points on a grid.
(c) Draw the curve of best fit for the data.
(d) What is the relationship between the time and the number of cells?

2. The table below gives the estimated world population since 1500 A.D.

Year	Population (in millions)
1600	500
1800	1000
1930	2000
1950	2500
1960	3000
1970	3600
1980	4400
1990	5500

(a) Plot the points on a grid.
(b) Draw the curve of best fit for the data.
(c) What is the relationship between the year and the population?

3. Westgate Marina has Thunder class sailboats for sale. The following table gives the cost of several boats and their age.

Age (in years)	Cost (in $1000)	Age (in years)	Cost (in $1000)
1	14	7	4
3	8	10	2
4	7	2	11
5	5	8	3
9	4	7	5
3	9	1	15
6	5	2	13
3	10	5	7
8	4	9	3
4	8	1	16
8	5	10	3

(a) Plot the points on a grid.
(b) Draw the curve of best fit for the data.
(c) What is the relationship between the age and the cost?

4. To conduct the following experiment you will need a measuring tape, a stick or pole, and a sunny day.
(a) Record the length of the shadow of the pole every three minutes from one hour before noon to one hour after noon.
(b) Plot the points on a grid.
(c) Draw the curve of best fit, if there is one.
(d) Are the length of the shadow and the time of day related?

5. To conduct the following experiment you will need a round balloon and a measuring tape.
(a) Record the diameter of the balloon and the number of breaths it took to reach that size.
(b) Plot the ordered pairs on a grid.
(c) Draw the curve of best fit, if there is one.
(d) Are the diameter and the number of breaths related?

3.2 BINARY RELATIONS

The study of how numbers relate to each other is the basis of mathematics. The following table shows the relationship between your distance from a storm and the time between the flash of lightning and the thunderclap.

Time between Flash and Thunder (s)	Distance from Storm (m)
1	330
2	660
3	990
4	1320
5	1650
6	1980

> A relation is a set of ordered pairs.

The above information could be displayed as a set of ordered pairs This set of ordered pairs

$$\{(1, 330), (2, 660), (3, 990), (4, 1320), (5, 1650), (6, 1980)\}$$

is called a binary relation. The first component represents the time between flash and thunder and the second component the distance from the storm.

The pairs of numbers are called ordered pairs since the order of the components is important. We have decided to write the time in seconds first and the distance in metres second.

Bicycle

2

Binary

Using our definitions, what does (10, 3330) mean?

Does (15, 2) have any meaning in this example?

The set of first components of a relation is called the domain of the relation and the set of second components the range of the relation. In our example

the domain is the set $\{1, 2, 3, 4, 5, 6\}$
and the range is the set $\{330, 660, 990, 1320, 1650, 1980\}$.

EXAMPLE 1. State the domain and the range of each of the following.
(a) $\{(2, 3), (4, 4), (7, 6), (8, 9)\}$
(b) $\{(-7, 3), (2, 3), (5, 3)\}$
(c) $\{(-1, -12), (-1, 6), (-1, 9)\}$
(d) $\{(a, b), (d, q), (m, x)\}$

SOLUTION:
(a) Domain: $\{2, 4, 7, 8\}$
    Range: $\{3, 4, 6, 9\}$

(b) Domain: $\{-7, 2, 5\}$
    Range: $\{3\}$

(c) Domain: $\{-1\}$
   Range: $\{-12, 6, 9\}$

(d) Domain: $\{a, d, m\}$
   Range: $\{b, q, x\}$

Sets of ordered pairs are often derived from real situations.

EXAMPLE 2. In a scientific experiment, a marble is dropped from a tower. The following table shows the total distance (to the nearest tenth of a metre) travelled by the marble after each of the first five seconds.

Time (s)	Distance (m)
1	4.9
2	19.6
3	44.1
4	78.4
5	122.5

(a) What does (2, 19.6) mean?
(b) What meaning, if any, do the following have?
   (i) (2.5, 30.6)
   (ii) (0, 0)
   (iii) (-1, 4.9)
(c) What distance did the marble fall during the first, second, and third seconds?
(d) If the relationship between time (t) and distance (d) is given by the formula

$$d = 4.9t^2$$

continue the table for the total distance fallen after 6 s, 7 s, and 8 s.

SOLUTION:
(a) (2, 19.6) means that after 2 s the marble has fallen 19.6 m.
(b) (i) (2.5, 30.6) means that after 2.5 s the marble has fallen 30.6 m.
   (ii) (0, 0) means that at the time of release the marble had not yet travelled any distance.
   (iii) (-1, 4.9) is meaningless since time cannot be negative.
(c) The solution in a table:

Time interval	Distance (m)
second 1	4.9
second 2	$19.6 - 4.9 = 14.7$
second 3	$44.1 - 19.6 = 24.5$

(d)

Time (s)	Distance (m)
6	176.4
7	240.1
8	313.6

EXERCISE 3.2

A 1. A hockey team needs a minimum of 6 players.

(a) Complete the following table.

Number of Hockey Teams	Minimum Number of Players Needed
1	
2	
3	
4	
. . .	
50	

(b) State the domain of the relation.
(c) State the range of the relation.
(d) What does (25, 150) mean?
(e) What meaning, if any, do the following have?

    (i) (0, 0)
    (ii) (3, $19\frac{1}{2}$)
    (iii) (12, 4)

(f) Complete the following for the given relation.

    (i) (20, ■)
    (ii) (31, ■)
    (iii) (■, 240)

2. State the domain and range of each of the following.

(a) {(5, 6), (7, 12), (8, 41)}
(b) {(−3, −7), (0, 6), (3, 11), (5, 20)}
(c) {(2, 7), (5, 7)}
(d) {(−6, 3), (−6, 8), (−6, 14)}
(e) {(a, b), (c, d), (e, f), (g, h)}
(f) {(3, 11), (4, 11), (7, 11), (15, 11)}

B 3. When Achilles had his famous race with a tortoise, he ran 400 m every minute.

(a) Complete the following table in your notebook.

Time (min)	Distance (m)
1	
2	
	3600
	5400
20	

(b) What does (6, 2400) mean?
(c) Complete the following for the given relation.

    (i) (■, 3200)
    (ii) (7, ■)
    (iii) (11, ■)

(d) What meaning, if any, do the following have.

    (i) (5, 2000)
    (ii) ($2\frac{1}{2}$, 1000)
    (iii) (7, 100)

4. A mathematician has hired you to work for 14 d. The first day he will pay you $1, the second day $2, the third day $4, and so on, always doubling the pay of the previous day.

(a) Complete the following table in your notebook.

Day	Pay ($)
1	1
2	2
3	4
4	8
.	
.	
.	
.	
.	
14	

(b) List the relation as a set of ordered pairs in the form (day, pay).
(c) List the elements of the domain.
(d) List the elements of the range.

5. As the number of sides of a polygon increases, so does the number of diagonals you are able to draw.

(a) Complete the following table.

Number of Sides	Number of Diagonals
3	0
4	2
5	
6	
7	
8	

(b) List the relation as a set of ordered pairs in the form (number of sides, number of diagonals).
(c) List the elements of the domain.
(d) List the elements of the range.

(e) Why does $(4\frac{1}{2}, 3)$ have no meaning?
(f) What is the formula for determining the number of diagonals when you are given the number of sides the polygon has?

6. Bingo is a popular game where ordered pairs are used. For example, the "caller" may call (B, 7), which means "under the B, 7." All the possible ordered pairs the "caller" can call form a relation. What is the domain and range of this relation?

C 7. A circle may be cut into a maximum of 2 pieces with one straight cut. Two straight cuts will produce 4 pieces (cuts do not have to pass through the centre).

(a) Complete the following table.

Number of Cuts	Maximum Number of Pieces
0	1
1	2
2	4
3	
4	
5	

(b) List the relation as a set of ordered pairs in the form (number of cuts, number of pieces).
(c) List the elements of the domain.
(d) List the elements of the range.
(e) Why will $(3\frac{1}{2}, \blacksquare)$ have no meaning?
(f) What is the maximum number of pieces you will get with 6 cuts?
(g) The formula for determining the maximum number of pieces when you are given the number of cuts is

$$\frac{1}{2}(n^2 + n + 2)$$

where n is the number of cuts.
   (i) Test the formula using the values in your table.
   (ii) Find the number of pieces when there are 12 cuts.

3.3 GRAPHING RELATIONS

In this section we will draw the graphs of binary relations.

EXAMPLE 1. The table below gives the length of the shadow for objects of various heights at a certain time. Draw the graph of this relation.

Height (m)	Length of Shadow (m)
2	3
4	6
5	7.5
6	9
9	13.5

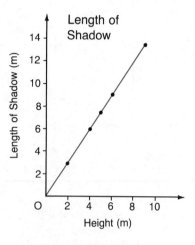

SOLUTION:

I. Draw and label the axes.

II. Plot the ordered pairs from the table.

III. Join the ordered pairs with a smooth curve.

IV. Give the graph a title.

EXAMPLE 2. The table below gives the total distance travelled by a falling object after each of the first four seconds. Draw the graph of this relation.

Time (s)	Distance (m)
1	4.9
2	19.6
3	44.1
4	78.4

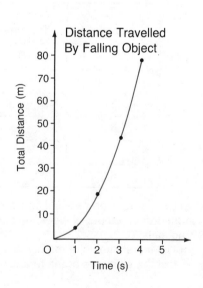

SOLUTION:

I. Draw and label the axes.

II. Plot the ordered pairs from the table.

III. Join the ordered pairs with a smooth curve.

EXERCISE 3.3

B 1. The table gives the temperature inside the earth according to how far below the earth's crust the temperature is recorded.

Depth (km)	Temperature (°C)
0	20
1	30
2	40
3	50

Draw the graph of this relation.

2. The table gives the area of a square for a given length of a side.

Length of Side (cm)	Area (cm²)
1	1
2	4
3	9
4	16
5	25

Draw the graph of this relation.

3. A large percent of the mass of the human body is water. The table gives the total mass for several people and the mass of water for each.

Total Mass (kg)	Mass of Water (kg)
30	21.6
40	28.8
50	36
60	43.2

Draw the graph of this relation.

4. Terri hit a golf ball down the fairway. The table gives the distance travelled by the ball versus the height.

Distance (m)	Height (m)
0	0
10	4.4
20	7.5
30	9.4
40	10.0
50	8.5
60	5.1
65	3.2
70	0

Draw a graph of this relation.

5. Radioactive sodium has a half-life of fifteen hours. This means that it takes fifteen hours for half the atoms of an amount of radioactive sodium to change into atoms of another element. Suppose you start with 1000 g of radioactive sodium. The table gives the amount remaining versus time.

Time (h)	Sodium (g)
0	1000
15	500
30	250
45	
60	
75	
90	

Complete the table and draw the graph of this relation.

3.4 INTERPOLATING AND EXTRAPOLATING FROM GRAPHS

Sound travels at a speed of 1200 km/h. When an aircraft breaks the sound barrier, it is flying at the speed of sound. This speed is called Mach 1.

The table below gives three Mach speeds.

Mach Number	1	2	3
Speed (km/h)	1200	2400	3600

These points are graphed on a grid. From the graph we can determine the Mach number for various speeds. For example, a speed of 3000 km/h has a Mach value of 2.5. To get this answer we used the graph to determine points that were not given. This is called interpolation since the values are between the given ordered pairs.

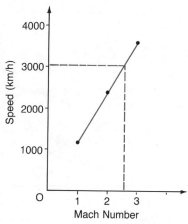

What is the speed for a Mach value of 1.5?

To determine data that are beyond the given ordered pairs, we extend the graph in the appropriate direction. For example, a Mach value of 3.5 means a speed of 4200 km/h. This is called extrapolation.

What is the Mach value for a speed of 900 km/h?

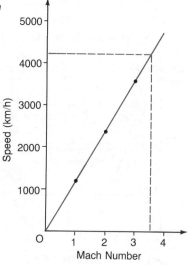

EXERCISE 3.4

1. The table gives the distance travelled by a car at a speed of 100 km/h.

Time (h)	Distance (km)
1	100
2	200
3	300
4	400

(a) Draw a graph of this relation.
(b) Use interpolation to determine the distance travelled in 1.25 h
(c) Use interpolation to determine the time required to travel 225 km.
(d) Use extrapolation to determine the distance travelled in $5\frac{1}{2}$ h.
(e) Use extrapolation to determine the time required to travel 80 km.

2. If you hang a mass to the end of a spring, the greater the mass, the longer the length of stretch of the spring.

The table gives the length of a certain spring for several masses.

Mass (kg)	Length of Spring (cm)
0	10
10	15
20	20
30	25
40	30

(a) Draw a graph of this relation.
(b) Determine the length of the spring for a mass of 12 kg.
(c) Determine the mass that gives a length of 22 cm.
(d) Determine the length of the spring for a mass of 42.5 kg.
(e) Determine the mass that gives a length of 32.5 cm.

3. The table gives the area of square pieces of astroturf for a given length.

Length (m)	Area (m²)
2	4
3	9
4	16
5	25
6	36

(a) Draw a graph of this relation.
(b) What is the area of the square with sides 3.5 m?
(c) What is the area of the square with sides 1.5 m?
(d) If the area of the square is 40 m², what is the length of each side?

4. Radioactive fluoride has a half-life of two hours. Suppose you start with 100 g of radioactive fluoride. The table gives the approximate amount of fluoride remaining versus time.

Time (h)	Fluoride (g)
0	100
2	50
4	25
6	13.5

(a) Draw a graph of this relation.
(b) Determine the amount of fluoride remaining after 1 h.
(c) After how much time will there be 40 g of fluoride remaining.
(d) Determine the amount of fluoride remaining after 7 h.

3.5 GRAPHING GENERAL RELATIONS

Graphs help us to visualize real situations.

EXAMPLE. When you turn on a hot water faucet the temperature of the water depends on how many seconds the water has been running. Sketch a graph of this relation.

SOLUTION:
Draw and label horizontal and vertical axes.

The initial temperature of the water will be close to room temperature since this is the water that was in the pipes. The temperature of the water will quickly rise once the water from the hot water tank starts coming out. The next phase will be a decrease in temperature once you have drained the tank, and the temperature will level off to the temperature of the water supplied by the city.

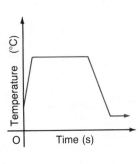

EXERCISE 3.5

B 1. The distance required to stop a car depends on how fast the car is moving. Sketch a graph of stopping distance versus speed of the car. State a reasonable domain and range for this relation.

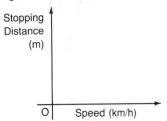

2. If you start driving at a constant speed with a full tank of gasoline, the number of litres of gasoline remaining in the tank depends on how far you have driven. Sketch a graph of litres of gasoline remaining versus distance travelled. State a reasonable domain and range for this relation.

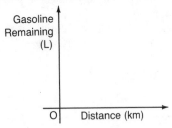

3. The time of sunset depends on the time of year. Sketch a graph of time of sunset versus day of the year. State a reasonable domain and range for this relation.

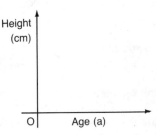

4. Your height depends on your age. Sketch a graph of height (in centimetres) versus age (in years). State a reasonable domain and range for this relation.

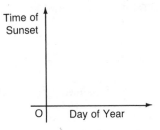

5. You fill an electric kettle with cold water and plug in the kettle. Sketch a graph of the water temperature versus the length of time the kettle is plugged in. State a reasonable domain and range for this relation.

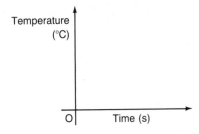

6. The number of people that attend a rock concert is determined by the popularity of the band. Sketch a graph of attendance versus popularity. Does this relation have a domain and range?

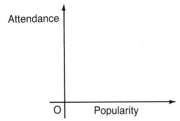

7. The number of greeting cards a greeting card store sells depends on the time of year. Sketch a graph of number of cards sold versus the month of the year.

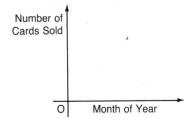

8. If you drop an object from the top of a tall building, the speed of the falling object depends on how long it has been falling. Sketch a graph of speed versus time.

9. The height of a batted baseball depends on the length of time since it was hit. Sketch a graph of height versus time elapsed since hitting. State a reasonable domain and range for this relation.

10. The water pressure on the hull of a diving submarine depends on the depth of the submarine. Sketch a graph of pressure versus depth. State a reasonable domain and range for this relation.

11. Suppose you are the last person to get on a ferris wheel. Once you are seated, the wheel starts to rotate. Your height above the ground depends on the length of time you have been riding. Sketch a graph of height versus time. State a reasonable domain and range for this relation.

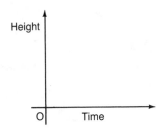

MIND BENDER

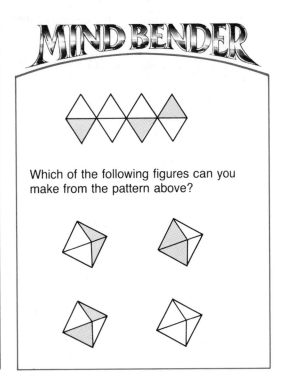

Which of the following figures can you make from the pattern above?

3.6 DIRECT VARIATION

The following table gives the distance travelled by a plane flying at a constant speed of 200 km/h.

Time (h)	Distance (km)
1	200
2	400
3	600
4	800
5	1000

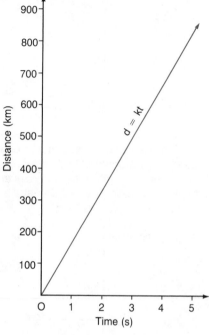

From the table we see that if the time is doubled, the distance is doubled. If the time is tripled, the distance is tripled. If the time is cut in half, the distance is cut in half. We say that the distance varies directly as the time. This is an example of direct variation.

In a direct variation, the ratios of the corresponding values are the same.

$$\frac{200}{1} = 200, \quad \frac{400}{2} = 200, \quad \frac{600}{3} = 200, \quad \frac{800}{4} = 200, \quad \frac{1000}{5} = 200$$

Then $\frac{d}{t} = k$, or $d = kt$, where k is the constant of variation.

The symbol
$\propto$
is read
"varies as."

> For direct variation
>
> $d \propto t$ or $d = kt$
>
> and the graph is a straight line.

EXAMPLE. The amount Bill earns varies directly as the number of hours he works. If he earned $52 in eight hours, how much will he earn in eleven hours?

SOLUTION:
First find the constant, k.

$$\frac{e}{h} = k, \text{ where e represents earnings}$$
$$h \text{ represents the hours}$$

$$\frac{52}{8} = k$$

$$k = 6.5$$

Therefore, $\dfrac{e}{h} = 6.5$ or $e = 6.5$ h.

When h = 11,

$$\dfrac{e}{h} = 6.5$$

$$\dfrac{e}{11} = 6.5$$

$$e = 71.50$$

or

$$e = 6.5 \text{ h}$$
$$= 6.5(11)$$
$$= 71.50$$

Bill will earn $71.50 in 11 h.

EXERCISE 3.6

1. x varies directly as y.
When x = 30, y = 45.
(a) Find the value of k and write the equation.
(b) Find x when y = 105.

2. m varies directly as n.
When m = 50, n = 20.
(a) Find the value of k and write the equation.
(b) Find m when n = 70.

3. r varies directly as t. When r = 66, t = 22.
(a) Find the value of k and write the equation.
(b) Find t when r = 39.

4. c varies directly as d.
When c = 120, d = 180.
(a) Find the value of k and write the equation.
(b) Find d when c = 95.

5. The number of words typed varies directly as the length of time spent typing. John can type 260 words in 5 min.

(a) Find the value of k and write the equation.
(b) How many words can he type in 17 min?
(c) How long will it take him to type a 1300 word science project?

6. The height that a ball bounces varies directly as the height from which it is dropped. A ball dropped from 24 cm will bounce 18 cm.
(a) Find the value of k.
(b) How far will the ball bounce if it is dropped from 300 cm?
(c) If the ball bounces 150 cm, from what height was it dropped?

7. The price of peanuts varies directly as the mass of the peanuts bought. A mass of 2.5 kg of peanuts costs $12.25.
(a) Find the value of k and write the equation.

(b) How much will 8.2 kg of peanuts cost?
(c) How many kilograms of peanuts will you receive for $34.30?

8. The cost of having an automobile repaired varies directly as the number of hours the mechanic spends working on it. It costs $212.50 for 5 h of labour.
(a) Find the value of k and write the equation.
(b) How much will it cost for 7.5 h of labour?
(c) How long did the mechanic work if the labour costs were $148.75?

INVERSE VARIATION

The table gives the time required to clean a stadium according to the number of people working.

Number of People	1	2	3	4	6	12
Time (h)	12	6	4	3	2	1

This is an example of an inverse variation.

EXERCISE

1. Use the pattern in the table to explain why it is called an inverse variation.

2. Draw the graph of this relation.

3.7 PARTIAL VARIATION

The following table gives the cost for a banquet at the Longhorn Restaurant.

Number of People	Cost ($)
10	350
20	600
30	850
40	1100

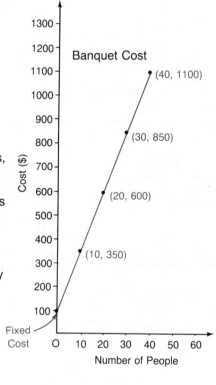

From the table we see that as the number of people increases, the cost increases. However, by extending the graph to the vertical axis we see that there is a fixed cost of $100 for every banquet. This cost is to cover expenses such as heat, hydro, and room rental, that do not change regardless of how many people attend the banquet. This is an example of a partial variation. An equation for this relation is

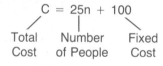

C = 25n + 100

Total Cost   Number of People   Fixed Cost

For partial variation, the equation is of the form $y = mx + b$ and the graph is a straight line.

The total cost of a banquet depends on the number of people, which varies, and the fixed cost of $100.

EXAMPLE. It costs $0.10 to print each newspaper plus a fixed cost of $1000 to set up the press.
(a) Write the partial variation equation.
(b) How much will it cost to print 20 000 newspapers?

SOLUTION:
(a) C = 0.1n + 1000, where C represents the cost
                     n represents the number of newspapers.

(b) C = 0.1n + 1000
    = 0.1(20 000) + 1000
    = 2000 + 1000
    = 3000

It costs $3000 to print 20 000 newspapers.

EXERCISE 3.7

1. The table gives the cost of producing bicycles.

Number of Bicycles	Cost ($)
10	3000
20	5000
30	7000

(a) Draw a graph of this partial variation.

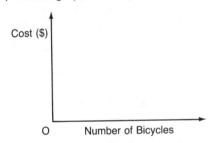

Cost ($)

O   Number of Bicycles

(b) What is the fixed cost?
(c) Write the partial variation equation.
(d) How much will it cost to produce 70 bicycles?

2. The table gives the cost of manufacturing dresses.

Number of Dresses	Cost ($)
1000	7000
2000	12 000
3000	17 000
4000	22 000

(a) Draw a graph of this partial variation.
(b) What is the fixed cost?

(c) Write the partial variation equation.
(d) Find the cost of manufacturing 30 000 dresses.

3. It costs $0.05 to print each advertising flyer plus a fixed cost of $75.
(a) Write the partial variation equation.
(b) How much will it cost to print 50 000 flyers?

4. The total cost to take seven basketball players to a tournament was $1900. The fixed cost was $500.
(a) Determine the partial variation equation.
(b) How much would it cost to take eleven players to the tournament?

5. It costs $375 to take 25 students to the art gallery. The fixed cost is $125.
(a) Determine the partial variation equation.
(b) How much would it cost to take 20 students to the art gallery.
(c) If the total cost of a trip is divided evenly among the students attending, what is the difference in cost per student when 20 go as opposed to 25? Explain the difference.

C 6. The table gives the time required to travel 100 km at various speeds.

Speed (km/h)	1	5	10	20	50	100
Time (h)	100	20	10	5	2	1

As the speed increases, the time decreases. As the speed decreases, the time increases. We say that the speed varies inversely as the time.

(a) Draw the graph of this relation.
(b) How long will it take to travel the 100 km at 40 km/h?

3.8 PROBLEM SOLVING

1. There are three numbers less than one thousand that are both perfect squares and perfect cubes. What are they?

2. Student tickets for the Air Show cost $3.00 each. Adult tickets cost $5.00 each. After paying expenses of $200.00, the profit from the show was $538.00. If 87 adult tickets were sold, how many student tickets were sold?

3. The diagram below shows the excavation for an archaeological dig.

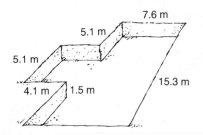

(a) What is the area of the dig?
(b) What was the volume of the soil removed?

4. If you use whole numbers only, how many rectangles can you draw that have a perimeter of 72 m?

5. Arrange the following numbers into pairs that total twenty-six.

$$22, \quad 6, \quad 10, \quad 2, \quad 18, \quad 4,$$
$$8, \quad 12, \quad 24, \quad 14, \quad 16, \quad 20$$

6. The area of a square is 64 cm². Find the circumference of a circle that is inscribed in the square.

7. If $x^{0.2503} = 5$, what is the value of $x^{0.7509}$?

8. Find the numbers between 100 and 2000 that are both squares and cubes of integers.

9. Which is better, a 30% discount or 2 successive discounts of 15%?

10. Some bowling leagues make it possible for bowlers of different abilities to compete by assigning bowlers handicaps. A handicap is calculated using the formula

$$H = 0.8(200 - A)$$

where H is the handicap and
        A is the bowler's average.
Handicaps are rounded to the nearest whole number. Jill has an average of 167.
(a) What is her handicap?
(b) If she bowls a game of 156, what will her score be with her handicap?

11. Write 116 as the sum of four perfect squares.

12. Salami costs $2.75/kg and liverwurst costs $3.05/kg. James bought 3 kg of salami and some liverwurst. He received $9.55 change from $30.00. How much liverwurst did he buy?

13. Find the product.

$$(1 - \tfrac{1}{2})(1 - \tfrac{1}{3})(1 - \tfrac{1}{4}) \cdots (1 - \tfrac{1}{65})$$

14. A rectangle has an area of 120 m². The length and width are whole numbers.
(a) What are the possibilities for the length and width?
(b) Which length and width give the smallest perimeter?

15. Two runners start running laps from the same place at the same time. One runner takes 70 s to run a lap. The other runner takes 80 s to run a lap. When will the two runners be even with each other?

16. A watch gains 12 min/h. What is the correct time if the watch was properly set at 3:00 and it now reads 10:00?

17. Ed Hurdlman averages 120 km/h, 80 km/h, and 40 km/h over a 240 km course on 3 successive runs. Calculate his average speed for the 3 runs.

18. In three successive years, the cost of living rose 7%, 7.5%, and 6.5%. Find the percentage increase in the cost of living over the three years to the nearest tenth of a percent.

19. The tank of a midsize car is one-sixth full of gasoline. If 4 L of gasoline are added, then the tank will be one-quarter full. What is the capacity of the tank?

20. Harriet is preparing a poster with the words MIND BENDER across the top. The ten letters and the space in the words MIND BENDER are to be centred at the top of a sheet of paper that is 45 cm wide. Each letter is 1.8 cm wide. The space between consecutive letters is 0.6 cm and the space between words is 2.4 cm. How far from the left edge of the paper should Harriet start her lettering?

21. Six students try out for the three lead roles in the school play. How many ways can the cast for these parts be chosen?

22. Barbara Jones receives a bonus if her team wins 60% of the games. So far the team has won 75 of 100 games and there are 50 games left to play. How many of the remaining games must the team win so that Barbara will receive a bonus?

23. If x is a negative integer, arrange the following monomials from smallest to largest.

$$\frac{13x}{24}, \quad \frac{12x}{23}, \quad \frac{11x}{24}, \quad \frac{11x}{21}, \quad \frac{11x}{20}$$

24.

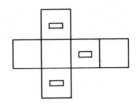

Which of the following figures can you make from the pattern above?

(a)

(b)

(c)

(d)

Each letter represents a different digit in this subtraction.

```
  N I N E
- F O U R
  F I V E
```

3.9 REVIEW EXERCISE

1. The table gives the age and height of several students.

Age (a)	Height (cm)
10	131
11	140
10	129
12	152
13	160
14	172
13	158
11	142
13	163
12	150
14	175
14	169
10	127
11	139
12	149

(a) Plot the points on a grid.
(b) Draw a curve of best fit for the data.

2. Eight centimetres of snow contains about the same amount of water as one centimetre of rain.

Rain (cm)	Snow (cm)
1	8
2	16
3	24
4	32
5	40

(a) Draw a graph of this relation.
(b) If it snows 20 cm, how much rain would this be?

3. State the domain and range of each of the following.
(a) {(3, 4), (−2, 9), (−1, 7), (0, 8)}
(b) {(2, 0), (4, 4), (6, 8), (8, 10)}
(c) {(1, −2), (1, −1), (1, 0), (1, 1)}
(d) {(3, −2), (2, −2), (1, −2)}

4. Carbon 14 is used by scientists to determine the age of fossils. All living plants and animals contain the same amount of carbon 14 per kilogram of mass. When they die, the carbon 14 begins to change to nitrogen 14. Carbon 14 has a half-life of 5700 a.

The table gives the percent of C 14 remaining in a dinosaur according to the number of years after its death.

Years after Death	Percent of C 14 Remaining
0	100
5700	50
11 400	25
17 100	12.5
22 800	6.24

(a) Draw a graph of this relation.
(b) A scientist found bones that contained 40% of the original amount of C 14. What was the approximate age of the bones?

(c) What percent of C 14 would there be if a fossil was 20 000 a old?

5. The table gives the distance travelled by an airplane at a speed of 500 km/h.

Time (h)	Distance (km)
1	500
2	1000
3	1500
4	2000

(a) Draw a graph of this relation.
(b) Use interpolation to determine the distance travelled in 2.75 h.
(c) Use interpolation to determine the time required to travel 1100 km.
(d) Use extrapolation to determine the distance travelled in 5.25 h.
(e) Use extrapolation to determine the time required to travel 250 km.

6. You are the driver of a car in a 200 m race. The track is straight. Sketch a graph of speed versus time from the start of the race to the finish.

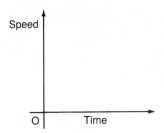

7. The height of a punted football depends on the number of seconds since it was punted. Sketch a graph of height versus time.

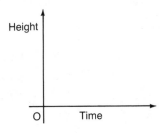

8. x varies directly as y. When x = 80, y = 60.
(a) Find the value of k and write the equation.
(b) Find x when y = 150.

9. The cost of alligator food varies directly as the mass of food bought. A 3.5 kg bag of alligator food costs $23.45.
(a) Find the value of k and write the equation.
(b) How much will 53.5 kg of alligator food cost?
(c) How much alligator food can you buy for $402.00?

10. The table gives the cost of producing rock videos.

Number of Videos	Cost ($)
1000	10 000
2000	17 000
3000	24 000
4000	31 000

(a) Draw a graph of this partial variation.

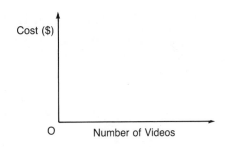

(b) What is the fixed cost?
(c) Write the partial variation equation.
(d) How much will it cost to produce 5300 rock videos?

3.10 CHAPTER 3 TEST

1. The table gives the cost of riding in a carriage through the park.

Distance (km)	Cost ($)
1	8
2	16
3	24
4	32

(a) List the relation as a set of ordered pairs.
(b) List the elements of the domain.
(c) List the elements of the range.

2. The table gives the distance travelled by an express train.

Time (h)	Distance (km)
1	300
2	600
3	900
4	1200

(a) Draw a graph of this relation.
(b) Use interpolation to determine the distance travelled in 3.75 h.
(c) Use extrapolation to determine the time required to travel 200 km.

3. An ice cube tray is filled with water and placed in the freezer. Sketch a graph of the water temperature versus the length of time the tray is in the freezer.

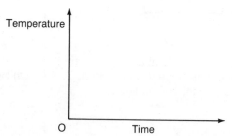

4. The cost of granular chlorine for a swimming pool varies directly as the amount purchased. Five kilograms of chlorine costs $14.00.

(a) Find the value of k and write the equation.
(b) How much will 9.5 kg of chlorine cost?
(c) How much chlorine can you buy for $36.40?

SLOPE AND EQUATIONS OF LINES

CHAPTER

4

The advancement and perfection of mathematics are intimately connected with the prosperity of the State.

Napoleon

REVIEW AND PREVIEW TO CHAPTER 4

THE PYTHAGOREAN THEOREM

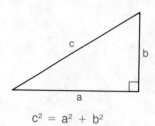

$$c^2 = a^2 + b^2$$

EXERCISE

1. Use the Pythagorean Theorem to determine the missing dimension.

(a)

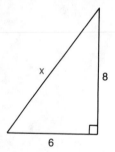

(b)

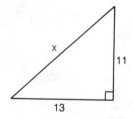

(c)

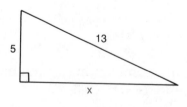

(d)

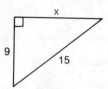

(e)

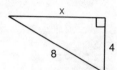

(f)

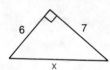

(g)

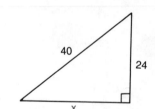

(h)

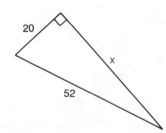

2. Determine the missing dimension.

(a)

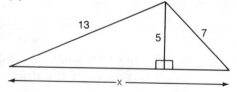

(b)

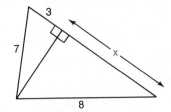

(c)

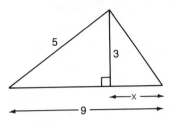

(d)

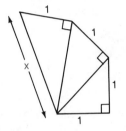

FORMULAS AND EQUATIONS

EXERCISE

1. Express each of the following in terms of the indicated variable.

(a) If $A = \ell w$, then $\ell = \blacksquare$ and $w = \blacksquare$.

(b) If $I = prt$, then $p = \blacksquare$ and $t = \blacksquare$.

(c) If $C = 2\pi r$, then $r = \blacksquare$.

(d) If $V = \ell wh$, then $\ell = \blacksquare$ and $w = \blacksquare$.

(e) If $D = st$, then $s = \blacksquare$ and $t = \blacksquare$.

(f) If $A = \frac{1}{2}bh$, then $h = \blacksquare$ and $b = \blacksquare$.

(g) If $P = 2(\ell + w)$, then $\ell = \blacksquare$ and $w = \blacksquare$.

(h) If $A = \dfrac{h}{2}(a + b)$, then $h = \blacksquare$ and $b = \blacksquare$.

2. Solve for y.

(a) $x + y = 7$ (b) $x - y = 9$

(c) $x + 2y = 6$ (d) $2x + 3y = 8$

(e) $2x - 5y = 10$ (f) $4x + 5y - 20 = 0$

SQUARE ROOTS

n	$\sqrt{n}$	n	$\sqrt{n}$
1	1.000	21	4.582
2	1.414	22	4.690
3	1.732	23	4.795
4	2.000	24	4.898
5	2.236	25	5.000
6	2.449	26	5.099
7	2.645	27	5.196
8	2.828	28	5.291
9	3.000	29	5.385
10	3.162	30	5.477
11	3.316	31	5.567
12	3.464	32	5.656
13	3.605	33	5.744
14	3.741	34	5.830
15	3.872	35	5.916
16	4.000	36	6.000
17	4.123	37	6.082
18	4.242	38	6.164
19	4.358	39	6.244
20	4.472	40	6.324

MICRO MATH

The following program computes the square root of a number.

NEW

```
10 REM SQUARE ROOT
20 PRINT "ENTER YOUR NUMBER"
30 INPUT N
40 S=SQR(N)
50 PRINT N,S
60 END
```

RUN

To make the program reiterative, add these statements.

```
52 PRINT "ANOTHER QUESTION?"
54 INPUT Z$
56 IF Z$ = "Y" THEN 20
```

4.1 SLOPE

The slope of a line is the measure of the amount of steepness of the line. The slope of a line is defined to be the quotient of the vertical change (called the rise) divided by the horizontal change (called the run).

$$\text{Slope} = \frac{\text{rise}}{\text{run}} = \frac{\text{vertical change}}{\text{horizontal change}}$$

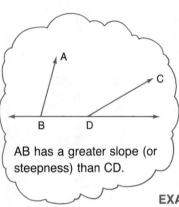

AB has a greater slope (or steepness) than CD.

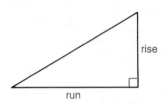

EXAMPLE 1. Find the slope of the line through A(2, 1) and B(6, 4).

SOLUTION:
The vertical change or rise of AB is 3 (the difference in the y-coordinates). The horizontal change or run is 4 (the difference in the x-coordinates).

$$\text{Slope of line} = \frac{\text{rise of AB}}{\text{run of AB}}$$
$$= \frac{3}{4}$$

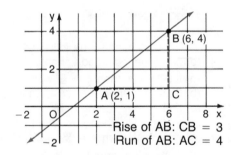

Rise of AB: CB = 3
Run of AB: AC = 4

The rise is the vertical change or the difference in the y-coordinates and is denoted by Δy (read "delta y"). Similarly, the run, the difference in the x-coordinates, is denoted by Δx. The letter m is used to denote slope.

$$\text{Slope} = \frac{\text{rise}}{\text{run}}$$
$$= \frac{\Delta y}{\Delta x}$$
$$= m$$

EXAMPLE 2. Find the slope of the line segment joining A(3, −2) to B(6, 5).

SOLUTION:

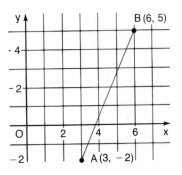

$$m_{AB} = \frac{\Delta y}{\Delta x}$$

$$m_{AB} = \frac{5 - (-2)}{6 - 3}$$

$$= \frac{7}{3}$$

or

$$m_{BA} = \frac{\Delta y}{\Delta x}$$

$$m_{BA} = \frac{-2 - 5}{3 - 6}$$

$$= \frac{-7}{-3}$$

$$= \frac{7}{3}$$

The slope of AB is the same as the slope of BA.

EXAMPLE 3. Find the slope of the line ℓ through A(4, −2) and B(−5, 6).

SOLUTION:
Since the slope of a line is the same as the slope of any segment of the line, to find the slope of ℓ, all we need do is find the slope of AB.

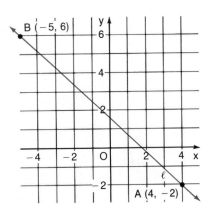

$$m_{AB} = \frac{\Delta y}{\Delta x}$$

$$m_{AB} = \frac{6 - (-2)}{-5 - 4}$$

$$= \frac{8}{-9}$$

$$= -\frac{8}{9}$$

In going from left to right,
if a line falls its slope is a negative number.
In going from left to right,
if a line rises its slope is a positive number.

EXAMPLE 4. Find the slope of the line through A(4, 1) and B(−2, 1).

SOLUTION:
The graph of the line through A and B is horizontal.

$$m_{AB} = \frac{\Delta y}{\Delta x}$$

$$m_{AB} = \frac{1 - 1}{-2 - 4}$$

$$= \frac{0}{-6}$$

$$= 0$$

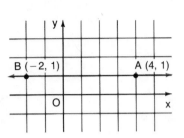

The slope of a horizontal line is zero.

EXAMPLE 5. Find the slope of the line through A(2, 3) and B(2, −4).

SOLUTION:
The graph of the line through A and B is vertical.

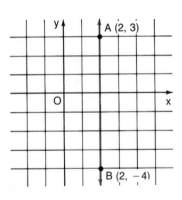

$$\Delta y = -4 - 3$$
$$= -7$$

$$\Delta x = 2 - 2$$
$$= 0$$

Hence $\frac{\Delta y}{\Delta x}$ is undefined and the slope of the line is not defined by a real number.

The slope of a vertical line is not defined by a real number.

We can summarize the previous results as follows.

Two Points	Graph	m_{AB}	Slope	Description of Line
A(2, 1) B(6, 4)		$m_{AB} = \frac{3}{4}$	positive	The line rises from left to right.
A(4, −2) B(−5, 6)		$m_{AB} = -\frac{8}{9}$	negative	The line falls from left to right.
A(4, 1) B(−2, 1)		$m_{AB} = 0$	zero	The line is horizontal.
A(2, 3) B(2, −4)		m_{AB} is not defined by a real number.	undefined	The line is vertical.

EXAMPLE 6. Find the slope of the line through $P(x_1, y_1)$ and $Q(x_2, y_2)$.

SOLUTION:

$$m = \frac{\Delta y}{\Delta x}$$

$$m = \frac{y_2 - y_1}{x_2 - x_1}, \quad x_2 \neq x_1$$

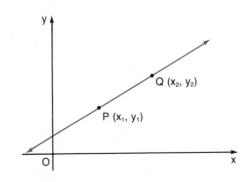

Given two points on a line, the slope of the line may be found using

$$m = \frac{y_2 - y_1}{x_2 - x_1}, \qquad x_2 \neq x_1$$

EXERCISE 4.1

A 1. (a) Without calculating, determine whether the slope of each line is positive, negative, or zero, or whether the slope is undefined.
(b) State the rise.
(c) State the run.
(d) Determine the slope of the line, where possible.

(i)

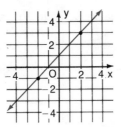

(ii)

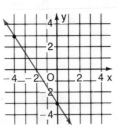

(iii)

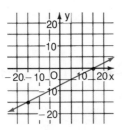

(iv)

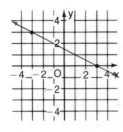

(v)

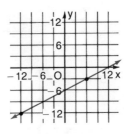

(vi)

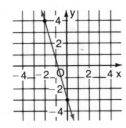

(vii)

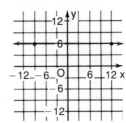

(viii)

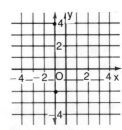

(ix)

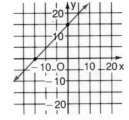

B 2. Determine the slopes of the lines through the following points.

(a) A(1, 1), B(4, 3)
(b) C(0, 2), D(4, 6)
(c) E(5, 7), F(9, 11)
(d) G(0, 0), H(5, 6)
(e) K(5, 3), L(7, 3)
(f) M(−3, 4), N(5, −2)
(g) P(−3, −1), Q(−5, 7)
(h) R(2, −3), S(0, 4)

3. Determine the slopes of the line segments joining the following pairs of points.

(a) A(6, −8), B(−3, 2)
(b) C(7, −3), D(8, −3)
(c) E(5, 7), F(5, −2)
(d) G(−2, −1), H(−5, −4)
(e) K(−6, 7), L(−6, −5)
(f) M(8, 0), N(0, 8)
(g) R($\frac{1}{2}$, 3), S(2, −3)

(h) P($\frac{1}{3}$, $\frac{1}{2}$), Q(2, 2$\frac{1}{2}$)

(i) W(2$\frac{1}{5}$, −3), R(−3$\frac{1}{2}$, $\frac{1}{2}$)

(j) B(−$\frac{1}{2}$, 3), A(−$\frac{1}{2}$, −4)

(k) A(3.2, −4.6), B(−2.4, 8.8)
(l) G(1.75, −0.3), D(−2.25, −1.7)
(m) E(−1.86, −2.14), F(3.58, −0.72)
(n) G(11.9, −9.3), H(15.4, 6.7)

4. Sketch the graph of each of the following and then determine the slope of each line where x, y ∈ R.

(a) y = 3x − 2
(b) y = 4 − x
(c) 2x + 3y = 6
(d) 5x − 3y = 15
(e) y = $\dfrac{x - 1}{3}$
(f) 2x − y − 4 = 0
(g) f(x) = 2x − 7
(h) f:x → 2 − 3x

C 5. (a) A line through (3, 1) and (4, y) has a slope m = 7.
Find y.
(b) A line through (6, −2) and (3, y) has a slope m = 2.
Find y.

(c) A line through (4, −7) and (−2, y) has a slope m = −$\frac{2}{3}$.
Find y.
(d) A line through (−2, −3) and (x, 5) has a slope m = 2.
Find x.

6. Find x such that
A(1, −2), B(x, 3), and C(−3, −4)
are collinear.

7. A line contains the points A(2, 5) and B(300, −450). Find another point on the line.

CALCULATOR MATH

We know that division by zero is not defined in the set of real numbers. How does your calculator respond to a division by zero?

Press C 8 ÷ 0 =

MICRO MATH

How does your computer respond to division by zero?

In BASIC, type

PRINT 8/0

In BASIC, the PRINT statement can also be written as

? 8/0

In LOGO, type

PRINT 8/0

4.2 LINEAR EQUATIONS: POINT-SLOPE FORM

In this section we will find equations of lines. The slope of a line is equal to the slope of any line segment contained in the line. By using the definition of slope, we can determine the equation of a line given the slope of the line and any point on the line.

EXAMPLE 1. (a) Determine an equation of a line through (3, 1) with slope m = 2.
(b) Express the equation in the form $Ax + By + C = 0$.

> $Ax + By + C = 0$ where A, B, C $\in$ R, is called the standard form for the equation of a straight line.

SOLUTION:

(a) We must find an equation in x and y that satisfies the given conditions.

Let (x, y) be any point on the line, other than (3, 1).
The slope of the line is 2.

$$m = \frac{\Delta y}{\Delta x}$$

or $$\frac{\Delta y}{\Delta x} = m$$

then $$\frac{(y - 1)}{(x - 3)} = 2$$

and $$y - 1 = 2(x - 3)$$

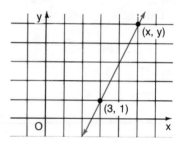

(b) Express in the standard form $Ax + By + C = 0$.

$$y - 1 = 2(x - 3)$$
$$y - 1 = 2x - 6$$
$$2x - 6 - y + 1 = 0$$
$$2x - y - 5 = 0$$

In this example, A = 2, B = -1, and C = -5.

EXAMPLE 2. Find the equation of the line through (x_1, y_1) with slope m.

SOLUTION:

Let (x, y) be any point on the line other than (x_1, y_1). The slope of the line is m.

$$\frac{\Delta y}{\Delta x} = m$$

then $$\frac{(y - y_1)}{(x - x_1)} = m$$

and $$y - y_1 = m(x - x_1)$$

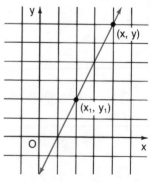

> **Linear Equation : Point-Slope Form**
>
> Given a point on the line, (x_1, y_1), and the slope of the line, m, an equation of the line may be expressed as
>
> $$y - y_1 = m(x - x_1).$$

EXAMPLE 3. (a) Find an equation of the line through $(2, -3)$ with slope $m = -2$.
Express the equation in standard form.
(b) Use this equation to find two other points on the line. Check your solutions.

SOLUTION:

(a) $\qquad y - y_1 = m(x - x_1)$

$(x_1, y_1) = (2, -3) \qquad$ and $\qquad m = -2$

$$y - (-3) = -2(x - 2)$$
$$y + 3 = -2(x - 2)$$
$$y + 3 = -2x + 4$$
$$2x + y - 1 = 0$$

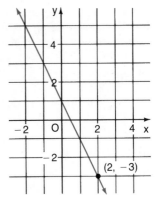

(b) To find other points on the line, it is convenient to express the equation in the form $y = mx + b$.

$$2x + y - 1 = 0$$
$$y = -2x + 1$$

when $x = 1$,

$$y = -2(1) + 1$$
$$= -2 + 1$$
$$= -1$$

when $x = 3$,

$$y = -2(3) + 1$$
$$= -6 + 1$$
$$= -5$$

Two other points on the line are $(1, -1)$ and $(3, -5)$. We check our solutions by showing that the points satisfy the equation of the line.

Check.

For $x = 1$ and $y = -1$,

L.S. $= 2x + y - 1$
$\quad = 2(1) + (-1) - 1$
$\quad = 2 - 1 - 1$
$\quad = 0$
R.S. $= 0$

For $x = 3$ and $y = -5$,

L.S. $= 2x + y - 1$
$\quad = 2(3) + (-5) - 1$
$\quad = 6 - 5 - 1$
$\quad = 0$
R.S. $= 0$

EXERCISE 4.2

A 1. State the following equations in standard form $(Ax + By + C = 0)$ and state the values of A, B, and C.
(a) $5x + 3y = 7$ (b) $3x = 2y - 4$
(c) $4x = 3 - 5y$ (d) $7x + 2 = -3y$
(e) $5y = 2 - 3x$ (f) $2y - 3 = 7x$
(g) $5 = 3y - 4x$ (h) $3x - 4y = 0$
(i) $2x + 7 = 0$ (j) $3 - 4y = 0$
(k) $0 = 2 - 3y + 4x$ (l) $y = 2x - 7$

B 2. Determine an equation of the line through the given point having the given slope. Express the equation in standard form.
(a) $(3, 2)$; $m = 4$
(b) $(5, 7)$; $m = 2$
(c) $(-5, 2)$; $m = -3$
(d) $(-4, -1)$; $m = -1$
(e) $(-6, -4)$; $m = 3$
(f) $(4, -2)$; $m = -6$
(g) $(6, 8)$; $m = \frac{1}{2}$
(h) $(-3, 5)$; $m = -\frac{1}{3}$
(i) $(\frac{1}{2}, -2)$; $m = -\frac{1}{2}$
(j) $(\frac{1}{4}, -\frac{1}{5})$; $m = \frac{2}{3}$

3. Find an equation of the line through the given point and having the given slope. Use the equation to find two other points on the line. Graph your solutions.
(a) $(1, 2)$; $m = 2$
(b) $(-1, -3)$; $m = 6$
(c) $(3, -4)$; $m = -2$
(d) $(-5, 2)$; $m = -3$
(e) $(0, 1)$; $m = 3$
(f) $(6, 0)$; $m = \frac{1}{2}$
(g) $(-2, -1)$; $m = -\frac{1}{2}$
(h) $(5, -3)$; $m = \frac{1}{3}$
(i) $(0.6, 0.3)$; $m = -0.1$

4. Determine an equation of the line with slope $m = 2$ and passing through the point $(5, 0)$.

5. Determine an equation of the line with slope $m = -3$ and passing through the point $(0, -2)$.

6. Determine an equation of the line through $(-5, 6)$ and
(a) having slope $m = 4$.
(b) parallel to the x-axis.
(c) parallel to the y-axis.

7. Determine the equation of the x-axis.

8. Determine the equation of the y-axis.

9. Determine an equation of the line through $(-5, 2)$ and having slope $m = 2$.

10. Find an equation of the line passing through $(3, 5)$ and $(5, 7)$.

11. Find an equation of a line passing through the origin, and parallel to the line $y = x$.

12. Find an equation of a line passing through (a, b) with slope 1.

MICRO MATH

Many of the answers in this exercise can be verified using the following BASIC program.

NEW

```
100 REM GIVEN A SLOPE AND A POINT,
105 REM FIND THE EQUATION
110 REM IN THE FORM AX + BY + C = 0.
120 PRINT "WHAT IS THE SLOPE";
130 INPUT M
140 PRINT "X-COORDINATE OF POINT";
150 INPUT X1
160 PRINT "Y-COORDINATE OF POINT";
170 INPUT Y1
180 PRINT "THE EQUATION IS";
190 IF M < 0 THEN PRINT -M;
    "X + Y + ("; -Y1 + M*X1; ") = 0"
200 IF M > 0 THEN PRINT M;
    "X - Y + ("; Y1 - M*X1; ") = 0"
210 IF M = 0 THEN PRINT " Y ="; Y1
220 END
```

RUN

4.3 LINEAR EQUATIONS: TWO-POINT FORM

We can determine the equation of a line given two points on the line.

EXAMPLE 1. Find the equation of the line through $(-1, -3)$ and $(5, 6)$. Express the equation in standard form.

SOLUTION:

Since we know two points on the line, we can determine the slope of the line.

$$m = \frac{y_2 - y_1}{x_2 - x_1}$$

$$m = \frac{6 - (-3)}{5 - (-1)}$$

$$= \frac{9}{6}$$

$$= \frac{3}{2}$$

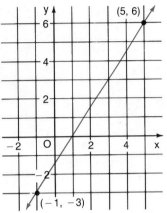

We now have the slope of the line ($m = \frac{3}{2}$) and a point on the line, $(5, 6)$ or $(-1, -3)$.

$$y - y_1 = m(x - x_1)$$

$$y - 6 = \frac{3}{2}(x - 5)$$

$$y - 6 = \frac{3}{2}x - \frac{15}{2}$$

$$2y - 12 = 3x - 15$$

Using the point $(-1, -3)$ and the slope $m = \frac{3}{2}$ will give the same result.

The equation is $3x - 2y - 3 = 0$.

EXAMPLE 2. Find the equation of the line through $(-1, -3)$ and $(5, -3)$. Express the equation in standard form.

SOLUTION:

We first determine the slope of the line.

$$m = \frac{y_2 - y_1}{x_2 - x_1}$$

$$m = \frac{-3 - (-3)}{5 - (-1)}$$

$$= \frac{0}{6}$$

$$= 0$$

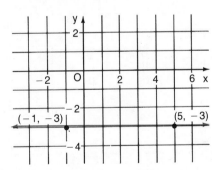

We now have the slope of the line ($m = 0$) and a point on the line, $(-1, -3)$ or $(5, -3)$

$$y - y_1 = m(x - x_1)$$

$$y - (-3) = 0(x - 5)$$

$$y + 3 = 0$$

The equation of the line in standard form is $y + 3 = 0$.

In the following chart we shall observe the graph of Ax + By + C = 0 when one or more of the values of A, B, and C is zero.

Ax + By + C = 0	Table of Values	Graph	Observation
$0x + 2y + 5 = 0$ $2y + 5 = 0$ $A = 0$ $B = 2$ $C = 5$	<table><tr><td>x</td><td>y</td></tr><tr><td>0</td><td>-2.5</td></tr><tr><td>3</td><td>-2.5</td></tr></table>		A horizontal line.
$3x + 0y + 6 = 0$ $3x \quad + 6 = 0$ $x \quad + 2 = 0$ $A = 3$ $B = 0$ $C = 6$	<table><tr><td>x</td><td>y</td></tr><tr><td>-2</td><td>0</td></tr><tr><td>-2</td><td>3</td></tr></table>		A vertical line.
$3x + 4y + 0 = 0$ $3x + 4y \quad = 0$ $A = 3$ $B = 4$ $C = 0$	<table><tr><td>x</td><td>y</td></tr><tr><td>0</td><td>0</td></tr><tr><td>4</td><td>3</td></tr></table>		A line through the origin (0, 0).
$0x + 4y + 0 = 0$ $4y \quad = 0$ $y \quad = 0$ $A = 0$ $B = 4$ $C = 0$	<table><tr><td>x</td><td>y</td></tr><tr><td>0</td><td>0</td></tr><tr><td>3</td><td>0</td></tr></table>		A horizontal line through the origin (0, 0). (The x-axis.)
$3x + 0y + 0 = 0$ $3x \quad = 0$ $x \quad = 0$ $A = 3$ $B = 0$ $C = 0$	<table><tr><td>x</td><td>y</td></tr><tr><td>0</td><td>0</td></tr><tr><td>0</td><td>3</td></tr></table>		A vertical line through the origin (0, 0). (The y-axis.)

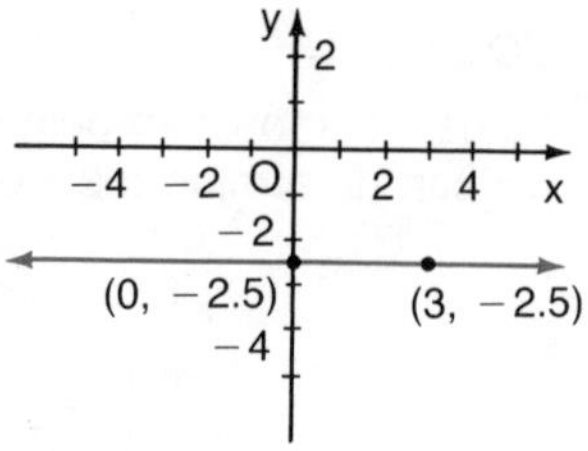

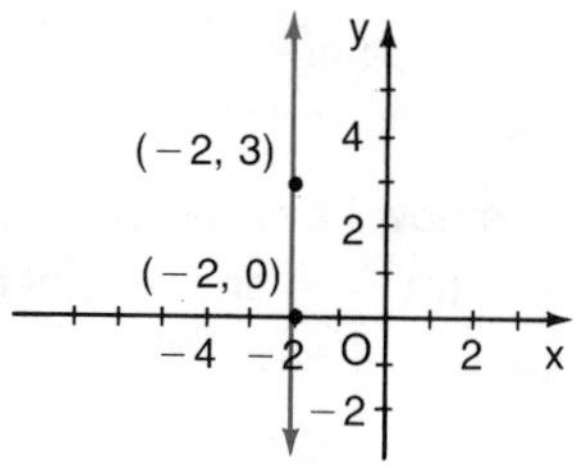

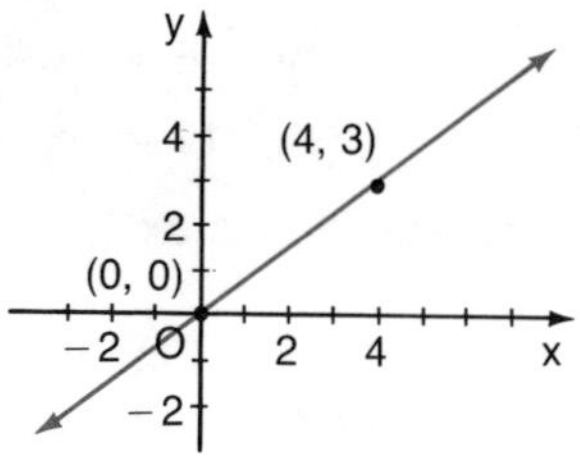

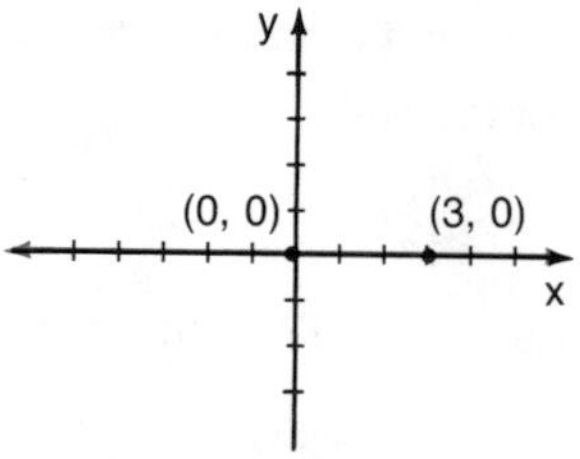

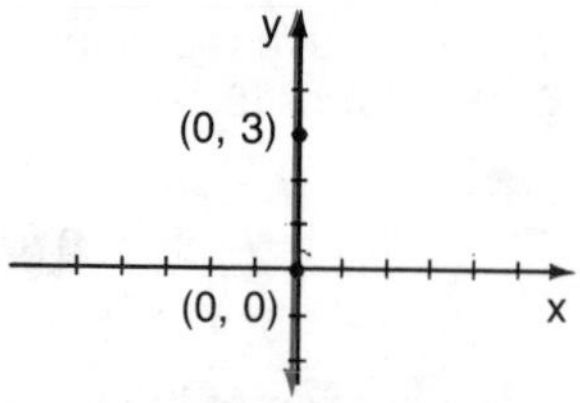

The observations are summarized as follows.

For the line Ax + By + C = 0,

If A = 0, then the line is horizontal.
If B = 0, then the line is vertical.
If C = 0, then the line passes through the origin (0, 0).

EXERCISE 4.3

A 1. In the following chart, determine the values of A, B, and C. Determine whether the line is horizontal or vertical, and whether it passes through the origin.

Ax + By + C = 0	A	B	C	Description of the Line
(a) 2x + 3 = 0				
(b) 3y + 5 = 0				
(c) x + y = 0				
(d) 2x − 7 = 0				
(e) 5x − 4y = 0				
(f) x = 0				
(g) y = 0				

2. From the following graphs, determine whether A, B, or C is zero in the equation Ax + By + C = 0.

(a) 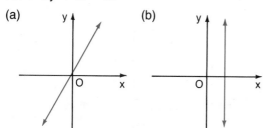 (b)

(c) 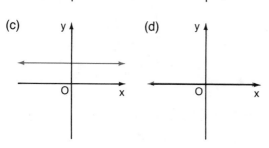 (d)

B 3. Find an equation of the line through the following pairs of points. Express the equation in standard form.

(a) (2, 3) and (3, 5)
(b) (1, 4) and (3, 10)
(c) (−1, −5) and (−3, 5)
(d) (−3, −2) and (−6, 7)
(e) (−1, 0) and (3, −16)
(f) (4, 2) and (2, 1)
(g) (−5, 2) and (1, 4)
(h) (6, 4) and (−5, 4)
(i) (3, −5) and (3, 6)
(j) (2, ½) and (3, −4)
(k) (1.5, 3) and (2.5, 7)
(l) (−0.8, −0.3) and (−1, −0.6)
(m) (−2.2, 5.4) and (−3.4, 7.2)
(n) (15.4, −47.5) and (−3.6, 0)

4. Determine an equation of the line through (−4, 2) and (−2, 10). Use the equation to determine two other points on the line.

5. Find an equation of the line through (4, −1) and (0, 2). Express the equation in standard form.

6. Find an equation of the line passing through the points (5, 0) and (0, −4).

7. Find an equation of the line passing through the points (0, −5) and (1, 0).

8. Find an equation of the line through (a, 0) and (0, b).

4.4 GRAPHING USING INTERCEPTS

Relations may be graphed using the intercepts. The x-intercept of a relation is the x-coordinate of the point where the relation intersects the x-axis. The y-intercept of a relation is the y-coordinate of the point where the relation intersects the y-axis.

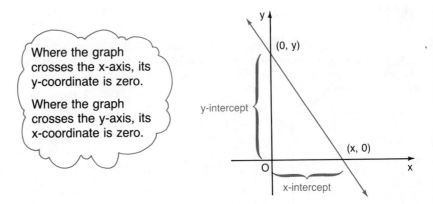

Where the graph crosses the x-axis, its y-coordinate is zero.

Where the graph crosses the y-axis, its x-coordinate is zero.

> To find the x-intercept, let y = 0.
>
> To find the y-intercept, let x = 0.

EXAMPLE. Graph the relation $4x - 3y = 12$, x, y ∈ R.

SOLUTION:
To find the x-intercept, let y = 0.

$$4x - 3y = 12$$
$$4x - 3(0) = 12$$
$$4x = 12$$
$$x = 3$$

To find the y-intercept, let x = 0.

$$4x - 3y = 12$$
$$4(0) - 3y = 12$$
$$-3y = 12$$
$$y = -4$$

3 is called the x-intercept and -4 the y-intercept.

EXERCISE 4.4

A 1. State the x- and y-intercepts of each of the following.
(a) $2x + 3y = 6$
(b) $4x + 3y = 12$
(c) $3x + y = 9$
(d) $x + 4y = 8$
(e) $5x - 2y = 10$
(f) $7x - 3y = 21$
(g) $4x - 5y = -20$
(h) $3x - 5y = -15$
(i) $7x + 2y - 14 = 0$
(j) $8x - 3y + 24 = 0$
(k) $y = 4x - 8$
(l) $y = -3x + 12$

B 2. Use the x- and y-intercepts to graph the following relations.
(a) $4x + 5y = 20$
(b) $3x - 4y = 12$
(c) $2x + y = 4$
(d) $5x + 3y = 15$
(e) $x - y = -7$
(f) $5x + 2y = -10$
(g) $2x + 7y - 14 = 0$
(h) $x - 3y + 6 = 0$

3. Use the x- and y-intercepts to graph each of the following.
(a) $y = 3x - 6$
(b) $y = -2x + 4$
(c) $y = -x - 3$
(d) $y = \frac{1}{2}x + 2$
(e) $y = -\frac{1}{3}x + 1$
(f) $\frac{x}{2} + \frac{y}{3} = 1$
(g) $\frac{x}{4} - \frac{y}{2} = 3$
(h) $\frac{2}{3}x - \frac{1}{4}y = -2$

C 4. State the x- and y-intercepts of each of the following, if possible.
(a) $\{(x, y) \mid 2x - 3 = 0, x, y \in R\}$
(b) $\{(x, y) \mid y + 3 = 0, x, y \in R\}$
(c) $\{(x, y) \mid y = x^2 - 9, x, y \in R\}$
(d) $\{(x, y) \mid y = 2x^2 - 8, x, y \in R\}$
(e) $\{(x, y) \mid x^2 + y^2 = 25, x, y \in R\}$
(f) $\{(x, y) \mid 9x^2 + 4y^2 = 36, x, y \in R\}$

5. State the equation of a relation whose graph does not have an x-intercept.

6. State the equation of a relation whose graph does not have a y-intercept.

7. Find a defining equation for each of the following.

(a)

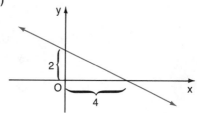

(b)

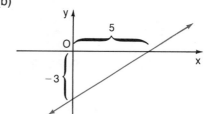

(c)

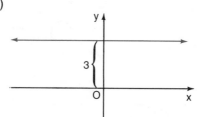

8. Find a general equation of the line with x-intercept a and y-intercept b.

4.5 LINEAR EQUATIONS: SLOPE Y-INTERCEPT FORM

We saw in Chapter 3 that for a partial variation, the equation was in the form $y = mx + b$ and that the graph was a straight line. In this section we shall further investigate straight lines expressed in the form $y = mx + b$.

EXAMPLE 1. Find an equation of the line through $(0, -3)$ with $m = -4$.

SOLUTION:

$$y - y_1 = m(x - x_1)$$
$$y - (-3) = -4(x - 0)$$
$$y + 3 = -4x$$
$$y = -4x - 3$$

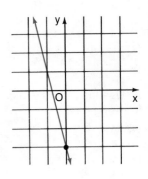

EXAMPLE 2. Find an equation of the line through $(0, b)$ with slope m.

SOLUTION:

$$y - y_1 = m(x - x_1)$$
$$y - b = m(x - 0)$$
$$y - b = mx$$
$$y = mx + b$$

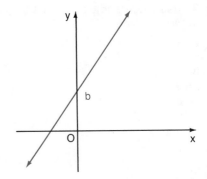

Linear Equation: Slope y-Intercept Form

The graph of the equation of a line expressed in the form

$$y = mx + b, \quad x, y \in R$$

has a slope m and a y-intercept b.

EXAMPLE 3. State the slope and y-intercept of the line
$2x - 3y = 7$.

SOLUTION:

Express the equation in the form $y = mx + b$.

$$2x - 3y = 7$$
$$-3y = -2x + 7$$
$$\frac{-3y}{-3} = \frac{-2x}{-3} + \frac{7}{-3}$$
$$y = \tfrac{2}{3}x - \tfrac{7}{3}$$
$$y = mx + b$$

The slope $m = \tfrac{2}{3}$ and y-intercept $b = -\tfrac{7}{3}$.

The following chart shows the graphs of $y = mx$ for various positive values of m.

$y = mx + b$	Table of Values		Slope m	y-intercept b	Graph	Observation
$y = \tfrac{1}{3}x$	x: 0, 3	y: 0, 1	$\tfrac{1}{3}$	0	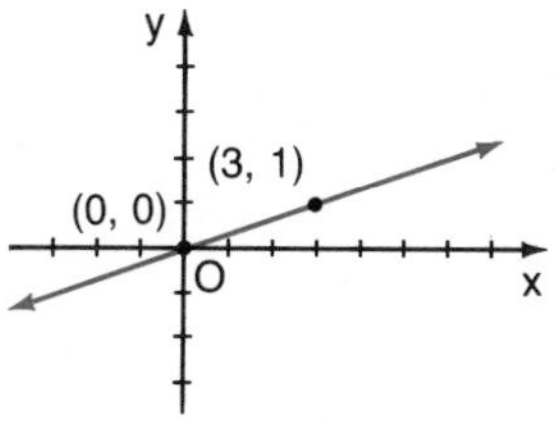 (3, 1) (0, 0)	A line passing through the origin and having a positive slope.
$y = x$	x: 0, 2	y: 0, 2	1	0	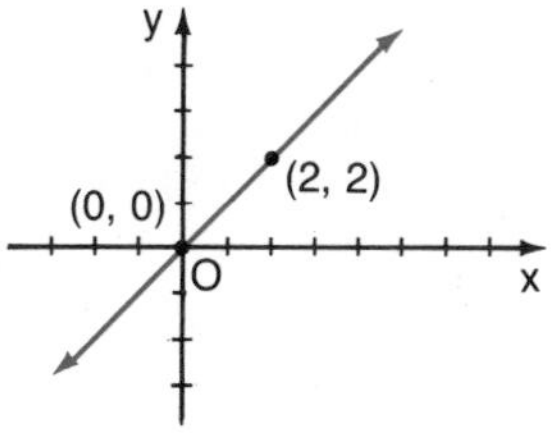 (2, 2) (0, 0)	A line passing through the origin and forming an angle of 45° with the positive x-axis.
$y = 3x$	x: 0, 1	y: 0, 3	3	0	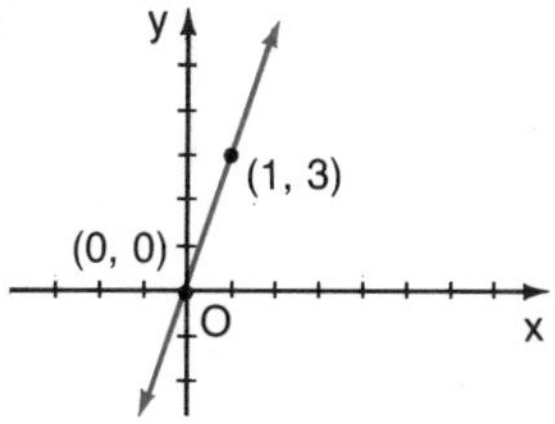 (1, 3) (0, 0)	A line passing through the origin and having a positive slope.

We conclude that for equations of the form $y = mx$ where $m > 0$, the line passes through the origin and rises to the right as x increases.

By graphing the equations $y = -\frac{1}{3}x$, $y = -x$, and $y = -3x$, we observe that for equations of the form $y = mx$ where $m < 0$, the line passes through the origin and falls to the right as x increases.

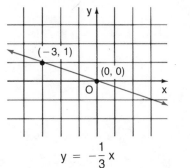

$$y = -\frac{1}{3}x$$

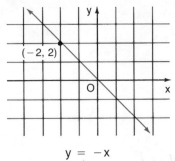

$$y = -x$$

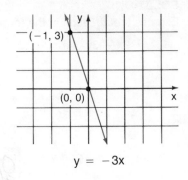

$$y = -3x$$

The following chart shows the graphs of $y = x + b$ for various values of b.

$y = mx + b$	Table of Values		Slope m	y-intercept b	Graph	Observation
$y = x - 1$	x	y	1	−1		A line having a y-intercept of −1 and forming an angle of 45° with the x-axis.
	0	−1				
	2	1				
$y = x$	x	y	1	0		A line passing through the origin and forming an angle of 45° with the x-axis.
	0	0				
	2	2				
$y = x + 2$	x	y	1	2		A line having a y-intercept of 2 and forming an angle of 45° with the x-axis.
	0	2				
	2	4				

We observe that for an equation of the form $y = x + b$, the line forms an angle of 45° with the right portion of the x-axis. The y-intercept is determined by the value of b.

EXERCISE 4.5

1. State the slope and y-intercept of each of the following.
(a) $y = 4x + 6$
(b) $y = x - 4$
(c) $y = -2x - 3$
(d) $y = -7x + 4$
(e) $y = \frac{1}{2}x - 6$
(f) $y = -\frac{2}{3}x + 7$
(g) $y + 7 = 3x$
(h) $y - 6 = -2x$ ·
(i) $y = 5$
(j) $x = 3$
(k) $y = -2$
(l) $x = -4$
(m) $3x + y = 2$
(n) $y - 2x = 0$

2. State a linear equation of a line whose graph has the given slope and y-intercept.
(a) $m = 2$; $b = 3$
(b) $m = 4$; $b = -2$
(c) $m = -2$; $b = -4$
(d) $m = 0$; $b = 3$
(e) $m = -1$; $b = 0$
(f) $m = -\frac{1}{2}$, $b = -2$
(g) $m = 0.2$; $b = 1.7$
(h) $m = -1.5$; $b = -4.6$
(i) $m = -\frac{4}{5}$; $b = 0$
(j) $m = 0$; $b = -\frac{1}{5}$
(k) $m = 15.3$; $b = -45.6$

3. Match the equations with the graphs below.
(a) $y = x$
(b) $y = 3x$
(c) $y = -5x$
(d) $y = x + 3$
(e) $y = x - 5$
(f) $y = 0$

(i)

(ii)
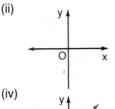

(iii)
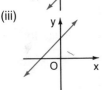

(iv)

(v)
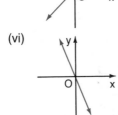

(vi)

4. State the slope and y-intercept of each of the following.
(a) $2x + 3y = 8$
(b) $3x - 2y = 5$
(c) $5x + 2y - 4 = 0$
(d) $2x + 5y = 0$
(e) $7x - 3y + 2 = 0$
(f) $2y - 4 = 7x$
(g) $2y - 7 = 0$
(h) $3x + 5 = 0$
(i) $3x + 0.5y = 4$
(j) $1.2x - 0.3y = 0.12$
(k) $0.4x + 0.5y - 0.2 = 0$
(l) $14.4x + 1.2y = 0$

5. Sketch the graphs of the lines with the following slopes and y-intercepts.
(a) $m = 2$; $b = 4$
(b) $m = 3$; $b = -2$
(c) $m = -2$, $b = 5$
(d) $m = -4$; $b = -6$
(e) $m = \frac{1}{2}$, $b = 1$
(f) $m = -\frac{1}{3}$; $b = -2$

INVESTIGATION:

The following exercises will prepare you for the next section.

6. Draw the graph of each of the following on the same set of axes.
(a) $y = 2x + 4$
(b) $y = 2x + 3$
(c) $y = 2x - 3$
(d) $y = 2x + 6$
(i) How are the graphs of these four lines related?
(ii) State the slope of each line.
(iii) What conclusion can you draw?

7. (a) Draw the graphs of each pair of lines on a set of axes.
(i) $y = 2x + 2$ $y = -\frac{1}{2}x - 3$
(ii) $y = 3x - 4$ $y = -\frac{1}{3}x + 2$
(iii) $y = -4x + 1$ $y = -\frac{1}{4}x - 2$

(b) Measure the angle formed by each pair of lines.
(c) For each pair of lines above, calculate the product of the slopes
$$m_1 \times m_2$$

(d) Draw a conclusion.
(e) Test your conclusion using these lines.
$$y = -x + 5 \qquad y = x - 3$$

4.6 PARALLEL AND PERPENDICULAR LINES

In this section we will investigate the slopes of parallel and perpendicular lines.

Parallel Lines	Perpendicular Lines
Two lines are parallel if they have the same slope.	Two lines are perpendicular if the product of their slopes is -1.
$m_1 = m_2$	$m_1 \times m_2 = -1$

Lines parallel to the y-axis are not included in the above statements, since lines parallel to the y-axis have no slope.

EXAMPLE.   Determine an equation of a line through $(-4, 1)$ and perpendicular to the line $6x - 3y = 7$.

SOLUTION:
In order to use $y - y_1 = m(x - x_1)$ to determine the equation we must know a point on the line and the slope of the line. A point on the line is $(-4, 1)$. To find the required slope we first find the slope of $6x - 3y = 7$.

$$6x - 3y = 7$$
$$-3y = -6x + 7$$
$$y = 2x - \frac{7}{3}$$

The slope of $6x - 3y = 7$ is 2. The slope of lines perpendicular to this line is $-\frac{1}{2}$ since $2(-\frac{1}{2}) = -1$.

$$y - y_1 = m(x - x_1)$$
$$y - 1 = -\frac{1}{2}(x + 4)$$
$$y - 1 = -\frac{1}{2}x - 2$$
$$2y - 2 = -x - 4$$
$$x + 2y + 2 = 0$$

The equation is $x + 2y + 2 = 0$.

EXERCISE 4.6

A 1. Given the slopes of two lines, determine whether the lines are

(a) parallel.
(b) perpendicular.
(c) neither perpendicular nor parallel.

(i) $m_1 = \frac{2}{3}, m_2 = \frac{3}{2}$

(ii) $m_1 = \frac{7}{2}, m_2 = -\frac{2}{7}$

(iii) $m_1 = \frac{1}{2}, m_2 = \frac{5}{10}$

(iv) $m_1 = 2, m_2 = -\frac{4}{8}$

(v) $m_1 = -\frac{3}{2}, m_2 = \frac{3}{2}$

(vi) $m_1 = -1, m_2 = 1$

(vii) $m_1 = \frac{4}{5}, m_2 = \frac{16}{20}$

(viii) $m_1 = \frac{1}{3}, m_2 = -\frac{3}{9}$

(ix) $m_1 = -\frac{2}{7}, m_2 = \frac{21}{6}$

(x) $m_1 = \frac{4}{20}, m_2 = \frac{10}{50}$

(xi) $m_1 = 1\frac{1}{3}, m_2 = -\frac{8}{6}$

(xii) $m_1 = 0, m_2 = -1$

(xiii) $m_1 = 0.5, m_2 = -2$

(xiv) $m_1 = 0.25, m_2 = 4$

(xv) $m_1 = 0.1, m_2 = 1$

(xvi) $m_1 = -0.8, m_2 = 1.25$

B 2. State the slope of a line

(a) parallel to the following lines.
(b) perpendicular to the following lines.

(i) $y = 2x + 5$

(ii) $y = 3x - 2$

(iii) $y = -3x + 1$

(iv) $y = -x + 4$

(v) $y = \frac{1}{2}x + 7$

(vi) $y = -\frac{2}{3}x - 4$

(vii) $y = -\frac{3}{4}x$

(viii) $y = \frac{5}{4}x + 3$

(ix) $y + 7x = 4$

(x) $y - 3x + 6 = 0$

(xi) $3x + y - 4 = 0$

(xii) $5x + 2y = 7$

(xiii) $5x - 4y + 3 = 0$

(xiv) $3x - y = 4$

(xv) $5x - 4 = 7y$

(xvi) $2y - 4 = -3x$

3. Determine an equation of the line through $(-2, 4)$ and parallel to $2x - y - 4 = 0$.

4. Determine an equation of the line through $(-3, -1)$ and parallel to $4x + 2y = 5$.

5. Find an equation of the line perpendicular to $2x - y + 4 = 0$ and through $(-5, 6)$.

6. Find an equation of the line through $(-6, 0)$ and perpendicular to $4x + 3y - 7 = 0$.

7. (a) Plot the points A(4, 2), B(−2, 1), and C(2, −2).
(b) Determine an equation of the line through A and parallel to BC.
(c) Determine an equation of the line through B and perpendicular to AC.

8. Prove that the following points are the vertices of a right angled triangle.
(a) A(−2, 5), B(6, 8), C(1, −3)
(b) P(−6, 1), Q(−2, −7), R(−4, −8)

9. Prove that the following points are the vertices of a parallelogram.
(a) A(2, 1), B(14, 11), C(6, 5), D(−6, −5)
(b) P(−5, −2), Q(1, −1), R(4, 4), S(−2, 3)

MICRO MATH

The following program will calculate the slope of a line segment.

NEW

```
10 REM SLOPE CALCULATOR
20 PRINT "(X1,Y1)";
30 INPUT X1,Y1
40 PRINT "(X2,Y2)";
50 INPUT X2,Y2
60 IF X1=X2 THEN PRINT "VERTICAL
   SEGMENT; IT HAS NO SLOPE": GOTO 90
70 M=(Y2-Y1)/(X2-X1)
80 PRINT "THE SLOPE IS"; M
90 END
```

RUN

4.7 PROBLEM SOLVING USING LINEAR EQUATIONS AND GRAPHS

In this section we will see how a linear function can be used as a mathematical model for some practical problems. We will take some liberties in using mathematical equations and graphs to solve problems since not all mathematical models fit real world situations. However, the "fit" is usually close enough for most practical purposes.

The problem solving model in Chapter 1 suggests that drawing a graph and determining an equation are good planning techniques.

READ

EXAMPLE. The Arco Chemical Supply Co. sells distilled water to be used in chemistry experiments. Sample prices that appear in their catalogue are

2 L cost $1.75
5 L cost $4.00

How much would 8 L of water cost?

PLAN

SOLUTION:
Plot the graph of this relation.

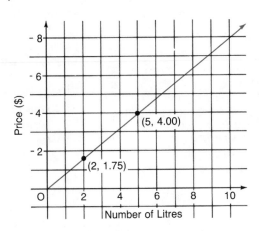

Now find an equation for this relation expressing price in terms of litres.
In this problem we will replace x by L(litres) and y by p (price).

$E=mc^2$

$$\text{Slope } m = \frac{\Delta y}{\Delta x}$$

$$\text{Slope } m = \frac{\Delta p}{\Delta L}$$

$$= \frac{4.00 - 1.75}{5 - 2}$$

$$= \frac{2.25}{3}$$

$$= 0.75$$

$y - y_1 = m(x - x_1)$ becomes $p - p_1 = m(L - L_1)$.

Use m = 0.75 and the point (5, 4.00).

$$p - p_1 = m(L - L_1)$$
$$p - 4.00 = 0.75(L - 5)$$
$$p - 4.00 = 0.75\,L - 3.75$$
$$p = 0.75\,L + 0.25$$

SOLVE

Substitute L = 8.

$$p = 0.75\,L + 0.25$$
$$= 0.75(8) + 0.25$$
$$= 6.00 + 0.25$$
$$= 6.25$$

Use the graph to check the answer.

ANSWER

8 L will cost $6.25.

When linear functions are used to represent practical situations, the slopes and y-intercepts may have particular meanings. In the above example,
(i) the slope represented the price per litre.
(ii) the y-intercept of 0.25 probably represents a handling charge that the company adds to all orders.

EXERCISE 4.7

3 For each of the following, plot a graph, then solve the problem by first finding an equation representing the situation. Assume that a linear relation is the best mathematical model that fits the situation. When the domain is N it will be convenient to draw the graph as though x ∈ R instead of indicating the relation as a series of points on the plane.

(b) Determine the cost of a banquet for 150 people.
(c) How many people could attend if you paid $2330?
(d) What quantity does the slope of the relation represent?
(e) Determine the y-intercept of the relation. What meaning does the y-intercept have?

1. The Vasco Restaurant has banquet facilities for 300 people. When the owner quotes a price for a banquet he is including the room rent plus the cost of the meal. A banquet for 50 people costs $800. One hundred people will cost $1250.

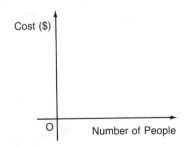

(a) Determine the cost of a banquet for 200 people.

2. The Ace Plumbing Supply Company advertises that it will take approximately 4 h for its 180 L home hot water tank to heat cold water to the required hot water temperature. An inspector filled the tank with cold water and found that after 2 h the temperature of the water was 35°C and after 3 h it was 47.5°C.

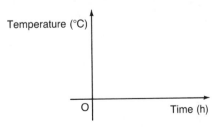

(a) What will be the water temperature after 1 h of heating?

(b) How long will it take for the water to reach 50°C?
(c) Determine the y-intercept. What meaning does the y-intercept have?

3. The student council decides to provide a band and a lunch for the graduation dance. If 200 people attend, the cost will be $1600. If 300 people attend, the price increases to $1900. The fire regulations will permit a maximum of 500 people at the dance.

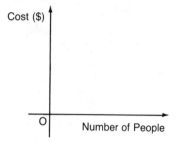

(a) Determine the cost of the dance if 400 people attend.
(b) Determine how many people should attend if the council wishes to spend $2350.
(c) Because of fire regulations, what is the maximum that the dance could cost?
(d) What quantity does the slope of the relation represent?
(e) Determine the y-intercept. What meaning does the y-intercept have?

4. In order to determine the gasoline consumption of a new car, the company representative filled the tank with gasoline and proceeded to drive around the test track at a constant speed. After driving 100 km, 80 L of gas remained in the tank. After 300 km, 40 L of gas remained.

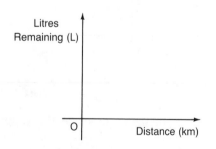

(a) Determine how many litres of gasoline remain after 400 km of driving.
(b) What is the capacity of the gas tank (in litres)?
(c) How many kilometres could you expect to drive on a full tank of gasoline?
(d) How many litres of gasoline will the car use in going 350 km?
(e) What quantity does the slope of the relation represent?

5. Since light travels much faster than sound, you will see the lightning before you hear the thunderclap. If the storm is 660 m away, the time difference between flash and thunderclap is 2 s. The time difference is 5.4 s for a distance of 1782 m.

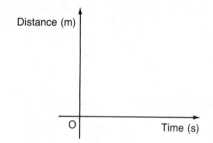

(a) Determine the distance from the storm if the time interval is 6.2 s.
(b) If the distance from the storm is 1320 m, what is the time difference between flash and thunderclap?

6. An object is thrown down from a cliff with an initial velocity of 20.0 m/s. After 4 s its velocity is 59.2 m/s.

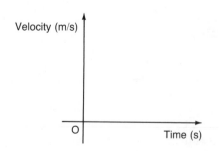

(a) What is its velocity after 5 s?
(b) At what time was its velocity 54.3 m/s?

4.8 PRIME NUMBERS

A prime number is a whole number that has exactly two divisors. The first six prime numbers are

$$2, \quad 3, \quad 5, \quad 7, \quad 11, \quad \text{and} \quad 13$$

1. List all of the prime numbers less than 100.

In 1742, Christian Goldbach wrote a letter to Leonhard Euler in which he stated that every even whole number greater than 2 can be written as the sum of two prime numbers. Euler was unable to prove or disprove Goldbach's conjecture and it remains unsolved to this day.

2. Write the following numbers as the sum of two primes. The first two have been done for you.
(a) $8 = 3 + 5$ (b) $14 = 7 + 7$
(c) $22 = \blacksquare + \blacksquare$ (d) $36 = \blacksquare + \blacksquare$
(e) $44 = \blacksquare + \blacksquare$ (f) $62 = \blacksquare + \blacksquare$

The prime numbers 13 and 15 are called twin primes because their difference is exactly 2.

3. How many twin primes are there less than 100?

For centuries, mathematicians have tried to find a formula that gives only prime numbers. One potential formula was $n^2 - n + 41$

For $n = 1$, $1^2 - 1 + 41 = 41$ (prime)
For $n = 2$, $2^2 - 2 + 41 = 43$ (prime)
For $n = 3$, $3^2 - 3 + 41 = 47$ (prime)

4. The formula produces primes for values of n up to and including 40. Write a computer program to evaluate the formula to $n = 40$.

5. Why does the formula break down when $n = 41$?

Another attempt at a formula to produce prime numbers was made by Fermat. His formula was $2^{2^n} + 1$

6. Evaluate this expression for $n = 1, 2, 3$, and 4. The resulting numbers are all primes.

7. Fermat's formula breaks down for $n = 5$. When $n = 5$ the formula gives the number 4 294 967 297. Euler discovered that this number is divisible by 641. Show that it is.

In 1644, Father Marin Mersenne asserted that $2^p - 1$ is prime for

$p = 2, 3, 5, 7, 13, 17, 19, 31, 67, 127$, and 257. This assertion stood for 250 a.

8. Evaluate $2^p - 1$ for $p = 2, 3, 7$, and 13.

In 1903, Frank Cole gave a lecture before the American Mathematical Society; however, he gave it without speaking a word. At that time it was commonly believed that $2^{67} - 1$ was prime. Cole multiplied 2^{67} and then subtracted 1. Then he moved to another chalkboard and wrote

761 838 257 287
× 193 707 721
———————————

He multiplied it out and got the same result as on the first chalkboard. Cole had factored $2^{67} - 1$. He then received the only standing ovation ever given at a meeting of the American Mathematical Society.

4.9 FAMILIES OF LINES

In our earlier work we saw that equations of the form $y = mx$ represent lines passing through the origin. An infinite number of such lines can be obtained by substituting real values for m.

EXAMPLE 1. Graph $y = mx$ where $m \in \{-4, -1, 0, 1, 4\}$.

SOLUTION:
The equation $y = mx$ originates from the equation $y = mx + b$ where b is a constant equal to zero.

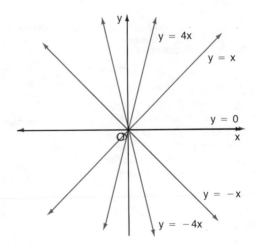

The lines are $y = -4x$, $y = -x$, $y = 0$, $y = x$, and $y = 4x$.

Each line passes through the origin.

The uniqueness of each line is determined by the value of the slope m.

Since all lines share the common characteristic that $b = 0$, they are said to belong to a family of lines. Individual members of the family are identified by individual values of m, and we say that m is the parameter in the family of lines defined by $y = mx + 0$.

> $y = mx$, $m \in R$ represents an infinite family of lines passing through the origin.

EXAMPLE 2. Graph and describe the family of lines defined by
$y = 2x + b$ where $b \in \{-8, -6, -4, -2, 0, 1, 2, 3, 6\}$.

SOLUTION:
In this family, all lines have the same slope $m = 2$.
Hence all lines of the family are parallel.

Individual members of the family are determined by the values of
the parameter b, the y-intercept.

$y = 2x + b$ represents a family of parallel lines whose slopes
are 2.

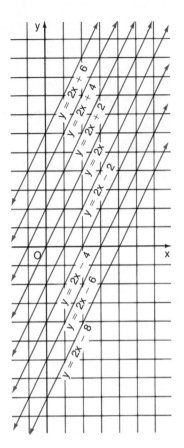

> $y = mx + b$ where m is a constant and $b \in R$,
> represents an infinite family of parallel lines
> with a given slope m.

EXAMPLE 3. Graph and describe the family of lines $y = mx + 2, m \in R$.

SOLUTION:
In this family, the y-intercept is a constant
equal to 2. Hence all lines have the same
y-intercept, 2.

Individual members of the family are
determined by the values of the
parameter m, the slope.

The graph shows members of the family
obtained by substituting

$m = -2, -1, -\frac{1}{2}, 0, \frac{2}{5}, 1$, and 2.

$y = mx + 2, m \in R$ represents an infinite
family of lines having a y-intercept of 2.

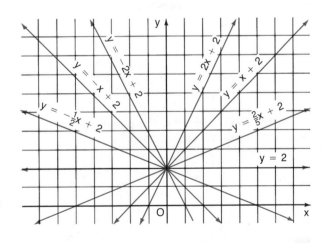

> $y = mx + b$ where b is a constant and $m \in R$, represents an
> infinite family of lines having a given y-intercept.

EXAMPLE 4.   Graph and describe the family of lines represented by y = b, b ∈ R.

SOLUTION:

The equation y = b represents the family of
lines y = 0x + b with constant slope of 0.
Hence y = b represents a family of horizontal
lines.

Individual members are identified by
the values of the parameter b, the y-intercept.

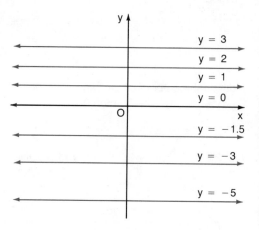

---

y = b,   b ∈ R represents an infinite family of lines parallel to the
x-axis.

EXAMPLE 5.   Graph and describe the family of lines determined by
x = a,   a ∈ {−2, −1, 0, 1, 2}.

SOLUTION:

Individual members can be identified by
substituting the various values for the
parameter a.

x = −2
x = −1
x = 0
x = 1
x = 2

All graphs are vertical lines. The parameter a
represents the x-intercept of each line.

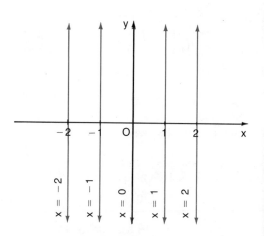

---

x = a,   a ∈ R represents an infinite family of lines parallel to the
y-axis.

EXAMPLE 6. Graph and describe the family of lines determined by $y + 2 = m(x - 3)$, $m \in R$.

SOLUTION:

The equation for this family can be obtained by substituting the point $(3, -2)$ into the point-slope form of the line.

$$y - y_1 = m(x - x_1)$$

The parameter m identifies the individual slope of each member of the family.

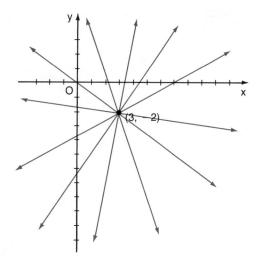

$y - b = m(x - a)$ where a and b are constants and $m \in R$ represents a family of lines passing through the given point (a, b).

EXERCISE 4.9

A 1. Identify the parameter in each of the following families.

(a) $y = mx - 3$, $m \in R$
(b) $y = b$, $b \in \{-2, -1, 0, 1, 2\}$
(c) $y - 4 = m(x + 3)$, $m \in I$
(d) $x = a$, $a \in R$
(e) $y = 3x + b$, $b \in R$

B 2. Determine the equation for the family of lines

(a) having y-intercepts 5.
(b) parallel to the x-axis.
(c) passing through the point $(4, 5)$.
(d) having slopes -3.
(e) parallel to the y-axis.
(f) passing through the origin $(0, 0)$.

3. Express in the form $y = mx + b$.

(a) $3x - 2y + 5 = 0$
(b) $-2x + 4y = 6$
(c) $x + y = 16$

(d) $\dfrac{y - 2}{x + 3} + \dfrac{2}{5} = 0$

(e) $\dfrac{y + 4}{x - 3} = \dfrac{2}{3}$

4. Graph and describe the following families of lines.

(a) $y = b$, $b \in \{0, 1, 2, 3\}$
(b) $x = a$, $a \in R$
(c) $y = 3x + b$, $b \in \{-4, -2, 0, 2, 4\}$
(d) $y = -2x + b$, $b \in R$
(e) $y = mx$, $m \in R$
(f) $y + 1 = m(x + 4)$, $m \in R$
(g) $y = m(x - 2)$, $m \in R$

C 5. Graph and describe the following families of lines.

(a) $3x + 2y = c$
(b) $mx - y = 5$
(c) $2x - ny = 3$

4.10 LENGTH OF A LINE SEGMENT

The length of a horizontal line segment may be determined by calculating $|\Delta x|$.

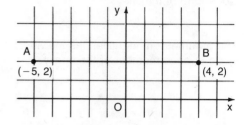

$$
\begin{aligned}
\text{Length of AB} &= |\Delta x| \\
&= |4-(-5)| \\
&= 9
\end{aligned}
$$

The length of a vertical line segment may be determined by calculating $|\Delta y|$.

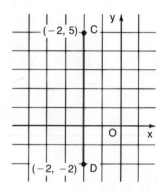

$$
\begin{aligned}
\text{Length of CD} &= |\Delta y| \\
&= |(-2)-5| \\
&= 7
\end{aligned}
$$

The length of a line segment that is neither horizontal nor vertical may be found using the Pythagorean theorem.

EXAMPLE 1. Find the length of the line segment joining A(3, 2) to B(10, 6).

SOLUTION:
Draw line segment AB.
Construct right triangle ABC.

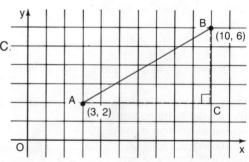

$$
\begin{aligned}
\text{Length of BC} &= |\Delta y| \\
&= |6 - 2| \\
&= 4
\end{aligned}
$$

$$
\begin{aligned}
\text{Length of AC} &= |\Delta x| \\
&= |10 - 3| \\
&= 7
\end{aligned}
$$

Use the Pythagorean relationship.
$$
\begin{aligned}
(AB)^2 &= (AC)^2 + (BC)^2 \\
AB &= \sqrt{(AC)^2 + (BC)^2} \\
&= \sqrt{7^2 + 4^2} \\
&= \sqrt{49 + 16} \\
&= \sqrt{65}
\end{aligned}
$$

Since $(AC)^2 = (\Delta x)^2$ and $(BC)^2 = (\Delta y)^2$ the length formula may be generalized as follows.

> **Length of a Line Segment**
> $\ell = \sqrt{(\Delta x)^2 + (\Delta y)^2}$
> $\ell = \sqrt{(x_2 - x_1)^2 + (y_2 - y_1)^2}$

EXAMPLE 2. Find the length of the line segment joining C(2, −3) to D(−3, 1).

SOLUTION:

$$CD = \sqrt{(\Delta x)^2 + (\Delta y)^2}$$
$$CD = \sqrt{(-5)^2 + (4)^2}$$
$$= \sqrt{25 + 16}$$
$$= \sqrt{41}$$

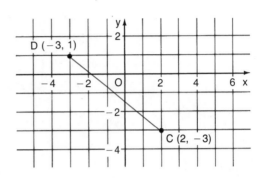

EXERCISE 4.10

A 1. Determine the length of the line segment joining the given points.

(a) (3, 2) and (3, 7)
(b) (4, 8) and (10, 8)
(c) (−3, 7) and (8, 7)
(d) (9, −3) and (−2, −3)
(e) (7, −4) and (7, −11)
(f) (−5, 0) and (12, 0)
(g) (0, −9) and (0, 6)
(h) (−5, 4) and (−5, −6)
(i) (1, −5) and (−7, −5)
(j) (2, −8) and (2, −9)
(k) (1.4, −3.2) and (−2.6, −3.2)
(l) (−1.3, 0.8) and (−1.3, −2.4)

B 2. Calculate the lengths of the following line segments.

(a) A(4, 2), B(7, 9)
(b) R(2, 1), T(10, 6)
(c) S(−3, 5), M(2, 8)
(d) P(−4, 6), Q(−7, −9)
(e) D(−5, 0), E(7, −11)
(f) K(0, 0), L(−7, −6)

(g) C(−3, −8), F(2, 7)
(h) R(−1, 3), S(6, −5)
(i) M(0, −2), N(4, −3)
(j) A(−1, 1), B(1, −1)
(k) C(1.2, −0.8), D(2.2, 1.2)
(l) R(1.5, 15.5), T(−3.5, 7.5)
(m) E(6.6, −0.1), F(4.2, 0.9)
(n) G(−1.3, 4.5), H(−7.4, 8)

3. Find the lengths of the sides of a triangle with vertices A(5, 6), B(−1, 2), and C(1, −3).

4. A quadrilateral has vertices A(4, 6), B(−3, 2), C(−5, −5), and D(6, −1). Find the lengths of the diagonals.

5. Prove that C(−1, 2) is the midpoint of the line segment joining A(−5, 7) and B(3, −3).

6. The coordinates of the endpoints of a diameter of a circle are (5, 2) and (−3, −4). What is the length of the radius of the circle?

4.11 MIDPOINT OF A LINE SEGMENT

It is possible to calculate the coordinates of the midpoint of a line segment when the coordinates of the endpoints are known.

> If A has coordinates (x_1, y_1) and B has coordinates (x_2, y_2), then the coordinates of the midpoint M of the segment AB are
>
> $$\left(\frac{x_1 + x_2}{2}, \frac{y_1 + y_2}{2}\right).$$

EXAMPLE 1. Determine the coordinates of the midpoint M of the segment AB with endpoints A(1, −2) and B(7, 6).

SOLUTION:

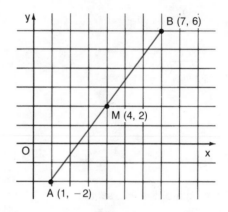

Substituting into the formula for midpoint:

$$M\left(\frac{x_1 + x_2}{2}, \frac{y_1 + y_2}{2}\right)$$

The midpoint for A(1, −2) and B(7, 6) is

$$\left(\frac{1 + 7}{2}, \frac{-2 + 6}{2}\right)$$

$$= (4, 2)$$

$$x = \frac{x_1 + x_2}{2} \qquad y = \frac{y_1 + y_2}{2}$$
$$x = \frac{1 + 7}{2} \qquad y = \frac{-2 + 6}{2}$$
$$= 4 \qquad\qquad = 2$$

EXAMPLE 2. Prove that M, whose coordinates are given in each of the following diagrams, is the midpoint of the given segment AB.

(a)

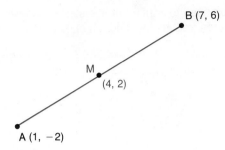

(b)

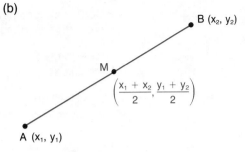

SOLUTION:
Use the formula for the length of a line segment.

(a) $AB = \sqrt{(7-1)^2 + (6+2)^2}$
$= \sqrt{6^2 + 8^2}$
$= \sqrt{100}$
$= 10$

$AM = \sqrt{(4-1)^2 + (2+2)^2}$
$= \sqrt{3^2 + 4^2}$
$= \sqrt{25}$
$= 5$

$MB = \sqrt{(7-4)^2 + (6-2)^2}$
$= \sqrt{3^2 + 4^2}$
$= \sqrt{25}$
$= 5$

(b) $AB = \sqrt{(x_2 - x_1)^2 + (y_2 - y_1)^2}$

$AM = \sqrt{\left(\dfrac{x_1 + x_2}{2} - x_1\right)^2 + \left(\dfrac{y_1 + y_2}{2} - y_1\right)^2}$

$= \sqrt{\left(\dfrac{x_1 + x_2 - 2x_1}{2}\right)^2 + \left(\dfrac{y_1 + y_2 - 2y_1}{2}\right)^2}$

$= \sqrt{\dfrac{(x_2 - x_1)^2}{4} + \dfrac{(y_2 - y_1)^2}{4}}$

$= \sqrt{\dfrac{(x_2 - x_1)^2 + (y_2 - y_1)^2}{4}}$

$= \tfrac{1}{2}\sqrt{(x_2 - x_1)^2 + (y_2 - y_1)^2}$

$MB = \sqrt{\left(x_2 - \dfrac{x_1 + x_2}{2}\right)^2 + \left(y_2 - \dfrac{y_1 + y_2}{2}\right)^2}$

$= \tfrac{1}{2}\sqrt{(x_2 - x_1)^2 + (y_2 - y_1)^2}$

Hence $AM = MB = \tfrac{1}{2} AB$ and M is the midpoint of AB.

EXERCISE 4.11

A 1. Determine the midpoint of the line segment whose endpoints are the following.

(a) (3, 4) and (5, 4)
(b) (2, 3) and (2, 9)
(c) (4, −2) and (9, −2)
(d) (−1, 5) and (−1, −2)
(e) (3, 0) and (6, 0)
(f) (0, −1) and (0, 7)
(g) (−1.2, 3.4) and (3.2, 3.4)
(h) $(\tfrac{1}{2}, -\tfrac{5}{2})$ and $(\tfrac{3}{2}, -\tfrac{5}{2})$

B 2. Determine the midpoints of the line segments whose endpoints are the following.

(a) A(3, 4), B(7, −2)
(b) C(2, −1), D(4, 5)
(c) E(5, −4), F(−1, −2)
(d) G(3, 2), H(7, 5)
(e) M(2, −9), N(−3, −1)
(f) P(4, −5), Q(−2, 2)
(g) R($3\tfrac{1}{2}$, 2), S($-1\tfrac{1}{2}$, 4)
(h) X(−1.2, 7.3), Y(3.2, 2.7)

4.12 PROPERTIES OF PLANE FIGURES

Coordinate geometry can be used to confirm or investigate certain properties of triangles, squares, rectangles, and parallelograms.

EXAMPLE 1. The three points A(0, 5), B(2, 3), and C(5, 0) are on the line $x + y = 5$. Show that $AB + BC = AC$.

SOLUTION:
We must show that $AB + BC = AC$.

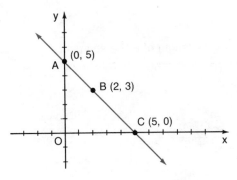

$$\ell = \sqrt{(x_2 - x_1)^2 + (y_2 - y_1)^2}$$

L.S. $= AB + BC$
$= \sqrt{(2 - 0)^2 + (3 - 5)^2} + \sqrt{(5 - 2)^2 + (0 - 3)^2}$
$= \sqrt{2^2 + (-2)^2} \qquad + \sqrt{3^2 + (-3)^2}$
$= \sqrt{8} \qquad\qquad + \sqrt{18}$
$= \sqrt{4 \times 2} \qquad\; + \sqrt{9 \times 2}$
$= 2\sqrt{2} \qquad\qquad + 3\sqrt{2}$
$= 5\sqrt{2}$

R.S. $= AC$
$= \sqrt{(5 - 0)^2 + (0 - 5)^2}$
$= \sqrt{5^2 + (-5)^2}$
$= \sqrt{50}$
$= \sqrt{25 \times 2}$
$= 5\sqrt{2}$

L.S. $=$ R.S.

$\therefore AB + BC = AC$

We generalize the results of Example 1 in the following statement.

> If three points A, B, and C are collinear, then $AB + BC = AC$.

EXAMPLE 2. The diagonals of a square are equal.
Verify this statement for the square whose vertices are A(2, 2), B(5, 2), C(5, 5), and D(2, 5).

SOLUTION:

We must verify that AC = BD.

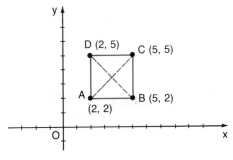

$$\ell = \sqrt{(x_2 - x_1)^2 + (y_2 - y_1)^2}$$

L.S. = AC	R.S. = BD
$= \sqrt{(5 - 2)^2 + (5 - 2)^2}$	$= \sqrt{(5 - 2)^2 + (2 - 5)^2}$
$= \sqrt{3^2 + 3^2}$	$= \sqrt{3^2 + (-3)^2}$
$= \sqrt{18}$	$= \sqrt{18}$
$= 3\sqrt{2}$	$= 3\sqrt{2}$

L.S. = R.S.

∴ AC = BC

The lengths of the diagonals of the square are equal.

EXERCISE 4.12

B **1.** Opposite sides of a square are parallel.
Verify this statement for the square whose vertices are
A(4, 8), B(8, 7), C(7, 3), and D(3, 4).

2. The diagonals of a square are perpendicular.
Verify this statement for the square whose vertices are
A(6, 10), B(10, 9), C(9, 5), and D(5, 6).

3. The diagonals of a parallelogram bisect each other.
Verify this statement for the parallelogram whose vertices are
P(−1, −3), Q(4, −2), R(5, 3), and S(0, 2).

4. The line segment joining the midpoint of two sides of a triangle is parallel to the third side and equal to one half of it.
Verify this relationship for the triangle whose vertices are A(3, −4), B(−3, 2), and C(5, 4) using the midpoints P and Q of AB and AC respectively.

5. The midpoints of the sides of any quadrilateral are the vertices of a parallelogram.
Verify this statement for the quadrilateral whose vertices are A(−2, 4), B(0, 8), C(6, 6), and D(4, −2).

6. (a) Graph the quadrilateral whose vertices are A(5, 5), B(−1, 1), C(−3, −5), and D(3, −1).
(b) Show that ABCD is a parallelogram by finding the slopes of the sides.
(c) Show that AB = DC and BC = AD.

7. In an isosceles triangle the line drawn from the vertex formed by the two equal sides to the midpoint of the other side is perpendicular to the other side.
Verify this statement for the triangle whose vertices are D(4, 1), E(6, 6), and F(8, 1).

4.13 FUNCTIONS

We have defined a relation as a set of ordered pairs. In this section we will consider a special kind of relation called a function. The table shown gives the length of a year on the planets as compared to Earth.

Planet	Length of Year (compared to earth)
Mercury	0.24
Venus	0.62
Earth	1
Mars	1.9
Jupiter	12
Saturn	29
Uranus	84
Neptune	165
Pluto	248

This table may also be represented as a correspondence or mapping.

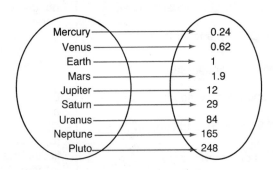

As a set of ordered pairs, we have

{(Mercury, 0.24), (Venus, 0.62), (Earth, 1), (Mars, 1.9), (Jupiter, 12), (Saturn, 29), (Uranus, 84), (Neptune, 165), (Pluto, 248)}.

Corresponding to each planet there is one, and only one, number. This relation describes a function.

A function is a relation such that for every first element there is one, and only one, second element.

{(3, 5), (7, 11), (8, 15), (9, 22)}   Function

{(3, 6), (4, 7), (4, 12), (5, 13)}   Not a function (Why?)

{(6, 4), (7, 4), (8, 4), (9, 4)}   Function

{(3, 8), (3, 9), (3, 10), (3, 11)}   Not a function

EXAMPLE 1.
(a) Illustrate the relation defined by
     $\{(x, y) \mid y = 3x - 2, x \in \{1, 2, 3, 4\}\}$
as a mapping.
(b) State the domain and range of the relation.
(c) Is the relation a function? Explain.

SOLUTION:

x	3x − 2	y
1	3(1) − 2	1
2	3(2) − 2	4
3	3(3) − 2	7
4	3(4) − 2	10

(a) Relation as a mapping.

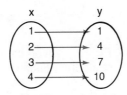

(b) Domain: {1, 2, 3, 4}
     Range: {1, 4, 7, 10}
(c) Yes. For every first element there is one, and only one, second element.

Another way to describe this function is by $(x, 3x - 2)$. This states that the first element is transformed or mapped into the second element by the operation indicated.

EXAMPLE 2.   Given $x \in \{-2, -1, 0, 1, 2\}$.
(a) Illustrate the relation defined by (x, x^2) as a mapping.
(b) State the domain and range.
(c) Is the relation a function? Explain.

SOLUTION:

(a) The ordered pair (x, x^2) states that the first element is transformed or mapped into the second element by squaring the first element.

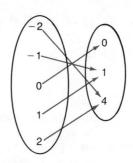

> **FUNCTION**
> For each element in the domain there is one element in the range.

(b) Domain: $\{-2, -1, 0, 1, 2\}$
    Range: $\{0, 1, 4\}$

(c) Yes. For every first element there is one, and only one, second element. (Only one arrow starts from each element of the domain.)

Another way to illustrate a function is by arrow notation. For example,

$$f:x \rightarrow 2x - 1.$$

This states that the first element is mapped or transformed into the second element by multiplying x by 2 and then subtracting 1. The letter f, in f:x, is used for identification only; it distinguishes one mapping from another. Examples of other mappings are

> A function is a mapping.
>
> f maps or transforms one element x into an element y.
>
> $f:x \rightarrow y$

$$g:x \rightarrow x + 5$$
$$m:x \rightarrow x^2 + 3$$
$$h:x \rightarrow 2x^2 - 4$$

EXAMPLE 3. Given $h:x \rightarrow 2x + 4$, $x \in \{0, 1, 2, 3, 4\}$.
(a) Illustrate the relation as a mapping.
(b) List the ordered pairs of h.
(c) State the domain and range of h.
(d) Is h a function? Explain.

SOLUTION:

(a)

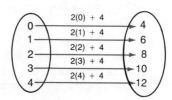

(b) $\{(0, 4), (1, 6), (2, 8), (3, 10), (4, 12)\}$
(c) Domain: $\{0, 1, 2, 3, 4\}$
    Range: $\{4, 6, 8, 10, 12\}$
(d) Yes. For each element in the domain there is one, and only one, element in the range.

EXERCISE 4.13

A 1. State which of the following relations are functions. Explain your answer.
(a) {(1, 3), (2, 5), (3, 7), (4, 9), (5, 11)}
(b) {(−2, 0), (−1, 2), (0, 4), (1, 6), (2, 8)}
(c) {(−3, 4), (−1, 7), (1, 9), (1, 11)}
(d) {(5, 4), (7, 11), (6, 4), (2, 11)}
(e) {(3, 6), (4, 6), (9, 6), (10, 6)}
(f) {(−3, 5), (−3, 7), (−3, 9), (−3, 11)}
(g) {(8, −3), (9, −3), (7, 6), (8, −2)}
(h) {(red, 3), (green, 4), (blue, 5)}
(i) {(15, 33), (15$\frac{1}{2}$, 33), (16, 34), (16, 35)}

2. State which of the following relations are functions. Explain your answer.

(a)   (b)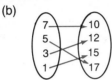

(c) 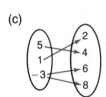 (d)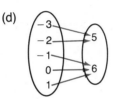

3. Given that a mapping is defined by the ordered pair (x, x + 7), state the missing element in each of the following.
(a) (5, ■)   (b) (0, ■)   (c) (−3, ■)
(d) (■, 8)   (e) (■, 21)   (f) (■, 0)
(g) (−16, ■)   (h) (−5, ■)   (i) (■, −8)

4. Given that f:x → x − 4, state the missing element in each of the following.
(a) (6, ■)   (b) (14, ■)   (c) (10, ■)
(d) (■, 5)   (e) (■, 0)   (f) (■, −3)
(g) (−5, ■)   (h) (−10, ■)   (i) (■, −6)

5. (a) In your mathematics class is the relation defined by (student, age) a function? Explain.
(b) Is the relation (age, student) a function? Explain.

6. In your mathematics class is the relation defined by (eye colour, student) a function? Explain.

B 7. (a) Illustrate the relation defined by {(x, y) | y = 2x − 3, x ∈ {1, 2, 3, 4, 5}} as a mapping.
(b) State the domain and range of the relation.
(c) Is the relation a function? Explain.

8. (a) Illustrate the relation defined by {(x, y) | y = x² + 2, x ∈ {−2, −1, 0, 1, 2}} as a mapping.
(b) State the domain and range of the relation.
(c) Is the relation a function? Explain.

9. Given x ∈ {0, 1, 2, 3, 4}.
(a) Illustrate the relation defined by (x, 3x + 4) as a mapping.
(b) State the domain and range.
(c) Is the relation a function? Explain.

10. Given x ∈ {1, 3, 5, 7, 9}.
(a) Illustrate the relation defined by $\left(x, \dfrac{x + 3}{2}\right)$ as a mapping.
(b) Is the relation a function? Explain.

11. Given f:x → 5x − 4, x ∈ {0, 1, 2, 3, 4}.
(a) List the ordered pairs of f.
(b) State the domain and range of f.
(c) Is f a function? Explain.

12. Given g:x → $\frac{1}{2}$x + 3, x ∈ {0, 2, 4, 6}.
(a) List the ordered pairs of g.
(b) Is g a function? Explain.

13. Given h:x → 2x² − 4, x ∈ {−2, −1, 0, 1, 2}.
(a) List the ordered pairs of h.
(b) Is h a function? Explain.

14. List as a set of ordered pairs the possible "calls" of a baseball umpire. For example, (1, 2) means 1 ball and 2 strikes. Is the relation a function? Explain.

C 15. List the ordered pairs of the relation defined by {(x, y) | x = y², y ∈ {−2, −1, 0, 1, 2}}. Is the relation a function? Explain.

4.14 FUNCTION NOTATION

Function notation is another way to express a mapping, such as f:x → 2x + 5. This mapping can be written as

$$f(x) = 2x + 5$$

where f(x) is read "f of x" or "f at x."

Identifies the function.

f(x)

States the variable used in the function.

If $\qquad$ f(x) = 2x + 5,

then $\qquad$ f(3) = 2(3) + 5

$\qquad\qquad$ = 6 + 5

$\qquad\qquad$ = 11

Note that f(3) means the value of the function when x = 3.

This is a very convenient method of determining the ordered pairs of a function.

We now have several methods to name functions.

$$y = 2x + 5$$

$$\{(x, y) \mid y = 2x + 5\}$$

$$f:x \rightarrow 2x + 5$$

$$(x, 2x + 5)$$

$$f(x) = 2x + 5$$

EXAMPLE 1. If h(x) = 4x − 5, find

(a) h(6) $\qquad\qquad\qquad\qquad$ (b) h(−3)
(c) h(0) $\qquad\qquad\qquad\qquad$ (d) h(m)

and state the ordered pair associated with each.

SOLUTION:

(a) h(x) = 4x − 5
$\qquad$ h(6) = 4(6) − 5
$\qquad\qquad$ = 24 − 5
$\qquad\qquad$ = 19

Ordered pair: (6, 19)

(b) $\quad$ h(x) = 4x − 5
$\qquad$ h(−3) = 4(−3) − 5
$\qquad\qquad$ = −12 − 5
$\qquad\qquad$ = −17

Ordered pair: (−3, −17)

(c) h(x) = 4x − 5
$\qquad$ h(0) = 4(0) − 5
$\qquad\qquad$ = 0 − 5
$\qquad\qquad$ = −5

Ordered pair: (0, −5)

(d) h(x) = 4x − 5
$\qquad$ h(m) = 4(m) − 5
$\qquad\qquad$ = 4m − 5

Ordered pair: (m, 4m − 5)

EXAMPLE 2. If $f(x) = 2x + 1$ and $g(x) = 1 - 2x$, find
(a) f(2) (b) g(-2) (c) f[g(-1)]

SOLUTION:

(a) $f(x) = 2x + 1$
$\ \ \ f(2) = 2(2) + 1$
$\ \ \ \ \ \ \ \ = 4 + 1$
$\ \ \ \ \ \ \ \ = 5$

(b) $g(x) = 1 - 2x$
$\ \ g(-2) = 1 - 2(-2)$
$\ \ \ \ \ \ \ \ = 1 + 4$
$\ \ \ \ \ \ \ \ = 5$

(c) $g(x) = 1 - 2x$
$\ \ g(-1) = 1 - 2(-1)$
$\ \ \ \ \ \ \ \ = 1 + 2$
$\ \ \ \ \ \ \ \ = 3$
Since $g(-1) = 3$,
then $f[g(-1)] = f(3)$
$\ \ \ \ \ \ \ \ \ \ \ \ \ \ \ = 2(3) + 1$
$\ \ \ \ \ \ \ \ \ \ \ \ \ \ \ = 6 + 1$
$\ \ \ \ \ \ \ \ \ \ \ \ \ \ \ = 7$

f[g(x)] can be written
(f ∘ g)(x).

EXERCISE 4.14

A 1. If $f(x) = 4x + 3$, find
(a) f(1)   (b) f(2)   (c) f(-2)   (d) f(0)
(e) f(10)   (f) f(-7)   (g) f(-100) (h) f(50)
(i) f(6)   (j) f(-5)   (k) f(a)   (l) f(b)

2. If $g(x) = 3x - 5$, find
(a) g(2)   (b) g(7)   (c) g(-3)   (d) g(0)
(e) g(10)   (f) g(-10)   (g) g(-7)   (h) g(20)
(i) g(-4)   (j) g(m)   (k) g(t)   (l) g(a²)

3. If $h(x) = x^2$, $f(x) = 2x + 5$, and $g(x) = 1 + 3x$, find
(a) h(2)   (b) g(-3)   (c) f(0)   (d) h(0)
(e) g(4)   (f) h(-2)   (g) f(-6)   (h) g(-4)
(i) f(4)   (j) h($\frac{1}{2}$)   (k) f($\frac{1}{2}$)   (l) g($-\frac{1}{3}$)

B 4. If $f(x) = x^2 + 4$, find
(a) f(2)   (b) f(-3)   (c) f(6)   (d) f(-2)
and state the ordered pair associated with each.

5. If $g(x) = \frac{1}{2}x - 4$, find
(a) g(2)   (b) g(-4)   (c) g(6)   (d) g(9)
and state the ordered pair associated with each.

6. If $h(x) = x^2 - 3x + 7$, find
(a) h(1)   (b) h(2)   (c) h(-3)   (d) h(0)

7. Given $h(x) = (x + 1)^2$, find
(a) h(2)   (b) h(4)   (c) h(-1)   (d) h(-4)

8. If $g(x) = 4x - 7$, find
(a) g(3) + g(2)
(b) g(7) + g(1)
(c) g(-2) - g(4)
(d) g(5) + g(-3) - g(6)

9. Given $f(x) = x^2 + 1$ and $h(x) = (x - 1)^2$, find
(a) f(4) + h(2)   (b) h(3) + f(-3)
(c) f(-2) - h(-1)   (d) h(-4) - f(2)

10. If $m(x) = 5x - 4$ and $g(x) = 2x^2$, find
(a) m(5) + g(3)
(b) g(-2) - m(1)
(c) 2[m(-1)] + 3[g(-4)]
(d) 4[g(-1)] - 3[m(-1)]

C 11. Given $m(x) = 3x - 4$ and $n(x) = 1 - 2x$, find
(a) m(-3)   (b) n(0)   (c) m[n(-1)]
(d) n[m(3)]   (e) m[m(2)]   (f) m[n(3)]

12. Given $f(x) = x^2$ and $g(x) = x^2 + 2$, find
(a) f(-4)   (b) g(2)   (c) f[g(0)]   (d) g[f(-2)]

13. If $f(x) = 5x - 10$, find x so that
(a) f(x) = 0
(b) f(x) = 25
(c) f(x) = -35

14. If $g(x) = (x + 1)(x - 2)$, find x so that $g(x) = 0$.

4.15 PROBLEM SOLVING

1. Marcia has a three litre jar and a five litre jar. How can she get exactly four litres of water from a well using these two jars?

2. A rubber ball will bounce half the height it drops. A ball is dropped from 200 m. How far will the ball have travelled after it hits the ground for
(a) the second time?
(b) the third time?
(c) the fourth time?
(d) the fifth time?

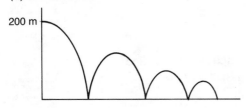

200 m

3. It is 10:00. What time will it be 99 999 999 999 h from now?

4. The sum and difference of two squares can be primes. For example,

$$9 + 4 = 13 \quad \text{and} \quad 9 - 4 = 5$$

Can the sum and difference of two prime numbers be squares?

5. A commuter must travel from Eagle to Riverside and back every day. There are four roads joining the two towns. The commuter would like to vary the trips as much as possible and always return on a different road. How many different ways can the round trip be made?

Eagle

Riverside

6. Two bees are sitting on flowers 180 m apart. One bee can fly at a speed of 4 m/s, while the other flies at 5 m/s. The bees start to fly back and forth between the two flowers.
(a) After how long will they meet each other for the first time?
(b) After how long will they meet each other for the second time?

7. The legend states that the inventor of the game of chess asked to be rewarded with wheat. He wanted one grain of wheat put on the first square of the chess board, 2 grains on the second, 4 grains on the third, 8 grains on the fourth, and so on. The total number of grains was $2^{64} - 1$, which is several thousand times the world's annual wheat crop. To approximate 2^{64}, enter 2 on your calculator and then press the squaring key several times. How many times would you need to press it?

8. The number 3 can be written using four 4s as follows.

$$(4 + 4 + 4) \div 4 = 3$$

Write expressions for 0, 1, 2, 4, 5, 6, 7, 8, 9, and 12 using four 4s.

9. Two teenagers and four adults wish to cross a river in a small boat. The boat can carry only one adult at a time, or one or two teenagers.
(a) What is the least number of crossings the boat must make to carry all six people across?
(b) What is the least number of crossings the boat must make if there are five adults?

10.

21

How many ways can you write the number 21 as the sum of consecutive whole numbers?

11.

45

The number 45 can be written as the sum of consecutive whole numbers as follows.

$$14 + 15 + 16 = 45$$

Find four other ways to write 45 as the sum of consecutive whole numbers.

12.

81

Write the whole number 81 as the sum of consecutive whole numbers in as many ways as possible.

13. For a science project, Ellen and Joe proposed a new temperature scale, which they called the Exinor scale. In the Exinor scale, water freezes at 50°E and boils at 200°E. Complete the following table by expressing the missing values to the nearest tenth of a degree.

Celsius (°C)	Exinor (°E)
0	50
10	
15	
30	
	100
	120
	140
100	200

14. A pipe 250 m long needs to be cut into pieces 25 m long. Each cut takes three minutes. How long will it take to cut the pipe?

15. Which positive numbers less than 49 are divisible by both 8 and 12?

16. How many ways can you receive change for a quarter if at least one coin is a nickel?

17. How many whole numbers less than 50 can be written as the sum of two perfect squares?

18. Frank has 1000 small washers, 1000 medium washers, and 1000 large washers. How many packages can be filled if each package must contain 8 small washers, 5 medium washers, and 6 large washers?

19. How many rectangles are there?

20.

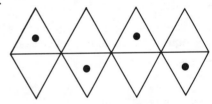

Which of the following figures can you make from the pattern above?

(a)

(b)

(c)

(d)

4.16 REVIEW EXERCISE

1. State the slope and y-intercept of each of the following.
(a) y = 7x + 6   (b) 3x + y = 14
(c) 4x − y − 7 = 0   (d) y = ⅓x − 4
(e) 4x + 2y − 7 = 0   (f) x = 7
(g) y = −4   (h) 3x − 5y = 9
(i) 4x − 7y + 11 = 0
(j) −2x + 3y = 12

2. Determine the length of the line segment joining the two given points.
(a) (5, 2) and (5, 7)
(b) (3, 8) and (5, 8)
(c) (−2, 8) and (−2, 15)
(d) (−4, 16) and (−4, 0)

3. Determine the coordinates of the midpoint of the line segment joining the two given points.
(a) (7, −4) and (1, −4)
(b) (3, 4) and (3, −7)
(c) (−4, −6) and (−11, −6)
(d) (5, −12) and (5, 3)

4. Determine the parameter in each of the following equations representing families of lines.
(a) y = 4x + b, b ∈ R
(b) y = b, b ∈ R
(c) y − 4 = m(x + 3), m ∈ R
(d) x = a, a ∈ R
(e) y = mx, m ∈ R
(f) y = mx − 4, m ∈ R

5. State which of the following relations are functions.
(a) {(5, 6), (6, 8), (7, 10), (8, 13)}
(b) {(4, −3), (5, −3), (6, −3), (7, −3), (8, −3)}
(c) {(−1, 6), (−2, 7), (−1, 8), (−3, 9)}
(d) {(5, −4), (5, 0), (5, 4)}

6. Given that h:x → x + 5, state the missing element in each of the following.
(a) (2, ■)   (b) (8, ■)
(c) (■, 10)   (d) (■, 4)
(e) (0, ■)   (f) (■, 0)
(g) (−11, ■)   (h) (■, −5)

7. If f(x) = 2x + 1, g(x) = 3x − 1, and h(x) = x², find.
(a) f(2)   (b) g(4)
(c) h(2)   (d) g(20)
(e) h(−3)   (f) h(0)
(g) f(−10)   (h) g(−5)
(i) f(½)   (j) g(−⅓)
(k) f(a)   (l) g(b)

8. Determine the slopes of the line segments joining the following pairs of points.
(a) A(5, −3), B(−4, 6)
(b) C(−1, 7), D(−4, 8)
(c) E(−3, −5), F(5, −9)
(d) G(0, −11), H(1, −5)
(e) K(1.2, −5.6), L(0.2, 0.4)
(f) M(3, −2.5), N(4, −7.5)

9. Determine an equation of the line through the given point having the given slope.
(a) (4, 6); m = 7
(b) (−3, −5); m = −1
(c) (−5, 8); m = −2
(d) (3, −7); m = ½
(e) (−4, 0); m = −1.4
(f) (1.4, −0.8); m = −0.2

10. Determine an equation of the line through (−4, −5) and
(a) having slope m = −2.
(b) parallel to the y-axis.
(c) parallel to the x-axis.

11. Find an equation of the line through the following pairs of points.
(a) (3, 4) and (1, −1)
(b) (−4, −6) and (5, −2)
(c) (3, −7) and (−2, 5)
(d) (1.2, −0.6) and (−0.8, 0.4)

12. Express in the form y = mx + b.
(a) 2x + y = 3   (b) 3x − y = 7
(c) x + 2y = 4   (d) 3x − 4y = 12
(e) y − 4 = 3x   (f) $\frac{y + 2}{x − 1} = \frac{1}{2}$
(g) y − 3 = 4(x + 7)   (h) $\frac{y − 4}{x + 1} = \frac{−3}{2}$

13. Find an equation of the line through (6, −5) and parallel to 4x − 2y + 7 = 0.

14. Find an equation of the line through (−3, −4) and perpendicular to 4x + 2y − 6 = 0.

15. Calculate the lengths of the following line segments.

(a) A(5, 6), B(−4, 3)
(b) C(−3, 7), D(−6, 4)
(c) G(−11, 5), H(4, −1)
(d) M(1.4, −0.6), N(−0.6, 3.4)

16. A quadrilateral has vertices A(4, 6), B(−5, 2), C(−6, −7), and D(8, −3). Find the lengths of the diagonals.

17. Determine the equation for the family of lines

(a) parallel to the x-axis.
(b) passing through the point (7, −2).
(c) having y-intercepts 5.
(d) having slopes 4.

18. Graph and describe the following families of lines.

(a) y = mx, m ∈ {−2, −1, 0, 1, 2}
(b) y = −5x + b, b ∈ {−4, −2, 0, 2, 4}
(c) y + 3 = m(x − 4), m ∈ R
(d) x = a, a ∈ R
(e) y = mx − 4, m ∈ R

19. Determine the midpoints of the segments whose endpoints are given as follows.

(a) A(3, −5), B(−1, 7)
(b) C(4, −2), D(2, 2)
(c) G(4, −3), H(7, −1)
(d) M(−1, 0), N(−5, 3)
(e) P(3.7, 4.2), Q(2.3, −2.2)
(f) R(2½, ½), S(−1½, 1½)

20. If f(x) = 3x − 2 and h(x) = (x − 2)², find

(a) f(−4)
(b) h(−2)
(c) f(1) + h(1)
(d) h(4) − f(−2)
(e) 2[f(4)] + 3[f(−1)]
(f) 4[h(2)] − 2[f(−4)]

21. The Barko Publishing Company specializes in printing student yearbooks. An order of 400 books costs $3000. An order of 600 books costs $4000.
(a) Plot a graph of this relation.

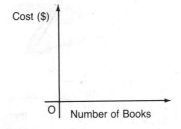

(b) Find an equation of this relation expressing cost in terms of the number of books ordered.
(c) What quantity does the slope of the relation represent?
(d) From the graph determine the cost of 300 books.
(e) From the equation determine the cost of 200 books.
(f) If an order costs $3500, how many books were ordered?
(g) Determine the y-intercept of the relation.
(h) What meaning does the y-intercept have?

MICRO MATH

The following program will calculate the length and the midpoint of a line segment.

NEW

```
10 REM LENGTH AND MIDPOINT CALCULATOR
20 PRINT "(X1,Y1)";
30 INPUT X1,Y1
40 PRINT "(X2,Y2)";
50 INPUT X2,Y2
60 L=SQR((X2-X1)*(X2-X1)+(Y2-Y1)*
   (Y2-Y1))
70 X=(X1+X2)/2
80 Y=(Y1+Y2)/2
90 PRINT "THE LENGTH OF THE SEGMENT
   IS"; L
100 PRINT "THE MIDPOINT IS (";
    X; ","; Y; ")"
110 END
```

RUN

4.17 CHAPTER 4 TEST

1. Determine the slope of the line
(a) whose equation is $y = -2x + 4$.
(b) whose equation is $3x - 4y = 12$.
(c) whose equation is $y = -2$.
(d) perpendicular to the line $y = -2x + 3$.
(e) parallel to the line $x + \dfrac{y}{2} = 3$.
(f) passing through the points $(3, 6)$ and $(5, 10)$.

2. Determine an equation of the line
(a) passing through $(-1, -3)$ whose slope is 2.
(b) passing through the points $(-1, 3)$ and $(1, 5)$.
(c) whose slope is -1 and whose y-intercept is 4.
(d) passing through $(2, 3)$ and parallel to the y-axis.
(e) passing through the point $(4, -1)$ and perpendicular to the line

$$y = -\frac{x}{3} + 2.$$

3. Calculate the length of the segment whose endpoints are $A(-3, 5)$ and $B(9, 0)$.

4. Determine the midpoint of the segment whose endpoints are $C(-5, 3)$ and $D(-3, 7)$.

5. Graph the relation $3x - 5y = 15$ using intercepts.

6. Determine the equation for the family of lines
(a) whose y-intercepts are 7.
(b) passing through the point $(3, -2)$.

7. Graph and describe the following family of lines.
(a) $y = b, b \in R$
(b) $y = mx + 3, m \in R$

8. One end of a coil spring is hooked to the ceiling and the other end is allowed to dangle freely. When a 5 kg mass is attached, the length of the spring is 22 cm. When an 8 kg mass is attached, the spring is 31 cm long.
(a) Plot a graph for this relation.
(b) Find an equation for this relation expressing length in terms of mass.
(c) From the graph determine the length of the spring when a 2 kg mass is attached.
(d) If the spring is 25 cm long, what mass is attached?
(e) Determine the y-intercept of the relation.
(f) What meaning does the y-intercept have?

4.18 CUMULATIVE REVIEW FOR CHAPTERS 1 TO 4

1. Find the decimal equivalent, the period, and the length of the period for each of the following.

(a) $\frac{7}{8}$

(b) $\frac{3}{7}$

(c) $\frac{2}{9}$

(d) $\frac{2}{25}$

2. Express as a common fraction.

(a) 0.04

(b) $0.\overline{4}$

(c) $0.\overline{13}$

3. Graph each set on a number line.

(a) $\{x \in R \mid -3 < x \leq 1\}$
(b) $\{x \in R \mid x \geq -1\} \cap \{x \in R \mid x \leq 4\}$
(c) $\{x \in R \mid x < 0\} \cup \{x \in R \mid x > 3\}$

4. Find a rational and an irrational number between the given numbers.

(a) 2.145 271 ...
   2.144 316 ...
(b) 0.127 127 ...
   0.127

5. Change to a mixed radical.

(a) $\sqrt{18}$

(b) $\sqrt{162}$

(c) $\sqrt{75}$

(d) $\sqrt{72}$

6. Change to an entire radical.

(a) $2\sqrt{5}$

(b) $5\sqrt{7}$

(c) $4\sqrt{3}$

(d) $2\sqrt{2}$

7. Simplify.

(a) $2\sqrt{5} \times 3\sqrt{7}$

(b) $2\sqrt{3} \times 3\sqrt{12}$

(c) $(2\sqrt{3})^3$

(d) $3\sqrt{2}(2\sqrt{3} - 5)$

(e) $4\sqrt{2}(\sqrt{2} + \sqrt{18})$

(f) $(3\sqrt{2})^2(2\sqrt{3})^2$

(g) $\frac{4\sqrt{24}}{2\sqrt{12}}$

(h) $\frac{18\sqrt{18}}{54\sqrt{2}}$

8. Simplify.

(a) $3\sqrt{5} - \sqrt{2} + 2\sqrt{5} + 5\sqrt{2}$
(b) $2\sqrt{2} + \sqrt{8}$
(c) $3\sqrt{27} + 5\sqrt{3}$
(d) $5\sqrt{8} + 2\sqrt{32}$
(e) $\sqrt{3} + \sqrt{27} + \sqrt{12}$

9. Find the value of x to the nearest tenth using the Pythagorean relationship.

(a)

(b)

10. Simplify.

(a) $(3ab^2)(2a^2b^3)$

(b) $(-2x^2y)(3x^3)(y^2)$

(c) $\frac{16a^3b}{24ab^2}$

(d) $\frac{(3a^2)^3}{9a^5}$

(e) $\left(\frac{2xy^2}{3x^2y}\right)^2$

(f) $\frac{(2abc)(3a^2b)}{(2ac)^2}$

11. Evaluate.

(a) $2^{-3} \times 2^3$

(b) $\left(\frac{3}{5}\right)^{-2}$

(c) $2^{-1} + 3^{-1}$

(d) $3^0 - \left(\frac{1}{2}\right)^{-1}$

12. Simplify.

(a) $(2x^2 + 3x - 1) + (x^2 - 7x + 2)$
(b) $(3a - 2b + 4) - (2a + b - 6)$
(c) $2(x - y) + 3(2x + 5y)$
(d) $3x(x - 3) - 4x^2(-x + 2)$

13. Factor, if possible.

(a) $12abc - 4ab + 8bc$
(b) $2a^2x + 4ax - 8a^3x^2$
(c) $9x^2 - 25$
(d) $x^2 + 3x - 10$

14. Simplify the following and state the restrictions on the variables.

(a) $\frac{3x}{6x + 9x^2}$

(b) $\frac{x + 4}{x^2 - 16}$

(c) $\frac{x + 5x + 6}{x^2 + 6x + 9}$

(d) $\frac{2x + 4}{2} \div \frac{x^2 - 4}{x - 2}$

15. Simplify.

(a) $\frac{2x}{3} + \frac{4x}{5}$

(b) $\frac{2a}{5} + \frac{3a - 1}{2}$

16. Solve the following where x ∈ R.
(a) $3x - 2(2x + 3) = 2$
(b) $2x - 3(x - 1) = 2(x + 1)$
(c) $\frac{3}{4}x - 2 = 4$

17. Solve the following inequalities where x ∈ R.
(a) $3x + 2(2x + 1) < 9$
(b) $\frac{x - 1}{3} \geq \frac{x + 2}{2}$

18. The table gives the cost of renting ice-time at a local arena.

Time (h)	Cost ($)
1	40
2	80
3	120
4	160

(a) List the relation as a set of ordered pairs.
(b) List the elements of the domain.
(c) List the elements of the range.

19. The table gives the cost of printing advertisement flyers.

Number	Cost ($)
1000	50
2000	100
3000	150
4000	200

(a) Draw a graph of this relation.
(b) Use interpolation to determine the cost of printing 2750 flyers.
(c) Use extrapolation to determine the number of flyers that can be printed for $275.

20. A parachutist jumps from a plane. Moments later, the parachute opens. Sketch a graph of the parachutist's speed of descent versus the time of descent.

21. The table shows the cost of making a long distance telephone call.

Time (min)	Cost ($)
1	0.71
2	1.31
3	1.91
4	2.51

(a) What is the fixed cost?
(b) Write the partial variation equation.
(c) How much will it cost to talk for 10 min?

22. The amount of beef needed for a banquet varies directly as the number of people attending. Six kilograms are needed to prepare 20 plates.
(a) Find the value of k and write the equation.
(b) How much beef is needed to prepare 25 plates?
(c) How many plates can be prepared with 12.6 kg of beef?

23. Determine the slope of the line
(a) whose equation is $y = 3x - 4$.
(b) whose equation is $2x - 3y = 6$.
(c) whose equation is $y - 3 = 0$.
(d) parallel to the line $y = 2x - 5$.
(e) perpendicular to the line $y = -\frac{2x}{3} + 4$.
(f) passing through the points $(2, -4)$ and $(3, -6)$.

24. Determine an equation of the line
(a) passing through $(3, -2)$ whose slope is 3.
(b) passing through the points $(3, 4)$ and $(1, 2)$.
(c) whose slope is -2 and whose y-intercept is 5.
(d) passing through $(3, -5)$ and parallel to the y-axis.
(e) passing through $(1, 2)$ and perpendicular to the line $y = \frac{1}{2}x + 4$.

25. Determine the equation of the family of lines
(a) whose y-intercepts are 3.
(b) passing through the point $(-1, 2)$.

SYSTEMS OF EQUATIONS

CHAPTER

5

Each problem that I solved became a rule which served afterwards to solve other problems.

Descartes

REVIEW AND PREVIEW TO CHAPTER 5

EQUATIONS IN ONE VARIABLE

EXERCISE

1. Solve the following equations.
   (a) $x - 3 = 12$
   (b) $w + 7 = 11$
   (c) $3x = 15$
   (d) $\frac{1}{2}b = 6$
   (e) $2x + 1 = 15$
   (f) $2x - 3 = 13$
   (g) $\frac{x}{3} = 5$
   (h) $-3d = -21$
   (i) $-3 + 4n = 17$

2. Solve the following equations.
   (a) $3m + 1 = 16$
   (b) $2t - 4 = -20$
   (c) $5y - 10 = -10$
   (d) $3 - d = 4$
   (e) $5 = 2a + 1$
   (f) $4x + 16 = 0$

3. Solve.
   (a) $4x + 7 = 2x - 3$
   (b) $3a - 14 = 6 - 2a$
   (c) $5b + 6 = 7b - 2$
   (d) $4x - 3 = 6x - 11$
   (e) $2 + 3y - 4 = -5y + 6$
   (f) $-6x - 4 = 6 + 4x + 20$

4. Solve.
   (a) $5(x - 3) = 2(x + 6)$
   (b) $6(m + 2) = 4(m - 3)$
   (c) $2(2b - 1) + 4 = 5(b + 1)$
   (d) $5(a - 3) - 2a = -6$
   (e) $7 - 2(1 - 3x) + 16 = 8x + 11$
   (f) $4b - (3b - 1) - 3 + 6(b - 2) = 0$

5. Solve.
   (a) $\frac{x}{3} = \frac{1}{2}$
   (b) $\frac{m - 1}{3} = 6$
   (c) $\frac{x}{3} - \frac{1}{2} = \frac{1}{4}$
   (d) $\frac{a + 2}{2} = \frac{a - 1}{3}$
   (e) $\frac{x + 1}{2} + \frac{x + 1}{3} = 5$

   (f) $\frac{2m + 1}{3} - \frac{m + 1}{4} = 3$
   (g) $\frac{a + 7}{6} + \frac{1}{2} = \frac{a - 2}{4}$
   (h) $\frac{1 - 3x}{4} - \frac{x - 1}{3} = -x$

6. Solve the following equations for x. a, b, c ≠ 0.
   (a) $ax + b = c$
   (b) $ab - x = c$
   (c) $bc + x = a$
   (d) $\frac{x}{a} - b = c$
   (e) $\frac{x}{a} - \frac{b}{c} = \frac{1}{d}$
   (f) $\frac{x}{b} = a - c$

7. Solve for x. a, b, c ≠ 0.
   (a) $ax - bx = c$
   (b) $ax + bx = a + b$
   (c) $ax - bx = a^2 - b^2$
   (d) $\frac{x}{a} - \frac{x}{b} = \frac{a}{b}$
   (e) $\frac{x}{a} - \frac{x}{b} - \frac{x}{c} = 1$
   (f) $ax + bc = cx$

SIMPLIFICATION

EXERCISE

1. Simplify the following.
   (a) $3x(x - 5) - 2x(x + 4)$
   (b) $(x - 3)(x + 4)$
   (c) $(x + 7)^2$
   (d) $3x(x + 2) - x(x - 5)$
   (e) $(2x - 5)(2x + 5)$
   (f) $(3x + 2)^2$
   (g) $4x(3 - x) + 2x(5 + 2x)$

2. Simplify.
   (a) $3x[2x - (x + 2)]$
   (b) $4x^2 - x[3x - 2(x - 1)]$
   (c) $[x - 3(x + 2) - 5x] - 3x$
   (d) $4x[2x - 5(x + 1)] + 3x$
   (e) $3x[x - 2(x + 3)] + 5(x - 2)$

FACTORING

EXERCISE

1. Factor.
(a) $a^2 - b^2$ (b) $a^2 - 2ab + b^2$
(c) $a^2 - a - 12$ (d) $a^2 + a - 20$
(e) $a^2 - ab$ (f) $a^2 - 5ab + 6b^2$
(g) $a^2 - 2ab - 8b^2$

2. Factor.
(a) $a^3 - ab$ (b) $a^2b - ab^2$
(c) $a^2b + b^3$ (d) $a^3 + 2a^2b + ab^2$

INTERSECTION AND UNION OF SETS

$A = \{a, b, c, d\}$ $B = \{a, b, e, f\}$

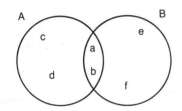

INTERSECTION

The intersection of A and B is the set containing the members that are in both A and B.

$$A \cap B = \{a, b\}$$

UNION

The union of A and B is the set containing the members that are in A or B.

$$A \cup B = \{a, b, c, d, e, f\}$$

EXERCISE

1. $A = \{1, 2, 3, 4, 5\}$, $B = \{2, 4, 6, 8\}$ and $C = \{5, 6, 7, 8\}$. Find the following.
(a) $A \cap B$
(b) $A \cup B$
(c) $A \cap (B \cup C)$
(d) $(A \cap B) \cup (A \cap C)$

TABLES OF VALUES

EXERCISE

1. Complete the tables for the given equations.

(a) $y = 3x - 2$

x	y
-2	
0	
2	

(b) $y = x^2 - 1$

x	y
-1	
0	
1	

(c) $y = 5 - 2x$

x	y
4	
-3	
-2	

(d) $y = 2(x^2 - 4)$

x	y
4	
-1	
-4	

GRAPHING ON A NUMBER LINE

EXERCISE

1. Graph the solution set of the following.
(a) $2x + 3 \leq 11$, $x \in 1$
(b) $3x - 1 > 8$, $x \in I$
(c) $3 - 2x < 15$, $x \in R$
(d) $4 - x \leq 5$, $x \in R$
(e) $3x + 5 > x - 11$, $x \in R$
(f) $2 - 3x \leq 2x + 7$, $x \in R$
(g) $3(x - 1) > 5x - 13$, $x \in R$

2. Graph the solution set of the following, where $x \in R$.
(a) $3x + 1 \geq 7$ and $2x - 3 \leq 7$
(b) $3x - 1 < 8$ and $4x + 1 \geq -7$
(c) $1 - 3x > 2x - 4$ or $1 - x \leq 2x - 5$
(d) $2(x - 3) + 7 > 3x + 5$ and $7 \leq 2(1 - 2x) + 1$
(e) $5 - (x - 4) \geq 3(1 - x) - 4$ or $3x + 2(x - 1) \leq 8 - (x + 4)$

5.1 ORDERED PAIRS AND SOLUTION SETS

An equation in one variable, such as $2x + 3 = 11$, has one real value as a solution. In this case, the solution set is $\{4\}$. We can verify that 4 is a solution by substituting $x = 4$ in the equation.

$$2x + 3 = 11$$

$$\begin{aligned} \text{L.S.} &= 2x + 3 & \qquad \text{R.S.} &= 11 \\ \text{L.S.} &= 2(4) + 3 & \\ &= 8 + 3 & \\ &= 11 & \end{aligned}$$

Since L.S. = R.S., 4 is the solution set.

The solution set for an equation in two variables, such as $2x + y = 7$, consists of an infinite number of ordered pairs. Some of these ordered pairs are $(0, 7)$, $(1, 5)$, $(2, 3)$, and $(-1, 9)$. We can verify that any one of these is the solution set by substituting the values for x and y in the equation.

EXAMPLE 1. Is $(-1, 9)$ in the solution set of $2x + y = 7$ where $x, y \in R$?

SOLUTION:
For $x = -1$ and $y = 9$,

$$\begin{aligned} \text{L.S.} &= 2x + y & \qquad \text{R.S.} &= 7 \\ &= 2(-1) + 9 & \\ &= -2 + 9 & \\ &= 7 & \end{aligned}$$

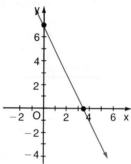

Since L.S. = R.S., $(-1, 9)$ is in the solution set of $2x + y = 7$.

EXAMPLE 2. Does $(3, 6)$ satisfy the relation $y = 4x - 7$?

SOLUTION:
For $x = 3$ and $y = 6$,

$$\begin{aligned} \text{L.S.} &= y & \qquad \text{R.S.} &= 4x - 7 \\ &= 6 & &= 4(3) - 7 \\ & & &= 12 - 7 \\ & & &= 5 \end{aligned}$$

Since L.S. $\neq$ R.S., $(3, 6)$ does not satisfy $y = 4x - 7$ and $(3, 6)$ is not in the solution set.

The results of Example 2 are shown in the graph at the right. Note that $(3, 6)$ is not on the graph of $y = 4x - 7$.

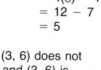

There is an infinite number of ordered pairs that satisfy the equation $x + y = 6$. Some of them are (5, 1), (4, 2), (3, 3), and (2, 4). Similarly, there is an infinite number of ordered pairs that satisfy the equation $x - y = 2$. Examples are (5, 3), (4, 2), (6, 4), and (1, −1). Note that (4, 2) is the only ordered pair that satisfies both equations.

EXAMPLE 3. Does the ordered pair (−3, 2) satisfy both equations?
$$x + y = -1$$
$$2x + 5y = 4$$

SOLUTION:

Substitute $x = -3$ and $y = 2$ in both equations.

For $x + y = -1$

L.S. $= x + y$ R.S. $= -1$
    $= -3 + 2$
    $= -1$

(−3, 2) satisfies $x + y = -1$.

For $2x + 5y = 4$

L.S. $= 2x + 5y$ R.S. $= 4$
    $= 2(-3) + 5(2)$
    $= -6 + 10$
    $= 4$

(−3, 2) satisfies $2x + 5y = 4$.

(−3, 2) satisfies both equations.

The results of Example 3 are shown on the graph at the right. Note that the point (−3, 2) is on lines $x + y = -1$ and $2x + 5y = 4$.

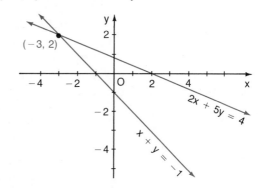

EXERCISE 5.1

B **1.** Check the ordered pairs following the equation to see whether or not the pair is an element of the solution set.

(a) $x + y = 14$;   (2, 12), (0, 14), (−1, 16), (4, 9), (−7, 19), (20, −6)

(b) $2x + y = 13$;   (0, 12), (1, 11), (7, −1), (5, 2), (−3, 20), (10, −7)

(c) $x - y = 8$;   (9, 1), (4, 4), (2, −6), (13, 4), (−6, −14), (3, −5)

(d) $x - y = -2$;   (4, 6), (3, 6), (−3, 5), (−3, −5), (−3, −1), (−2, 0)

2. State the missing element of each ordered pair so that the ordered pair belongs to the solution set of the equation.

(a) $x + y = 9$;
(4, ■), (■, 1), (−3, ■), (■, −5), (12, ■)

(b) $x - y = 6$;
(9, ■), (■, 2), (5, ■), (■, −3), (−8, ■)

(c) $2x + y = 15$;
(1, ■), (5, ■), (7, ■), (■, 3), (■, −5)

3. In each case, state the ordered pair that satisfies both equations.

(a) $x + y = 4$
   $x - y = 2$ (2, 2), (5, 3), (3, 1), (1, 3)

(b) $x - y = 1$
   $x + y = 7$ (3, 2), (9, −2), (12, −5), (4, 3)

(c) $2x + y = 7$
   $x + y = 5$ (1, 5), (2, 3), (0, 7), (−2, 7)

4. Find the ordered pair that satisfies both equations.

(a) $x + y = 9$ (b) $x + y = 11$
   $x - y = 3$ $x - y = 3$

(c) $x - y = 4$ (d) $x - y = 6$
   $x + y = 10$ $x + y = 8$

5.2 GRAPHICAL SOLUTIONS OF LINEAR SYSTEMS

When you find all the ordered pairs that satisfy two equations, such as $y = 2x + 1$ and $y = -x + 7$, you have solved a system of linear equations. In this section we will deal with graphical solutions.

EXAMPLE 1.   Find the point of intersection of the graphs defined by $y = 2x + 1$ and $y = -x + 7$.

SOLUTION:

$y = 2x + 1$

x	y
0	1
1	3
2	5
3	7

$y = -x + 7$

x	y
0	7
2	5
4	3
6	1

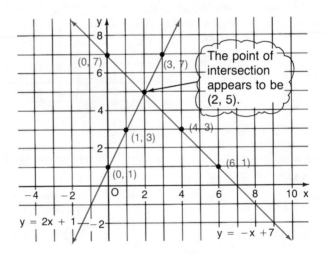

The point of intersection appears to be (2, 5).

Check (2, 5) in $y = 2x + 1$.

L.S. $= y$
$\quad = 5$

R.S. $= 2x + 1$
$\quad = 2(2) + 1$
$\quad = 5$

Check (2, 5) in $y = -x + 7$.

L.S. $= y$
$\quad = 5$

R.S. $= -x + 7$
$\quad = -(2) + 7$
$\quad = 5$

Since the point (2, 5) satisfies both equations, we say that the solution of this linear system is (2, 5).

EXAMPLE 2. Solve the following graphically.

$$y + 2x = -5 \quad \text{①}$$
$$y - 3x = 5 \quad \text{②}$$

SOLUTION:

Express each equation in the form $y = mx + b$.

$$y + 2x = -5 \qquad\qquad y - 3x = 5$$
$$y = -2x - 5 \qquad\qquad y = 3x + 5$$

x	y
1	−7
0	−5
−1	−3

x	y
1	8
0	5
−1	2

Draw the graphs.

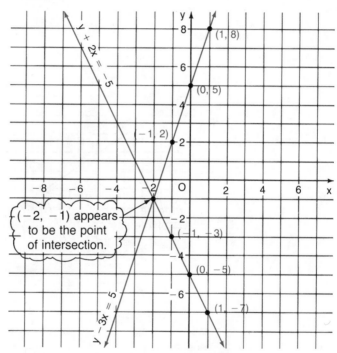

$(-2, -1)$ appears to be the point of intersection.

We check the point of intersection by substituting into both equations.

Check in ①.

L.S. $= y + 2x$
$= (-1) + 2(-2)$
$= -1 - 4$
$= -5$
R.S. $= -5$

Check in ②.

L.S. $= y - 3x$
$= (-1) - 3(-2)$
$= -1 + 6$
$= 5$
R.S. $= 5$

L.S. $=$ R.S.

The solution is $(-2, -1)$.

EXAMPLE 3. Solve the following graphically. Check your solution.

$$2x + 3y = -12 \quad \text{①}$$
$$2x - y = -4 \quad \text{②}$$

SOLUTION:
In this case it is convenient to use the intercept method to draw the graphs of the relations.

For $2x + 3y = -12$, when $x = 0$, $y = -4$
and   when $y = 0$, $x = -6$.

Two ordered pairs are $(0, -4)$ and $(-6, 0)$.

For $2x - y = -4$, when $x = 0$, $y = 4$
and   when $y = 0$, $x = -2$.

Two ordered pairs are $(0, 4)$ and $(-2, 0)$.

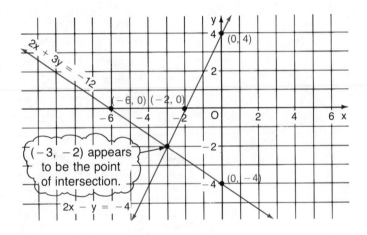

We check the point of intersection by substituting it into both equations.

Check in ①.

L.S. $= 2x + 3y$
     $= 2(-3) + 3(-2)$
     $= -6 - 6$
     $= -12$
R.S. $= -12$

Check in ②.

L.S. $= 2x - y$
     $= 2(-3) - (-2)$
     $= -6 + 2$
     $= -4$
R.S. $= -4$

L.S. $=$ R.S.

The solution is $(-3, -2)$.

EXERCISE 5.2

A 1. State three ordered pairs that satisfy each of the following.

(a) $y = x + 3$　　(b) $y = 2x - 1$
(c) $y = 3x + 1$　　(d) $y = 2 - x$
(e) $y = -x + 4$　　(f) $y = -2x - 1$
(g) $y = 4x + 2$　　(h) $y = 3x$
(i) $y = -x$　　　(j) $y = 2x - 3$

2. Use the "intercept method" to find two ordered pairs that satisfy each of the following.

(a) $2x + 3y = 6$　　(b) $4x + 5y = 20$
(c) $x + 2y = 8$　　(d) $3x + y = 9$
(e) $5x - 3y = 15$　　(f) $3x - 4y = -12$
(g) $x + y = 7$　　(h) $x - y = 4$
(i) $x - y = -3$　　(j) $3x - 2y = 7$

B 3. Determine graphically the points of intersection. Check your answer.

(a)

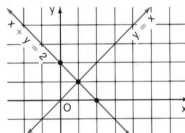

(b)

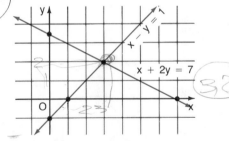

(c)

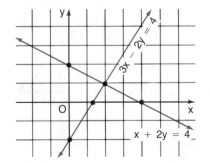

4. Solve the following graphically. Check your solution.

(a) $y = x + 2$　　(b) $y = 2x - 1$
　 $y = 4 - x$　　　 $y = 8 - x$
(c) $y = 1 - 2x$　　(d) $y = x + 8$
　 $y = x + 7$　　　 $y = -3x$
(e) $y = 2x - 1$　　(f) $y = -3x + 10$
　 $y = 4x - 3$　　　 $y = 2x + 5$

5. Solve the following graphically. Use the intercept method to draw the graphs.

(a) $x - y = -4$　　(b) $3x - 2y = 12$
　 $x + 2y = 2$　　　 $2y - x = -8$
(c) $2x + y = 12$　　(d) $5x - 2y = 10$
　 $3x - 2y = 18$　　　 $x + 2y = 2$

C 6. Solve the following graphically. How many points of intersection are there for each pair of equations?

(a) $y = x + 4$　　(b) $2x + 3y = 6$
　 $y = x - 2$　　　 $4x + 6y = 12$
(c) $y = -2x + 2$　　(d) $4x - 3y = 12$
　 $y = -2x - 4$　　　 $12x - 9y = 36$

MICRO MATH

The following program will print ordered pairs that satisfy a given equation.

NEW

```
100 REM ORDERED PAIRS
110 PRINT "FOR THE EQUATION Y=MX+B"
120 PRINT "WHAT IS THE VALUE OF M";
130 INPUT M
140 PRINT "WHAT IS THE VALUE OF B";
150 INPUT B
160 PRINT "SOME ORDERED PAIRS ARE:"
170 FOR X= -10 TO 10
180 Y = M*X + B
190 PRINT "("; X; ","; Y; ")"
200 NEXT X
210 END
```

RUN

5.3 ALGEBRAIC SOLUTIONS OF LINEAR SYSTEMS: SUBSTITUTION

In the previous section the solution to a system of linear equations was determined by inspection. This method is not reliable enough to determine points of intersection whose coordinates are very large or whose coordinates are not integers as shown in the graphs below.

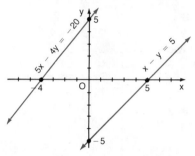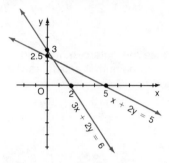

The solution is $(-40, -45)$.

The solution is $(0.5, 2.25)$.

An algebraic method is more reliable for solving a linear system. This section introduces the algebraic method of substitution.

There are many ordered pairs that satisfy $y - 2x = 7$. Solving for y, we obtain $y = 2x + 7$.

We can verify that $(x, 2x + 7)$ is an ordered pair that satisfies the equation by substitution.

L.S. $= y - 2x$		R.S. $= 7$
$= (2x + 7) - 2x$		
$= 2x + 7 - 2x$		
$= 7$		

We now use this idea to solve the system.

EXAMPLE 1. Solve. $\quad y - 2x = 7 \quad$ ①
$$y + x = 4 \quad ②$$

SOLUTION:

We know that $(x, 2x + 7)$ satisfies equation ①. At the point of intersection of the two lines, $(x, 2x + 7)$ must also satisfy ②.

$$y + x = 4$$
$$(2x + 7) + x = 4$$
$$2x + 7 + x = 4$$
$$3x + 7 = 4$$
$$3x = -3$$
$$x = -1$$

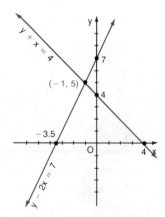

From ① we have
$$y = 2x + 7$$
$$= 2(-1) + 7$$
$$= -2 + 7$$
$$= 5$$

The solution is $(-1, 5)$.

EXAMPLE 2. Solve by substitution.

$$2x + y = 6 \quad \text{①}$$
$$3x - 2y = 2 \quad \text{②}$$

SOLUTION:
From ①

$$2x + y = 6$$
$$y = 6 - 2x$$

Substitute in ②.

$$3x - 2y = 2$$
$$3x - 2(6 - 2x) = 2$$
$$3x - 12 + 4x = 2$$
$$7x = 14$$
$$x = 2$$

Substitute $x = 2$ in ①.

$$2x + y = 6$$
$$2(2) + y = 6$$
$$4 + y = 6$$
$$y = 2$$

Check in ①.

L.S. $= 2x + y$
$= 2(2) + 2$
$= 4 + 2$
$= 6$
R.S. $= 6$

Check in ②.

L.S. $= 3x - 2y$
$= 3(2) - 2(2)$
$= 6 - 4$
$= 2$
R.S. $= 2$

The solution is (2, 2).

EXERCISE 5.3

B 1. Solve by substitution.

(a) $2x + y = 6$
$3x + 2y = 10$

(b) $3x + y = 2$
$5x + 2y = 3$

(c) $x + 4y = 3$
$2x + 5y = 3$

(d) $x - 2y = 4$
$2x - 3y = 7$

(e) $x - 2y = 3$
$5x + 4y = 8$

(f) $2a + b = 2$
$3a - 2b = 3$

(g) $m + 3n = 2$
$3m - 6n = 1$

(h) $x + 2y = 4$
$2x - 6y = 3$

C 2. Solve by substitution. Check your solution.

(a) $3x + 4y = 9$
$5x - 8y = 4$

(b) $5x + 4y = 5$
$3x - 2y = 3$

(c) $2x + 5y = 6$
$4x + 15y = -8$

(d) $2a + 3b = 3$
$10a + 6b = -3$

(e) $3m - 2n = 5$
$4m + 14n = 15$

(f) $3x + 2y = 12$
$2x + 3y = 13$

(g) $5a - 8b = 8$
$10a + 4b = 1$

(h) $3m - 4n - 10 = 0$
$5m - 12n - 6 = 0$

5.4 ALGEBRAIC SOLUTIONS OF LINEAR SYSTEMS: COMPARISON

Linear systems can also be solved algebraically by the method of comparison. This method uses the transitive property of equality.

Transitive Property of Equality			
If	$2 + 3 = 5$	If	$a = b$
and	$5 = 4 + 1,$	and	$b = c,$
then,	$2 + 3 = 4 + 1.$	then	$a = c.$

EXAMPLE 1. Solve. $\quad y = 2x + 3 \quad$ ①
$\qquad\qquad\qquad\quad\ y = x + 4 \quad$ ②

SOLUTION:

> At the point of intersection, the x-coordinate of equation ① equals the x-coordinate of equation ②, and the y-coordinate of equation ① equals the y-coordinate of equation ②.

Since $\quad y = 2x + 3 \quad$ ① $\qquad$ or $\qquad 2x + 3 = y$
and $\quad\ y = x + 4 \quad$ ②
then by the transitive property of equality,

$$2x + 3 = x + 4$$
$$2x - x = 4 - 3$$
$$x = 1$$

Substitute $x = 1$ in $y = 2x + 3$.

$$y = 2x + 3$$
$$y = 2(1) + 3$$
$$y = 2 + 3$$
$$y = 5$$

Check in ①.

L.S. $= y$
$\quad\ = 5$
R.S. $= 2x + 3$
$\qquad = 2(1) + 3$
$\qquad = 5$

Check in ②.

L.S. $= y$
$\quad\ = 5$
R.S. $= x + 4$
$\qquad = 1 + 4$
$\qquad = 5$

The solution is $(1, 5)$.

EXAMPLE 2. Solve by comparison.
$$3x + 2y = 12 \quad ①$$
$$2x + 3y = 13 \quad ②$$

SOLUTION:
Solve both equations for the same variable, y.

In ①, $\quad 3x + 2y = 12 \qquad$ In ②, $\quad 2x + 3y = 13$
$\qquad\qquad 2y = -3x + 12 \qquad\qquad\qquad 3y = -2x + 13$
$\qquad\qquad y = \dfrac{-3x + 12}{2} \qquad\qquad\qquad y = \dfrac{-2x + 13}{3}$

By the transitive property of equality,

$$\frac{-3x + 12}{2} = \frac{-2x + 13}{3}$$

The Transitive Property of Equality

If $\dfrac{-3x + 12}{2} = y$

and $y = \dfrac{-2x + 13}{3}$

then $\dfrac{-3x + 12}{2} = \dfrac{-2x + 13}{3}$

Clear fractions.

$$6\left[\frac{-3x + 12}{2}\right] = 6\left[\frac{-2x + 13}{3}\right]$$

LCD of 2 and 3 is 6.

$$3(-3x + 12) = 2(-2x + 13)$$
$$-9x + 36 = -4x + 26$$
$$-9x + 4x = 26 - 36$$
$$-5x = -10$$
$$x = 2$$

Substitute $x = 2$ in ①.

$$3x + 2y = 12$$
$$3(2) + 2y = 12$$
$$6 + 2y = 12$$
$$2y = 6$$
$$y = 3$$

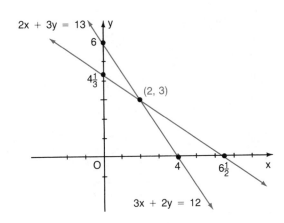

Check in ①.

L.S. $= 3x + 2y$
$= 3(2) + 2(3)$
$= 6 + 6$
$= 12$
R.S. $= 12$

Check in ②.

L.S. $= 2x + 3y$
$= 2(2) + 3(3)$
$= 4 + 9$
$= 13$
R.S. $= 13$

The solution is (2, 3).

To begin your solution it is not always necessary to solve both equations for y. All that is required is that both equations be solved for the same variable.

EXAMPLE 3. Solve by comparison.

$$2x + 3y = 16 \quad ①$$
$$5x - 2y = 2 \quad ②$$

SOLUTION:

Solve both equations for the same variable.

In ①, $\quad 2x + 3y = 16$ 　　　　In ②, $\quad 5x - 2y = 2$

$$2x = -3y + 16 \qquad\qquad\qquad 5x = 2y + 2$$

$$x = \frac{-3y + 16}{2} \qquad\qquad\qquad x = \frac{2y + 2}{5}$$

By the transitive property of equality,

$$\frac{-3y + 16}{2} = \frac{2y + 2}{5}$$

The LCD of 2 and 5 is 10.

$$10\left[\frac{-3y + 16}{2}\right] = 10\left[\frac{2y + 2}{5}\right]$$

$$5(-3y + 16) = 2(2y + 2)$$

$$-15y + 80 = 4y + 4$$

$$-19y = -76$$

$$y = 4$$

Substitute in ①.

$$2x + 3y = 16$$
$$2x + 3(4) = 16$$
$$2x + 12 = 16$$
$$2x = 4$$
$$x = 2$$

Check in ①.

L.S. $= 2x + 3y$
　$= 2(2) + 3(4)$
　$= 4 + 12$
　$= 16$
R.S. $= 16$

Check in ②.

L.S. $= 5x - 2y$
　$= 5(2) - 2(4)$
　$= 10 - 8$
　$= 2$
R.S. $= 2$

The solution is $x = 2$ and $y = 4$.

EXERCISE 5.4

A 1. Solve each of the following equations for the indicated variable.

(a) $3x + y = 7$
　　$y = \blacksquare$

(b) $x + 2y = 4$
　　$x = \blacksquare$

(c) $2x + 3y = 2$
　　$y = \blacksquare$

(d) $3x + 2y = 4$
　　$x = \blacksquare$

(e) $5x + 2y = 20$
　　$y = \blacksquare$

(f) $5x + 2y = 20$
　　$x = \blacksquare$

(g) $3x - 2y = 12$
　　$x = \blacksquare$

(h) $3y - 4x = 11$
　　$y = \blacksquare$

(i) $5x - y = 7$
　　$y = \blacksquare$

(j) $2y - x = 4$
　　$x = \blacksquare$

(k) $2a + 3b + 4 = 0$
　　$a = \blacksquare$

(l) $5a - 3b - 2 = 0$
　　$b = \blacksquare$

(m) $2x - 3y - 4 = 0$
　　$y = \blacksquare$

(n) $-3x + 2y - 3 = 0$
　　$x = \blacksquare$

(o) $3b - 5a - 6 = 0$
　　$a = \blacksquare$

(p) $3m - 7n = 4$
　　$n = \blacksquare$

B 2. Solve by comparison.

(a) $y = 3x + 2$
$y = x + 6$

(b) $y = 2x - 3$
$y = 3x - 4$

(c) $y = -4x + 7$
$y = 2x - 5$

(d) $y = 5x + 9$
$y = -x - 9$

(e) $x = 2y + 3$
$x = y - 4$

(f) $x = 3 - 4y$
$x = 2y - 9$

(g) $a = 3b + 7$
$a = 2b - 4$

(h) $n = 4m - 3$
$n = 2 - m$

3. Solve by comparison and check your solution.

(a) $y = 3x - 4$
$3y - x = 4$

(b) $x = 2y + 6$
$2x + y = 2$

(c) $y = 2x - 3$
$x + 2y = 4$

(d) $y = 3x - 1$
$3y - 2x = 4$

4. Solve by comparison and check your solution.

(a) $2x + 3y = 6$
$2x + 4y = 8$

(b) $2x - 3y = 2$
$5x + 6y = 5$

(c) $5x + 3y = 7$
$8x + 9y = 7$

(d) $2x - 4y = 5$
$5x + 12y = 7$

(e) $2x - 4y - 5 = 0$
$3x + 8y - 4 = 0$

(f) $3b - 2a - 4 = 0$
$6a - 5b + 12 = 0$

(g) $3m = 5 - 2n$
$15m + 4n - 1 = 0$

(h) $2a = 5 - 3b$
$4a = 9b + 5$

(i) $2x + 3y - 4 = 0$
$3x + 15y + 1 = 0$

(j) $2m + 3n = 0$
$m - 6n = -5$

PIERRE FERMAT (1601–1665)

Fermat was not a professional mathematician. He was a French lawyer and civil servant whose hobby was mathematics. Whenever he had some spare time he did mathematics for the fun of it. But he found enough spare time to invent two of the major areas of mathematics; analytic geometry and differential calculus. Not bad for an amateur! Fermat never published his discoveries, and so although he invented analytic geometry at the same time as Descartes, he did not receive credit for it at the time. Fermat was also one of the founders of two other areas of mathematics: probability theory and number theory. A major concern in number theory is to solve equations allowing only integers as solutions. For example, the problem known as Fermat's Last Theorem states that if n is an integer larger than 2, then there are no integers x, y, z such that $x^n + y^n = z^n$. (Of course for $n = 2$ we know some solutions such as $x = 3$, $y = 4$, $z = 5$. The assertion is that for $n > 2$ the equation $x^n + y^n = z^n$ has no solution in integers. For example, for $n = 3$ it says that no perfect cube can be expressed as the sum of two perfect cubes.) Fermat claimed that he had proved this theorem. In the margin of a book he wrote, "I have discovered a truly remarkable proof which this margin is too small to contain." However, he never published a proof, and to this day nobody has been able to prove or disprove it, although certain special cases have been proved. (For example, Euler gave proofs for the cases $n = 3$ and 4 and later mathematicians have shown that it is true when $n \leqslant 619$.) Fermat's Last Theorem is still the most famous unsolved problem in mathematics!

5.5 ALGEBRAIC SOLUTIONS OF LINEAR SYSTEMS: ADDITION OR SUBTRACTION

In the method of comparison, we obtained a single equation in one variable when we used the transitive property of equality. In solving a linear system of two variables, another way to eliminate one of the variables is by addition or subtraction.

This method uses the following properties of equality.

Properties of Equality			
If $\quad\quad 5 = 5$ and $\quad\quad 3 = 3,$		If $\quad\quad a = b$ and $\quad\quad c = d,$	
then $\quad 5 + 3 = 5 + 3$ and $\quad 5 - 3 = 5 - 3.$		then $\quad a + c = b + d$ and $\quad a - c = b - d.$	

EXAMPLE 1. Solve.

$$x + y = 9 \quad ①$$
$$x - y = 3 \quad ②$$

SOLUTION:

$$x + y = 9 \quad ①$$
$$\underline{x - y = 3} \quad ②$$

Add. $\quad\quad 2x = 12$

$\quad\quad\quad\quad x = 6$

Substitute in ①.

$$x + y = 9$$
$$6 + y = 9$$
$$y = 3$$

Check in ①.

L.S. $= x + y$
$\quad = 6 + 3$
$\quad = 9$
R.S. $= 9$

Check in ②.

L.S. $= x - y$
$\quad = 6 - 3$
$\quad = 3$
R.S. $= 3$

The solution is (6, 3).

EXAMPLE 2. Solve.

$$x + 5y = 4 \quad ①$$
$$x + 3y = 2 \quad ②$$

SOLUTION:

Adding will not eliminate one of the unknowns. Subtracting will.

$$x + 5y = 4$$
$$\underline{x + 3y = 2}$$

Subtract. $\quad 2y = 2$

$\quad\quad\quad\quad y = 1$

Substitute in ①.
$$x + 5y = 4$$
$$x + 5(1) = 4$$
$$x + 5 = 4$$
$$x = -1$$

Check in ①.

L.S. $= x + 5y$
$= (-1) + 5(1)$
$= -1 + 5$
$= 4$
R.S. $= 4$

Check in ②.

L.S. $= x + 3y$
$= (-1) + 3(1)$
$= -1 + 3$
$= 2$
R.S. $= 2$

The solution is $(-1, 1)$.

EXAMPLE 3. Solve. $\quad 3x + 2y = 34 \quad$ ①
$\qquad\qquad\qquad 5x - 3y = -13 \quad$ ②

SOLUTION:

Neither addition nor subtraction eliminates one of the variables if the equations are left in their present form. Elimination will not occur until either the x terms or y terms are identical or opposites. To achieve this we can multiply both sides of an equation by the same number.

METHOD I.

Eliminating y

> The ordered pairs that satisfy $x + y = 6$ are the same ordered pairs that satisfy $2x + 2y = 12$. Multiplying both sides of an equation by the same number does not change the relation.

① $\qquad 3x + 2y = 34$
② $\qquad 5x - 3y = -13$

① $\times$ 3 $\quad 9x + 6y = 102$
② $\times$ 2 $\quad \underline{10x - 6y = -26}$
Add. $\qquad\quad 19x = 76$
$\qquad\qquad\qquad x = 4$

Substitute in ①.

$$3x + 2y = 34$$
$$3(4) + 2y = 34$$
$$12 + 2y = 34$$
$$2y = 22$$
$$y = 11$$

Check in ②.

L.S. $= 5x - 3y$
$= 5(4) - 3(11)$
$= 20 - 33$
$= -13$
R.S. $= -13$

METHOD II.

Eliminating x

① $\qquad 3x + 2y = 34$
② $\qquad 5x - 3y = -13$

① $\times$ 5 $15x + 10y = 170$
② $\times$ 3 $\underline{15x - 9y = -39}$
Subtract. $\qquad 19y = 209$
$\qquad\qquad\qquad y = 11$

Substitute in ②.

$$5x - 3y = -13$$
$$5x - 3(11) = -13$$
$$5x - 33 = -13$$
$$5x = 20$$
$$x = 4$$

Check in ①.

L.S. $= 3x + 2y$
$= 3(4) + 2(11)$
$= 12 + 22$
$= 34$
R.S. $= 34$

The solution is $(4, 11)$.

EXERCISE 5.5

A 1. Solve for x and y.
(a) x + y = 6
   x − y = 4
(b) x − y = 3
   x + y = 7
(c) x + y = 8
   x − y = −2
(d) x + y = 8
   −x + y = 6
(e) 2x + y = 5
   x + y = 4
(f) x + 2y = 4
   x + y = 2
(g) 3x + y = 6
   2x − y = 4
(h) 3x + 2y = 2
   x − 2y = 2
(i) x + 3y = 7
   x + y = 3
(j) 4x − 2y = 12
   3x + 2y = 9

B 2. Solve and check.
(a) x + 3y = 10
   3x + 2y = 16
(b) 3x + y = 12
   2x + 5y = 21
(c) 2a + b = 10
   3a − 2b = 8
(d) x − 3y = 1
   3x − 2y = 17
(e) 2a + 5b = 19
   3a − b = 3
(f) 4x − y = 7
   6x + 5y = 17

3. Solve and check.
(a) 3x − 2y = 5
   2x + 3y = 12
(b) m − 2n = 3
   2m − 3n = 4
(c) 3x − 2y = −8
   4x + 3y = −5
(d) 2a + 3b = 11
   3a − 2b = −16
(e) 5x + 3y + 19 = 0
   2x − 5y = 11
(f) 5m + 2n − 5 = 0
   2m + 3n − 13 = 0

(g) 3x = 4y + 5
   5x + 3y + 11 = 0
(h) 10 = 3x − 4y
   5x − 12y = 6

4. Solve and check.
(a) 4x − 9y = 4
   6x + 15y = −13
(b) 8x − 9y = 41
   4x + 3y = 3
(c) 8x + 3y = −14
   7y − 12x = 21
(d) 3a − 2b + 26 = 0
   5a + b + 26 = 0
(e) 3b − 2a + 2 = 0
   7a − 6b = −11
(f) 4x + 3y + 3 = 0
   8x = 9y − 1
(g) 2x − 8y + 1 = 0
   6x = 7 − 16y
(h) 6x − 2y = 1
   9x − 4y = 4

Determine the pattern. Find the missing number.

9	8	20	3
16	4	32	12
15	9	29	5
23	13	50	14
9	12	▨	16

5.6 PROBLEM SOLVING

READ

Determine whether the points A and B are in the same region of the figure.

PLAN

We can try to trace a path from one point to the other, or we can try to develop an easier method by solving simpler problems, then looking for a pattern.

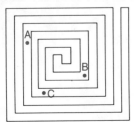

SOLVING SIMPLER PROBLEMS
In the following simpler situations, A and B are not in the same region.

In the following situations, A and B are in the same region.

In each of the cases, draw a line segment joining the points A and B.

LOOK FOR A PATTERN
How many times does each segment intersect a boundary of the curve?

SOLVE

From your observations, solve the original problem.

ANSWER

Give your answer.
Summarize your findings in a general statement.

EXERCISE 5.6

1. Determine whether the points A and B are in the same region.
Determine whether C is in the interior or the exterior of the closed region.

(a)

(b)

5.7 LINEAR SYSTEMS WITH RATIONAL COEFFICIENTS

EXAMPLE. Solve.

$$\frac{x}{2} - \frac{y}{3} = 3 \quad \text{①}$$

$$2x - \frac{y}{2} = 7 \quad \text{②}$$

SOLUTION:

Our work is often simplified by clearing fractions. Express the fractions in the first equation in terms of their lowest common denominator (LCD).

$$\frac{x}{2} - \frac{y}{3} = 3$$

$$6\left[\frac{x}{2} - \frac{y}{3}\right] = 6[3]$$

Multiplying both sides by 6, the result is

$$3x - 2y = 18$$

We use this method to clear fractions from both equations before continuing the solution.

$$\frac{x}{2} - \frac{y}{3} = 3 \quad \text{①}$$

$$2x - \frac{y}{2} = 7 \quad \text{②}$$

| ① × 6 | $3x - 2y = 18$ |
| ② × 2 | $4x - y = 14$ |

$$3x - 2y = 18$$

② × 2 $\underline{8x - 2y = 28}$

$$-5x = -10$$

$$x = 2$$

Substitute.

$$3x - 2y = 18$$
$$3(2) - 2y = 18$$
$$6 - 2y = 18$$
$$-2y = 12$$
$$y = -6$$

Check in ②.

L.S. $= 2x - \dfrac{y}{2}$ R.S. $= 7$

$$= 2(2) - \frac{(-6)}{2}$$

$$= 4 + 3$$

$$= 7$$

The solution is $(2, -6)$.

EXERCISE 5.7

B 1. Solve the following.

(a) $\dfrac{x}{3} + \dfrac{y}{4} = 2$

$\dfrac{2x}{3} - \dfrac{y}{2} = 0$

(b) $\dfrac{4a}{3} - \dfrac{b}{4} = 9$

$\dfrac{5a}{6} + b = 1$

(c) $x - y = 6$

$\dfrac{2x}{3} + \dfrac{y}{3} = 1$

(d) $\dfrac{x}{3} - \dfrac{y}{6} = -\dfrac{2}{3}$

$\dfrac{x}{12} - \dfrac{y}{4} = 1\frac{1}{2}$

(e) $\frac{1}{2}x + y = -4$

$\dfrac{x}{2} - \dfrac{3y}{2} = 1$

(f) $\frac{1}{3}m - \frac{1}{6}n = \frac{1}{2}$

$\dfrac{m}{5} - \dfrac{3n}{10} = \dfrac{1}{2}$

2. Solve.

(a) $0.2x - 0.3y = -0.1$
$0.5x - 0.4y = 0.8$

(b) $0.2x - 0.3y = -0.6$
$0.5x + 0.2y = 2.3$

(c) $0.3a - 0.5b = 1.2$
$0.7a - 0.2b = -0.1$

(d) $1.2m + 0.6n = 0$
$3.5m + 1.7n = 0.01$

(e) $4x + 5y = -0.5$
$3x + 7y = 0.6$

(f) $7c - 2d = -4.3$
$8c - 5d = -4.1$

(g) $0.5x - 1.3y = 1.23$
$4x - 2y = 0.6$

(h) $3x + 2y = 2$
$4x - 3y = 7.2$

3. Solve.

(a) $5(x - 3) + 2(y + 4) = 10$
$3(x + 4) - 4(y + 3) = -21$

(b) $2(3x - 1) - (y + 4) = -7$
$4(1 - 2x) - 3(3 - y) = -12$

(c) $2(x - 1) - 3(y - 3) = 0$
$3(x + 2) - (y - 7) = 20$

(d) $4(x - 4) - (y - 3) = -18$
$5(x + 1) + 2(y - 2) = -28$

(e) $5(x + 5) - 2(y - 3) = 62$
$4(x - 7) - (y + 4) = -9$

(f) $3(x + 3) - (y + 6) = -2$
$5(2x - 1) - 3(3y - 2) = 7$

(g) $3(x - 15) - (2y - 3) = -2$
$4(2x - 35) - 3(1 - 2y) = 77$

(h) $3(x + 5) + 2(y - 3) = 9$
$5(2x - 1) - 3(2y - 3) = 4$

C 4. Solve.

(a) $\dfrac{x - 2}{3} + \dfrac{y + 1}{5} = 2$

$\dfrac{x + 2}{7} - \dfrac{y + 5}{3} = -2$

(b) $\dfrac{x - 5}{3} + \dfrac{y + 1}{2} = 1$

$\dfrac{x - 1}{5} + \dfrac{y + 2}{3} = 2$

(c) $\dfrac{3(x - 2)}{2} - \dfrac{y - 2}{4} = 11$

$\dfrac{2(x + 2)}{5} - \dfrac{y}{3} = 6$

(d) $\dfrac{2x - 1}{5} - \dfrac{3y + 2}{4} = -2$

$\dfrac{3x + 1}{5} + \dfrac{5y - 3}{3} = 14$

(e) $\dfrac{2}{3}x + \dfrac{y - 1}{4} = 6$

$\dfrac{5x}{6} - \dfrac{y + 3}{4} = 2$

(f) $\dfrac{x - 1}{3} + \dfrac{y + 2}{4} = 4$

$\dfrac{x + 1}{2} - \dfrac{y - 2}{2} = 2$

5.8 LINEAR SYSTEMS WITH LITERAL COEFFICIENTS

In this section we will use the method of elimination by addition or subtraction to solve linear systems with literal coefficients.

EXAMPLE 1.   Solve for x and y.

$$ax - 2by = 3ab \quad ①$$
$$2ax + by = ab \quad ②$$

SOLUTION:

$$ax - 2by = 3ab \quad ①$$
$$2ax + by = ab \quad ②$$

$$① \times 2 \qquad 2ax - 4by = 6ab$$
$$\underline{\qquad\qquad 2ax + by = ab}$$

Subtract.
$$-5by = 5ab$$
$$y = -a, \quad b \neq 0$$

Substitute in ①.

$$ax - 2by = 3ab$$
$$ax - 2b(-a) = 3ab$$
$$ax + 2ab = 3ab$$
$$ax = ab$$
$$x = b, \quad a \neq 0$$

The solution is (b, −a).

EXAMPLE 2.   Solve for x and y.

$$ax + by = c \quad ①$$
$$dx + ey = f \quad ②$$

SOLUTION:

$$ax + by = c$$
$$dx + ey = f$$

$$① \times e \qquad aex + bey = ce$$
$$② \times b \qquad \underline{bdx + bey = bf}$$

Subtract.
$$aex - bdx = ce - bf$$
$$x(ae - bd) = ce - bf$$
$$(ae - bd)x = ce - bf$$
$$x = \frac{ce - bf}{ae - bd}, \quad (ae - bd) \neq 0$$

The value of y may be found by substitution. However, it may be simpler, in cases similar to this example, to start again and eliminate x by addition or subtraction.

$$\boxed{\begin{array}{c} \text{General Solution of Linear System} \\ \text{in Two Unknowns} \\[4pt] x = \dfrac{ce - bf}{ae - bd}, \quad ae - bd \neq 0 \\[10pt] y = \dfrac{af - cd}{ae - bd}, \quad ae - bd \neq 0 \end{array}}$$

EXERCISE 5.8

A 1. Solve the following for x.

(a) $ax = b$

(b) $mx = n$

(c) $nx = a + b$

(d) $(m + n)x = a + b$

(e) $\dfrac{x}{a} = b$

(f) $\dfrac{x}{m} = -n$

(g) $(a + b)x = 4$

(h) $x(m - n) = -2y$

(i) $ax + bx = 6$

(j) $cx - dx = t$

(k) $gx - hx = c + d$

(l) $bx - ax = t - s$

(m) $2ax + bx = m$

(n) $4cx - 3tx = b - a$

2. Solve for y.

(a) $3y - by = m$

(b) $5y + 4 = by - 7$

(c) $\dfrac{3y}{b} - \dfrac{y}{2a} = 4$

(d) $ay - by + c = 0$

(e) $3a - 2y + 5by = 3$

B 3. Solve for x and y.

(a) $x - y = a + b$
$x + y = a - b$

(b) $bx + ay = 2ab$
$bx - ay = 4ab$

(c) $6mx + 13ny = 4mn$
$2mx + 5ny = 2mn$

(d) $2ax + 3by = ab$
$3ax + 4by = 3ab$

(e) $ax - 3by = 2ab$
$3ax + 4by = 5ab$

(f) $2x + y = a - b$
$x - y = a + b$

4. Solve for x and y.

(a) $2ax + y = m$
$bx - y = n$

(b) $ax + y = 3$
$x + by = 2$

(c) $3x + ay = 4$
$ax + 2y = 6$

(d) $ax + y = 2$
$bx - y = 4$

(e) $mx + ny = g$
$dx + ey = h$

(f) $ax - by = c$
$dx - ey = f$

WORD LADDER

Start with the word "lead" and change one letter at a time to form a new word until you reach "gold." The best solution has the fewest steps.

l e a d
_ _ _ _
_ _ _ _
_ _ _ _
_ _ _ _
_ _ _ _
g o l d

5.9 CLASSIFYING AND INTERPRETING LINEAR SYSTEMS

A system of two linear equations in two variables will satisfy one of the following cases.

Linear Systems
I. The system has exactly one solution. This is true when the lines determining the system intersect at a point. Such a system is said to be consistent. 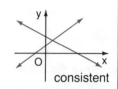 consistent
II. The system has no solution. This is true when the lines determining the system are parallel. Such a system is said to be inconsistent. 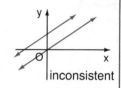 inconsistent
III. The system has an unlimited number of solutions. This is true when the two equations defining the system determine the same straight line. Such a system is said to be dependent. 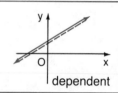 dependent

A brief analysis of a linear system will help us to classify it and understand the nature of its solution even before a formal algebraic solution is attempted.

EXAMPLE. Analyse the information systems. Classify them as consistent, inconsistent, or dependent.

(a) $2x + y = 4$ ①
    $2x + y = 7$ ②

(b) $2x + y = 4$ ①
    $4x + 2y = 8$ ②

(c) $2x + y = 4$ ①
    $x + 3y = 7$ ②

SOLUTION:

All of the above equations represent straight lines.

(a) Expressing both lines in the form $y = mx + b$, we observe that both have slope -2. Therefore, the lines are either parallel or coincidental. Since the y-intercepts are different, they must be parallel. Since these lines do not intercept there will be no solution.

The system is inconsistent.

(b) Expressing both lines in the form $y = mx + b$, we observe that both have slope -2. Therefore, the lines are either parallel or coincidental. Multiplying equation ② by $\frac{1}{2}$ produces $2x + y = 4$, the same equation as ①. Hence the two equations represent the same line and will intersect at all points along the line. $\{(x, y) \mid 2x + y = 4, x, y \in R\}$.

The system is dependent.

(c) Expressing both lines in the form $y = mx + b$, we observe that the slopes are -2 and $-\frac{1}{3}$. Hence the lines are not parallel and will intersect at a single point.

The system is consistent.

EXERCISE 5.9

A 1. By inspection classify the following linear systems as consistent, inconsistent, or dependent.

(a) $y = 2x + 1$
$y = -3x + 2$

(b) $x - 2y = 3$
$3x - 6y = 9$

(c) $x + 2y = 6$
$x + 2y = 12$

(d) $y = -4x + 3$
$y = -4x - 6$

(e) $y = 3x - 4$
$y = -x + 7$

(f) $y = x + 4$
$2y = 2x + 8$

(g) $4x + 2y = 7$
$4y = -8x + 3$

(h) $2x - 3y = 7$
$5x + 2y = 10$

(i) $2y = 6x - 4$
$y - 3x = -2$

(j) $4x - 3y = 9$
$8x - 6y = 18$

B 2. Classify the following systems and give the solution set.

(a) $2x - 3y = 7$
$2x - 3y = 5$

(b) $x + y = 4$
$2x + 2y = 8$

(c) $x + y = 2$
$x - 2y = -1$

(d) $y = 2x - 1$
$2y = x + 4$

(e) $x - 4y = 8$
$2x - 8y = 8$

(f) $x + 5y = 4$
$x + 3y = 2$

C 3. Classify the following systems.

(a) $x + 2y = 3$
$2x + y = 3$
$3x - y = 2$

(b) $x + 2y = 2$
$2x + 4y = 4$
$x + 2y = 1$

EXTRA

A FLOW CHART FOR SYSTEMS OF EQUATIONS

The flow chart at the right can be used to solve and classify linear systems.

Classify and solve. $\quad ax + by = c$
$\quad\quad\quad\quad\quad\quad\quad\quad\quad\quad dx + ey = f$

EXAMPLE. Classify the following systems as consistent, inconsistent, or dependent, and give the solution set.

(a) $3x + 2y = 6$
$6x + 4y = 12$

(b) $x + 2y = 6$
$2x + 4y = 5$

SOLUTION:

(a) Let $a = 3$, $b = 2$, $c = 6$, $d = 6$, $e = 4$, and $f = 12$.

$ae = bd = 12$
$af = cd = 36$

The system is dependent.

The solution set is $\{(x, y) \mid 3x + 2y = 6, x, y \in R\}$

(b) Let $a = 1$, $b = 2$, $c = 6$, $d = 2$, $e = 4$, and $f = 5$.

$ae = bd = 4$
$af \neq cd$

The system is inconsistent.

The solution set is $\emptyset$.

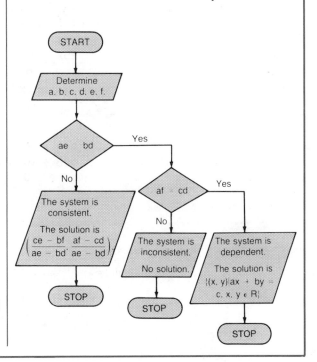

START

Determine
a, b, c, d, e, f.

ae bd   —Yes→

No

The system is consistent.

The solution is
$\left(\dfrac{ce - bf}{ae - bd}, \dfrac{af - cd}{ae - bd} \right)$

STOP

af cd   —Yes→

No

The system is inconsistent.

No solution.

STOP

The system is dependent.

The solution is
$\{(x, y) \mid ax + by = c, x, y \in R\}$

STOP

5.10 SYSTEMS OF THREE LINEAR EQUATIONS IN THREE VARIABLES

The addition or subtraction method can also be used to solve linear systems of three equations in three variables.

EXAMPLE. Solve the following for x, y, and t.

$$3x - 2y + 4t = 11 \quad ①$$
$$2x + 3y - t = 5 \quad ②$$
$$x + 4y - 2t = 3 \quad ③$$

SOLUTION:

Step 1.

Eliminate y from ① and ②.

$$3x - 2y + 4t = 11 \quad ①$$
$$2x + 3y - t = 5 \quad ②$$

① × 3 $9x - 6y + 12t = 33$
② × 2 $\underline{4x + 6y - 2t = 10}$
Add. $13x + 10t = 43 \quad ④$

Step 2.

Eliminate y from ② and ③.

$$2x + 3y - t = 5 \quad ②$$
$$x + 4y - 2t = 3 \quad ③$$

② × 4 $8x + 12y - 4t = 20$
③ × 3 $\underline{3x + 12y - 6t = 9}$
Subtract. $5x + 2t = 11 \quad ⑤$

Step 3.

Solve the system of equations ④ and ⑤.

Eliminate t from ④ and ⑤.

$$13x + 10t = 43 \quad ④$$
$$5x + 2t = 11 \quad ⑤$$

$$13x + 10t = 43$$
⑤ × 5 $\underline{25x + 10t = 55}$
Subtract. $-12x = -12$
$$x = 1$$

Substitute x = 1 in ④.

$$13x + 10t = 43$$
$$13(1) + 10t = 43$$
$$13 + 10t = 43$$
$$10t = 30$$
$$t = 3$$

Step 4.

Substitute x = 1 and t = 3 in ①.

$$3x - 2y + 4t = 11$$
$$3(1) - 2y + 4(3) = 11$$
$$3 - 2y + 12 = 11$$
$$-2y = -4$$
$$y = 2$$

Step 5.

Check in ②.

L.S. $= 2x + 3y - t$ R.S. $= 5$
     $= 2(1) + 3(2) - 3$
     $= 2 + 6 - 3$
     $= 5$

The solution is $x = 1$, $y = 2$, and $t = 3$.

The above steps for solving a linear system of three equations in three variables can be summarized in the following flow chart.

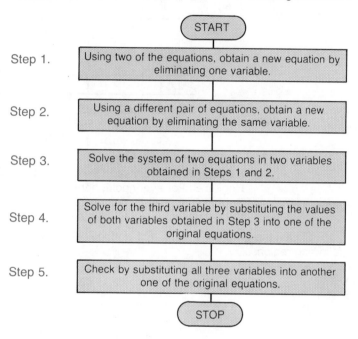

START

Step 1.   Using two of the equations, obtain a new equation by eliminating one variable.

Step 2.   Using a different pair of equations, obtain a new equation by eliminating the same variable.

Step 3.   Solve the system of two equations in two variables obtained in Steps 1 and 2.

Step 4.   Solve for the third variable by substituting the values of both variables obtained in Step 3 into one of the original equations.

Step 5.   Check by substituting all three variables into another one of the original equations.

STOP

Some systems can be solved using fewer steps.

EXERCISE 5.10

B 1. Solve the following.

(a) $2a + 3b + c = 15$
    $3a + 2b - c = 10$
    $4a + b + 2c = 15$

(b) $4x - 2y + 3t = 27$
    $2x + 3y - 4t = -6$
    $3x + 5y - 2t = 12$

(c) $3a - 2b - 3c = 22$
    $2a - 3b + 4c = 0$
    $4a + b - 2c = 16$

(d) $2x + 5y - 3m = -7$
    $3x - 2y - 4m = 16$
    $5x + 2y - 5m = 4$

(e) $3a + 4b - 2c = -5$
    $5a + 7b + 6c = 1$
    $2a - 13b + 5c = 3$

(f) $2x - 2y - 2d = 9$
    $3x + 4y - 4d = 0$
    $x - y + 2d = 3$

(g) $2a + b - 2c + d = 7$
    $3a + 2b + 2c - d = 12$
    $2a + 3b - c + 2d = 10$
    $4a - b + 3c - 2d = 12$

(h) $x - y = 1$
    $x + m = 2$
    $m - y = 7$

5.11 GRAPHING INEQUALITIES IN TWO VARIABLES

The graph of a linear relation divides the plane into 3 distinct regions. Consider the graph of the relation $y = x$, $x, y \in R$.

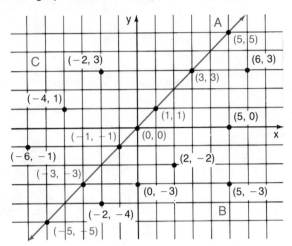

Region A: For every point here, $y = x$.
Region B: For every point here, $y < x$.
Region C: For every point here, $y > x$.

EXAMPLE 1. Sketch the graph of $y = 2x + 1$ and indicate on the graph the following regions.
(a) $y = 2x + 1$
(b) $y > 2x + 1$
(c) $y < 2x + 1$

SOLUTION:

The region where $y = 2x + 1$ is the straight line. In order to determine the regions $y > 2x + 1$ and $y < 2x + 1$, we select a test point, $(-3, 4)$, not on the line, and determine which of the two remaining relations the test point satisfies.

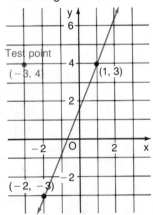

For the relation $y = 2x + 1$
when $y = 4$, L.S. $= y$
$= 4$

when $x = -3$, R.S. $= 2x + 1$
$= 2(-3) + 1$
$= -5$

At the point $(-3, 4)$, since $4 > -5$
L.S. $>$ R.S.
In the region of the test point, $y > 2x + 1$.

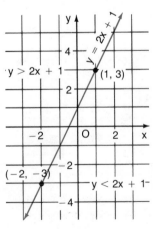

EXAMPLE 2. Sketch the graph of $3x - 2y = 6$ and indicate the following regions.

(a) $3x - 2y = 6$

(b) $3x - 2y > 6$

(c) $3x - 2y < 6$

SOLUTION:

For this example it is convenient to use the "intercept method" to draw the graph. In this case the point $(0, 0)$ is a convenient test point.

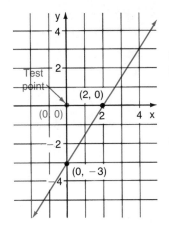

For the relation $3x - 2y = 6$
when $x = 0$ and $y = 0$, L.S. $= 3x - 2y$
$$= 3(0) - 2(0)$$
$$= 0$$
R.S. $= 6$

At the point $(0, 0)$, since $0 < 6$
$$\text{L.S.} < \text{R.S.}$$
In the region of the test point $3x - 2y < 6$.

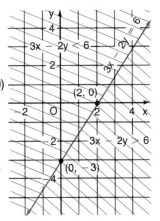

EXAMPLE 3. Draw the graph of $y \leqslant 2x - 3$.

SOLUTION:

In this problem we are asked to show two of the three regions, namely $y = 2x - 3$ and $y < 2x - 3$.

First, draw the boundary line $y = 2x - 3$. In this case the point $(0, 0)$ is a convenient test point.

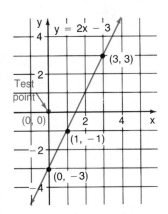

For the relation $y = 2x - 3$
when $y = 0$, L.S. $= y$
$$= 0$$

when $x = 0$, R.S. $= 2x - 3$
$$= 2(0) - 3$$
$$= -3$$

At the point $(0, 0)$, since $0 > -3$
$$\text{L.S.} > \text{R.S.}$$
In the region of the test point $y > 2x - 3$.

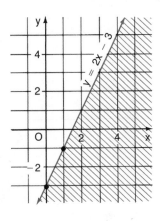

The region $y < 2x - 3$ is on the other side of the line. The graph of $y \leqslant 2x - 3$ is shown at right. Some sort of markings or shading must be used to indicate the required region.

EXAMPLE 4. Draw the graph of $2x + 3y > 6$.

SOLUTION:
Draw the boundary line $2x + 3y = 6$. The intercept method is convenient for this example. The test point selected lies anywhere except on the line. In this example we will use $(4, 3)$ as the test point.

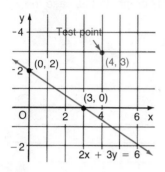

For the relation $2x + 3y = 6$
When $x = 4$ and $y = 3$, L.S. $= 2x + 3y$
$$= 2(4) + 3(3)$$
$$= 17$$
R.S. $= 6$

At the point $(4, 3)$, since $17 > 6$
L.S. $>$ R.S.
In the region of the test point $2x + 3y > 6$.
The graph of $2x + 3y > 6$ is shown at right.

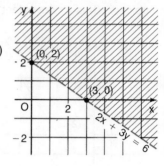

The line $2x + 3y = 6$ is shown as a broken line since it is not part of the solution.

EXAMPLE 5. Draw the graph of $\{(x, y)|y \leqslant -2, x, y \in R\}$.

SOLUTION:
Draw the boundary line $y = -2$. A test point will show the region where $y < -2$ is below the boundary line.

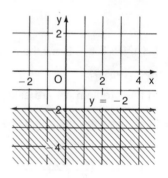

For $y > mx + b$, the required region is above the line.

For $y < mx + b$, the required region is below the line.

These rules hold only when the defining relation is expressed in the form

$$y > mx + b \quad \text{or} \quad y < mx + b.$$

EXERCISE 5.11

B 1. (a) Draw the graph of each of the following.
    (i) $y > 2x + 1$
    (ii) $y > 3x - 4$
    (iii) $y > -x + 6$
    (iv) $y > -3x - 1$
  (b) For $y > mx + b$, is the required region above the line or below the line?

2. (a) Draw the graph of each of the following.
    (i) $y < 3x + 4$
    (ii) $y < 2x - 5$
    (iii) $y < -x - 5$
    (iv) $y < -2x + 3$
  (b) For $y < mx + b$, is the required region above the line or below the line?

3. Draw the graph of each of the following relations and indicate the 3 regions associated with each for $x, y \in R$.
(a) $y = x + 2$
(b) $y = 3x - 4$
(c) $y = x - 5$
(d) $4x + 3y = 12$
(e) $5x - 2y = 10$
(f) $y = 3 - 2x$
(g) $x - 3y = 6$
(h) $2x - y = -4$
(i) $y = \dfrac{x + 1}{2}$
(j) $y = \tfrac{1}{3}x - 1$
(k) $3x - y - 6 = 0$
(l) $x + y = 0$

4. Draw the graph of each of the following relations and indicate the 3 regions associated with each.
(a) $\{(x, y) \mid x = 3, x, y \in R\}$
(b) $\{(x, y) \mid y = -4, x, y \in R\}$
(c) $\{(x, y) \mid x = -5, x, y \in R\}$
(d) $\{(x, y) \mid y = 0, x, y \in R\}$

Draw the graph of each of the following for $x, y \in R$.

5. (a) $y \geqslant 3x + 5$
(b) $y \leqslant 2x - 1$
(c) $y < 4 + 2x$
(d) $y > -3x + 2$

(e) $y \geqslant 5x - 1$
(f) $y \leqslant -x - 5$
(g) $y < -4x$
(h) $y > 4 - 3x$

6. (a) $2x - 3y \geqslant 6$
(b) $5x + 4y \leqslant 20$
(c) $4x - 3y > 12$
(d) $x + 3y < 9$
(e) $3x - 5y - 15 \geqslant 0$
(f) $x + 4y < 2$
(g) $9x - 2y > -18$
(h) $2y - 7x \geqslant 14$

7. (a) $\{(x, y) \mid x \geqslant 2, x, y \in R\}$
(b) $\{(x, y) \mid y < 3, x, y \in R\}$
(c) $\{(x, y) \mid x < -3, x, y \in R\}$
(d) $\{(x, y) \mid y \geqslant -2, x, y \in R\}$
(e) $\{(x, y) \mid x \geqslant 0, x, y \in R\}$
(f) $\{(x, y) \mid y \geqslant 0, x, y \in R\}$

8. (a) $y \geqslant \dfrac{x - 1}{3}$
(b) $y < \dfrac{1 - 2x}{2}$
(c) $y > -\tfrac{1}{2}x + 4$
(d) $\dfrac{x}{3} - \dfrac{y}{4} \leqslant 1$
(e) $y - 2 < 3x$
(f) $y - 2x \geqslant 0$

MIND BENDER

$\blacksquare\blacksquare \times \blacksquare = \blacksquare\blacksquare$

Put 5 different digits in the spaces to make the statement true. The digits must total 27.

5.12 INTERSECTION AND UNION OF LINEAR INEQUALITIES

In this section we shall determine the intersection or union of two or more linear inequalities. Recall that for an intersection we use "and" or "∩". For union we use "or" or "∪".

EXAMPLE 1. Graph the following.
$\{(x, y) \mid y \geq 2x - 1 \text{ and } y \leq -x + 2\}$

SOLUTION:
Graph each relation on the same set of axes.

The intersection is the double shaded region which contains all the points that satisfy both inequalities.

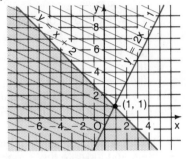

EXAMPLE 2. Graph the following.
$\{(x, y) \mid 2x - 3y < 6 \text{ and } 5x + 3y \leq 15\}$

SOLUTION:
Graph each relation on the same set of axes.

The intersection is the double shaded region. As indicated on the graph, the point (3, 0) is not included in the intersection.

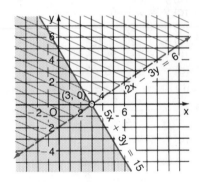

EXAMPLE 3. Graph the following.
$\{(x, y) \mid x \leq 5 \text{ and } x \geq -1\} \cap \{(x, y) \mid y \leq 4 \text{ and } y \geq -2\}$

SOLUTION:
Graph each relation on the same set of axes. The required intersection is the shaded region.

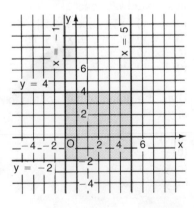

EXERCISE 5.12

A 1. State the quadrant or quadrants defined by each of the following.

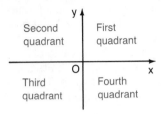

Unless otherwise stated, x, y ∈ R.

(a) {(x, y) | y ⩾ 0 and x ⩾ 0}
(b) {(x, y) | x ⩽ 0 and y ⩾ 0}
(c) {(x, y) | x ⩾ 0 or y ⩾ 0}
(d) {(x, y) | y ⩽ 0 and x ⩾ 0}
(e) {(x, y) | x ⩽ 0 or y ⩽ 0}
(f) {(x, y) | y ⩽ 0 and x ⩽ 0}
(g) {(x, y) | x ⩽ 0 or y ⩾ 0}

B 2. Graph the following.

(a) {(x, y) | y ⩾ x + 3 and y ⩽ −x + 4}
(b) {(x, y) | y ⩽ 2x + 1 and y ⩽ 3 − 2x}
(c) {(x, y) | y > 3x + 2 or y ⩽ 2 − 2x}
(d) {(x, y) | y < ½x + 3 and y > x − 5}
(e) {(x, y) | y ⩽ 2x and y ⩾ −3x}

3. Graph the following.

(a) {(x, y) | x + 2y ⩽ 4 and x − 3y ⩾ 6}
(b) {(x, y) | 2x + 3y ⩾ 6 and 4x + 3y ⩽ 12}
(c) {(x, y) | x − y < 5 or x + 3y > 9}
(d) {(x, y) | 2x − y ⩾ 8 and 2x + y < 6}
(e) {(x, y) | 3x − y < 9 or x − 5y ⩽ −10}

4. Graph the following.

(a) {(x, y) | x ⩾ 2 and y ⩽ 3}
(b) {(x, y) | y ⩾ −2 and x ⩽ −1}
(c) {(x, y) | x ⩽ 3 and x ⩾ −2}
(d) {(x, y) | y < 4 and y > −2}
(e) {(x, y) | x < 3 or y ⩽ 2}

5. Graph the following.

(a) {(x, y) | x ⩽ 4 and y ⩽ 3 and
   x ⩾ −2 and y ⩾ −5}
(b) {(x, y) | x ⩽ −1 and x ⩾ −4 and
   y ⩽ 6 and y ⩾ 1}

(c) {(x, y) | x ⩾ 5 or y ⩾ 4 or x ⩽ −3}
(d) {(x, y) | x > 4 and x < 7 and
   y > −2 and y < 5}
(e) {(x, y) | x ⩽ −2 and x > −6 and
   y ⩽ −1 and y > −5}
(f) {(x, y) | y < 3 and x ⩽ −2 and x ⩾ −5}

6. Graph the following.

(a) {(x, y) | 5x + 2y ⩽ 10 and
   x ⩾ 0 and y ⩾ 0}
(b) {(x, y) | 3y − 4x ⩽ 12 and
   x ⩽ 0 and y ⩾ 0}
(c) {(x, y) | 6x − 5y ⩽ 30 and
   3x − 2y ⩽ 6 and x ⩾ 0 ∩ y ⩾ 0}
(d) {(x, y) | 7x + 5y ⩽ 35 and
   x − y ⩽ 1 and 5y − 6x ⩽ 30}
(e) {(x, y) | 7x + 3y ⩽ 21 and
   4x + 5y ⩽ 20 and x ⩾ 0 and y ⩾ 0}
(f) {(x, y) | 5x + 4y ⩽ 20 and
   3y − 4x ⩽ 12 and y ⩾ 0}
(g) {(x, y) | 4x + 5y ⩽ 20 and
   5y − 6x ⩽ 30 and y ⩾ −3}

Place the digits 1, 2, 3, 4, 5, 6, 7, and 8 at the vertices of a cube so that the sum of the four numbers at the vertices of each face is equal.

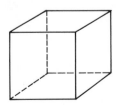

5.13 PROBLEM SOLVING: LINEAR PROGRAMMING

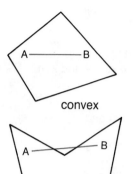

convex

not convex

Linear programming is a branch of mathematics which uses graphs of linear inequalities and linear equations to solve practical problems.

Linear programming solutions are based on the fact that given
(a) a graph of a convex polygonal region, and
(b) a linear expression, the maximum or minimum value of the expression over the region occurs at the vertices of the region.

Suppose we are given the convex region as shown. The maximum or minimum value of any expression over the region, say $3x + 4y$, will occur at one of the vertices.

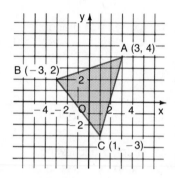

At A(3, 4), $3x + 4y = 3(3) + 4(4)$
$= 25$

At B(−3, 2), $3x + 4y = 3(−3) + 4(2)$
$= −1$

At C(1, −3), $3x + 4y = 3(1) + 4(−3)$
$= −9$

The maximum value of $3x + 4y$ over the region is 25 and the minimum value is −9.

The maximum or minimum values may also occur at other points in the region, but all we need test are the vertices in order to determine the maximum and minimum values.

Using the region in the graph above and the expression $4y − 3x$, we find

At A(3, 4), $4y − 3x = 4(4) − 3(3)$
$= 7$

At B(−3, 2), $4y − 3x = 4(2) − 3(−3)$
$= 17$

At C(1, −3), $4y − 3x = 4(−3) − 3(1)$
$= −15$

The maximum value of $4y − 3x$ over the region occurs at B and the minimum value at C.

EXAMPLE 1. Sketch the graph of the region defined by
$$x - 2y \geq -11, \qquad 4x - y \leq 12, \qquad x + y \geq -2$$
and determine the maximum and minimum values of $4x + 2y$ over the region.

SOLUTION:
Not only must we graph the region, but we must solve the appropriate simultaneous equations in order to determine the vertices of the region.

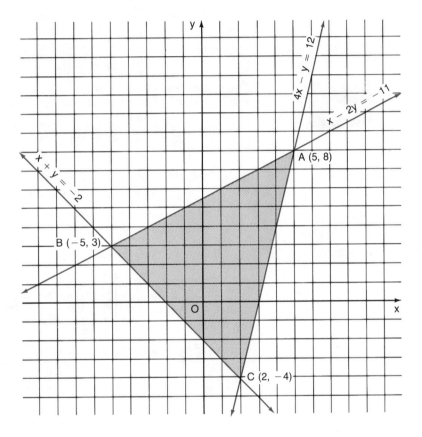

At A(5, 8), $4x + 2y = 4(5) + 2(8)$
$$= 36$$

At B(−5, 3), $4x + 2y = 4(-5) + 2(3)$
$$= -14$$

At C(2, −4), $4x + 2y = 4(2) + 2(-4)$
$$= 0$$

The maximum and minimum values of $4x + 2y$ over the region occur at A(5, 8) and B(−5, 3) respectively. The maximum is 36 and the minimum is −14.

EXAMPLE 2. The Acme Gem Co. makes two types of artificial gems for rings—a red stone and a blue stone. Each blue stone requires 1 min at the cutting machine and 3 min at the polishing machine. A red stone takes 2 min at the cutting machine and 2 min at the polishing machine. The cutting machine is available for a maximum of 100 min/d and the polishing machine 180 min/d.

Assuming that the company can sell all the stones they make and that the profit on each blue stone is $2 and on each red $3, how many of each should be made each day in order to maximize the profit?

SOLUTION:

PLAN

Let x represent the number of blue stones made each day.
Let y represent the number of red stones made each day.

The restrictions are as follows:

$x \geqslant 0, y \geqslant 0$ The company will not make a negative number of stones.

$x + 2y \leqslant 100$ The time on the cutting machine must be less than or equal to 100 min.

$3x + 2y \leqslant 180$ The time on the polishing machine must be less than or equal to 180 min.

Graph the solution set of the four inequalities.

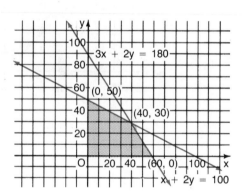

SOLVE

The profit expression to be maximized is $2x + 3y$.

At (0, 0), $2x + 3y = 2(0) + 3(0) = 0$

At (60, 0), $2x + 3y = 2(60) + 3(0) = 120$

At (40, 30), $2x + 3y = 2(40) + 3(30) = 170$

At (0, 50), $2x + 3y = 2(0) + 3(50) = 150$

ANSWER

A maximum profit will be realized if 40 blue stones and 30 red stones are made each day.

EXERCISE 5.13

B 1. Determine the maximum and minimum values of each expression over the given region.

(a) (i) 4x + 5y
     (ii) 2x − 5y
     (iii) x + 7y

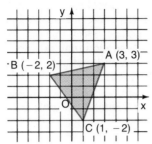

(b) (i) 5x − 3y
     (ii) x + 7y
     (iii) 2x − y

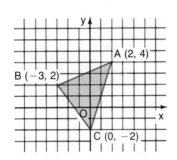

(c) (i) 5y − 3x
     (ii) 4x + 5y
     (iii) 7y − x

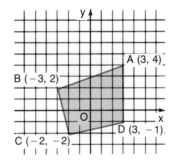

(d) (i) 3x − 6y
     (ii) 5y − x
     (iii) −3x − 4y

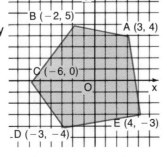

(e) (i) 2x − 4y
     (ii) 5x + 3y
     (iii) x − y

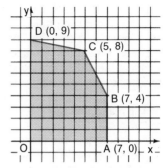

(f) (i) 3x + 4y
     (ii) 5x − 2y
     (iii) 3y − 2x

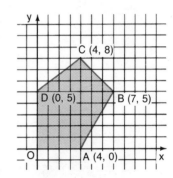

2. Sketch the graph of each of the following regions and determine the maximum and minimum values of the given expression over the region.

(a) (i) Region: 5x + 4y ⩽ 20, x ⩾ 0, y ⩾ 0
     (ii) Expression: 2x + 4y

(b) (i) Region: x + y ⩽ 10, x + 2y ⩽ 16, x ⩾ 0, y ⩾ 0
     (ii) Expression: 5x + 7y

(c) (i) Region: x + 2y ⩽ 20, 2x + y ⩽ 16, x ⩾ 0, y ⩾ 0
     (ii) Expression: 7x − y

(d) (i) Region: y ⩽ 2x + 4, y ⩽ −8x + 14, y ⩾ −3x − 1
     (ii) Expression: 3y − 4x

(e) (i) Region: 2x + 3y ⩽ 27, 2x + y ⩽ 13, x ⩾ 0, y ⩾ 0
     (ii) Expression: 5x + 4y

3. The All Pro Sports Company makes 2 models of footballs—Standard and Championship. Each Standard model requires 2 min at the cutting machine and 1 min at the stitching machine. Each Championship model requires 1 min at the cutting machine and 2 min at the stitching machine. Since both machines are needed for other jobs, the cutting machine is available for a maximum of 180 min/d and the stitching machine 120 min/d.

Assuming that the company can sell all of the footballs made and that the profit on each Standard football is $10 and on each Championship football $12, how many of each type should be made each day in order to maximize the profit?

4. To raise money, the student council decides to make necklaces and bracelets during the lunch hours and then sell them to students. The Grade 12 students will drill holes in the beads and the Grade 11 students will string them. The beads for each bracelet require 4 min to drill and 4 min to string. For each necklace, the drilling time is 5 min and 6 min are required for stringing. The Grade 11 students can provide 132 min/d for stringing and the Grade 12 students 120 min/d for drilling.

Assuming that they sell everything they make and that the profit on each bracelet is $3 and on each necklace $4, how many of each should they make each day in order to maximize their profit?

5. The Ace Electronics Company makes 2 types of radios—portable and table. Both radios must be processed by machine A and machine B. Each portable model requires 6 min at machine A and 10 min at B. Each table model requires 5 min at A and 5 min at B. Machine A is available for 120 min/d and machine B 160 min/d.

Assuming that they sell all the radios they make and that the profit on each portable is $30 and on each table model $20, how many of each should they make each day in order to maximize the profit?

6. The National Instrument Company makes two types of student calculators—Super I and Super II. Each calculator must be processed by three machines—A, B, and C. Super I requires 3 min at A, 3 min at B, and 1 min at C. Super II requires 2 min at A, 4 min at B, and 2 min at C. Machine A is available for 240 min/d, B 300 min/d, and C 140 min/d.

Assuming that all the calculators made are sold and that the profit on Super I is $25 and on Super II $30, how many of each should be made each day in order to maximize the profit?

7. The Wake Up Company makes 2 models of toasters—Standard and Deluxe. The Standard model must be processed for 1 min on machine A, 1 min on B, and 3 min on C. The Deluxe model requires 1 min on A, 5 min on B, and 1 min on C. Machine A is available for 200 min/d, B 600 min/d, and C 480 min/d. If the profit on each Standard model is $15 and on each Deluxe $20, how many of each should be made each day in order to maximize the profit?

8. The Cuddly Company makes stuffed animals for children. To make a stuffed bear it takes 3 min at the cutting machine, 5 min at the sewing machine, and 3 min at the stuffing machine. Each rabbit requires 4 min at the cutting machine, 6 min at the sewing machine, and 1 min at the stuffing machine. The cutting machine is available for 196 min/d, the sewing machine 300 min/d, and the stuffing machine 141 min/d.

Assuming maximum sales and that the profit on each bear is $4 and on each rabbit $5, how many of each should be made each day in order to maximize the profit?

9. The Aqua Marine Company builds sailboats and motorboats. It takes 6 d to build a sailboat and 2 d to build a motorboat. The profit on a sailboat is $5000 and the profit on a motorboat is $2000. The factory operates 24 d per month and at least two of each kind of boat must be built per month. How many of each kind of boat must be built per month in order to have a maximum profit?

10. A computer manufacturer has 1000 chips to use in producing home personal computers and portable computers. Each home computer requires 5 chips, while each portable computer requires 20 chips. The costs of assembly are $80 for a home computer and $120 for a portable computer. Assembly costs are limited to $15 000 and the profits are $100 on a home computer and $250 on a portable computer. How many of each kind of computer should be manufactured to have a maximum profit?

5.14 PROBLEM SOLVING

1. Radio waves travel at a speed of 300 000 km/s. Sound waves travel at 300 m/s. A radio performance was broadcast from an outdoor band shell in Vancouver. Jane Evans was at the live performance, sitting 50 m from the stage. Carl Rodgers listened to the radio at his home in Melbourne, Australia, 13 600 km from Vancouver. Who heard the sound first and why?

2. How many times between one o'clock in the afternoon and one o'clock in the morning will the hands on a clock cross?

3. The digits on a calculator are made up of 7 lines.

If our number system needed more than the digits from 0 to 9, how many new digits could be formed on a calculator so that

(a) all lines are continuous or connected.
(b) all new digits are as high as the others.

4. Place the numbers from 21 to 29 in the circles so that the sum along each side is 100.

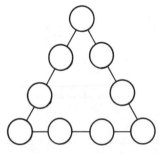

5. A book has 546 pages. How many digits were used to number the pages of the book?

6. Each letter in the multiplication represents a different digit.

$$BE \times BE = HUB$$

Find the value of each letter.

7. Sixty-four people entered a tennis tournament. Justine was responsible for determining opponents. She decided to give each player a number from 1 to 64. Then 1 played 2, 3 played 4, 5 played 6, and so on. The winner of 1 versus 2 played the winner of 3 versus 4, and so on. This procedure continued until a winner was determined. Before the tournament started, Justine was given the names of the four best players so that she could "seed" them. "Seeding" good players means placing them in the list of 64 players so that they don't meet each other (assuming they win their games) until the second to last round. Which of the numbers from 1 to 64 could Justine have assigned to the four best players?

8. (a) If St. Patrick's day is on a Monday, how many more Mondays are there in the year?
(b) St. Patrick's day is on a Monday. On what day will the next Valentine's day fall?

9. A wheel rotates 12 times in a minute. Through how many degrees does it rotate in one second?

10. How many numbers between 100 and 500 begin or end with a 3?

11. Two cars are 900 km apart. They start to drive towards each other and they meet in five hours. One car is twice as fast as the other. What is the speed of the slower car?

12. If Terry counts the number of tapes he has by twos, by threes, by fours, by fives, and by sixes, there is always one tape left over. If he counts by sevens, there are none left over. What is the smallest number of tapes that Terry could have?

13. Use a calculator to prime factor 23 256.

14. Express the following continued fraction in the form $\dfrac{a}{b}$.

$$1 + \cfrac{1}{1 + \cfrac{1}{1 + \cfrac{1}{2}}}$$

15. The playground supervisors purchased 24 adult's shirts from one manufacturer at $14 each and 16 children's shirts at $7 each from another manufacturer. What should the selling price be in order to sell the shirts at one price without profit?

16. An ice-cream wagon offers three kinds of ice-cream and three kinds of toppings. How many different sundaes can be made using two scoops of ice-cream and two toppings?

17. A rectangular field has a length that is twice the width. The field is surrounded by a fence with posts 6 m apart. If there are 150 posts in total, what are the dimensions of the field?

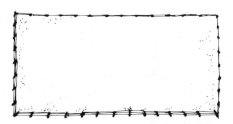

18. Tulip Car Rentals charges $13.50/d plus $0.05/km. Lenore rented a car for three days. When she left the Tulip parking lot the odometer on the car read 13 433.8 km. When she returned the car, the odometer read 14 219.8 km. How much did she owe for the use of the car?

19.

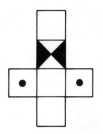

Which of the following figures can you make from the pattern above?

(a)   (b)

(c)   (d)

MIND BENDER

Find the missing digits in this division.

5.15 REVIEW EXERCISE

1. State 3 ordered pairs that satisfy each of the following.

(a) $y = x + 4$ (b) $y = x - 7$
(c) $y = -x + 1$ (d) $y = 2x - 3$
(e) $y = -4x$ (f) $y = 3 - x$

2. Use the intercept method to determine 2 points that satisfy each of the following.

(a) $4x + 3y = 12$ (b) $2x + y = 6$
(c) $3x - 2y = 6$ (d) $5x - 2y = 10$
(e) $7x - 3y = -21$ (f) $x - y = 4$

3. State which of the following ordered pairs satisfy the equation $2x + 3y = 24$.

(a) $(12, 0)$ (b) $(2, 6)$ (c) $(0, 9)$ (d) $(1, 7)$
(e) $(3, 6)$ (f) $(6, 4)$ (g) $(10, 2)$ (h) $(-1, 9)$

4. State which of the following ordered pairs satisfy the equation $y = 4x - 6$.

(a) $(1, -3)$ (b) $(-2, -14)$
(c) $(0, -6)$ (d) $(3, 7)$
(e) $(2, 2)$ (f) $(-1, -7)$
(g) $(10, 36)$ (h) $(-5, -26)$

5. Solve each of the following equations for the indicated variable.

(a) $2x + y = 4$; y (b) $x - 3y = 7$; x
(c) $3x + 2y = 5$; y (d) $2a + 3b = 4$; a
(e) $3m - 2n = 2$; m (f) $4d - 3e = 7$; e
(g) $4x - 3y = 0$; x (h) $2x + 3y - 4 = 0$; y

6. Determine whether the ordered pair satisfies the relation.

(a) $3x - 2y \geqslant 6$; $(1, -3)$
(b) $7x + 2y < 10$; $(-1, 8)$
(c) $3x - y > 4$; $(-1, -6)$
(d) $y \geqslant 2x - 5$; $(1, -2)$
(e) $5x + 3y < 2$; $(1, -1)$
(f) $y < 1 - 4x$; $(-2, 8)$
(g) $3y - 2x < -2$; $(2, 0)$
(h) $6x + 7y > -3$; $(-3, 2)$

7. Solve the following graphically.

(a) $y = x + 3$ (b) $x + y = 7$
     $y = -x + 1$ $x - y = 3$
(c) $y = 2x - 1$ (d) $x + 2y = 0$
     $y = 3x - 4$ $2x - y = -10$

8. Solve. Check your solution.

(a) $5x - 2y = -9$ (b) $3x + y = 13$
     $3x + 7y = 11$ $2x + 3y = 18$
(c) $5x - 4y + 13 = 0$ (d) $2x - 3y = -10$
     $7x - y + 9 = 0$ $4x + y = 1$
(e) $2x + 3y = -18$ (f) $x + 5y = 16$
     $3x - 5y = 11$ $2x + 3y = 11$
(g) $4x = 3y + 1$ (h) $2x - y - 15 = 0$
     $8x + 15y = 9$ $5x + 4y - 18 = 0$
(i) $6x = 5y - 3$
     $3x + 10y + 4 = 0$
(j) $7x + 8y = 1$
     $14x - 10y + 11 = 0$

9. Solve.

(a) $\frac{2}{3}x + \frac{1}{4}y = 3$ (b) $\frac{3x}{2} - \frac{2y}{3} = 2$

     $\frac{1}{3}x - \frac{1}{2}y = -1$ $\frac{3x}{4} - \frac{y}{6} = 2$

(c) $\frac{7x}{10} - y = -13$ (d) $\frac{x}{4} + \frac{y}{6} = 1\frac{1}{4}$

     $\frac{3}{5}x + \frac{1}{6}y = -5$ $\frac{x}{5} - \frac{y}{2} = -\frac{9}{10}$

(e) $4x + 3y = -1.9$
     $2x - 7y = 3.3$
(f) $0.1x - 0.4y = 1.9$
     $0.4x + 0.5y = -0.8$
(g) $2x - 5y = -3.1$
     $x + 7y = 3.2$
(h) $0.4x - 0.3y = 2.4$
     $0.6x + 0.7y = -1$

10. Classify each of the following linear systems as consistent, inconsistent, or dependent.

(a) $y = 3x + 4$ (b) $x + 2y = 6$
     $y = 3x - 7$ $2x + 4y = 12$
(c) $x - 3y = 7$ (d) $2x - y = 4$
     $x + 4y = 17$ $2x - y = 15$
(e) $7x + 5y = 21$ (f) $2x = 3y + 7$
     $7x + 6y = 21$ $6x - 9y - 21 = 0$

11. Solve for x and y.

(a) $ax + by = 4ab$ (b) $4ax - 3by = 6ab$
     $ax - by = 2ab$ $2ax - 2by = 7ab$
(c) $2ax - y = 4ab$ (d) $ax + by = c$
     $3ax + y = 6ab$ $mx - ny = d$

12. Draw the graph of each of the following.
(a) $y \geqslant 2x - 4$ (b) $y < 3x + 5$
(c) $2x - 3y \leqslant 12$ (d) $4x + 5y > 20$
(e) $y > -2x + 3$ (f) $3x - 4y < -24$
(g) $\{(x, y) \mid x \geqslant -2, x, y \in R\}$
(h) $\{(x, y) \mid y < 3, x, y \in R\}$

13. Graph the following.
(a) $\{(x, y) \mid y \geqslant x + 1 \text{ and } y \leqslant -2x + 7\}$
(b) $\{(x, y) \mid y < 2x + 8 \text{ and } y \geqslant 3 - 3x\}$
(c) $\{(x, y) \mid y > 2x - 3 \text{ and } y < x + 5\}$
(d) $\{(x, y) \mid 2x + 3y \leqslant 6 \text{ and } 5x - 2y \geqslant 20\}$
(e) $\{(x, y) \mid x - 3y > 12 \text{ or } 2x + y > 6\}$
(f) $\{(x, y) \mid x \geqslant 3 \text{ and } y \geqslant -2\}$
(g) $\{(x, y) \mid 4x - 3y \leqslant 24 \text{ and } y < 6 - 3x\}$

14. Determine the maximum and minimum values of $4x - 5y$ and $2x + 5y$ over each of the following regions.

(a)

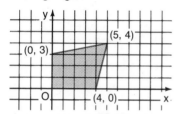

(b)

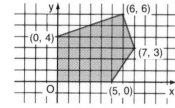

(c)
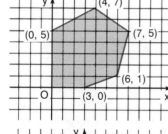

(d)
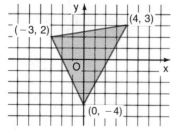

15. Sketch the graph of the region bounded by $x + y \leqslant 10$, $x + 2y \leqslant 16$, $x \geqslant 0$, and $y \geqslant 0$. Determine the maximum and minimum values of $4x + 2y$ over this region.

16. Sketch the graph of the region bounded by $y \leqslant -2x + 6$, $y \leqslant -x + 5$, $x \geqslant 0$, and $y \geqslant 0$. Determine the maximum and minimum values of $3x - 2y$ over this region.

17. Solve the following systems of equations.
(a) $2a + 3b - 4c = 21$
    $3a - 2b + 2c = -4$
    $4a + 5b + 3c = 17$
(b) $5a - 3b + 4c = -3$
    $6a + 2b - 3c = -26$
    $2a - 5b - 11c = 14$
(c) $a + b = -1$
    $b + c = -2$
    $a + c = 9$
(d) $2a + 3b + 2c - 4d = 8$
    $3a - b + 3c - 2d = 19$
    $4a + 2b + c + d = 6$
    $2a + b - 4c + 2d = -12$

18. The Summertime Clothing Company makes bikinis and swimming trunks. A bikini requires 2 min at the cutting machine, the trunks 1 min each. Sewing a bikini takes 3 min, while the trunks take 4 min each. There is a maximum of 140 min/d available for cutting and 360 min/d for sewing. If the profit on each bikini is $5.00 and on each set of trunks $4.00, how many of each should be made in a day in order to maximize the profit?

19. To raise money for the graduation dance the student council decides to make and sell ice cream sundaes during the lunch period. A Super sundae requires 2 scoops of vanilla, 2 scoops of chocolate, and 1 scoop of maple walnut. A Super Duper sundae has 1 scoop of vanilla, 3 scoops of chocolate, and 3 scoops of maple walnut. There are 280 scoops of vanilla, 360 scoops of chocolate, and 300 scoops of maple walnut available. There is a profit of $0.50 on a Super sundae and $1.00 on a Super Duper. If they can sell all the sundaes they make, how many of each should be made in order to maximize the profit?

5.16 CHAPTER 5 TEST

1. Determine whether the ordered pair satisfies the relation.
(a) $2x - y = 5$; $(1, -3)$ (b) $3x + 2y = 7$; $(1, -2)$
(c) $x - 2y \leqslant 5$; $(1, -2)$ (d) $y > \dfrac{x}{2} - 3$; $(2, 1)$

2. Solve the following graphically.
(a) $y = 3x + 2$ (b) $2x - y = 5$
    $y = 2x + 3$ $x + 3y = 6$

3. Solve and check your solution.
(a) $y = 7x - 2$ (b) $3x + 2y = 2$
    $x + y = 6$ $x + 3y = -4$
(c) $2x + 3y = 34$ (d) $y = 4x - 7$
    $3x - 5y = 13$ $y = \dfrac{x}{2} + 7$

4. Graph.
(a) $\{(x, y) \mid y > 2x + 4, x, y \in R\}$
(b) $\{(x, y) \mid 2x - 3y \leqslant 6, x, y \in R\}$
(c) $\{(x, y) \mid x \geqslant 3 \text{ and } y > -2, x, y \in R\}$
(d) $\{(x, y) \mid x > 0 \text{ and } y > 0\} \cap \{(x, y) \mid 2x - y < 2\}$

5. Determine the maximum and minimum values of the expression $3x + 4y$ over the region given below.

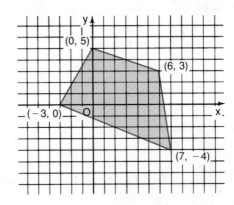

6. Sketch the graph of the region bounded by $2x + y \leqslant 8$, $x \geqslant 0$, and $y \geqslant 0$. Determine the maximum and minimum values of $3x + 4y$ over the region.

PROBLEM SOLVING AND WORD PROBLEMS

CHAPTER

6

Beside the mathematical arts there is no infallible knowledge, except it be borrowed from them.

Robert Recorde

REVIEW AND PREVIEW TO CHAPTER 6

PERCENT IN PRACTICAL PROBLEMS

EXERCISE

1. John bought a portable radio that was priced at $152.00. If the rate of sales tax was 7%, how much did he pay for the radio?

2. Stephanie bought a used car that listed at $5550.00. If the rate of sales tax was 7%, how much did she pay for the car?

3. A credit union offers a 9% interest rate on deposits of multiples of $500 if they are left in the credit union for one year. The student council deposits $1500. What is the interest after one year?

4. A salesman sells a car for $7550.00. If his commission is 5%, how much does he receive for this sale?

5. Carol sells real estate. Her commission is 6% on each sale. If she sells a property for $156 000.00, what is her commission?

6. A large department store has a "10% Day" when everything is discounted 10%. If you buy a pair of shoes priced at $32.50, how much is the discount?

7. A new car dealer pays you a salary of $300 a week plus commission of 3% on all sales. If your sales total $42 250.00 for the week, how much would you earn?

8. A variety store sells pens priced at $3.00. If the rate of sales tax is 7%, how much would you pay for a pen?

9. A jeweller bought a diamond ring for $1500.00. If his rate of mark-up is 80% of his cost price, what would you pay for the ring?

10. A large department store has a "10% Day" when everything bought on this day is discounted 10%. If you buy a sweater priced at $40.00, what will you pay for the sweater if the rate of sales tax is 7%?

11. The science club decides to set up a tropical fish aquarium. The local pet store delivered, on request, the following items:

    tank   : $75.00
    tank stand: $35.00
    gravel   : $8.00
    pump   : $22.00
    filter   : $15.00

If the rate of sales tax is 7%, how much is the bill from the pet shop?

12. A bank offers an interest rate of 11% on deposits left in the bank for one year. If you deposit $1200.00 under these conditions, what will the interest amount to after one year?

13. Sarah purchased the following items from a department store: a blouse priced at $10.37, slacks priced at $25.53, and a jacket priced at $41.30. If the rate of sales tax is 7%, how much was her total bill?

14. A variety store owner buys bread from a bakery for $1.10 a loaf. If his rate of markup is 20%, what will you pay for a loaf of bread?

15. A television set priced at $780.00 is put on sale at 25% off. If the rate of sales tax is 7%, what would you pay for the set?

16. A new car lists for $16 780.00. If you have a trade-in valued at $2100.00 and the rate of sales tax is 7%, what will you pay for the car?

17. A bank pays interest of 12.5% on deposits left in the bank for one year. If you deposit $2500.00, how much is the interest after one year?

18. A car dealer pays you $200.00 a week plus 2% of your total sales. If your sales totalled $58 000.00 for the week, how much would you be paid?

19. Mario's weekly sales for a four week period were $8900.00, $12 100.00, $14 700.00, and $7900.00. If he is paid $150.00 a week plus 3% of sales, how much did he earn in the four weeks?

20. Marina bought the following items at a hardware store.
    (i) a hammer priced at $8.57
    (ii) nails priced at $2.36
    (iii) paint priced at $18.07
    (iv) a paint brush priced at $4.00
If the rate of sales tax is 7%, what was her total bill?

USING MATHEMATICAL SYMBOLS

EXERCISE

1. Write each of the following as a mathematical expression.

(a) The sum of two and three.
(b) The product of six and two.
(c) The difference of seven and five.
(d) The positive square root of seven.
(e) The square of five.
(f) Four less than eight.
(g) Five more than two.
(h) Three times as large as five.
(i) Six more than ten.
(j) Pi is an element of the set of real numbers.

(k) Sixteen diminished by five.
(l) Twelve increased by seven.
(m) Twenty-four diminished by eight.
(n) The square of sixteen.
(o) The sum of the squares of four and three.
(p) The square of the sum of four and three.
(q) Four more than twice three.
(r) Three less than twice four.
(s) Twice five increased by two.

EQUATIONS IN ONE VARIABLE

EXERCISE

1. Solve the following equations, $x \in R$.
(a) $3(2x - 1) = 9$
(b) $-2(x + 5) = 3x + 6$
(c) $3x + 2(x - 3) = 3(2x - 1) + 2$
(d) $(x + 2)(x - 3) = (x - 5)(x + 6) + 4x$
(e) $(x - 3)(x + 3) = (x - 5)(x + 5) + 4x$
(f) $(x - 4)(x + 5) = x(x - 5) - 2$
(g) $3(2x - 3) - 2(x + 4) = 3(2x - 5) + 6$
(h) $(x + 1)(x - 1) = (x + 2)x$
(i) $3(x - 5) + 2(x - 1) = 3(x - 1)$
(j) $(2x - 5)(3x + 2) - 6x(x - 1) = -4x$

EQUATIONS IN TWO VARIABLES

EXERCISE

1. Solve the following systems of equations.
(a) $3x + y = 5$
    $2x + y = 3$
(b) $y = 5x + 13$
    $y = -2x - 8$
(c) $3x - 2y = 8$
    $6x - 5y = 20$

6.1 PROBLEM SOLVING TECHNIQUES

In this chapter, we apply the READ—PLAN—SOLVE—ANSWER problem solving model to problems using equations.

READ

Read the problem carefully. Understand what the problem is telling you and what it is asking you to find.

PLAN

Classify the information

Classify what is unknown, what you are required to find, and what facts you are given or already know about the unknown(s).

Introduce the variable(s)

Represent each unknown in terms of a variable.

Set up an equation

Translate the words and the information given in the problem into an algebraic expression in the form of an equation.

SOLVE

Solve the equation(s)

In previous chapters you have experienced many different methods of solving equations.

ANSWER

Check your solution

Re-read the question and substitute the values that you have obtained. Do they work?

State your solution

Since the problem was presented in words, the answer should be presented in words. Use a complete sentence. Make sure you answer exactly what was asked for in the question.

Step 1. READ

Step 2. PLAN

Classify the information.

EXAMPLE. In each of the following questions, identify
(a) what is unknown.
(b) what you are required to find.
(c) the facts that you do know about the unknowns.

(i) Mary is twice as old as Paul. The sum of their ages is 63. How old is Paul?
(ii) Michelle has 3 more dimes than nickels. Altogether she has $2.10. How many nickels does she have?
(iii) The sum of three consecutive integers is 96. Find the integers.
(iv) The sum of two numbers is 80. Their difference is 6. Find the smaller number.

SOLUTION:

(i) Unknowns: Mary's age
                        Paul's age

   Required to find: Paul's age

   Known facts: Mary is twice as old as Paul
                        the sum of their ages is 63

(ii) Unknowns: number of nickels
                        number of dimes

   Required to find: number of nickels

   Known facts: (number of dimes) = 3 + (number of nickels)
                        total sum is $2.10 or 210¢
                        nickels are worth $0.05 or 5¢
                        dimes are worth $0.10 or 10¢

(iii) Unknowns: 3 integers (first, second, third)

   Required to find: all three integers

   Known facts: they are integers
                        they are consecutive
                        each one is 1 more than the preceding one
                        their sum is 96

(iv) Unknowns: 2 numbers (a smaller and a larger)

   Required to find: the smaller

   Known facts: larger + smaller = 80
                        larger − smaller = 6

EXERCISE 6.1

B In each of the following questions, identify
(a) what is the unknown.
(b) what you are required to find.
(c) the facts you are given and what is already known.

1. The sum of two numbers is 58. Their difference is 16. Find the numbers.

2. Two computer diskettes contain a total of 77 programs. There are 37 more in one diskette than the other. How many programs does each diskette contain?

3. The sum of two numbers is 77. When the smaller is subtracted from the larger, the result is 37. Find the numbers.

4. The sum of two numbers is 1253. The larger number is 277 more than the smaller number. Find the numbers.

5. The sum of two numbers is 73. Twice the larger plus 3 times the smaller is 162. Find the numbers.

6. When 5 times the larger of two numbers is added to 7 times the smaller, the result is 373. Eight times the larger less 5 times the smaller is 208. Find the numbers.

7. Seven times the larger of two numbers plus 6 times the smaller is 487. Nine times the larger increased by 7 times the smaller is 614. Find the numbers.

8. Two school events attracted a total of 1120 people. One event attracted 594 more people than the other. Find the attendance at each event.

9. Five times the smaller of two numbers added to six times the larger is 291. When 10 times the smaller is increased by 13 times the larger, the result is 613. Find the numbers.

10. Eight times the larger of two numbers decreased by 5 times the smaller is 589. Four times the larger increased by 7 times the smaller is 371. Find the numbers.

11. When the larger of two numbers is multiplied by 7, and the product is added to 10 times the smaller number, the result is 645. Five times the larger diminished by eight times the smaller is 67. Find the numbers.

12. The difference between two numbers is 63. When the larger is subtracted from twice the smaller, the result is 49. Find the numbers.

13. The sum of two numbers is 799. Twice the smaller number is 50 more than the larger number. Find the numbers.

14. Two numbers have a difference of 412 and a sum of 1104. Find the numbers.

15. Two numbers have a difference of 118. The larger is 27 less than twice the smaller. Find the numbers.

16. The sum of two numbers is 1990. When 318 is subtracted from five times the smaller the result is three times the smaller. Find the numbers.

17. Jack has 34 bills in fives and twos. The total value of these bills is $116. How many two dollar bills does he have?

18. Anne has $197.00 made up of $5 and $2 bills. If there are 61 bills in all, how many $2 bills are there?

19. Fred has three times as many $2 bills as he has $5 bills. In total, Fred has $561. How many $5 bills does Fred have?

20. There are 6 more $5 bills than $10 bills. The value of the bills is $255.00. How many $5 bills are there?

21. The automatic sandwich machine contained 132 coins in dimes and quarters. The value of the coins was $21.30. How many quarters were there?

22. Maria has 14 coins in dimes and quarters. The value of the coins is $2.75. How many of each are there?

23. The sum of two numbers is 362, and their difference is 114. Find the numbers.

24. A picture is 4 cm longer than it is wide. The perimeter is 40 cm. What are the dimensions of the picture?

25. Kumar has 99 albums and cassettes. There are 35 more albums than cassettes. How many of each are there?

26. Giselle has $228 in $2 bills and $5 bills. There are 80 bills. How many of each does she have?

27. The sum of two numbers is 1005. Twice the smaller is 36 more than the larger. Find the numbers.

Determine the pattern. Find the missing number.

25	52	31	26
9	4	7	5
38	28	18	19
7	20	7	

6.2 TRANSLATING WORDS INTO MATHEMATICAL EXPRESSIONS

The PLAN stage of the problem solving model involves the introduction of one or more variables, and the translation of the information from words to an algebraic statement.

EXAMPLE 1. Introduce one variable to represent the unknown and translate the information into an equation.

(a) When 14 is added to five times a number, the result is 49.

(b) Twice the car's speed decreased by 13 km/h is 139 km/h.

SOLUTION:

(a) The number is the unknown.

Let x represent the number.

$$5x + 14 = 49$$

(b) The car's speed is the unknown.

Let s represent the speed in km/h.

$$2s - 13 = 139$$

EXAMPLE 2. Introduce different variables to represent the unknowns and translate the information into an equation.

(a) The sum of two numbers is 17.

(b) Four times the length less five times the width is 138.

SOLUTION:

(a) The two numbers are the unknowns.

Let x represent the first number.
Let y represent the second number.

$$x + y = 17$$

(b) The two unknowns are the length and width.

Let ℓ represent the length.
Let w represent the width.

$$4\ell - 5w = 138$$

EXAMPLE 3. Introduce variables to represent the unknowns and translate the information into an equation.

(a) The number of nickels and dimes is 19.

(b) The value of the nickels and dimes is $1.55.

SOLUTION:

(a) Let x represent the number of nickels.

Let y represent the number of dimes.

$$x + y = 19$$

(b) Let x represent the number of nickels.

Let y represent the number of dimes.

$$0.05x + 0.10y = 1.55$$

EXERCISE 6.2

B 1. Write the following as algebraic expressions in one variable.

(a) 3 times a number
(b) a number increased by 4
(c) a number decreased by 3
(d) the length increased by 5 m
(e) Mary's age two years ago
(f) John's age five years from now
(g) twice the width increased by 3
(h) one-half the speed
(i) eight points less than the winner
(j) three times the volume decreased by 20
(k) the value, in cents, of x quarters
(l) one-half Susan's age six years ago
(m) one-third of Tom's age ten years from now
(n) six times a number decreased by 2
(o) four times as many people
(p) the value, in cents, of y dimes
(q) nine percent of the selling price
(r) twelve percent of the cost price
(s) interest, after one year, from an investment at 10% per annum
(t) interest, after one year, from an investment at 12% per annum

2. Write each of the following as an equation in one variable.

(a) A number increased by 35 is 82.
(b) Five times a number is 185.
(c) Four times a number less 47 is 293.
(d) When 57 is added to 9 times a number the result is 795.
(e) Six times the number of students less 87 is 999.
(f) Sam's age five years ago was 17.
(g) Sue's age thirteen years from now will be 27.
(h) Three times Bill's age five years ago was 48.
(i) Five times Tom's age plus 13 is 163.
(j) Twice the length increased by 4 is 26.
(k) Three times the width decreased by 7 is 92.
(l) One-half the length plus 11 is 43.
(m) Twice the car's speed increased by 31 is 165.
(n) Robert drove 400 km in 8 h. Find his speed.
(o) Fran averaged 60 km/h for 7.5 h. How far did she drive?

(p) How long will it take to drive 490 km at 35 km/h?
(q) 5% of the total price is $30.
(r) 7% of the cost price is $1.40.
(s) The bag of quarters had a total value of $17.75.

3. Write the following as expressions in two variables.

(a) The sum of the length and the width.
(b) Twice the length added to three times the width.
(c) Three times the length decreased by the width.
(d) The sum of Jeff's age and 3 times Kerry's age.
(e) The value of x nickels and y dimes.
(f) The value of x nickels and y quarters.
(g) The value of x $2 bills and y $5 bills.
(h) Five times Paul's age decreased by 4 times Hal's age.
(i) Twice the length increased by 3 plus 4 times the width.

4. Write the following as algebraic equations in two variables.

(a) The sum of 2 numbers is 50.
(b) The difference between 2 numbers is 40.
(c) There are a total of 35 boys and girls in the class.
(d) Grant counted 8 more cars than trucks.
(e) Larry's history and physics marks totalled 170.
(f) Twice one number plus 3 times another is 48.
(g) Four times the number of dimes less twice the number of quarters is 33.
(h) The sum of Linda's and Bob's age is 35.
(i) Eight times Greg's age plus Harry's age two years ago is 251.
(j) The length plus 3 times the width is 48.
(k) Seven times the length less 5 times the width is 38.
(l) Twelve times the length less 5 times the width is 487.
(m) The value of the dimes and quarters was 180¢.
(n) The $10 bills and $5 bills had a total value of $765.00.

6.3 SOLVING PROBLEMS USING TWO VARIABLES — PART I

We now combine the planning skills developed in the previous sections with the techniques of solving linear systems to solve word problems.

READ

EXAMPLE 1. The sum of two numbers is 340 and their difference is 174. Find the numbers.

SOLUTION:

PLAN

Let x represent the larger number.
Let y represent the smaller number.

$E=mc^2$

$$x + y = 340 \quad ①$$
$$x - y = 174 \quad ②$$

Add.
$$2x = 514$$
$$x = 257$$

SOLVE

Substitute in ①.
$$x + y = 340$$
$$257 + y = 340$$
$$y = 83$$

ANSWER

Check.

The sum of two numbers is 340.

$$257 + 83 = 340$$

The difference between them is 174.

$$257 - 83 = 174$$

Therefore, the numbers are 257 and 83.

Match each problem with a system of equations.

1. Two numbers have a difference of 412 and a sum of 1104. Find the numbers.

2. Two numbers have a difference of 118. The larger is 27 less than twice the smaller. Find the numbers.

3. The sum of two numbers is 1990. When 318 is subtracted from five times the smaller the result is three times the smaller. Find the numbers.

4. Jack has 34 bills in fives and twos. The total value of these bills is $116. How many two dollar bills does he have?

(a) $x + y = 34$
   $5x + 2y = 116$

(b) $x - y = 412$
   $x + y = 1104$

(c) $x - y = 118$
   $x + 27 = 2y$

(d) $x - y = -118$
   $x - 2y = 27$

(e) $x + y = 34$
   $5x - 2y = 116$

(f) $x + y = 1990$
   $5x - 318 = 3x$

READ

EXAMPLE 2. When 4 times the larger of 2 numbers is added to 3 times the smaller, the result is 68. Seven times the larger less 5 times the smaller is 37. Find the numbers.

SOLUTION:

PLAN

Let x represent the larger number.
Let y represent the smaller number.

$$4x + 3y = 68 \quad ①$$
$$7x - 5y = 37 \quad ②$$

SOLVE

① × 5	$20x + 15y = 340$
② × 3	$21x - 15y = 111$
Add.	$41x = 451$
	$x = 11$

Substitute in ①.

$$4x + 3y = 68$$
$$4(11) + 3y = 68$$
$$44 + 3y = 68$$
$$3y = 24$$
$$y = 8$$

ANSWER

Check.

4 times the larger plus 3 times the smaller is 68.

$$4(11) + 3(8) = 44 + 24$$
$$= 68$$

7 times the larger less 5 times the smaller is 37.

$$7(11) - 5(8) = 77 - 40$$
$$= 37$$

The numbers are 11 and 8.

Match each problem with a system of equations.

1. Anne has $197.00 made up of $5 and $2 bills. If there are 61 bills in all, how many $2 bills are there?

(a) $2x - 5y = 0$
$2x + 5y = 561$

(b) $\quad x - y = 6$
$5x + 10y = 255$

2. Fred has three times as many $2 bills as he has $5 bills. In total, Fred has $561. How many $5 bills does Fred have?

(c) $\quad x + y = 61$
$5x + 2y = 197$

3. There are 6 more $5 bills than $10 bills. The value of the bills is $255.00. How many $5 bills are there?

(d) $\quad x + y = 132$
$25x + 10y = 2130$

4. The automatic sandwich machine contained 132 coins in dimes and quarters. The value of the coins was $21.30. How many quarters were there?

(e) $2x + 5y = 561$
$3x - y = 0$

(f) $\quad x + y = 61$
$5x - 2y = 197$

EXERCISE 6.3

Use the problem solving model to solve the following.

B 1. The sum of 2 numbers is 255. When the smaller is subtracted from the larger, the result is 39. Find the numbers.

2. The sum of 2 numbers is 1584. Their difference is 58. Find the numbers.

3. The sum of 2 numbers is 1211 and their difference is 283. Find the numbers.

4. The mass of an excavator is twice that of a farm tractor. The sum of their masses is 21.9 t. Find both masses.

5. The sum of 2 numbers is 249. Twice the larger plus 3 times the smaller is 591. Find the numbers.

6. When 6 times the larger of 2 numbers is added to 7 times the smaller, the result is 114. Ten times the larger less 9 times the smaller is 66. Find the numbers.

7. Seven times the larger of 2 numbers decreased by 5 times the smaller is 42. Nine times the larger increased by 8 times the smaller is 186. Find the numbers.

8. Seven times the smaller of 2 numbers plus 9 times the larger is 178. When 10 times the larger is increased by 11 times the smaller, the result is 230. Find the numbers.

9. Four times the mass of a baseball is 16 g less than the mass of a basketball. The sum of their masses is 756 g. Find both masses.

10. When the larger of 2 numbers is multiplied by 9 and added to 10 times the smaller, the result is 389. Seven times the larger diminished by 4 times the smaller is 67. Find the numbers.

11. The difference in 2 numbers is 92. When the larger is subtracted from 4 times the smaller, the result is 151. Find the numbers.

12. In one month, a company executive flew round trip twice from London, England to Rome, Italy. The next month the executive flew one-way to Quebec City, which was 690 km farther than all the trips of the previous month. How far is it from Rome to London and from London to Quebec City if the executive flew a total of 6410 km?

13. The sum of 2 numbers is 188. The larger number is 24 more than 3 times the smaller. Find the numbers.

14. Two numbers have a difference of 123. The larger is 22 more than twice the smaller. Find the numbers.

15. Two numbers have a difference of 218. The larger is 140 less than twice the smaller. Find the numbers.

16. The sum of 2 numbers is 46. When 30 is subtracted from 5 times the smaller, the result is 3 times the larger. Find the numbers.

17. The sum of Joan's age and her father's age is 67. Three times Joan's age increased by 7 is her father's age. How old is Joan?

18. Sal's father is 3 times as old as he is. In six years the sum of their ages will be 68. How old is Sal?

19. If you double Lucien's age and then subtract 6 you have Peter's age. Two years ago the sum of their ages was 29. How old is Lucien?

20. Twice Sally's age increased by 3 times Sue's age is 103. Five times Sally's age decreased by 4 times Sue's age is 16. How old will Sally be ten years from now?

21. Pat is 3 times older than her dog. Four years ago, she was 7 times older. How old is Pat's dog?

22. One-half of Bob's age plus one-third of Terry's age is 24. One-fifth of Bob's age less one-ninth of Terry's age is 3. How old is Terry?

23. The sum of the digits of a 2-digit number is 11. The difference between the number and the number formed by reversing the digits is 27. Find the number.

24. A secret agent, being a mathematician, transmitted an important 2-digit locker number in the following manner. "The difference in the digits is 4. The sum of the number and the number formed by reversing the digits is 132." Find the locker number.

25. The sum of the digits of a 2-digit number is 9. If the number is doubled and then increased by 18, the result is the number with the digits reversed. Find the number.

THE SUM OF THE SQUARES OF THE DIGITS

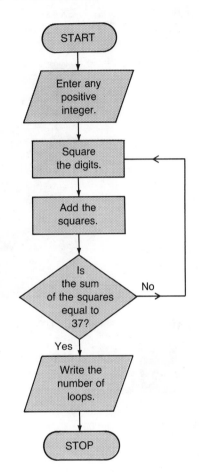

EXERCISE

1. Work through the flow chart using the following numbers.

(a) 25   (b) 63   (c) 125   (d) 58

2. What is the result if you choose 37 as the starting number?

3. Will this flow chart always result in a sequence that finishes with 37?

6.4 SOLVING PROBLEMS
USING TWO VARIABLES — PART II

In the following problems, we multiply a quantity by a unit value, to get a total value.

READ

EXAMPLE. The vending machine contains a total of 395 quarters and dimes. The total value of the coins is $66.80. How many of each are there?

PLAN

SOLVE

ANSWER

SOLUTION:

Let x represent the number of quarters.
Let y represent the number of dimes.

$$x + y = 395 \qquad ①$$
$$25x + 10y = 6680 \qquad ②$$

① × 10

$$10x + 10y = 3950$$
$$25x + 10y = 6680$$

Subtract.

$$-15x = -2730$$
$$x = 182$$

Substitute in ①.

$$x + y = 395$$
$$182 + y = 395$$
$$y = 213$$

Check.

There are 395 coins

$$182 + 213 = 395$$

Their total value is $66.80.

$$182(\$0.25) + 213(\$0.10) = \$45.50 + \$21.30$$
$$= \$66.80$$

There are 182 quarters and 213 dimes.

EXERCISE 6.4

B 1. Pierre has a total of $113 made up of $2 bills and $5 bills. If there are 31 bills in all, how many $2 bills does he have?

2. Ann has $300 made up of $5 and $10 bills. If there are 39 bills in all, how many $5 bills does she have?

3. Alan has twice as many $2 bills as $5 bills. Together they total $153. How many $5 bills does he have?

4. I have 6 more $5 bills than $10 bills. In all, I have $255. How many $5 bills do I have?

5. The pop machine contained $3.05 made up of dimes and quarters. There were 20 coins in all. How many dimes were there?

6. A parking meter contained 78 coins made up of dimes and nickels. The total value of the coins was $5.20. How many dimes does it contain?

7. A vending machine contained dimes and quarters. The number of quarters is 7 more than twice the number of dimes. The coins have a total value of $20.35. How many of each coin are there?

8. The athletic department bought a total of 29 basketballs and footballs at a cost of $1000. If basketballs cost $30 each and footballs $40 each, how many footballs were bought?

9. A movie theatre sold twice as many adult tickets as student tickets. The total receipts were $2299. If adult tickets cost $7 and students $5, how many of each were sold?

10. There were 296 tickets sold for the school athletic banquet. Adult tickets cost $10, student tickets $5. The receipts totalled $1910. How many student tickets were sold?

11. The school bookstore ordered a total of 130 mathematics and history books. A math book costs $19.00 and a history book $16.20. If the total bill was $2274.00, how many math books were bought?

C 12. Hans has some $2 bills and $5 bills which have a total value of $81. If he replaced the $2 bills with the same number of 5s and the $5 bills with the same number of 10s, he would have $175. How many $2 bills does he have?

13. The dance committee bought chips for 25¢ a bag and pop for 30¢ a can. The total bill was $155. At the dance, chips sold for 35¢ a bag and pop for 40¢ a can. The dance committee sold all the pop and chips and realized a profit of $55. How many cans of pop did they sell?

6.5 SOLVING PROBLEMS USING TWO VARIABLES — PART III

The problems in this section deal with investment.

READ

EXAMPLE. Mike invested $8000, part at 9% per annum and the remainder at 12% per annum. After one year the total interest earned on these investments was $810. How much did he invest at each rate?

PLAN

SOLUTION:
Let x be the amount invested at 9%.
Let y be the amount invested at 12%.

$$x + y = 8000 \qquad ① \qquad \text{Total money invested}$$
$$0.09x + 0.12y = 810 \qquad ② \qquad \text{Total interest earned}$$

SOLVE

$$① \times 9 \qquad 9x + 9y = 72\,000$$
$$② \times 100 \qquad \underline{9x + 12y = 81\,000} \qquad \text{Clear decimal fractions}$$
Subtract.
$$-3y = -9000$$
$$y = 3000$$
Substitute in ①.
$$x + 3000 = 8000$$
$$x = 5000$$

ANSWER

Check.

The total investment was $8000.

$$\$5000 + \$3000 = \$8000$$

The total interest earned was $810.

$$0.09(\$5000) + 0.12(\$3000) = \$450 + \$360$$
$$= \$810$$

He invested $5000 at 9% and $3000 at 12%.

EXERCISE 6.5

A 1. Complete the following statements.
(a) The interest, after 1 a, on $2000 at 10% is ■.
(b) The interest, after 1 a, on $300 at 9% is ■.
(c) The interest, after 1 a, on $3000 at 12% is ■.
(d) The interest, after 1 a, on $x at 7% is ■.

B 2. Peggy invested $1000, part at 8% per annum and the remainder at 9% per annum. After one year her total interest from these investments was $84. How much did she invest at each rate?

3. Ian invested $8000, part at 9% per annum and the remainder at 10% per annum. After one year his total interest from these investments was $740. How much did he invest at each rate?

4. The student council invested $6000, part at 7.5% per annum and the remainder at 8.5% per annum. The total interest, after one year, from these investments was $480. How much was invested at each rate?

6.6 SOLVING PROBLEMS USING TWO VARIABLES — PART IV

READ

EXAMPLE. A chemistry student was asked to make 100 L of 48% alcohol solution by volume by mixing 40% alcohol solution by volume and 60% alcohol solution by volume. How many litres of each must the student use?

PLAN

SOLVE

SOLUTION:

Let x represent the number of litres of 40% solution needed.
Let y represent the number of litres of 60% solution needed.

$$x + y = 100 \qquad ① \qquad \text{solution equation}$$
$$0.4x + 0.6y = (0.48)100 \qquad ② \qquad \text{alcohol equation}$$

$$① \times 4 \qquad 4x + 4y = 400$$
$$② \times 10 \qquad \underline{4x + 6y = 480}$$

Subtract.
$$-2y = -80$$
$$y = 40$$

Substitute in ①.
$$x + y = 100$$
$$x + 40 = 100$$
$$x = 60$$

ANSWER

Check.

100 L of solution are required.

$$60 \text{ L} + 40 \text{ L} = 100 \text{ L}$$

There must be 48 L of alcohol in the final solution.

$$0.4(60 \text{ L}) + 0.6(40 \text{ L}) = 24 \text{ L} + 24 \text{ L}$$
$$= 48 \text{ L}$$

EXERCISE 6.6

B 1. Complete the following.
(a) 100 kg of 30% salt solution by mass contains ■ kg of salt.
(b) 500 L of 40% alcohol solution by volume contains ■ L of alcohol.
(c) 2000 kg of 5% salt solution by mass contains ■ kg of salt.
(d) x L of 30% alcohol solution by volume contains ■ L of alcohol.
(e) y kg of 35% salt solution by mass contains ■ kg of salt.
(f) m kg of 9% silver alloy contains ■ kg of silver.

2. How many kilograms of 30% salt solution by mass and 40% salt solution by mass should be mixed to form 200 kg of 37% salt solution by mass?

3. A lab technician wants to make 500 kg of 28% alcohol solution by mixing 40% alcohol solution and 20% alcohol solution. How many kilograms of each type should be used?

4. A chemist mixes hydrochloric acid solutions of 30% strength and 40% strength to get 100 kg of hydrochloric acid solution of 34% strength. How many kilograms of each should be used?

5. How many kilograms of 9% silver alloy and 12% silver alloy should be combined to make 500 kg of 10.8% silver alloy?

6. How many kilograms of 35% salt solution and 45% salt solution should be mixed to make 500 kg of 43% salt solution?

6.7 SOLVING PROBLEMS USING TWO VARIABLES — PART V

READ

EXAMPLE. A store owner sells peanuts for $4.80/kg and raisins for $2.40/kg. He decides to mix raisins and peanuts and sell the mixture as a TV snack for $3.36/kg. He decides to make up 100 kg of the snack. How many kilograms of peanuts and raisins will he need?

PLAN

SOLUTION:
Let x represent the number of kilograms of peanuts needed.
Let y represent the number of kilograms of raisins needed.

	Number of Kilograms	Cost Per Kilogram	Value in Cents
Peanuts	x	480	480x
Raisins	y	240	240y
Mixture	100	336	33 600

$$x + y = 100 \quad ① \quad \text{Total mass of mixture}$$
$$480x + 240y = 33\ 600 \quad ② \quad \text{Total value of mixture}$$

$② \div 240$

$$\begin{array}{l} x + y = 100 \\ 2x + y = 140 \end{array}$$

Subtract.

$$-x = -40$$
$$x = 40$$

SOLVE

Substitute ①.

$$x + y = 100$$
$$40 + y = 100$$
$$y = 60$$

ANSWER

Check.

The mass of the mixture is 100 kg.

$$40 \text{ kg} + 60 \text{ kg} = 100 \text{ kg}$$

The value of the ingredients must be the same as the value of the mixture.

Ingredients: $4.80(40) + $2.40(60) = $192 + $144
$$= \$336.00$$

Mixture: $3.36(100) = $336.00

He will need 40 kg of peanuts and 60 kg of raisins.

EXERCISE 6.7

A 1. Complete the following.
  (a) The value of 10 kg of candy at $2.00/kg is ■.
  (b) The value of 6 kg of tea at $7.50/kg is ■.
  (c) The value of 20 kg of coffee at $6.00/kg is ■.
  (d) The value of x kg of peanuts at $3.10/kg is ■.
  (e) The value of y kg of soap at $4.50/kg is ■.
  (f) The value of m kg of tea at $3.07/kg is ■.

B 2. Jelly beans and mints, worth $2.10/kg and $2.70/kg respectively, were mixed to make 500 kg of mixture which sold for $2.52/kg. How many kilograms of mints were used?

3. Coffee that sells for $7.20/kg is mixed with coffee that sells for $4.80/kg to make 1200 kg of coffee that will sell for $5.60/kg. How many kilograms of each type of coffee were used?

4. A hardware store manager mixes nails that sell for $3.30/kg and nails that sell for $3.60/kg to get 100 kg of nails that he puts in 1 kg bags. He sells each bag for $3.42. How many kilograms of each type of nail does he use?

5. A department store manager decided to mix cashews and pecans to get 400 kg of nuts that sell for $10.08/kg. If cashews sell for $9.60/kg and pecans $10.80/kg, how many kilograms of each type of nuts did she use?

6. A merchant mixes tea that sells for $6.60/kg with tea that sells for $7.20/kg to get 200 kg of mixture that sells for $6.84/kg. How many kilograms of each type of tea did he use?

7. A store manager mixes tea worth $7.50/kg and tea worth $9.50/kg to make 200 kg of tea that sells for $8.35/kg. How many kilograms of each type of tea does she use?

8. A solution contains 25% copper sulphate. Another solution contains 50% copper sulphate. How much of each solution should be used to make 1000 mL of a solution that is 45% copper sulphate?

9. How many kilograms of soap powder that costs $0.80/kg should be mixed with soap powder that costs $1.50/kg to make 20 kg of a mixture of soap powder to cost $1.01/kg?

10. A gas station attendant wishes to make 100 L of 48% ethylene glycol solution by mixing some 40% solution with some 60% solution of ethylene glycol. How much of each solution should the attendant use?

11. Seth and Amanda mix nuts costing $4.50/kg with nuts costing $6.50/kg to form a mixture which costs $36.50 for a 7 kg box. How much of each kind of nuts should Seth and Amanda use for one box?

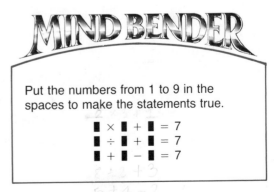

MIND BENDER

Put the numbers from 1 to 9 in the spaces to make the statements true.

■ × ■ + ■ = 7
■ ÷ ■ + ■ = 7
■ + ■ − ■ = 7

6.8 SOLVING PROBLEMS USING TWO VARIABLES — PART VI

In problems involving distance, speed, and time, it is often easier to classify the information in a table. Use the memory aid below to relate distance, speed, and time.

$$D = ST, \qquad \frac{D}{S} = T, \qquad \frac{D}{T} = S$$

READ

EXAMPLE. Jeanne took a trip from Brownsville to Montreal, a distance of 830 km. She travelled part of the way by bus and the rest of the way by plane. The bus averaged 40 km/h and the plane 500 km/h. The whole trip took 3.5 h. How many hours did she spend travelling by bus?

PLAN

SOLUTION:
Let x represent the time on the bus, in hours.
Let y represent the time flying, in hours.

	Distance (km)	Speed (km/h)	Time (h)
Bus	40x	40	x
Plane	500y	500	y
Totals	830		3.5

$E=mc^2$

$$40x + 500y = 830 \qquad ① \qquad \text{Distance equation}$$
$$x + y = 3.5 \qquad ② \qquad \text{Time equation}$$

① ÷ 10
② × 4
Subtract.

$$4x + 50y = 83$$
$$\underline{4x + 4y = 14}$$
$$46y = 69$$
$$y = 1.5$$

SOLVE

Substitute in ②.

$$x + y = 3.5$$
$$x + 1.5 = 3.5$$
$$x = 2$$

ANSWER

Check.

The total time is 3.5 h.

$$2\,h + 1.5\,h = 3.5\,h$$

The total distance is 830 km.

$$40(2)\,km + 500(1.5)\,km = 80\,km + 750\,km$$
$$= 830\,km$$

Jeanne travelled 2 h by bus.

EXERCISE 6.8

A 1. Complete the following statements.
(a) The distance travelled in 4 h at 60 km/h is ■ km.
(b) The time taken to travel 600 km at 50 km/h is ■ h.
(c) If you travel 400 km in 8 h your average speed is ■ km/h.
(d) The distance travelled in x h at 40 km/h is ■ km.
(e) The time taken to travel y km at 50 km/h is ■ h.
(f) The distance travelled in m h at 8 km/h is ■ km.
(g) The time taken to travel n km at 30 km/h is ■ h.

B 2. Jack drove at 50 km/h from Smithville to Dry Gulch. From Dry Gulch to Streetsville he drove at 80 km/h. The whole trip was 550 km and took 8 h. How far is it from Dry Gulch to Streetsville?

3. It took Maria 9 h to drive the 580 km between Devils Basin and Tumbleweed. The first part of the trip was through mountains and she averaged 60 km/h. Once out of the mountains, she averaged 70 km/h the rest of the way. How many hours did she spend driving through the mountains?

4. Fred took 7 h to drive from Cheyenne to Boothill, a total distance of 485 km. He drove most of the way at 80 km/h, but was slowed to 30 km/h for a time by a dust storm during the trip. How many hours did he spend driving through the dust storm?

5. It took the football team 5 h to travel from Titletown to Toronto, a total distance of 1320 km. Part of the trip was by bus and the remainder by plane. The bus averaged 40 km/h and the plane 600 km/h. How many hours were spent travelling by bus?

6. It is 395 km from Ski Valley to Vancouver. Kim made the trip in 6 h, travelling by bus and train. The train averaged 70 km/h and the bus 60 km/h. How much time was spent travelling by train?

7. The distance from the highway to Lake Snow was 160 km and Jacques made the trip in 11 h. For the first part of the journey he used a snowmobile and travelled at 20 km/h. The last part of the trip was made on skis, where he averaged 10 km/h. How far did he travel on skis?

8. Sarah spent 2 h more travelling by train than she did by bus. The train averaged 70 km/h and the bus 50 km/h. The total distance travelled was 740 km. How far did she travel by bus?

C 9. Flying into the wind, an aircraft made a 360 km trip in 2 h. The return trip with a tail wind took 1.5 h. Find the speed of the wind.

10. It took Ed 8 h to row 40 km upstream. The return trip, with the aid of the current, took 5 h. Find the speed of the current.

11. An aircraft flying into the wind can make an 1100 km trip in 2 h. The same aircraft can make the same trip in 1 h 50 min if flown with the wind. Find the speed of the wind.

12. Monica left Montreal driving at 30 km/h. Wendy left 2 h later and travelled the same road at 40 km/h. At what distance from Montreal will Wendy overtake Monica?

13. After robbing the bank, the James boys left Winchester on horseback at 20 km/h. The posse was slow getting organized and didn't start the chase until 1 h had passed. By having fresh horses, they managed to travel at 25 km/h. How far from Winchester did the posse overtake the James boys?

The sum of 3 consecutive integers is 222. Find the integers.

6.9 REVIEW EXERCISE

1. The sum of two numbers is 377 and their difference is 107. Find the numbers.

2. The sum of 2 numbers is 778 and their difference is 282. Find the numbers.

3. The sum of 2 numbers is 812 and their difference is 42. Find the numbers.

4. Three times the larger of 2 numbers increased by 4 times the smaller is 205. Six times the larger plus 3 times the smaller is 270. Find the numbers.

5. Four times the larger of 2 numbers decreased by 3 times the smaller is 152. Three times the larger increased by 5 times the smaller is 288. Find the numbers.

6. Three times the smaller of 2 numbers increased by 5 times the larger is 229. Four times the smaller decreased by 25 equals 3 times the larger. Find the numbers.

7. A bill of $424 was paid with $5 bills and $2 bills. A total of 128 bills were used. How many of them were fives?

8. After selling a total of 427 adult and student tickets the cashier at a theatre had receipts of $3263.50. If adult tickets sell for $8.50 and student tickets for $6.50, how many student tickets were sold?

9. The length of a rectangle is 19 m longer than the width. If the perimeter is 606 m, what are the dimensions of the rectangle?

10. The sum of Lisa's age and Ellen's age is 41. Five years from now the sum of their ages will be three times Lisa's present age. How old is Lisa?

11. A coffee machine contained $13.60 made up of dimes and quarters. If there are 97 coins, how many dimes are there?

12. The perimeter of a rectangle is 176 m. The length is equal to 3 times the width decreased by 4. Find the dimensions of the rectangle.

13. Adult and student tickets were sold for the school play. The total receipts were $2005. The number of student tickets sold was equal to three times the number of adult tickets sold decreased by 56. If student tickets cost $3.50 and adult tickets cost $5.00, how many adult tickets were sold?

14. Wayne invested $9000, part at 9% per annum and the remainder at 8% per annum. After one year the total interest from these investments was $750. How much was invested at 9%?

15. A lab technician needs to make 400 kg of 51% alcohol solution by combining 60% alcohol solution by mass and 40% alcohol solution by mass. How many kilograms of the 40% solution must be used?

16. Greta invests $5000, part at 7% per annum and the remainder at 6% per annum. After one year the total interest from these investments was $315. How much was invested at 7%?

17. It took Terry 7 h to drive the 390 km from Cold Bay to Morgan's Cove. He averaged 60 km/h for the first part of the trip, but was forced to complete the trip at 50 km/h due to a thunderstorm. How many hours did he spend driving at 50 km/h?

18. A merchant mixes tea that sells for $7.20/kg and tea that sells for $9.20/kg to make 100 kg of tea that he sells for $8.80/kg. How many kilograms of each type of tea did he mix?

19. The student council invested $4000, part at 8.5% per annum and the remainder at 9.5% per annum. After one year the interest from the 8.5% investment was $16 more than the interest from the 9.5% investment. How much was invested at 9.5%?

20. A chemist mixes hydrochloric acid solution of 50% strength and 40% strength to get 500 kg of hydrochloric acid solution of 46% strength. How many kilograms of the 50% solution are used?

21. A department store manager has one of her employees mix seeds that sell for $2.30/kg and seeds that sell for $3.20/kg to get 150 kg of mixture that sells for $2.72/kg. How many kilograms of each type must be used?

22. Vince left Trout Creek driving at 40 km/h. Sybil followed 2 h later driving at 50 km/h. How far down the road will Sybil overtake Vince?

23. Fritz invested $3000, part at 8% per annum and the remainder at 7% per annum. At the end of one year the interest from the 8% investment was $60 more than the interest from the 7% investment. How much was invested at each rate?

24. How would you invest $6400, part at 8% per annum and the remainder at 6% per annum so that at the end of the one year the interest from the 8% investment will be double the interest from the 6% investment?

25. The sum of the digits of a 2-digit number is 8. When 36 is added to the number, the digits are reversed. Find the number.

6.10 CHAPTER 6 TEST

1. The sum of 2 numbers is 84. The difference between them is 18. Find the numbers.

2. Six times the larger of 2 numbers plus 5 times the smaller is 145. Eight times the larger increased by 4 times the smaller is 164. Find the numbers.

3. Twice Tony's age increased by 6 is 3 times Jim's age. Two years ago the sum of their ages was 23. How old is Tony?

4. A parking meter contained 110 coins made up of dimes and nickels. If the value of the coins was $8.60, how many dimes did the meter contain?

5. A store owner mixed walnuts that sell for $7.50/kg and pecans that sell for $10.50/kg to make 200 kg of mixture that he sells for $8.25/kg. How many kilograms of walnuts did he use?

6. How many kilograms of 40% salt solution by mass and 20% salt solution by mass should be mixed to make 100 kg of 32% salt solution?

7. Holly took a trip of 1900 km, travelling by bus and plane. The bus averaged 60 km/h and the plane 700 km/h. If the total trip took 5 h, how many kilometres did she travel by bus?

MATRICES

CHAPTER

7

Mathematics is the predominant science of our time; its conquests grow daily, though without noise; he who does not employ it for himself will someday find it employed against himself.

J.F. Herbart

REVIEW AND PREVIEW TO CHAPTER 7

USING TABLES

EXERCISE

1. Using the table below, find.
(a) the square of 19
(b) the square root of 11
(c) the cube of 12
(d) the square root of 19
(e) the reciprocal of 12
(f) the cube root of 2744
(g) the square root of 289
(h) $\frac{1}{7}$

n	n²	n³	$\sqrt{n}$	$\dfrac{1}{n}$
1	1	1	1.000	1.0000
2	4	8	1.414	.5000
3	9	27	1.732	.3333
4	16	64	2.000	.2500
5	25	125	2.236	.2000
6	36	216	2.449	.1667
7	49	343	2.646	.1429
8	64	512	2.828	.1250
9	81	729	3.000	.1111
10	100	1000	3.162	.1000
11	121	1331	3.317	.0909
12	144	1728	3.464	.0833
13	169	2197	3.606	.0769
14	196	2744	3.742	.0714
15	225	3375	3.873	.0667
16	256	4096	4.000	.0625
17	289	4913	4.123	.0588
18	324	5832	4.243	.0556
19	361	6859	4.359	.0526
20	400	8000	4.472	.0500

2. A ringette league pays an honorarium to its convenor based on years of experience and level of certification. The pay schedule is as follows.

		Level of Certification		
		1	2	3
Years of Experience	0	1100	1350	1600
	1	1200	1450	1700
	2	1300	1550	1800
	$\geqslant 3$	1400	1650	1900

(a) What would be the honorarium for a convenor who
   (i) is just starting with level 1 certification?
   (ii) has held the position for 3 a with level 3 certification?
   (iii) has been the convenor for 6 a with level 2 certification?
(b) What is the yearly increase for experience?
(c) What is the increase from one level of certification to the other?

3. The following is a teacher's marks sheet for a grade 10 mathematics class.

	Date	Sept. 20	Oct. 8	Oct. 15	Oct. 23	Nov. 8	
Pupil's Names	Value of test	20	40	35	25	80	
Adams, M.		12	23	21	16	46	
Barclay, J.		12	26	24	18	54	
Carlson, P.		14	30	29	22	57	
Fleming, S.		14	22	19	15	45	
Hong, Y.		15	25	24	21	56	
Lepage, P.		13	25	25	20	55	
Murray, M.		9	21	14	13	43	
Rossi, J.		13	23	24	16	46	
Spina, M.		18	33	30	21	60	
VanDusen, L.		12	26	28	19	59	

(a) Find the class total for each test. Where would you write these totals on the table?
(b) Find each student's total. Where would you write these totals on the table?
(c) What percentage of students failed the first test?

7.1 REPRESENTING INFORMATION WITH MATRICES

It has become important to organize information in a logical manner in order to obtain quick and accurate access. Matrices help to perform this function. The matrix (the plural is matrices) is a powerful tool of mathematics and the sciences.

A matrix is a rectangular array of numbers enclosed by parentheses.

Last season's football record for a football division is

	Won	Lost	Tied
Cougars	8	4	2
Panthers	7	6	1
Tigers	6	6	2
Lions	4	9	1

We can present this information as a matrix as follows.

$$\begin{pmatrix} 8 & 4 & 2 \\ 7 & 6 & 1 \\ 6 & 6 & 2 \\ 4 & 9 & 1 \end{pmatrix}$$

The individual numbers are the entries of the matrix. The number of rows (horizontal) and columns (vertical) determine the dimensions of the matrix.

The example above is a 4 × 3 (four by three) matrix. The number of rows is always given first.

A matrix having only one row, such as (3 5 9), is called a row matrix. A matrix having only one column, such as $\begin{pmatrix} 5 \\ 2 \end{pmatrix}$, is called a column matrix.

EXAMPLE 1. Express the following information in a matrix. State the dimensions of the matrix.

(a) The scoring statistics of a hockey player.

	Goals	Assists	Points
Lemieux	48	62	110

(b) The results of a volleyball match.

Blues	15	11	15
Whites	12	15	7

SOLUTION:

(a) A representative matrix might be

$$(48 \ \ 62 \ \ 110)$$

Since this matrix has 1 row and 3 columns, its dimensions are 1×3.

This is a row matrix.

(b) A representative matrix might be

$$\begin{pmatrix} 15 & 11 & 15 \\ 12 & 15 & 7 \end{pmatrix}$$

Since this matrix has 2 rows and 3 columns, its dimensions are 2×3.

> Two matrices are equal if they have the same dimensions and the same corresponding entries.

EXAMPLE 2. State the value of x, y, and z if

$$\begin{pmatrix} 3 & 2 & 1 \\ x & 4 & x + y \end{pmatrix} = \begin{pmatrix} 3 & y & 1 \\ 4 & 4 & z \end{pmatrix}$$

SOLUTION:

By comparing corresponding entries, we obtain

$$2 = y \quad ①$$
$$x = 4 \quad ②$$
$$x + y = z \quad ③$$

Substitute results ① and ② into equation ③.

$$4 + 2 = z$$
$$6 = z$$

Hence $x = 4$, $y = 2$, and $z = 6$.

EXERCISE 7.1

A 1. State the dimensions of each matrix.

(a) $\begin{pmatrix} 2 & 3 & -5 \\ 7 & -1 & 6 \end{pmatrix}$ (b) $\begin{pmatrix} 5 & -4 \\ -3 & 2 \end{pmatrix}$

(c) $\begin{pmatrix} 3 & 7 \\ -2 & -1 \\ -4 & 3 \end{pmatrix}$ (d) $(8 \quad -9 \quad -10 \quad 2)$

2. For the matrix $\begin{pmatrix} 5 & -2 & 3 \\ 1 & 0 & 6 \\ -3 & 4 & 1 \end{pmatrix}$ state

(a) the entries in the third row.
(b) the entries in the second column.
(c) the entries in the second row.
(d) the entry in the first row and second column.
(e) the entry in the second row and third column.
(f) the dimensions of the matrix.

3. State the values of x, y, and z.

(a) $\begin{pmatrix} 3 & 0 \\ x & 4 \end{pmatrix} = \begin{pmatrix} 3 & y \\ 7 & 4 \end{pmatrix}$

(b) $\begin{pmatrix} -3 & 6 \\ -4 & 1 \end{pmatrix} = \begin{pmatrix} x & 6 \\ -4 & 1 \end{pmatrix}$

(c) $\begin{pmatrix} x & 2 \\ 3 & y \end{pmatrix} = \begin{pmatrix} -1 & 2 \\ 3 & -4 \end{pmatrix}$

B 4. Express the following information in matrix form.

Montreal has won 50 games, lost 8, and tied 10.
Pittsburgh has played 67 games, won 27, and lost 27.
Los Angeles has lost 28, played 67, and tied 13.
Washington has played 68 games, tied 13, and won 19.
Detroit has tied 8, lost 41, and played 65.

5. The matrix below gives the distances between several Canadian cities in kilometres.

(a) How far is it from Toronto to Regina?
(b) How far is it from Montreal to Vancouver?
(c) Write the column matrix that gives the distances from Halifax to the other cities.
(d) Write the row matrix that gives the distances from Saint John to the other cities.
(e) Write the row matrix that gives the "round trip" distances from Winnipeg to the other cities.
(f) Write the column matrix that gives the "round trip" distances from Edmonton to the other cities.
(g) Some road maps would show only half of the matrix. Why?

DISTANCES BETWEEN CANADIAN CITIES

	E	H	M	R	S	T	W	V
Edmonton	0	4950	3677	800	4600	3451	1344	1355
Halifax	4950	0	1273	4177	422	1821	3606	6003
Montreal	3677	1273	0	2904	933	549	2333	4730
Regina	800	4177	2904	0	3837	2680	571	1828
Saint John	4600	422	933	3837	0	1482	3266	5664
Toronto	3451	1821	549	2680	1482	0	2108	4505
Winnipeg	1344	3606	2333	571	3266	2108	0	2397
Vancouver	1355	6003	4730	1828	5664	4505	2397	0

7.2 MAGIC SQUARES AND MAGIC TRIANGLES

A magic square is a square array of numbers whose rows, columns, and diagonals add to the same sum. The number of rows and columns is called the order of the magic square. If the square is made up of consecutive integers starting with 1, then it is called a standard magic square. Some examples of standard magic squares are shown below.

1

Order 1

6	1	8
7	5	3
2	9	4

Order 3

Other magic squares can be obtained by rotating or reflecting a standard magic square. However, such squares are not considered to be different magic squares.

There is no standard magic square of order 2.

There is only one standard magic square of order 3.

There are 880 standard magic squares of order 4.

The sum of any row, column, or diagonal of a standard magic square can be calculated by the formula

$$S = \frac{n(n^2 + 1)}{2}$$

where n is the order.

A magic triangle is formed by placing consecutive integers along the sides of a triangle in such a way that the sum of the integers on each side is the same. The sum of the integers on one side is called the magic sum. Two standard magic triangles are shown below.

Order: 3
Magic Sum: 9

Order: 4
Magic Sum: 20

EXERCISE 7.2

1. Construct another magic square of order 3 by rotating the one given on this page.

2. Construct another magic square of order 4 by reflecting the one given on this page.

3. Construct a new standard magic square of
(a) order 4.   (b) order 5.

4. Calculate the sum of any row, column, or diagonal of a standard magic square of
(a) order 4.   (b) order 5.
(c) order 13.   (d) order 21.

5. Construct the following standard magic triangles.
(a) order 3; magic sum 10
(b) order 3; magic sum 11
(c) order 4; magic sum 28

7.3 ADDITION AND SUBTRACTION OF MATRICES

It is only possible to add matrices if they have the same dimensions. For example, the results for July and August for a baseball division are given as follows.

July	Won	Lost
Tigers	15	5
Jays	13	7
Sox	8	12
Reds	4	16

$$\text{or} \quad J = \begin{pmatrix} 15 & 5 \\ 13 & 7 \\ 8 & 12 \\ 4 & 16 \end{pmatrix}$$

August	Won	Lost
Tigers	7	14
Jays	15	6
Sox	8	12
Reds	10	10

$$\text{or} \quad A = \begin{pmatrix} 7 & 14 \\ 15 & 6 \\ 8 & 12 \\ 10 & 10 \end{pmatrix}$$

The two month totals are found by adding the elements in the corresponding positions.

$$J + A = \begin{pmatrix} 15 & 5 \\ 13 & 7 \\ 8 & 12 \\ 4 & 16 \end{pmatrix} + \begin{pmatrix} 7 & 14 \\ 15 & 6 \\ 8 & 12 \\ 10 & 10 \end{pmatrix}$$

$$= \begin{pmatrix} 22 & 19 \\ 28 & 13 \\ 16 & 24 \\ 14 & 26 \end{pmatrix}$$

The sum of two matrices of the same dimensions is the matrix whose entries are the sums of the corresponding entries of the matrices being added.

$$\begin{pmatrix} a & b \\ c & d \end{pmatrix} + \begin{pmatrix} e & f \\ g & h \end{pmatrix} = \begin{pmatrix} a+e & b+f \\ c+g & d+h \end{pmatrix}$$

The matrices $\begin{pmatrix} 4 & 3 \\ -1 & 5 \end{pmatrix}$ and $\begin{pmatrix} -1 & 3 & 4 \\ 5 & -2 & 6 \end{pmatrix}$ cannot be added because they do not have the same dimensions.

The negative of a matrix A is the matrix $-A$, each of whose entries is the negative of the corresponding entry in A.
For example,

$$\text{if } A = \begin{pmatrix} 3 & 5 \\ -2 & -4 \end{pmatrix}, \text{ then } -A = \begin{pmatrix} -3 & -5 \\ 2 & 4 \end{pmatrix}.$$

As with real numbers, we define subtraction of matrices in terms of addition.

$$\text{If } A = \begin{pmatrix} 2 & 4 \\ -1 & 3 \end{pmatrix} \text{ and } B = \begin{pmatrix} 5 & -3 \\ -6 & -2 \end{pmatrix},$$

$$\text{then} \quad A - B = A + (-B)$$

$$\begin{pmatrix} 2 & 4 \\ -1 & 3 \end{pmatrix} - \begin{pmatrix} 5 & -3 \\ -6 & -2 \end{pmatrix} = \begin{pmatrix} 2 & 4 \\ -1 & 3 \end{pmatrix} + \begin{pmatrix} -5 & 3 \\ 6 & 2 \end{pmatrix}$$

$$= \begin{pmatrix} -3 & 7 \\ 5 & 5 \end{pmatrix}$$

Matrix addition and subtraction can be used to represent real life situations related to inventory and production.

EXAMPLE 1. A car manufacturer produces 3 different models in its three Canadian plants. The production in its first two months is shown in the tables below.

First Month

Plant		Model		
		A	B	C
	X	85	115	120
	Y	90	112	125
	Z	88	110	122

Second Month

Plant		Model		
		A	B	C
	X	80	120	121
	Y	92	110	115
	Z	90	102	125

(a) Represent the monthly productions in separate matrices.
(b) Represent in one matrix the total inventory after two months.

SOLUTION:
(a) The matrix representing the production of the first month is

$$\begin{pmatrix} 85 & 115 & 120 \\ 90 & 112 & 125 \\ 88 & 110 & 122 \end{pmatrix}$$

The matrix representing the second month's production is

$$\begin{pmatrix} 80 & 120 & 121 \\ 92 & 110 & 115 \\ 90 & 102 & 125 \end{pmatrix}$$

(b) The matrix representing the manufacturer's total inventory after the first two months is

$$\begin{pmatrix} 85 & 115 & 120 \\ 90 & 112 & 125 \\ 88 & 110 & 122 \end{pmatrix} + \begin{pmatrix} 80 & 120 & 121 \\ 92 & 110 & 115 \\ 90 & 102 & 125 \end{pmatrix} = \begin{pmatrix} 165 & 235 & 241 \\ 182 & 222 & 240 \\ 178 & 212 & 247 \end{pmatrix}$$

EXAMPLE 2. Eastern and Western dealers received cars from all three plants. The distribution is represented by the following tables.

Eastern Dealers

		Model		
		A	B	C
Plant	X	30	45	40
	Y	34	40	51
	Z	40	31	54

Western Dealers

		Model		
		A	B	C
Plant	X	35	55	65
	Y	25	43	62
	Z	45	42	63

The balance of the inventory was exported.
(a) Represent the distribution to both Eastern and Western dealers as matrices.
(b) Represent the total Canadian distribution in one matrix.
(c) Represent in one matrix the inventory that was exported.

SOLUTION:
(a) In matrix form, Eastern and Western distributions were as follows.

For Eastern dealers

$$\begin{pmatrix} 30 & 45 & 40 \\ 34 & 40 & 51 \\ 40 & 31 & 54 \end{pmatrix}$$

For Western dealers

$$\begin{pmatrix} 35 & 55 & 65 \\ 25 & 43 & 62 \\ 45 & 42 & 63 \end{pmatrix}$$

(b) The total Canadian distribution is represented as the sum of the above matrices.

$$\begin{pmatrix} 30 & 45 & 40 \\ 34 & 40 & 51 \\ 40 & 31 & 54 \end{pmatrix} + \begin{pmatrix} 35 & 55 & 65 \\ 25 & 43 & 62 \\ 45 & 42 & 63 \end{pmatrix} = \begin{pmatrix} 65 & 100 & 105 \\ 59 & 83 & 113 \\ 85 & 73 & 117 \end{pmatrix}$$

(c) To determine the inventory that was exported, we subtract the total Canadian distribution from the total inventory.

$$\begin{pmatrix} 165 & 235 & 241 \\ 182 & 222 & 240 \\ 178 & 212 & 247 \end{pmatrix} - \begin{pmatrix} 65 & 100 & 105 \\ 59 & 83 & 113 \\ 85 & 73 & 117 \end{pmatrix} = \begin{pmatrix} 100 & 135 & 136 \\ 123 & 139 & 127 \\ 93 & 139 & 130 \end{pmatrix}$$

Total Inventory Matrix	Canadian Distribution Matrix	Export Distribution Matrix

EXERCISE 7.3

A 1. For each of the following, state.
(a) the negative of the matrix.
(b) the dimensions of the matrix.

(i) $\begin{pmatrix} 2 & 3 & -5 \\ 7 & -1 & 6 \end{pmatrix}$ (ii) $\begin{pmatrix} 5 & -4 \\ -3 & 2 \end{pmatrix}$

(iii) $\begin{pmatrix} 3 & 7 \\ -2 & -1 \\ -4 & 3 \end{pmatrix}$ (iv) $(8 \quad -9 \quad -10 \quad 2)$

(v) $\begin{pmatrix} 1 \\ -4 \\ 5 \end{pmatrix}$ (vi) (6)

(vii) $\begin{pmatrix} 3 & 5 & -7 \\ 4 & -2 & 6 \\ 9 & -3 & -5 \end{pmatrix}$ (viii) $\begin{pmatrix} 6 \\ -2 \end{pmatrix}$

B 2. Perform the indicated operations where possible.

(a) $\begin{pmatrix} 3 & 6 \\ 5 & 2 \end{pmatrix} + \begin{pmatrix} 4 & 5 \\ 3 & 7 \end{pmatrix}$ (b) $\begin{pmatrix} 6 \\ 3 \\ -2 \end{pmatrix} - \begin{pmatrix} -1 \\ 4 \\ -7 \end{pmatrix}$

(c) $\begin{pmatrix} 2 & -3 \\ 4 & 0 \\ -1 & 2 \end{pmatrix} + \begin{pmatrix} -5 & 4 \\ -7 & 3 \\ 6 & 4 \end{pmatrix}$

(d) $\begin{pmatrix} 5 & 3 & 6 \\ 4 & -1 & 0 \end{pmatrix} + \begin{pmatrix} -3 & 5 \\ 6 & 4 \end{pmatrix}$

(e) $\begin{pmatrix} 2 & 7 \\ 3 & 6 \end{pmatrix} - \begin{pmatrix} -4 & -5 \\ 2 & 7 \end{pmatrix}$

(f) $\begin{pmatrix} 5 & 6 \\ 8 & -3 \\ 1 & 0 \end{pmatrix} - \begin{pmatrix} -4 & 3 & 5 \\ 6 & -7 & 2 \end{pmatrix}$

3. Given $A = \begin{pmatrix} 1 & 2 \\ 3 & 4 \end{pmatrix}$, $B = \begin{pmatrix} -2 & 3 \\ 0 & 4 \end{pmatrix}$, and

$C = \begin{pmatrix} -1 & 2 \\ -3 & -4 \end{pmatrix}$, find each of the following

matrices.
(a) $A + B$ (b) $A + C$
(c) $A - C$ (d) $C - A$

(e) $(A + B) + C$ (f) $A + (B + C)$
(g) $(B - C) - (C + B)$

4. (a) During each of the last two years, Mr. Thomas taught 4 classes of grade 10 mathematics and 2 classes of grade 10 computer studies. Ms. Labelle taught 3 classes of each. The distribution of students taught by these two teachers in the last two years is shown in the table below.

	First Year		Second Year	
	Math	Computer Studies	Math	Computer Studies
Thomas	84	44	81	47
Labelle	63	66	62	65

(i) Represent the distribution of students for each year in separate matrices.
(ii) Represent in one matrix the total distribution of students taught by the two teachers over the two-year period.
(b) The distribution of students to receive a passing grade is shown in the table below.

	First Year		Second Year	
	Math	Computer Studies	Math	Computer Studies
Thomas	79	39	74	45
Labelle	59	61	56	61

(i) Represent the distribution of students receiving a passing grade for each year in separate matrices.
(ii) Use one matrix to represent the total distribution of students receiving a passing grade over the two-year period.
(iii) Represent in one matrix the total distribution of students who did not receive a passing grade.

7.4 SCALAR MULTIPLICATION

In matrix algebra, a real number is often called a scalar. Multiplying a matrix by a real number is called scalar multiplication.

If x is a real number, then $2x = x + x$. So if A is a matrix, then we write $2A = A + A$.

$$\text{If } A = \begin{pmatrix} 1 & 3 \\ 4 & 5 \end{pmatrix}$$

$$\text{then } 2A = A + A$$

$$= \begin{pmatrix} 1 & 3 \\ 4 & 5 \end{pmatrix} + \begin{pmatrix} 1 & 3 \\ 4 & 5 \end{pmatrix}$$

$$= \begin{pmatrix} 2 & 6 \\ 8 & 10 \end{pmatrix}$$

$$= \begin{pmatrix} 2 \times 1 & 2 \times 3 \\ 2 \times 4 & 2 \times 5 \end{pmatrix}$$

$$\text{Similarly, } 3A = A + A + A$$

$$= \begin{pmatrix} 1 & 3 \\ 4 & 5 \end{pmatrix} + \begin{pmatrix} 1 & 3 \\ 4 & 5 \end{pmatrix} + \begin{pmatrix} 1 & 3 \\ 4 & 5 \end{pmatrix}$$

$$= \begin{pmatrix} 3 & 9 \\ 12 & 15 \end{pmatrix}$$

$$= \begin{pmatrix} 3 \times 1 & 3 \times 3 \\ 3 \times 4 & 3 \times 5 \end{pmatrix}$$

If k is a real number and A is a matrix, then kA is the matrix obtained by multiplying each entry of A by k.

$$k\begin{pmatrix} a & b \\ c & d \end{pmatrix} = \begin{pmatrix} ka & kb \\ kc & kd \end{pmatrix}$$

EXAMPLE 1. If $A = \begin{pmatrix} 0 & 4 \\ 3 & 5 \end{pmatrix}$ and $B = \begin{pmatrix} -1 & 2 \\ -4 & 6 \end{pmatrix}$, find $2A + 3B$.

SOLUTION:

$$2A + 3B = 2\begin{pmatrix} 0 & 4 \\ 3 & 5 \end{pmatrix} + 3\begin{pmatrix} -1 & 2 \\ -4 & 6 \end{pmatrix}$$

$$= \begin{pmatrix} 0 & 8 \\ 6 & 10 \end{pmatrix} + \begin{pmatrix} -3 & 6 \\ -12 & 18 \end{pmatrix}$$

$$= \begin{pmatrix} -3 & 14 \\ -6 & 28 \end{pmatrix}$$

EXAMPLE 2. A food distributor's gross sales of fish, poultry, and meats in its first year of operation is shown in the table below.

	Fish	Poultry	Meats
Spring	$1200	$2300	$2400
Summer	$1400	$2400	$2800
Fall	$1500	$2000	$3000
Winter	$1400	$2000	$2800

A 10% increase in sales is forecasted for the next year.
(a) Represent the gross sales of the first year in matrix form.
(b) Represent the forecasted sales for the next year in matrix form.

SOLUTION:
(a) The matrix representing gross sales for the first year is

$$G = \begin{pmatrix} 1200 & 2300 & 2400 \\ 1400 & 2400 & 2800 \\ 1500 & 2000 & 3000 \\ 1400 & 2000 & 2800 \end{pmatrix}$$

(b) To obtain the forecasted gross sales, we multiply the previous matrix by the scalar 1.1

$$G = \begin{pmatrix} 1320 & 2530 & 2640 \\ 1540 & 2640 & 3080 \\ 1650 & 2200 & 3300 \\ 1540 & 2200 & 3080 \end{pmatrix}$$

EXERCISE 7.4

A 1. Perform each scalar multiplication.

(a) $3\begin{pmatrix} 4 & 0 \\ 1 & 5 \end{pmatrix}$

(b) $2\begin{pmatrix} 0 \\ 1 \\ -6 \end{pmatrix}$

(c) $-4(5 \quad -2 \quad -3)$

(d) $\frac{1}{2}\begin{pmatrix} 8 & 6 \\ 4 & -10 \end{pmatrix}$

(e) $5\begin{pmatrix} 3a & 2b \\ -5a & 3b \end{pmatrix}$

(f) $-2\begin{pmatrix} 5 & -7 \\ -3 & -1 \end{pmatrix}$

B 2. Perform the indicated operations.

(a) $2\begin{pmatrix} 4 & 3 \\ 7 & 1 \end{pmatrix} + 3\begin{pmatrix} 5 & 0 \\ -2 & -1 \end{pmatrix}$

(b) $3\begin{pmatrix} 2 & 1 \\ 0 & 5 \\ -3 & 6 \end{pmatrix} + 5\begin{pmatrix} -1 & -2 \\ 3 & 0 \\ 4 & -2 \end{pmatrix}$

(c) $2\begin{pmatrix} 3 & -1 \\ 4 & 2 \end{pmatrix} - 3\begin{pmatrix} -5 & 1 \\ -2 & 3 \end{pmatrix}$

(d) $2\begin{pmatrix} 3 & -1 & 0 \\ -2 & 1 & -2 \end{pmatrix} - 3\begin{pmatrix} -5 & 2 & 2 \\ -1 & 0 & 1 \end{pmatrix}$

(e) $2\begin{pmatrix} -5 & -3 \\ 4 & 1 \end{pmatrix} - \begin{pmatrix} -5 & 2 \\ 3 & -4 \end{pmatrix}$

3. If $A = \begin{pmatrix} 2 & -3 \\ 4 & 0 \end{pmatrix}$ and $B = \begin{pmatrix} -1 & 2 \\ -3 & 5 \end{pmatrix}$, find

each of the following.
(a) 3A
(b) 2B
(c) A − B
(d) 3A + 2B
(e) 2A − 3B
(f) 2B − 4A
(g) 2(A − B)
(h) 3(B − A)

4. Solve each equation for the 2 × 2 matrix X.

(a) $2X = \begin{pmatrix} 4 & -8 \\ 6 & -10 \end{pmatrix}$

(b) $3X = \begin{pmatrix} 9 \\ -6 \\ -12 \end{pmatrix}$

(c) $2X + \begin{pmatrix} 0 & 1 \\ 1 & 0 \end{pmatrix} = \begin{pmatrix} 4 & 5 \\ 3 & 8 \end{pmatrix}$

(d) $2X + \begin{pmatrix} 1 & 3 \\ -1 & 5 \end{pmatrix} = d\begin{pmatrix} -3 & 5 \\ 1 & 1 \end{pmatrix}$

(e) $X - \begin{pmatrix} 0 & 3 \\ 5 & -2 \end{pmatrix} = 2\begin{pmatrix} 4 & -1 \\ 3 & -5 \end{pmatrix}$

(f) $2X + \begin{pmatrix} 0 & 2 \\ -3 & 4 \end{pmatrix} = \begin{pmatrix} 2 & -4 \\ 1 & 0 \end{pmatrix} + X$

(g) $3X + \begin{pmatrix} 2 & 0 \\ -5 & 3 \end{pmatrix} = 3\begin{pmatrix} 5 & -2 \\ 0 & 3 \end{pmatrix}$

5. The number of students registered in a local university this year is as follows.

	Arts	Sciences
Winter Term	8500	6000
Intercession	8200	5600
Summer Term	4000	2500

Enrolment is expected to increase by 5% next year.
(a) Represent this year's enrolment in matrix form.
(b) Represent next year's forecasted enrolment in matrix form.

CALCULATOR MATH

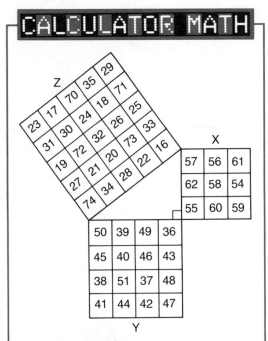

The triangle in the diagram is a right triangle. Z is the square on the hypotenuse and X and Y are the squares on the other two sides.

1. Verify that X, Y, and Z are each magic squares.
2. What is the magic number for each?
3. Verify that the square of the total of all the cells in Z equals the square of the total of all the cells in X plus the square of the total of all the cells in Y.

7.5 MULTIPLICATION OF MATRICES

It would seem that multiplication of matrices should be done in a manner similar to addition of matrices. However, if multiplication is done in this way, then the range of applications is extremely limited. Since we are interested in the applications of matrices we will multiply matrices in a way that turns out to be useful. At first the procedure may seem unnecessarily complicated. However, the applications will justify the method.

To multiply matrices it is not necessary that they have the same dimensions. What is necessary is that the number of columns of the first matrix be the same as the number of rows of the second matrix.

We will illustrate matrix multiplication by determining the revenue of a parking lot.

	Number of Cars	Number of Buses		Charge/vehicle in Dollars	
Monday	72	15		Cars	4
Tuesday	83	7		Buses	12

	Revenue in Dollars
Monday	m
Tuesday	t

Before applying matrix multiplication we will determine m and t by another procedure.

$$m = 72(4) + 15(12)$$
$$= 468$$

$$t = 83(4) + 7(12)$$
$$= 416$$

These calculations for m and t suggest a pattern for matrix multiplication.

$$\begin{pmatrix} 72 & 15 \\ 83 & 7 \end{pmatrix} \begin{pmatrix} 4 \\ 12 \end{pmatrix} = \begin{pmatrix} 468 \\ 416 \end{pmatrix}$$

The entry 468 is in row 1 and column 1 of the product matrix. It is obtained by multiplying, respectively, the entries in row 1 of $\begin{pmatrix} 72 & 15 \\ 83 & 7 \end{pmatrix}$ by those in column 1 of $\begin{pmatrix} 4 \\ 12 \end{pmatrix}$, and adding the results. That is,

$72 \times 4 + 15 \times 12 = 468.$

Similarly, the entry 416 is in row 2 and column 1 of the product matrix. It is obtained by multiplying the entries in row 2 of $\begin{pmatrix} 72 & 15 \\ 83 & 7 \end{pmatrix}$ by those in column 1 of $\begin{pmatrix} 4 \\ 12 \end{pmatrix}$, and adding the results. That is,

$83 \times 4 + 7 \times 12 = 416$.

You obtain the entries of the product matrix by adding the products of elements of a row of the first matrix with the corresponding elements of a column of the second matrix.

> The product of an m × n matrix A and an n × p matrix B is the m × p matrix whose entry in row i and column j is the sum of the products of corresponding elements of row i in A and column j in B.

A square matrix whose main diagonal from upper left to lower right has entries 1, while all other entries are 0, is called an identity matrix, usually represented by the letter I. An identity matrix, when multiplied by another square matrix A, leaves the matrix A unchanged.

EXAMPLE. Find the product.

$$\begin{pmatrix} 1 & 0 \\ 0 & 1 \end{pmatrix} \begin{pmatrix} 3 & -2 \\ 4 & -3 \end{pmatrix}$$

SOLUTION:

$$\begin{pmatrix} a & b \\ c & d \end{pmatrix} \begin{pmatrix} e & f \\ g & h \end{pmatrix} = \begin{pmatrix} ae + bg & af + bh \\ ce + dg & cf + dh \end{pmatrix}$$

$$\begin{pmatrix} 1 & 0 \\ 0 & 1 \end{pmatrix} \begin{pmatrix} 3 & -2 \\ 4 & -3 \end{pmatrix} = \begin{pmatrix} 3 & \\ & \end{pmatrix}$$

$$\begin{pmatrix} 1 & 0 \\ 0 & 1 \end{pmatrix} \begin{pmatrix} 3 & -2 \\ 4 & -3 \end{pmatrix} = \begin{pmatrix} 3 & -2 \\ & \end{pmatrix}$$

$$\begin{pmatrix} 1 & 0 \\ 0 & 1 \end{pmatrix} \begin{pmatrix} 3 & -2 \\ 4 & -3 \end{pmatrix} = \begin{pmatrix} 3 & -2 \\ 4 & \end{pmatrix}$$

$$\begin{pmatrix} 1 & 0 \\ 0 & 1 \end{pmatrix} \begin{pmatrix} 3 & -2 \\ 4 & -3 \end{pmatrix} = \begin{pmatrix} 3 & -2 \\ 4 & -3 \end{pmatrix}$$

EXERCISE 7.5

1. Perform the following multiplications, if possible.

(a) $\begin{pmatrix} 3 & 1 \\ 2 & 4 \end{pmatrix}\begin{pmatrix} 2 & 1 & 0 \\ 3 & 0 & 1 \end{pmatrix}$

(b) $\begin{pmatrix} 5 & -2 & 3 \\ 1 & 2 & -1 \end{pmatrix}\begin{pmatrix} 4 & 3 \\ 1 & -1 \\ 0 & 2 \end{pmatrix}$

(c) $\begin{pmatrix} 3 & 4 \\ -1 & 2 \end{pmatrix}\begin{pmatrix} 5 & 4 \\ 1 & -2 \\ 3 & 1 \end{pmatrix}$

(d) $(1 \quad -3 \quad 5)\begin{pmatrix} 3 \\ 0 \\ -3 \end{pmatrix}$

(e) $\begin{pmatrix} 2 & -1 & 2 \\ -3 & 4 & -1 \\ 5 & 0 & 3 \end{pmatrix}\begin{pmatrix} 5 & 2 & 5 \\ -1 & 2 & -1 \\ 4 & 3 & 4 \end{pmatrix}$

(f) $\begin{pmatrix} 4 & -2 & 3 \\ -1 & -3 & 5 \\ 3 & 1 & -2 \end{pmatrix}\begin{pmatrix} 3 \\ 0 \\ -1 \end{pmatrix}$

(g) $\begin{pmatrix} 5 \\ 2 \\ -1 \\ 3 \end{pmatrix}(4 \quad -2)$

(h) $\begin{pmatrix} 6 & 2 \\ -3 & 5 \\ 7 & -1 \end{pmatrix}\begin{pmatrix} 4 & -1 \\ 3 & 5 \\ 2 & -7 \end{pmatrix}$

(i) $\begin{pmatrix} 7 \\ 8 \end{pmatrix}\begin{pmatrix} -1 & -3 & 4 \\ 6 & 5 & -2 \end{pmatrix}$

(j) $\begin{pmatrix} 3 & -2 & 4 \\ 5 & 1 & 6 \\ 5 & 2 & -3 \end{pmatrix}\begin{pmatrix} 1 & 0 & 0 \\ 0 & 1 & 0 \\ 0 & 0 & 1 \end{pmatrix}$

(k) $\begin{pmatrix} 1 & 0 \\ 0 & 1 \end{pmatrix}\begin{pmatrix} -3 & 5 \\ 6 & 4 \end{pmatrix}$

(l) $\begin{pmatrix} -2 & -5 \\ -7 & 3 \end{pmatrix}\begin{pmatrix} 0 & 1 \\ 1 & 0 \end{pmatrix}$

(m) $\begin{pmatrix} 3 & -4 & 6 \\ 5 & -2 & 3 \\ 7 & 4 & 5 \\ 6 & 0 & -1 \end{pmatrix}\begin{pmatrix} -1 \\ 2 \\ -3 \end{pmatrix}$

(n) $\begin{pmatrix} 2 & 1 & -2 & 3 \\ 5 & 4 & 0 & -1 \\ 3 & -1 & -2 & 2 \end{pmatrix}\begin{pmatrix} 5 & 2 \\ -3 & 1 \\ 4 & -2 \\ -3 & 0 \end{pmatrix}$

C2. If $A = \begin{pmatrix} 2 & 1 \\ 3 & 2 \end{pmatrix}$, $B = \begin{pmatrix} 0 & -1 \\ 2 & -3 \end{pmatrix}$, and

$C = \begin{pmatrix} 1 & 2 \\ -1 & -2 \end{pmatrix}$, find.

(a) AB and BA
(b) BC and CB
(c) A(B + C) and AB + AC
(d) A(B − C) and AB − AC
(e) A(BC) and (AB)C
(f) (A − B)(A + B) and $A^2 - B^2$
(g) $(A - B)^2$ and $A^2 - 2AB + B^2$
(h) $(A + B)^2$ and $A^2 + 2AB + B^2$

MICRO MATH

The following BASIC program multiplies two 2 × 2 matrices.

$$X = \begin{pmatrix} a & b \\ c & d \end{pmatrix} \quad \text{and} \quad Y = \begin{pmatrix} e & f \\ g & h \end{pmatrix}$$

NEW

```
100 REM MULTIPLYING TWO 2X2 MATRICES
110 PRINT "FOR MATRIX X..."
120 PRINT "INPUT A, B, C, D"
130 INPUT A, B, C, D
140 PRINT "FOR MATRIX Y..."
150 PRINT "INPUT E, F, G, H"
160 INPUT E, F, G, H
170 PRINT "THE PRODUCT MATRIX XY IS:"
180 PRINT A*E+B*G; TAB(8); A*F+B*H
190 PRINT C*E+D*G; TAB(8); C*F+D*H
200 END
```

RUN

7.6 THE INVERSE OF A MATRIX

We can compare the identity element for multiplication of matrices to the identity element for multiplication of real numbers.

For real numbers, the identity element for multiplication in the set of real numbers is 1.

$$1 \times 3 = 3 \times 1 = 3$$
$$1 \times -2 = -2 \times 1 = -2$$
$$1 \times \tfrac{1}{2} = \tfrac{1}{2} \times 1 = \tfrac{1}{2}$$

Two real numbers whose product is the identity element 1 are said to be multiplicative inverses of each other.

$$3 \times \tfrac{1}{3} = \tfrac{1}{3} \times 3$$
$$= 1$$

$\tfrac{1}{3}$ is the multiplicative inverse of 3 and vice versa.

For 2×2 matrices, the identity element for

multiplication is $I = \begin{pmatrix} 1 & 0 \\ 0 & 1 \end{pmatrix}$.

$$\begin{array}{ccccc} IA & = & AI & = & A \\ \begin{pmatrix} 1 & 0 \\ 0 & 1 \end{pmatrix}\begin{pmatrix} 2 & 3 \\ 4 & 5 \end{pmatrix} & = & \begin{pmatrix} 2 & 3 \\ 4 & 5 \end{pmatrix}\begin{pmatrix} 1 & 0 \\ 0 & 1 \end{pmatrix} & = & \begin{pmatrix} 2 & 3 \\ 4 & 5 \end{pmatrix} \end{array}$$

Two matrices M and N such that MN = NM = I, where I is the identity matrix, are called inverses. We usually denote N by M^{-1}, which is called the inverse of M.

If $A = \begin{pmatrix} a & b \\ c & d \end{pmatrix}$, the inverse of A, written A^{-1} is obtained as follows.

$$A^{-1} = \begin{pmatrix} \dfrac{d}{ad - bc} & \dfrac{-b}{ad - bc} \\ \dfrac{-c}{ad - bc} & \dfrac{a}{ad - bc} \end{pmatrix} \qquad \text{where } ad - bc \neq 0.$$

EXAMPLE. Find the inverse of the matrix if it exists.

(a) $A = \begin{pmatrix} 2 & 3 \\ 1 & 4 \end{pmatrix}$

(b) $B = \begin{pmatrix} 3 & 4 \\ 6 & 8 \end{pmatrix}$

SOLUTION:

(a) If $A = \begin{pmatrix} a & b \\ c & d \end{pmatrix} = \begin{pmatrix} 2 & 3 \\ 1 & 4 \end{pmatrix}$,

then $ad - bc = 8 - 3$
$= 5$

Since $ad - bc \neq 0$, then A^{-1} exists.

$$A^{-1} = \begin{pmatrix} \frac{4}{5} & -\frac{3}{5} \\ -\frac{1}{5} & \frac{2}{5} \end{pmatrix}$$

Check.

$$A^{-1}A = \begin{pmatrix} \frac{4}{5} & -\frac{3}{5} \\ -\frac{1}{5} & \frac{2}{5} \end{pmatrix}\begin{pmatrix} 2 & 3 \\ 1 & 4 \end{pmatrix}$$

$$= \begin{pmatrix} \frac{8}{5} - \frac{3}{5} & \frac{12}{5} - \frac{12}{5} \\ -\frac{2}{5} + \frac{2}{5} & -\frac{3}{5} + \frac{8}{5} \end{pmatrix}$$

$$= \begin{pmatrix} 1 & 0 \\ 0 & 1 \end{pmatrix}$$

$$= I$$

$$AA^{-1} = \begin{pmatrix} 2 & 3 \\ 1 & 4 \end{pmatrix}\begin{pmatrix} \frac{4}{5} & -\frac{3}{5} \\ -\frac{1}{5} & \frac{2}{5} \end{pmatrix}$$

$$= \begin{pmatrix} \frac{8}{5} - \frac{3}{5} & -\frac{6}{5} + \frac{6}{5} \\ \frac{4}{5} - \frac{4}{5} & -\frac{3}{5} + \frac{8}{5} \end{pmatrix}$$

$$= \begin{pmatrix} 1 & 0 \\ 0 & 1 \end{pmatrix}$$

$$= I$$

(b) If $B = \begin{pmatrix} a & b \\ c & d \end{pmatrix} = \begin{pmatrix} 3 & 4 \\ 6 & 8 \end{pmatrix}$,

then $ad - bc = 24 - 24$
$$= 0$$

Since $ad - bc = 0$, then B^{-1} does not exist.

EXERCISE 7.6

A 1. Which of the following matrices have an inverse?

(a) $A = \begin{pmatrix} 2 & 1 \\ 0 & 2 \end{pmatrix}$

(b) $B = \begin{pmatrix} 2 & 1 \\ 5 & 3 \end{pmatrix}$

(c) $C = \begin{pmatrix} 2 & -1 \\ -4 & 2 \end{pmatrix}$

(d) $D = \begin{pmatrix} 2 & 1 \\ 1 & 0 \end{pmatrix}$

(e) $E = \begin{pmatrix} 3 & 0 \\ -1 & 0 \end{pmatrix}$

(f) $F = \begin{pmatrix} 3 & -7 \\ 2 & -5 \end{pmatrix}$

(e) $E = \begin{pmatrix} 4 & 6 \\ 2 & 3 \end{pmatrix}$

(f) $F = \begin{pmatrix} 1 & 4 \\ -2 & -6 \end{pmatrix}$

3. If $A = \begin{pmatrix} 1 & 2 \\ 1 & 3 \end{pmatrix}$ and $B = \begin{pmatrix} 2 & 1 \\ 5 & 3 \end{pmatrix}$, find.

(a) A^{-1}
(b) B^{-1}
(c) $B^{-1}A^{-1}$
(d) AB
(e) $(AB)^{-1}$
(f) What conclusion can you draw about $B^{-1}A^{-1}$ and $(AB)^{-1}$?

B 2. Find the inverse, if one exists, of each of the following matrices.

(a) $A = \begin{pmatrix} 3 & 1 \\ 2 & 1 \end{pmatrix}$

(b) $B = \begin{pmatrix} 5 & 3 \\ 1 & 1 \end{pmatrix}$

(c) $C = \begin{pmatrix} 4 & 6 \\ -2 & -2 \end{pmatrix}$

(d) $D = \begin{pmatrix} 5 & 0 \\ 1 & 2 \end{pmatrix}$

C 4. If $A = \begin{pmatrix} a & b \\ c & d \end{pmatrix}$ where $ad - bc \neq 0$, prove

that $A^{-1} = \begin{pmatrix} \dfrac{d}{ad - bc} & \dfrac{-b}{ad - bc} \\ \dfrac{-c}{ad - bc} & \dfrac{a}{ad - bc} \end{pmatrix}$ is the

inverse of A by verifying that $A^{-1}A = AA^{-1} = I$.

7.7 SOLVING LINEAR SYSTEMS USING MATRICES

A system of linear equations such as

$$x + 2y = 5$$
$$3x - 4y = -5$$

can be written as a linear matrix equation of the form AX = B, where

A is the matrix of coefficients $\begin{pmatrix} 1 & 2 \\ 3 & -4 \end{pmatrix}$,

X is the variable matrix, $\begin{pmatrix} x \\ y \end{pmatrix}$ and

B is the matrix of constants $\begin{pmatrix} 5 \\ -5 \end{pmatrix}$.

In this case, the linear matrix equation AX = B is

$$\begin{pmatrix} 1 & 2 \\ 3 & -4 \end{pmatrix}\begin{pmatrix} x \\ y \end{pmatrix} = \begin{pmatrix} 5 \\ -5 \end{pmatrix}$$

We can check this matrix equation by expanding the left side by matrix multiplication.

$$\begin{pmatrix} x + 2y \\ 3x - 4y \end{pmatrix} = \begin{pmatrix} 5 \\ -5 \end{pmatrix}$$

Since matrices are equal only when corresponding elements are equal, we obtain our original system.

$$x + 2y = 5 \quad \text{and} \quad 3x - 4y = -5$$

The procedure for solving a linear matrix equation in the form AX = B is similar to that of solving an equation in the form $3x = 7$; we multiply both sides by a multiplicative inverse.

Solve. $3x = 7$	Solve. AX = B
Multiply both sides by $\frac{1}{3}$, the multiplicative inverse of 3.	Multiply both sides by A^{-1}, the multiplicative inverse of the matrix A.
$\frac{1}{3}(3x) = \frac{1}{3}(7)$ $1x = \frac{7}{3}$ $x = \frac{7}{3}$	$A^{-1}AX = A^{-1}B$ $IX = A^{-1}B$ $X = A^{-1}B$

EXAMPLE. Given the linear system
$$3x + 2y = 7$$
$$4x + 3y = 10$$
(a) Express the system as a linear matrix equation.
(b) Find A^{-1} if it exists.
(c) Multiply both sides of the linear matrix equation by A^{-1}.
(d) Solve for x and y, and check.

SOLUTION:

(a) Let $A = \begin{pmatrix} 3 & 2 \\ 4 & 3 \end{pmatrix}$, $X = \begin{pmatrix} x \\ y \end{pmatrix}$, and $B = \begin{pmatrix} 7 \\ 10 \end{pmatrix}$.

The linear matrix equation is

$$AX = B$$

$$\begin{pmatrix} 3 & 2 \\ 4 & 3 \end{pmatrix}\begin{pmatrix} x \\ y \end{pmatrix} = \begin{pmatrix} 7 \\ 10 \end{pmatrix}$$

(b) If $A = \begin{pmatrix} 3 & 2 \\ 4 & 3 \end{pmatrix} = \begin{pmatrix} a & b \\ c & d \end{pmatrix}$,

then $ad - bc = 9 - 8$
$\qquad\qquad = 1.$

Hence, A^{-1} exists.

$$A^{-1} = \begin{pmatrix} \frac{3}{1} & -\frac{2}{1} \\ -\frac{4}{1} & \frac{3}{1} \end{pmatrix} = \begin{pmatrix} 3 & -2 \\ -4 & 3 \end{pmatrix}$$

(c) $\quad A^{-1} \qquad A \qquad X = \qquad A^{-1} \qquad B$

$$\begin{pmatrix} 3 & -2 \\ -4 & 3 \end{pmatrix}\begin{pmatrix} 3 & 2 \\ 4 & 3 \end{pmatrix}\begin{pmatrix} x \\ y \end{pmatrix} = \begin{pmatrix} 3 & -2 \\ -4 & 3 \end{pmatrix}\begin{pmatrix} 7 \\ 10 \end{pmatrix}$$

$$\begin{pmatrix} 1 & 0 \\ 0 & 1 \end{pmatrix}\begin{pmatrix} x \\ y \end{pmatrix} = \begin{pmatrix} 1 \\ 2 \end{pmatrix}$$

$$\begin{pmatrix} x \\ y \end{pmatrix} = \begin{pmatrix} 1 \\ 2 \end{pmatrix}$$

(d) By comparing the corresponding elements of the two equal matrices, we obtain $x = 1$ and $y = 2$.

Check.

For $3x + 2y = 7$,
if $x = 1$ and $y = 2$,

L.S. $= 3(1) + 2(2)$ R.S. $= 7$
$\quad = 3 + 4$
$\quad = 7$
$\qquad$ L.S. $=$ R.S.

For $4x + 3y = 10$,
if $x = 1$ and $y = 2$,

L.S. $= 4(1) + 3(2)$ R.S. $= 10$
$\quad = 4 + 6$
$\quad = 10$
$\qquad$ L.S. $=$ R.S.

$\therefore x = 1$ and $y = 2$.

EXERCISE 7.7

B 1. Solve the following systems of equations using matrices.

(a) $x + y = 5$
$2x - y = 4$

(b) $x + 2y = 6$
$x + 3y = 7$

(c) $2x - 3y = 12$
$x + 4y = -5$

(d) $2x + y = 13$
$3x - 2y = 9$

(e) $4x - y = 5$
$2x + 5y = -14$

(f) $4x - y = -2$
$7x - 2y = -5$

(g) $2x + 5y = -10$
$5x - 3y = -9$

(h) $3x + 2y = 1$
$4x - 3y = 24$

(i) $3x + 5y = 11$
$4x + 3y = 0$

(j) $4x + 5y + 6 = 0$
$3x - 2y = -16$

MICRO MATH

This program will calculate the inverse of the matrix

$$\begin{pmatrix} a & b \\ c & d \end{pmatrix}$$

if it exists.

NEW

```
100 REM INVERSE OF A 2X2
110 PRINT "ENTER A, B, C, D"
120 PRINT "SEPARATED BY COMMAS"
130 INPUT A, B, C, D
140 Q = A*D - B*C
150 IF Q <> 0 THEN 180
160 PRINT "NO INVERSE MATRIX."
170 GOTO 210
180 PRINT "THE INVERSE MATRIX IS"
190 PRINT D/Q; TAB(8); -B/Q
200 PRINT -C/Q; TAB(8); A/Q
210 END
```

RUN

Summary of Matrices

If $A = \begin{pmatrix} a & b \\ c & d \end{pmatrix}$, $B = \begin{pmatrix} e & f \\ g & h \end{pmatrix}$, and $k \in R$,

then

$$kA = \begin{pmatrix} ka & kb \\ kc & kd \end{pmatrix}$$

$$-A = \begin{pmatrix} -a & -b \\ -c & -d \end{pmatrix}$$

$$A + B = \begin{pmatrix} a + e & b + f \\ c + g & d + h \end{pmatrix}$$

$$A - B = \begin{pmatrix} a - e & b - f \\ c - g & d - h \end{pmatrix}$$

$$A^{-1} = \begin{pmatrix} \dfrac{d}{ad - bc} & \dfrac{-b}{ad - bc} \\ \dfrac{-c}{ad - bc} & \dfrac{a}{ad - bc} \end{pmatrix}$$

where $ad - bc \neq 0$

$$AB = \begin{pmatrix} ae + bg & af + bh \\ ce + dg & cf + dh \end{pmatrix}$$

7.8 A FORMULA FOR LINEAR SYSTEMS IN TWO VARIABLES

The system $\begin{array}{l} ax + by = e \\ cx + dy = f \end{array}$ where $ad - bc \neq 0$ can be represented in matrix form as

$\begin{pmatrix} a & b \\ c & d \end{pmatrix}\begin{pmatrix} x \\ y \end{pmatrix} = \begin{pmatrix} e \\ f \end{pmatrix}$. The linear matrix equation is $AX = B$. Multiplying both sides by A^{-1}

yields $X = A^{-1}B$.

$$A^{-1}AX = A^{-1}B$$
$$X = A^{-1}B$$

If $X = \begin{pmatrix} x \\ y \end{pmatrix}$, $A^{-1} = \begin{pmatrix} \dfrac{d}{ad-bc} & \dfrac{-b}{ad-bc} \\ \dfrac{-c}{ad-bc} & \dfrac{a}{ad-bc} \end{pmatrix}$, and $B = \begin{pmatrix} e \\ f \end{pmatrix}$,

then $\begin{pmatrix} x \\ y \end{pmatrix} = \begin{pmatrix} \dfrac{d}{ad-bc} & \dfrac{-b}{ad-bc} \\ \dfrac{-c}{ad-bc} & \dfrac{a}{ad-bc} \end{pmatrix}\begin{pmatrix} e \\ f \end{pmatrix}$

$\begin{pmatrix} x \\ y \end{pmatrix} = \begin{pmatrix} \dfrac{de-bf}{ad-bc} \\ \dfrac{af-ce}{ad-bc} \end{pmatrix}$

Hence $X = \dfrac{de-bf}{ad-bc}$ and $y = \dfrac{af-ce}{ad-bc}$.

EXAMPLE. Solve. $2x + 3y = 4$
$\qquad\qquad\qquad\quad x + 2y = 3$

SOLUTION:
Let $a = 2$, $b = 3$, $c = 1$, $d = 2$, $e = 4$,   and $f = 3$.

$\qquad x = \dfrac{(2)(4) - (3)(3)}{(2)(2) - (3)(1)}\qquad$ and $\qquad y = \dfrac{(2)(3) - (1)(4)}{(2)(2) - (3)(1)}$

$\qquad\quad = -1 \qquad\qquad\qquad\qquad\qquad\quad = 2$

EXERCISE 7.8

1. Solve.
(a) $2x - 3y = -5$
$\quad\ 3x + y = 9$

(b) $2x + 3y = 9$
$\quad -x + 4y = 23$

(c) $4x - 5y = 11$
$\quad -2x + 3y = -7$

7.9 PROBLEM SOLVING USING MATRICES

Our problem solving model in Chapter 1, suggests that making a table or chart is a good planning technique.

The organization of data into a more readable form may often lead to a clear and concise solution.

Matrices can contribute greatly to the solution of business problems by organizing large amounts of information into a concise form.

READ

EXAMPLE. A fresh fruit distributor supplies apples, peaches, and pears to four different stores. In one week, Store 1 bought 60 cases of apples, 40 cases of peaches, and 30 cases of pears. Store 2 bought 70 cases of apples, 30 cases of peaches, and 25 cases of pears. Store 3 bought 50 cases of apples, 20 cases of peaches, and 30 cases of pears. Store 4 bought 20 cases of pears, twice as many of peaches, and twice as many apples as peaches. Apples cost $15 per case, peaches $14 per case, and pears $12 per case. Determine the distributor's total income from each store.

PLAN

SOLUTION:

At first, the amount of information seems overwhelming. The table below will organize the data.

Number of Cases Ordered by Each Store

	Apples	Peaches	Pears
Store 1	60	40	30
Store 2	70	30	25
Store 3	50	20	30
Store 4	80	40	20

Cost per Case ($)

Apples	15
Peaches	14
Pears	12

We can further simplify the information using matrices.

Let A represent the amounts ordered by each store.

$$A = \begin{pmatrix} 60 & 40 & 30 \\ 70 & 30 & 25 \\ 50 & 20 & 30 \\ 80 & 40 & 20 \end{pmatrix}$$

Let C represent the costs of each case.

$$C = \begin{pmatrix} 15 \\ 14 \\ 12 \end{pmatrix}$$

SOLVE

Determining the total income for each store involves multiplying the number of cases ordered by each store by the corresponding cost per case. Matrix multiplication serves this purpose.

$$\begin{pmatrix} 60 & 40 & 30 \\ 70 & 30 & 25 \\ 50 & 20 & 30 \\ 80 & 40 & 20 \end{pmatrix} \begin{pmatrix} 15 \\ 14 \\ 12 \end{pmatrix} = \begin{pmatrix} 1820 \\ 1770 \\ 1390 \\ 2000 \end{pmatrix}$$

ANSWER

Store 1 paid $1820 for all 3 products; Store 2, $1770; Store 3, $1390; and Store 4, $2000.

The total income from all four stores, $6980, is obtained by adding the entries in the product matrix.

Sometimes a communication must be coded in such a way that it is difficult to decode. Matrices can be used to obtain a code that is relatively difficult to break. Matrix multiplication is used to encode the message, while at the other end, multiplication by the inverse matrix will easily decode it.

The message "RESCUE AT DAWN" is coded using the following steps.

Step 1.

Change each letter of the message to a number using the pattern:

R E S C U E A T D A W N
18 5 19 3 21 5 1 20 4 1 23 14

A B C D E F $\cdots$ X Y Z
1 2 3 4 5 6   24 25 26

Ignore spaces and punctuation.

Step 2.

Break the message up into groups of two numbers and express as 2×1 column matrices.

$$\begin{pmatrix} 18 \\ 5 \end{pmatrix} \begin{pmatrix} 19 \\ 3 \end{pmatrix} \begin{pmatrix} 21 \\ 5 \end{pmatrix} \begin{pmatrix} 1 \\ 20 \end{pmatrix} \begin{pmatrix} 4 \\ 1 \end{pmatrix} \begin{pmatrix} 23 \\ 14 \end{pmatrix}$$

Step 3.

Choose any 2×2 matrix that has an inverse, say $\begin{pmatrix} 3 & 1 \\ 2 & 1 \end{pmatrix}$.

$$\begin{pmatrix} 59 \\ 41 \end{pmatrix} \begin{pmatrix} 60 \\ 41 \end{pmatrix} \begin{pmatrix} 68 \\ 47 \end{pmatrix} \begin{pmatrix} 23 \\ 22 \end{pmatrix} \begin{pmatrix} 13 \\ 9 \end{pmatrix} \begin{pmatrix} 83 \\ 60 \end{pmatrix}$$

Multiply each column matrix by this encoding matrix.

Step 4.

Write the numbers horizontally.   59 41 60 41 68 47 23 22 13 9 83 60
Transmit this code.

When the message is received, it is converted into a set of
2 × 1 column matrices. Then each column matrix is multiplied
by the inverse of the coding matrix. In this case, the decoding

matrix is $\begin{pmatrix} 1 & -1 \\ -2 & 3 \end{pmatrix}$. The numbers are written horizontally, then

converted back to letters.
Another method for encoding a message might be to group the
numbers into groups of 4 to form 2 × 2 matrices. Each matrix can
then be added to a coding matrix. Decoding would be done by
subtracting the matrix.

Can you think of any other ingeneous ways of encoding a message?

EXERCISE 7.9

B 1. The Ace Sports Company supplies
baseballs, footballs, and basketballs to five
local high schools. The following table
indicates the number of each type of ball
ordered by each school.

	Base-balls	Foot-balls	Basket-balls
Churchill H.S.	30	10	15
Vanier H.S.	20	15	20
Central H.S.	15	20	25
High Park H.S.	20	15	30
Parkside H.S.	25	15	30

Baseballs cost $4 each, footballs $40 each,
and basketballs $30 each.

(a) Write the total order as a matrix.
(b) Write the cost of each as a column matrix.
(c) Use matrix multiplication to find the
amount owing to the company by each high
school.
(d) Use matrix multiplication to find the
company's income from footballs.
(e) Use matrix multiplication to find the
company's income from baseballs and
basketballs.

(f) Find the total amount owing to the
company by the five schools.

2. The following table indicates the number
of cases of canned peas, carrots, and corn
ordered by four different stores from a
cannery.

	Peas	Carrots	Corn
Store 1	30	20	10
Store 2	20	15	5
Store 3	40	30	20
Store 4	50	25	30

Peas cost $18 per case, carrots $16 per case,
and corn $14 per case.

(a) Write the total order as a matrix.
(b) Write the cost per case as a column
matrix.
(c) Using matrix multiplication, find the amount
owing to the cannery by each store.
(d) Find the total amount owing to the
cannery.

3. The following table represents the number of tickets issued for various traffic violations in Satellite City for the months of January, February, and March.

	No Parking	No Stopping	Careless Driving	Illegal U-turn
Jan.	157	84	24	12
Feb.	236	75	15	9
Mar.	173	72	10	13

The fines for these offences are $10, $20, $50, and $30 respectively.
(a) Write the violations as a matrix.
(b) Write the fines as a column matrix.
(c) Use matrix multiplication to determine the amount of money collected each month.
(d) What is the total amount collected over the three month period?

4. The Argus Instrument Company distributes four types of calculators — M51, M52, M61, and M62. The following table indicates the number of each type ordered by five stores.

	M51	M52	M61	M62
Store 1	10	20	10	30
Store 2	20	40	25	50
Store 3	30	30	40	20
Store 4	25	50	30	40
Store 5	20	30	50	40

Each M51, M52, M61, and M62 costs $20, $30, $50, and $80 respectively.
(a) Write the total order as a matrix.
(b) Write the cost of each as a column matrix.
(c) Use matrix multiplication to determine the amount owing by each store.
(d) Use matrix multiplication to determine the company's income from the M51 and M62 calculators.
(e) Find the total amount owing to the company from the five stores.

5. A pharmaceutical supply company receives the following orders from five different stores during the month of May.

Store I ordered 3 cases of toothpaste, 5 cases of deodorant, and 2 cases of bath powder. Store II ordered 6 cases of deodorant, 3 cases of bath powder, and 6 cases of toothpaste. Store III ordered 4 cases of bath powder, 5 cases of toothpaste, and 6 cases of deodorant. Store IV ordered 3 cases of deodorant, 2 cases of bath powder, and 6 cases of toothpaste. Store V ordered 4 cases of toothpaste, 5 cases of deodorant, and 2 cases of bath powder.

Toothpaste costs $60 per case, deodorant $84 per case, and bath powder $35 per case.
(a) Write the order as a matrix.
(b) Write the cost per case as a matrix.
(c) Use matrix multiplication to determine the total income from each store.
(d) Find the total amount owing to the company for the month of May.

6. Using the encoding matrix $\begin{pmatrix} 2 & 1 \\ 1 & 3 \end{pmatrix}$, encode the message

SEND MORE MONEY

7. Kelly receives the message

62 43 46 32 65 46 43 34 71 52 68 53

The decoding matrix for the day is
$\begin{pmatrix} 1 & -1 \\ -2 & 3 \end{pmatrix}$. Decode the message.

8. Philip receives the encoded message

12 29 35 85 41 102 34 83 29 72

Decode it using the decoding matrix $\begin{pmatrix} 1 & 1 \\ 2 & 3 \end{pmatrix}$.

9. Use the matrix $\begin{pmatrix} 3 & 1 \\ 5 & 2 \end{pmatrix}$ to encode the message

WILL LAND AT NOON

7.10 PROBLEM SOLVING

1. Ten students belong to the Mystery Writer's Club. They decide to form a committee of four to arrange for the speaker at their next meeting. How many committees with different members could be formed?

2. Peter tells two people about a song he has written that has a good chance of becoming a hit. Ten minutes later each of these people have told two others about the song. If each new person tells two others within ten minutes, how long will it take for at least 100 000 people to know about Peter's song?

3. Mark 25 points as shown below on a piece of paper.

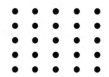

Connect 12 of the points with straight lines to form a perfect cross with 5 points on the inside and 8 points on the outside.

4. The number 1729 is the smallest whole number that can be represented in two different ways as the sum of two cubes. What are the two different ways?

5. The water-lily pads on a pond doubled in area every week. It took twenty weeks to go from one pad on the pond to a completely covered pond. What percent of the pond was covered after 17 weeks?

6. You have 3 groups with 3 eggs each. One of the nine eggs is lighter than the rest. The other 8 all have exactly the same mass. How can you determine which egg is the lighter egg with exactly two weighings?

7. Supply the missing information and solve the following problem.

The Bar-M Ranch has advertised a job that pays $3.50/h above the minimum wage required by law. How much would you earn if you worked 33.5 h per week for seven weeks at the Bar-M?

8. Place the numbers from 1 to 12 in the circles so that the sum along each row is 26.

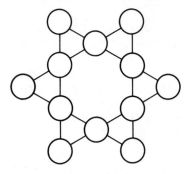

9. There are 12 teams in a minor hockey league. Ice-time has been reserved on Monday, Tuesday, and Thursday evenings until the end of the schedule.
(a) Draw-up a schedule so that each team plays each other team once and no team is idle on a game night.
(b) How many weeks does it take to complete the schedule?

10. Two campers leave a campsite in a canoe and paddle downstream at a constant speed of 8 km/h. Three hours later a camper leaves the campsite in a motorboat and travels downstream at a speed of 20 km/h. How long will it take the motorboat to overtake the canoe?

11. In a cashbox there are eight more nickels than dimes. The value of the nickels and dimes is $4.90. How many nickels are there?

12. Where on the surface of the earth can you walk 1 km due north, 1 km due west, and 1 km due south and arrive back at your starting-point?

13.

What is the size of the acute angle formed by the hands of a clock when the time is 1:20?

14. The gas tank of a car was half-full. Fifteen litres of gas were then removed from the tank leaving the tank $\frac{1}{8}$-full. What is the capacity of the tank?

15. The length of the base of an isosceles triangle is 65 cm. The perimeter of the triangle is 210 cm. What is the length of the other two sides?

16. A train travelling at 30 km/h is stopped $3\frac{1}{2}$ km from the station at 09:15. At what time would it have arrived at the station if it had not been stopped?

17. At 12:00 a tank is completely filled with milk at the processing plant. In 10 min intervals, one-half of the milk remaining in the tank is removed. What fraction of the tank is filled with milk at 12:30?

18. At 8:30 there were 10 000 cases of fruit on the shipping docks. After every half-hour, one-quarter of the cases remaining were shipped to stores. What fraction of the original number of cases remain at 10:00?

19. Bert's average on 12 math tests was 65. If Bert includes his most recent test, his new average mark will be 66. What is the value of the most recent test score?

20. A patio has an area of 36 m². The length and width of the patio are increased by 50%.
(a) What is the increase in area?
(b) What is the percentage increase in the area of the new patio over the original?

21.

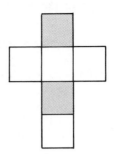

Which of the following figures can you make from the pattern above?
(a)

(b)

(c)

(d)

Using two of the four digits 1, 2, 3, 4 in the denominator and two in the numerator, form the greatest possible proper fraction.

7.11 REVIEW EXERCISE

1. For each of the following matrices
(a) state the dimensions.
(b) state the negative of the matrix.

(i) $\begin{pmatrix} 3 & 5 & 2 \\ 4 & 0 & -6 \end{pmatrix}$

(ii) $\begin{pmatrix} 1 & 4 \\ -6 & 5 \\ -3 & 0 \end{pmatrix}$

(iii) (7)

(iv) $\begin{pmatrix} 2 & 3 \\ -1 & 6 \end{pmatrix}$

(v) $\begin{pmatrix} 3 \\ 1 \\ 2 \end{pmatrix}$

(vi) $(5 \ \ 6 \ \ 8 \ \ -4)$

2. Solve for x, y, and z.

(a) $\begin{pmatrix} -1 & x \\ y & 4 \end{pmatrix} = \begin{pmatrix} -1 & 4 \\ -1 & z \end{pmatrix}$

(b) $(3 \ \ x \ \ -1) = (y \ \ 2 \ \ z)$

(c) $\begin{pmatrix} -2 & 0 \\ x & 3 \\ 2 & y \end{pmatrix} = \begin{pmatrix} -2 & 0 \\ 1 & 3 \\ z & 5 \end{pmatrix}$

3. Express as a single matrix.

(a) $\begin{pmatrix} 5 & 3 \\ 1 & 2 \end{pmatrix} + \begin{pmatrix} 3 & 0 \\ 5 & -2 \end{pmatrix}$

(b) $\begin{pmatrix} 6 & 8 \\ 5 & 7 \end{pmatrix} - \begin{pmatrix} 3 & 4 \\ 1 & 2 \end{pmatrix}$

(c) $\begin{pmatrix} 3 & -4 \\ 2 & 0 \\ -5 & -2 \end{pmatrix} + \begin{pmatrix} 5 & -6 \\ -3 & 4 \\ 1 & 3 \end{pmatrix}$

(d) $-3\begin{pmatrix} 4 & 2 & -5 \\ 1 & -3 & 0 \end{pmatrix}$

(e) $\begin{pmatrix} 6 & -4 \\ -3 & 0 \end{pmatrix} - \begin{pmatrix} 5 & -2 \\ -7 & 5 \end{pmatrix}$

(f) $2\begin{pmatrix} 3 & 5 \\ -2 & 4 \end{pmatrix}$

4. Which of the following products are possible?

(a) $\begin{pmatrix} 1 & 2 \\ 3 & 4 \end{pmatrix} \begin{pmatrix} 1 & 2 & 3 \\ 4 & 5 & 6 \end{pmatrix}$

(b) $(-1 \ \ 2)\begin{pmatrix} 1 & 2 \\ 3 & 4 \end{pmatrix}$

(c) $\begin{pmatrix} 1 & 2 \\ 3 & 4 \\ 5 & 6 \end{pmatrix}(-2 \ \ 0 \ \ 2)$

(d) $(1 \ \ 0)\begin{pmatrix} 2 \\ 1 \end{pmatrix}$

5. Perform the indicated operation.

(a) $\begin{pmatrix} 3 & 4 \\ -2 & 7 \end{pmatrix} + \begin{pmatrix} -5 & 2 \\ -4 & 6 \end{pmatrix}$

(b) $\begin{pmatrix} 5 & 7 \\ -2 & -1 \end{pmatrix} - \begin{pmatrix} -3 & 6 \\ 4 & 7 \end{pmatrix}$

(c) $3\begin{pmatrix} 4 & 1 \\ 2 & -6 \end{pmatrix} + 2\begin{pmatrix} -1 & 3 \\ 4 & -2 \end{pmatrix}$

(d) $\begin{pmatrix} 3 & 1 \\ 4 & -3 \\ -5 & 0 \end{pmatrix} + \begin{pmatrix} -2 & -3 \\ 5 & -6 \\ 7 & 4 \end{pmatrix}$

(e) $\begin{pmatrix} 2 & 3 & -2 \\ -1 & 4 & 6 \end{pmatrix} - \begin{pmatrix} -3 & -6 & 0 \\ 4 & 5 & 2 \end{pmatrix}$

6. Let $A = \begin{pmatrix} 2 & 1 \\ 0 & 3 \end{pmatrix}$, $B = \begin{pmatrix} 2 & 0 \\ -1 & -2 \end{pmatrix}$, and $C = \begin{pmatrix} 1 & -2 \\ -1 & 0 \end{pmatrix}$. Find.

(a) 2A
(b) −3B
(c) A + C
(d) A + B − C
(e) 2A − B
(f) 3(A − B)
(g) AB
(h) BA

7. Multiply, if possible.

(a) $\begin{pmatrix} 3 & 2 \\ 1 & 4 \end{pmatrix}\begin{pmatrix} 1 & 3 \\ 5 & 2 \end{pmatrix}$

(b) $\begin{pmatrix} 5 & -3 \\ 1 & 2 \end{pmatrix}(4 \ \ 6)$

(c) $\begin{pmatrix} 1 \\ 0 \\ 6 \end{pmatrix}\begin{pmatrix} 2 & 3 \\ 1 & 5 \end{pmatrix}$

(d) $(3 \ \ -5 \ \ 6)\begin{pmatrix} 5 \\ 0 \\ -1 \end{pmatrix}$

(e) $\begin{pmatrix} 1 & 0 & 0 \\ 0 & 1 & 0 \\ 0 & 0 & 1 \end{pmatrix} \begin{pmatrix} 3 & 4 & 1 \\ -2 & 4 & 2 \\ 3 & -1 & 5 \end{pmatrix}$

8. Solve for each variable.

(a) $4(x \quad y \quad z) = (-8 \quad 0 \quad 4)$

(b) $5\begin{pmatrix} 0 & x \\ y & 1 \end{pmatrix} = \begin{pmatrix} 0 & 15 \\ 10 & 5 \end{pmatrix}$

(c) $-2\begin{pmatrix} -1 & 0 \\ x & 4 \end{pmatrix} = \begin{pmatrix} y & 0 \\ -2 & 8 \end{pmatrix}$

(d) $2\begin{pmatrix} x & 3 \\ -2 & 1 \end{pmatrix} = 3\begin{pmatrix} 2 & y \\ -\frac{4}{3} & \frac{2}{3} \end{pmatrix}$

(e) $2\begin{pmatrix} 1 & -1 \\ 2 & 3 \end{pmatrix} + 3\begin{pmatrix} x & 1 \\ 0 & y \end{pmatrix} = \begin{pmatrix} 5 & 1 \\ z & 0 \end{pmatrix}$

9. Solve the following systems of equations using matrices.

(a) $x + y = 3$
$2x + y = 4$

(b) $x - y = 2$
$2x - y = 5$

(c) $x + 3y = 2$
$2x + 5y = 5$

(d) $x + y = -5$
$x - y = 1$

10. The Riley Sports Company supplies footballs, helmets, and shoulder pads to four high schools. The following table indicates the number of each ordered by each school.

	Footballs	Helmets	Shoulder Pads
Westview H.S.	20	25	16
East H.S.	15	14	18
St. Mary's H.S.	22	30	10
Glendale H.S.	14	16	12

Footballs cost $50 each, helmets $60 each, and shoulder pads $65 each.

(a) Write the total order as a matrix.
(b) Write the cost of each as a column matrix.
(c) Use matrix multiplication to determine the total amount owing by each school.
(d) Find the total amount owing to the company by the schools.

11. The Seaweed Frozen Food Company sells frozen jumbo shrimp, scallops, and lobster tails to four different restaurants. The following table shows the number of cases of each ordered by each restaurant.

	Shrimp	Lobster	Scallops
Restaurant A	7	10	5
Restaurant B	6	10	10
Restaurant C	7	5	7
Restaurant D	5	15	9

Jumbo shrimp cost $70 per case; lobster tails, $75 per case, and scallops $55 per case.

(a) Write the total order as a matrix.
(b) Write the cost per case as a column matrix.
(c) Using matrix multiplication, find the amount owing to the company by each restaurant.
(d) Find the total amount owing to the company.

12. The Micro Instrument Company distributes three types of calculators—T61, T62, and T63. The following table indicates the number of each type ordered by four different stores.

	T61	T62	T63
Store 1	10	20	20
Store 2	30	20	30
Store 3	20	30	10
Store 4	30	10	10

Each T61, T62, and T63 costs $10, $20, and $80 respectively. Determine Micro's total income from each store and the total income from all stores together.

13. Using the matrix $\begin{pmatrix} 3 & 4 \\ 2 & 3 \end{pmatrix}$ encode the message.

CODEWORD BLUE NOSE

7.12 CHAPTER 7 TEST

1. For the matrix $\begin{pmatrix} 1 & -3 \\ 2 & 0 \\ -1 & 4 \end{pmatrix}$

   (a) state its dimensions.
   (b) state its negative.

2. Solve for x, y, and z, given that

$$2\begin{pmatrix} 1 & -2 & x \\ 3 & -1 & y \end{pmatrix} = \begin{pmatrix} z & -4 & 4 \\ 6 & -2 & -2 \end{pmatrix}$$

3. Express as a single matrix.

   (a) $3\begin{pmatrix} 4 & 2 \\ -1 & 4 \end{pmatrix} + \begin{pmatrix} -5 & 3 \\ 8 & 2 \end{pmatrix}$

   (b) $2\begin{pmatrix} 1 \\ 4 \\ -6 \end{pmatrix} + 3\begin{pmatrix} 1 \\ 0 \\ 1 \end{pmatrix} - 4\begin{pmatrix} 5 \\ -2 \\ 3 \end{pmatrix}$

4. Multiply, if possible.

   (a) $\begin{pmatrix} 6 & -2 \\ 3 & 4 \end{pmatrix}\begin{pmatrix} 1 & 0 \\ 0 & 1 \end{pmatrix}$

   (b) $\begin{pmatrix} 2 & -1 \\ 3 & -2 \end{pmatrix}\begin{pmatrix} 4 & -1 & -3 \\ 1 & 2 & 4 \end{pmatrix}$

5. Solve the following systems of equations using matrices.
   (a) $x + y = 1$
   $x + 2y = 3$

   (b) $2x + 3y = 5$
   $x + 2y = 3$

6. In a track and field event involving many area schools, the number of first, second, and third place finishes in each division was recorded for each school. The table indicates the results of the top school.

	First	Second	Third
Midget	5	2	3
Junior	3	3	4
Senior	6	2	0

A first is worth 5 points; a second, 3 points; and a third, 1 point.
(a) Write the finishes as a matrix.
(b) Write the points per finish as a column matrix.
(c) Use matrix multiplication to determine the total points accumulated in each division.
(d) Determine the school's total points.

GEOMETRY AND DEDUCTIVE THINKING

CHAPTER

8

Nature has . . . some sort of arithmetical–geometrical coordinate system, because nature has all kinds of models.

Buckminster Fuller

BASIC TERMS IN GEOMETRY

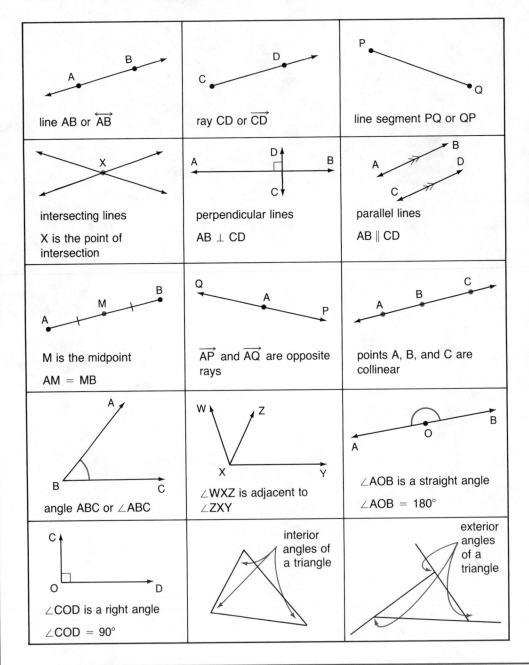

line AB or $\overleftrightarrow{AB}$

ray CD or $\overrightarrow{CD}$

line segment PQ or QP

intersecting lines

X is the point of intersection

perpendicular lines

AB ⊥ CD

parallel lines

AB ∥ CD

M is the midpoint

AM = MB

$\overrightarrow{AP}$ and $\overrightarrow{AQ}$ are opposite rays

points A, B, and C are collinear

angle ABC or ∠ABC

∠WXZ is adjacent to ∠ZXY

∠AOB is a straight angle

∠AOB = 180°

∠COD is a right angle

∠COD = 90°

interior angles of a triangle

exterior angles of a triangle

EXERCISE

1. In each of the following diagrams, name
(a) two triangles.
(b) a pair of parallel lines.
(c) two rays.
(d) two straight angles.
(e) an exterior angle of a triangle.
(f) a pair of adjacent angles.
(g) two obtuse angles.

(i)

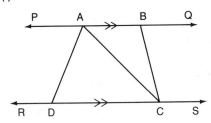

(ii)

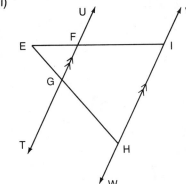

(iii)

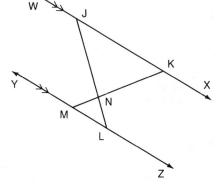

CLASSIFICATION OF TRIANGLES

By Angles	By Sides
acute	scalene
right	isosceles
obtuse	equilateral

EXERCISE

1. Classify each of the following triangles
(a) by sides.
(b) by angles.

(i)

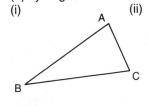

(ii)

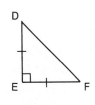

(iii)

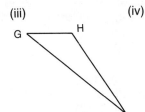

(iv)

USING A PROTRACTOR

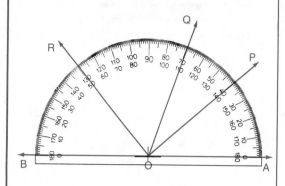

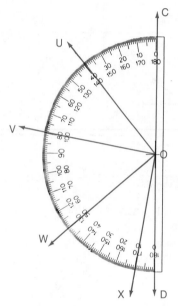

EXERCISE

From the diagrams state the measures of the following angles.

1. (a) ∠AOP   (b) ∠AOQ
   (c) ∠BOR   (d) ∠AOR
   (e) ∠BOQ   (f) ∠BOP

2. (a) ∠COU   (b) ∠COV
   (c) ∠DOX   (d) ∠DOW
   (e) ∠COW   (f) ∠DOV
   (g) ∠DOU   (h) ∠DOC

CONSTRUCTIONS

Bisector of an angle

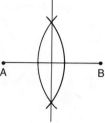

Right bisector of an angle

Perpendicular to a line "from" a point

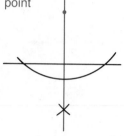

Perpendicular to a line "at" a point

Line parallel to a given line

An equilateral triangle

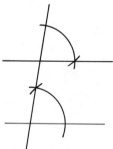

An angle congruent to a given angle

EXERCISE

Construct the following figures using the basic constructions.

1. Angles whose measures are
(a) 90°
(b) 45°
(c) 22.5°
(d) 120°
(e) 15°
(f) 135°

2. Angles whose measures are
(a) 67.5°
(b) 75°
(c) 165°
(d) 37.5°

3. (a) Bisect the angles of each of the following types of triangles.
   (i) acute
   (ii) right
   (iii) obtuse
(b) Using the point of intersection as centre, draw a perpendicular to one side, then draw a circle to touch each side once.

4. (a) Bisect the sides of each of the following types of triangles.
   (i) acute
   (ii) right
   (iii) obtuse
(b) Using the point of intersection as centre, draw a circle passing through the three vertices.

5. Draw the three altitudes of
 (i) an acute triangle.
 (ii) a right triangle.
 (iii) an obtuse triangle.

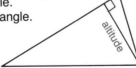

6. Draw the three medians of
 (i) an acute triangle.
 (ii) a right triangle.
 (iii) an obtuse triangle.

MICRO MATH

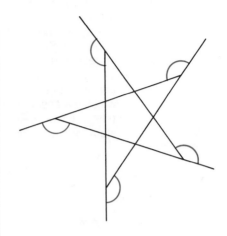

The external angles indicated in the five-point star above are equal in measure. Measure them with a protractor. Enter the following LOGO command, replacing the shaded box by the value obtained.

REPEAT 5 [FD 100 RT ■]

EXERCISE

1. Write the LOGO command that would produce the following star.

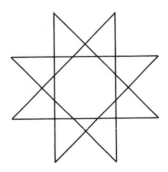

REPEAT 8 [FD 100 RT ■]

8.1 UNDEFINED AND DEFINED TERMS

The Ancient Greeks introduced the word "geometria", a combination of the words "geo" meaning earth and "metria" meaning measurement. It was so called because of its applications to land surveying and architecture.

A basic knowledge of geometric terms will facilitate our study of geometry. Some terms, such as point, line, and plane remain undefined but their meanings remain nevertheless understood. We come to know and understand these undefined terms better by agreeing to some basic properties about them. These basic properties which we assume to be true because of their self-evidence are called postulates or axioms. They will form the fundamental rules for our study of geometry.

Postulates	
	Through any two points there is exactly one line.
	Through any three noncollinear points there is exactly one plane.
	If two planes intersect, their intersection is a straight line.
	If two points are in a plane, then the line determined by these two points will lie entirely in the plane.

Other terms, called defined terms, are given meaning by statements known as definitions. A valid definition uses words that were either accepted as undefined or previously defined.

Examples of Undefined Terms	Examples of Defined Terms
B • A • — The points A and B.	B • (ray diagram) A • — The ray AB, written $\overrightarrow{AB}$.
B (line diagram) A — The line through A and B, called line AB.	B • (segment diagram) A • — The line segment AB.

EXAMPLE 1. Identify the undefined geometric terms used in the following definitions.

(a) A ray is a part of a line that consists of a point A and all points on the line on one side of A.

(b) A line segment (or simply *segment*) is a part of a line consisting of two points and the part of the line between them.

SOLUTION:
(a) A ray is defined in terms of line and point.

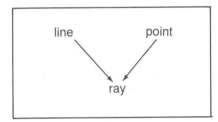

line   point

ray

(b) A segment is defined in terms of line and point.

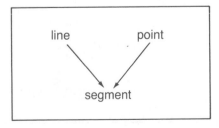

line   point

segment

We use undefined and previously defined terms in the following definitions involving angles and their measurements.

A degree (°) is $\frac{1}{180}$ of the rotation of a ray from one direction to its opposite.

An angle is the union of two rays with a common endpoint.

A right angle is an angle whose measure is 90°.

An acute angle is an angle whose measure is between 0° and 90°.

An obtuse angle is an angle whose measure is between 90° and 180°.

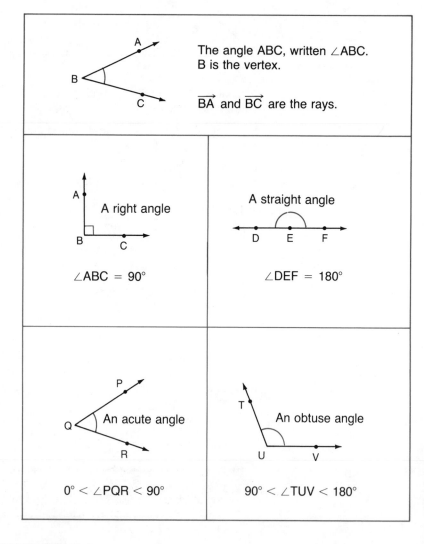

The angle ABC, written ∠ABC. B is the vertex.

$\overrightarrow{BA}$ and $\overrightarrow{BC}$ are the rays.

A right angle

∠ABC = 90°

A straight angle

∠DEF = 180°

An acute angle

0° < ∠PQR < 90°

An obtuse angle

90° < ∠TUV < 180°

EXAMPLE 2. Write a definition for each of the following. Indicate the undefined and previously defined terms.
(a) arm (or side) of an angle
(b) vertex of an angle
(c) complementary angles
(d) supplementary angles
(e) vertically opposite angles

SOLUTION:
(a) An arm (or side) of an angle is either of the two rays that form the angle.

(b) The vertex of an angle is the point common to the two rays that form the angle.

(c) Complementary angles are two angles, the sum of whose measures is 90°.

(d) Supplementary angles are two angles, the sum of whose measures is 180°.

(e) Vertically opposite angles are two angles whose arms are rays in the same line but in opposite directions.

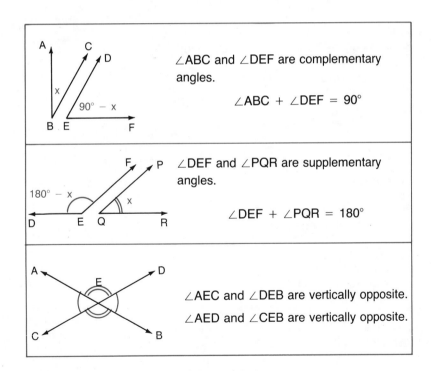

∠ABC and ∠DEF are complementary angles.

$$\angle ABC + \angle DEF = 90°$$

∠DEF and ∠PQR are supplementary angles.

$$\angle DEF + \angle PQR = 180°$$

∠AEC and ∠DEB are vertically opposite.

∠AED and ∠CEB are vertically opposite.

A good definition must be reversible without affecting its accuracy. The definition "a piano is a musical instrument with 88 black and white keys" is acceptable since the reversed statement would read, "a musical instrument with 88 black and white keys is a piano."

Read the following definitions relating to triangles by reversing the order.

A triangle is the union of three segments determined by three points not in a line.

A vertex of a triangle is a point which is common to two sides of a triangle.

Each of the three segments that form a triangle is called a side of the triangle.

EXERCISE 8.1

A 1. Read the following definitions by reversing the order within the definition.

(a) A right triangle is a triangle with one right angle.

(b) A scalene triangle is a triangle in which no two sides are of equal length.

(c) In a triangle, a side opposite an angle is a side which is not contained in the angle.

B 2. From the information provided in the diagrams of the Review and Preview to this chapter, write definitions for the following terms. Underline the undefined and previously defined terms used in your definitions.

(a) straight angle
(b) acute angle
(c) obtuse angle
(d) isosceles triangle
(e) equilateral triangle
(f) adjacent angles
(g) bisector of an angle
(h) opposite rays
(i) midpoint of a segment
(j) collinear points
(k) coplanar points
(l) intersecting lines
(m) perpendicular lines
(n) parallel lines
(o) altitude of a triangle
(p) median of a triangle
(q) right bisector of a segment

3. Draw diagrams that illustrate the following concepts.

(a) A line that intersects a segment at right angles and divides it into two equal segments is the right bisector of the segment.

(b) A point D is in the interior of ∠ABC if D is on the same side of ray BA as C and on the same side of ray BC as A.

(c) Concurrent lines are three or more lines intersecting at a common point.

(d) The centroid of a triangle is the point of intersection of the medians.

MICRO MATH

Using a protractor, measure the external angle shown in the 9-point star.

Try the following LOGO command, replacing the shaded rectangle by the measure of the external angle obtained above.

`REPEAT 9 [FD 100 RT ■]`

Give a single LOGO command that produces a 15-point star.

8.2 DEFINITION NETWORKS

Relationships between defined and undefined terms can be shown in a network.

Consider the following definitions.

> The vertex of an angle is defined in terms of point, ray, and angle.
>
> An angle is defined in terms of ray and point.
>
> A ray is defined in terms of line and point.

The network below shows the association of the defined and undefined terms.

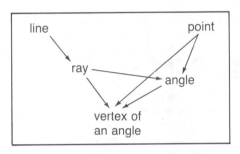

If two definitions are such that the first is given in terms of the second and the second in terms of the first, then at least one of these is unacceptable. In a network this would necessitate the use of a two-headed arrow.

EXAMPLE. Illustrate by constructing a network that at least one of the following definitions is unacceptable.

> A full revolution is a rotation of 360°.
>
> One degree (1°) is $\frac{1}{360}$ of a full revolution.

SOLUTION:
"Full revolution" is defined in terms of "rotation" and "degree."
"Degree" is defined in terms of a "full revolution."
The relationships between the terms are shown in the network below.

The double-headed arrow illustrates that one of the definitions is unacceptable.

EXERCISE 8.2

A 1. Illustrate by constructing a network that at least one definition in each of the following pairs is unacceptable.

(a) perpendicular lines: two lines which form right angles

 right angle: the angle formed by two perpendicular lines

(b) ray: a part of a line that consists of a point A and all points on the line on one side of A

 line: the union of two rays having opposite directions

2. On a large piece of paper, construct a network linking all the terms defined in this section.

8.3 DEDUCTIVE REASONING

Reasoning is a process of drawing conclusions from facts.
The ancient Egyptians and Babylonians used inductive reasoning to
make observations about shapes and figures that enabled them to
accurately survey fields and design structures.

> Inductive reasoning is the process of making general statements
> following the observation of a significant number of particular
> cases.

The process of inductive reasoning involves two steps:

I. Observing that a property is true for a variety of cases.
II. Concluding that the property is true for all cases and
stating this in a generalization.

Conclusions and generalizations obtained by inductive reasoning are
not infallible. To disprove a generalization, it suffices to find a
particular case in which a property does not hold true.
It was not until three thousand years after the Egyptians and
Babylonians that the Greeks began to organize geometry into a
science based on deductive reasoning.

> Deductive reasoning is a process that allows us to derive and
> establish new statements from facts that we have already
> accepted.

The general statements that are developed in this process and that
become new tools for the development and proof of more statements
are called theorems.
In the deductive process we use the rules of logical thinking to
justify our conclusions.

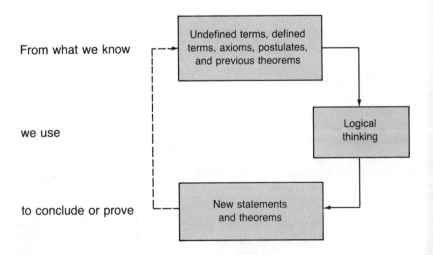

From what we know → Undefined terms, defined terms, axioms, postulates, and previous theorems

we use → Logical thinking

to conclude or prove → New statements and theorems

The Rule of Detachment is an example of a rule of logic which allows us to draw a conclusion. It has three parts which together are called an argument.

An argument.
  I. A conditional sentence in the form

    if   p   , then   q   .   } The hypotheses.

  II. A statement of fact.

  III. A conclusion.   } The conclusion.

The rule states that if you accept the conditional sentence, it suffices that the first part p is true in order to conclude the second part q.

The logic is shown in the following conversation.

Sue: "If it is raining, then I shall stay home."
Mike: "It is raining."   } The hypotheses.

Sue: "I shall stay home."   } The conclusion.

We can summarize the Rule of Detachment in the following way.

If   p   , then   q   .   Yes, I accept this statement. . .

and I admit that this is   p   true.

I can conclude this.   ∴ q

EXAMPLE 1.   What conclusion can be drawn from each pair of statements?

(a) If the Bears defeat the Cats, they will play in the playoffs.

  The Bears beat the Cats.

(b) If you get an "A" in all the math tests, you will get an "A" in the course.
  You got an "A" in all the tests.

SOLUTION:

(a) Hypotheses   { If the Bears defeat the Cats, then they will play in the playoffs.

  The Bears beat the Cats.

  Conclusion   { ∴ they will play in the playoffs.

(b) Hypotheses   { If you get an "A" in all the math tests, then you will get an "A" in the course.

  You got an "A" in all the tests.

  Conclusion   { ∴ you get an "A" in the course.

Many statements in geometry which may not at first appear to be conditional sentences can be rewritten in the form

"If ▩ , then ▩ ."

EXAMPLE 2. Express the following as conditional sentences in the form, "If p, then q."
(a) An equilateral triangle has three sides of equal length.
(b) When two planes intersect, their intersection is a straight line.

SOLUTION:
(a) If a triangle is equilateral, then it has three sides of equal length.
(b) If two planes intersect, then their intersection is a straight line.

EXERCISE 8.3

A 1. Express the following as conditional sentences in the form, "If p, then q."
(a) If you deposit your money in a savings account, you will earn interest.
(b) If we practise hard, we have a good chance of winning.
(c) The game is cancelled if it begins to rain heavily before the end of the fifth inning.
(d) On Tuesday we go swimming.
(e) A vote for me is a vote for progress.
(f) In a right triangle, the square of the hypotenuse equals the sum of the squares of the other two sides.
(g) When x = 3, 2x + 4 = 10.
(h) Two angles are congruent if their measures are equal.
(i) Two lines are perpendicular if they intersect at right angles.

B 2. What conclusions can be drawn from the following pairs of hypotheses?
(a) If I leave now, I will catch my bus.

I am leaving now.

(b) Whenever I study hard I pass the test.

I always study hard.

(c) If the witness was telling the truth, then the accused is guilty.

The witness was telling the truth.

(d) If he came in late last night, he is grounded.

He came in late last night.

THE CONTRAPOSITIVE

Each statement of the form,

"If p , then q ."

has a corresponding statement called the contrapositive. The contrapositive is obtained by negating both statements p and q and interchanging their order in the "If . . . then . . ." statement.

"If not q, then not p."

If the original "If . . . then . . ." statement is true, then its contrapositive is also true. For this reason, we say that a statement and its contrapositive are logically equivalent.

EXAMPLE. State the contrapositives of the following statements.

(a) If a figure is a quadrilateral, then it has four sides.
(b) If a triangle is equilateral, then it has three equal sides.

SOLUTION:
The contrapositive statements are as follows.
(a) If a figure does not have four sides, then it is not a quadrilateral.
(b) If a triangle does not have three equal sides, then it is not an equilateral triangle.

8.4 PROPERTIES OF GEOMETRIC FIGURES

Postulates or axioms are statements that we accept as true without proof. We use these statements to prove other statements called theorems. The theorems presented in this section will be proved later.

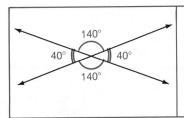

The Opposite Angles Theorem (OAT)

If two straight lines intersect, then the vertically opposite angles are equal.

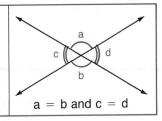

a = b and c = d

EXAMPLE 1. Solve for a and b.

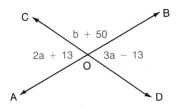

SOLUTION:

Since $\angle AOC = \angle BOD$ Opposite Angles Theorem
then $2a + 13 = 3a - 13$
and $a = 26$

Since $\angle AOB$ is a straight angle,
then $\angle AOB = 180°$
          $\angle AOC + \angle COB = 180°$
        $(2a + 13) + (b + 50) = 180$

> The assumption is that $(2a + 13)° + (b + 50)°$ is a straight angle.

and $2a + 13 + b + 50 = 180$
              $2a + b + 63 = 180$
            $2(26) + b + 63 = 180$
                  $b + 115 = 180$
                        $b = 65$

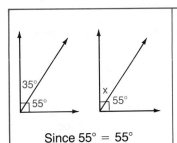

$35°$
$55°$
x
$55°$

Since $55° = 55°$
then $x = 35°$

The Complementary Angles Theorem (CAT)

If two angles are equal in measure, then their complements are equal in measure.

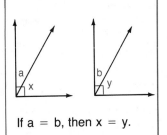

a
x
b
y

If a = b, then x = y.

EXAMPLE 2. In the figures, ∠CBD = ∠RQS. Solve for c.

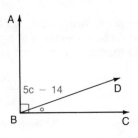

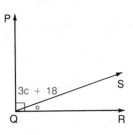

SOLUTION:

Since ∠CBD = ∠RQS

then ∠ABD = ∠PQS   Complementary Angles Theorem

and 5c − 14 = 3c + 18

2c = 32

c = 16

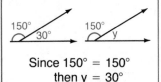 Since 150° = 150° then y = 30°	Supplementary Angles Theorem (SAT) If two angles are equal in measure, then their supplements are equal in measure.	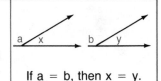 If a = b, then x = y.
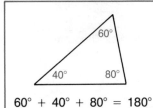 60° + 40° + 80° = 180°	Angle Sum of a Triangle Theorem (ASTT) The sum of the angles of a triangle is 180°.	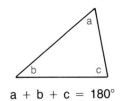 a + b + c = 180°
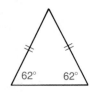	Isosceles Triangle Theorem (ITT) The angles opposite the equal sides of an isosceles triangle are equal in measure.	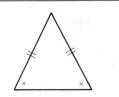

EXAMPLE 3. In △ABC, AB = AC and ∠BAC = 46°. Solve for x.

SOLUTION:

Since AB = AC

then ∠ACB = ∠ABC = x°   ITT

and 46 + x + x = 180   ASTT

2x = 134

x = 67

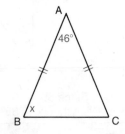

EXERCISE 8.4

B 1. Compute the measure of the indicated angles in the following.

(a)

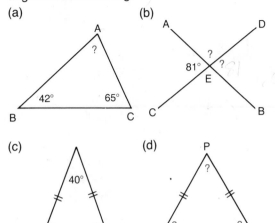

A
?
42°   65°
B   C

(b)

A   D
?
81° ?
E
C   B

(c)

40°
‖   ‖
?   ?
B   C

(d)

P
?
‖   ‖
?   ?
Q   ‖   R

(e)

A
63°
45°   ?
B   C   D

(f)

A
B 130°
C
120°   ?   E
D

2. Compute the value of x in the following.

(a)

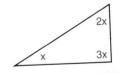

2x
x   3x

(b)

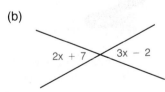

2x + 7   3x − 2

(c)

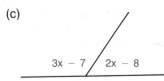

3x − 7   2x − 8

(d)

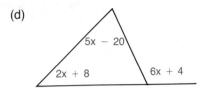

5x − 20
2x + 8   6x + 4

(e)

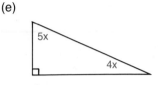

5x
4x

(f)

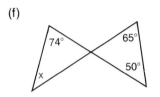

74°   65°
50°
x

MICRO MATH

8.5 LOGO

The LOGO computer language provides opportunities to study relationships and properties of geometric figures and apply them in creative ways.

Figures are drawn on the screen by typing various commands that move the "turtle" or "pencil." Some of the most basic commands are described below.

■ represents a numerical value

Command	Meaning	Example	Explanation
FD ■	move forward	FD 100	the turtle moves 100 units forward
BK ■	move backward	BK 50	the turtle moves 50 units backward
RT ■	right turn	RT 90	the turtle turns 90° clockwise
LT ■	left turn	LT 90	the turtle turns 90° counter-clockwise.

EXAMPLE 1. Provide the LOGO commands to draw a square with sides 100 units.

CS means Clear the Screen.

SOLUTION:
The commands are CS

```
FD 100    ①
RT 90     ②
FD 100    ③
RT 90     ④
FD 100    ⑤
RT 90     ⑥
FD 100    ⑦
RT 90     ⑧
```

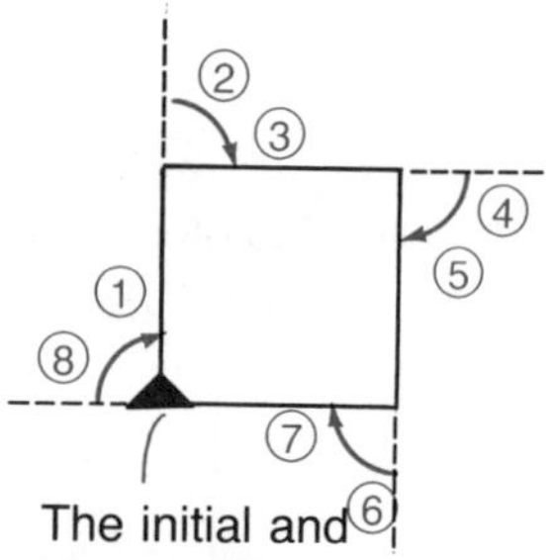

The initial and final position of the turtle.

The corresponding movements of the turtle are shown in the figure at the right.

In the example above, we notice that the two commands FD 100 and RT 90 are repeated four times. We can shorten the four pairs of commands into one "repeat" command.

REPEAT 4 [FD 100 RT 90]

Number of repetitions.   The group of commands to be repeated.

EXAMPLE 2. Give a single LOGO command to draw an equilateral triangle with sides 100 units.

SOLUTION:
Each interior angle of an equilateral triangle measures 60°. Hence each exterior angle measures 180° − 60° = 120°. After drawing one side, the turtle must turn 120° before drawing another side. This is repeated three times.

The command is   REPEAT 3 [FD 100 RT 120]

or   REPEAT 3 [FD 100 LT 120]

How will the two results differ?

   A regular polygon is a polygon in which all sides are equal and all angles are equal. In Examples 1 and 2, we observe that for these regular polygons, each turn has the same measure, the number of turns equals the number of sides, and the total number of degrees turned is 360°. In many introductory LOGO manuals, this is referred to as the "Total Turtle Turn Theorem."

EXERCISE 8.5

1. Complete the following table.

Figure	Number of Sides and Vertices	Degree Measure of Each Turn	Total Number of Degrees Turned	LOGO Command
Equilateral triangle	3	120°	360°	REPEAT 3 [FD 100 RT]
Square	4	90°	360°	REPEAT 4 [FD 100 RT 90]
Regular pentagon				
Regular hexagon				
Regular octagon				
Regular polygon of n sides				

2. (a) Write a LOGO command to draw a regular polygon with
     (i) 180 sides, each of length 1 unit.
     (ii) 360 sides, each of length 1 unit.
  (b) Use a computer to try your commands. What do the figures (i) and (ii) look like?

3. (a) Write the LOGO command to draw a square with sides 60 units.
  (b) Write the command that turns the turtle 30° clockwise.
  (c) Write a command that will repeat (a) and (b) twelve times. Try it on a computer.

8.6 THE NATURE OF PROOF

Euclid was the first to systematically prove relationships among figures using the method of deductive proof. In a deductive proof, we organize statements in such a way that the rule of detachment can be used to draw a conclusion that fully supports the statement that we want to prove.

Hypotheses   If a triangle has three equal sides, then it is equilateral.

                △ABC has three equal sides.

Conclusion   △ABC is equilateral.

Any defined term, undefined term, postulate, or previously proved statement or given fact can be used as an hypothesis. This method of proof allows us to prove a particular statement from the application of a general statement.

General: If an animal is a bear, then it hibernates.

Particular: Blackie is a bear.

Conclusion: Blackie hibernates.

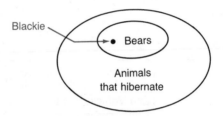

We first have a general statement in "If . . ., then . . ." form and we accept this statement as true. Our particular statement must relate to the "if . . ." part of the general statement so that we can conclude the "then . . ." part of the general statement as it relates to our particular statement.

EXAMPLE. △ABC is an isosceles triangle with AB = AC. Use the method of deductive proof to prove that ∠ABC = ∠ACB.

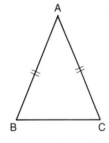

SOLUTION:
We use the Isosceles Triangle Theorem to form the general statement, and we use what is given to form the particular statement.
General: If a triangle is isosceles, then the angles opposite the equal sides are equal.
Particular: △ABC is isosceles.
Conclusion: ∠ABC = ∠ACB

We can simplify the steps in a deductive proof by accepting any statement that follows directly from a definition, postulate, or a previously established theorem. In these cases, we must provide a brief justification of the statement. In the following example, we apply the READ — PLAN — SOLVE — ANSWER problem solving model to proofs.

Problem Solving	Geometry Steps	Example
READ	State what is given. State what you are asked to prove.	*GIVEN:* △ABC with exterior angle ∠ACD and interior angles ∠ABC and ∠BAC *PROVE:* ∠ACD = ∠ABC + ∠BAC
PLAN 3·2·1	Draw a diagram. Where applicable, mark angles that are equal and segments that are congruent. Classify the information as relevant or irrelevant. Look for definitions, postulates, or theorems that connect what you are asked to prove with what is given. Work backwards step by step until you arrive at the given information. You may then be able to construct a proof by reversing your steps.	 *PLAN:* We can prove this if we can establish a relationship between ∠ACD and ∠ACB, then establish a similar relationship between (∠ABC + ∠BAC) and ∠ACB. The properties of equality would then lead to the result ∠ACD = ∠ABC + ∠BAC. The first relationship can be obtained from the definition of a straight angle, while the second can be obtained from the Angle Sum of a Triangle Theorem.
SOLVE	By following your plan, write the proof in two-column form. Each step of the proof consists of a statement and a reason.	*PROOF:*

PROOF:

Statements	Reasons
In △ABC,	
∠ACB + ∠ACD = 180°	straight angle
∠ACB + ∠ABC + ∠BAC = 180°	ASTT
∠ACD − ∠ABC − ∠BAC = 0	subtraction
∠ACD = ∠ABC + ∠BAC	

ANSWER	The final statement is what you were asked to prove. Generalize the results, if possible.	Exterior Angle Theorem (EAT) The degree measure of an exterior angle of a triangle is equal to the sum of the interior and non-adjacent angles.

A proof such as the preceding one, which is based strictly on accepted statements and logical reasoning is indisputable.

There are many times when statements are made in place of a real proof. Discuss the validity of the following as proofs.

I. Proof by Authority

If two students wish to prove a statement, they can consult an authority, for example, a teacher or look in a book. This is not always satisfactory, especially if you use an outdated text as your authority.

II. Proof by Inspection

Can you prove the following by just looking at the situation?
(a) AB is longer than CD.

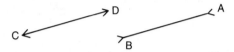

(b) AB, CD, and EF are parallel.

III. Proof by Analogy

If two things agree in at least one aspect, can we then reason that there will be agreement in yet another respect? For example, if the product of two natural numbers is always greater than either of the numbers, is it true that the product of two integers is always greater than either number? Since $-3 \times 4 = -12$ and the product is clearly less than -3 or 4, we see that we cannot always use analogy to prove statements.

IV. Proof by Induction

If you make a general statement following the observation of a significant number of particular cases, you are reasoning inductively. For example, if you went out in the rain 20 times and got wet every time, you could conclude that when you go out in the rain you will get wet. Can you conclude that a hockey team that has won its first 20 games will also win its twenty-first game? Although inductive reasoning is very useful in discovering new facts, it does not always prove statements beyond all doubt.

EXERCISE 8.6

B 1. Identify the method of proof for each.

(a) The sum of the angles of a triangle is 180°
because the teacher said so.

(b) △ABC is isosceles because it looks like
AB = AC.

(c) Since the set of integers is closed under
addition, the set of natural numbers is closed
under addition.

(d) Since Walter has scored three touchdowns
in every game so far, he will score three
touchdowns in the next game.

(e) To join the police force, you must be at
least 175 cm tall. Sharon is on the police
force. Sharon is at least 175 cm tall.

2. Rewrite one statement in "If . . ., then . . ."
form, then prove it using deductive reasoning.

(a) All cats are animals.
Jasper is a cat.
Prove that Jasper is an animal.

(b) All students at Eastern take music.
Diane attends Eastern.
Prove that Diane takes music.

(c) In order to take MTA2A a student must
have passed MTA1A.
Yvonne takes MTA2A.
Prove that Yvonne has passed MTA1A.

(d) The sum of the angles of a quadrilateral is
360°.
ABCD is a quadrilateral.
Prove that the sum of the angles of ABCD is
360°.

(e) The opposite angles of a parallelogram are
equal.
PQRS is a parallelogram.
Prove that the opposite angles of PQRS are
equal.

(f) A triangle with two equal sides has two
equal angles.
△ABC has two equal sides.
Prove that △ABC has two equal angles.

3. Prove that in a quadrilateral the sum of the
interior angles is 360°.

4. (a) Determine a formula for the sum of the
angles of an n-sided closed figure.

(b) Identify the method of proof used above.

Write two-column deductive proofs for the
following.

5. Opposite Angle Theorem

Given: AB and CD intersect at E.
Prove: ∠AED = ∠BEC

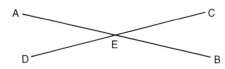

6. Supplementary Angle Theorem

Given: ∠ABC + ∠CBD = 180°;
∠PQR + ∠RQS = 180°;
∠ABC = ∠PQR
Prove: ∠CBD = ∠RQS

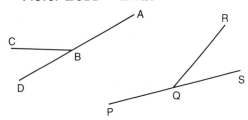

7. Complementary Angle Theorem

Given: ∠ABC + ∠CBD = 90°;
∠PQR + ∠RQS = 90°;
∠CBD = ∠PQR
Prove: ∠ABC = ∠RQS

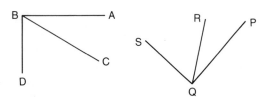

8. Given: BA ⊥ CA;
∠BAD = ∠ACD
Prove: ∠DAC = ∠DBA

⊥ means
"is perpendicular to."

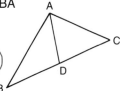

8.7 CONGRUENT TRIANGLES

Two figures are congruent if they are equal in all respects: lengths, angles, and areas. Two triangles are congruent if there is a one-to-one correspondence between their vertices so that the corresponding angles and sides are equal. We use the symbol ≅ to indicate that two figures are congruent,

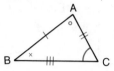   △ABC ≅ △DEF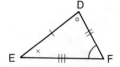

Note that △ABC and △DEF have been written to show the correspondence between the vertices of the triangles. The markings indicate that the corresponding angles and the corresponding sides are equal.

Corresponding Angles	Corresponding Sides
∠A = ∠D	AB = DE
∠B = ∠E	BC = EF
∠C = ∠F	CA = FD

EXAMPLE 1. Name the corresponding sides and angles indicated by the markings.

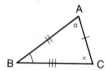

SOLUTION:
First we redraw the triangles in the same configuration.

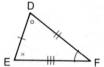

∠A = ∠D	AB = DF
∠B = ∠F	BC = FE
∠C = ∠E	CA = ED

EXAMPLE 2. State the measures of the unknown sides and angles given that △ABC ≅ △EFD.

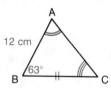   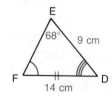

SOLUTION:

Using the correspondence,

$$A \leftrightarrow E, B \leftrightarrow F, \text{ and } C \leftrightarrow D$$

$\angle A = \angle E$	$AB = EF$
$\angle B = \angle F$	$BC = FD$
$\angle C = \angle D$	$CA = DE$

In △ABC, $\angle A = 68°$, AC = 9 cm, and BC = 14 cm.
In △EFD, $\angle F = 63°$ and EF = 12 cm.

What are the measures of $\angle C$ and $\angle D$?

EXERCISE 8.7

A 1. Given: △DEF ≅ △RST.
Complete the following congruence
correspondences.

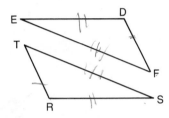

(a) $\angle$DEF → ■   (b) EF → ■
(c) $\angle$DFE → ■   (d) DE → ■
(e) $\angle$EDF → ■   (f) DF → ■

2. Determine the equal sides and angles
of the two congruent triangles from the
congruence correspondence between them.

$$\triangle PQR \cong \triangle STU$$

(a) PQ = ■   (b) $\angle$PQR = ■
(c) SU = ■   (d) $\angle$RPQ = ■
(e) QR = ■   (f) $\angle$QRP = ■

3. Name all pairs of equal angles and sides
in the given figures.

(a)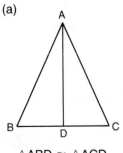

△ABD ≅ △ACD

(b)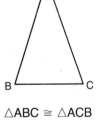

△ABC ≅ △ACB

(c) P

△TQS ≅ △PRS

(d)

△ABD ≅ △CDB

B 4. The Transitive Property of Congruence is
given as follows.

If △ABC ≅ △DEF and △DEF ≅ △LMN,
then △ABC ≅ △LMN.

(a) Make a diagram to show the transitive
property.
(b) Determine whether the reflexive property
holds true.

$$\triangle ABC \cong \triangle ABC$$

(c) Determine whether the symmetric property
holds true.

$$\triangle ABC \cong \triangle DEF \text{ and } \triangle DEF \cong \triangle ABC$$

5. State the measure of the unknown angles
and sides given that △DEF ≅ △PRQ.

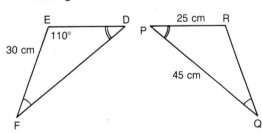

8.8 APPLICATION OF PROOF: THE SSS POSTULATE

Two triangles are congruent if the corresponding sides and the corresponding angles are equal. However, it is not always necessary to show all six of these equalities in order to prove that two triangles are congruent.

We can take three sticks with different lengths and form a triangle.

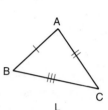

By rearranging the sticks, we can try to form other triangles. Each triangle that we make has the same shape and size as the first triangle, so the triangles are congruent. This demonstration is generalized as follows in the SSS postulate.

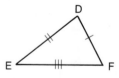

The SSS Postulate

If three sides of one triangle are respectively equal to the three sides of another triangle, then the triangles are congruent.

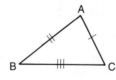

$$AB = DE$$
$$BC = EF$$
$$CA = FD$$
$$\triangle ABC \cong \triangle DEF$$

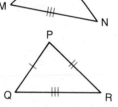

EXAMPLE.

GIVEN: $\triangle ABC$; $AB = AC$; D is the midpoint of BC

PROVE: $\angle ABC = \angle ACB$

PLAN: We can prove $\angle ABC = \angle ACB$ by proving $\triangle ABD \cong \triangle ACD$. We can prove $\triangle ABD \cong \triangle ACD$ by showing that the corresponding sides AB and AC, BD and CD, and AD are equal.

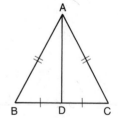

PROOF: Statements	Reasons

In △ABD and △ACD,
D is the midpoint of BC
    BD = CD
    AB = AC
    AD = AD
△ABD ≅ △ACD
∠ABC = ∠ACB
	given
	definition of midpoint
	given
	reflexive property
	SSS

We generalize this result and call it the Isosceles Triangle Theorem, Part I.

> **Isosceles Triangle Theorem (ITT) Part I**
>
> If a triangle has two equal sides, then the angles opposite the equal sides are equal.

EXERCISE 8.8

A 1. (a) Name pairs of triangles congruent by SSS.

(b) State the corresponding angles that are equal.

2. Prove that the triangles are congruent by naming the corresponding parts that are equal.

(a)

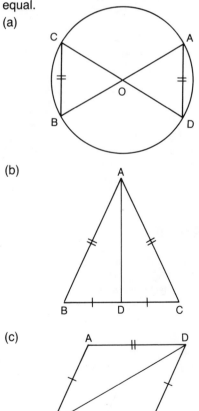

(b)

(c)

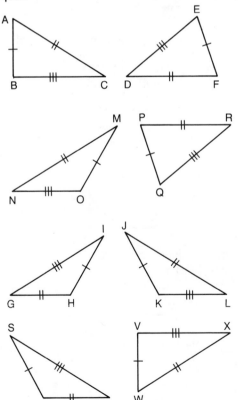

(d)

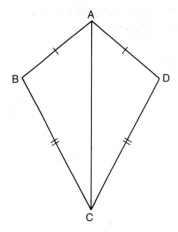

(e)

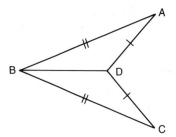

(f)

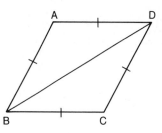

B Prove the following.

3. Given: △ABC; AB = AC
   Prove: (i) △ABC ≅ △ACB.
   (ii) ∠ABC = ∠ACB.

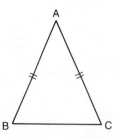

4. Given: rhombus ABCD
   Prove: (i) ∠BAD = ∠DCB
   (ii) ∠ABD = ∠CDB

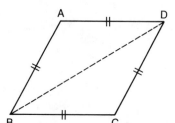

5. Given: △ABC; AB = AC; BD = CD
   Prove: (i) △ABD ≅ △ACD
   (ii) AD ⊥ BC

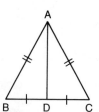

6. Given: AB and CD are chords of a circle centre O; AB = CD
   Prove: (i) △AOB ≅ △COD
   (ii) ∠AOB = ∠COD

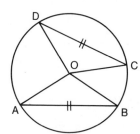

7. Given: quadrilateral ABCD;
   AB = CD; AD = CB
   Prove: ∠BAD = ∠DCB

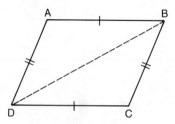

C 8. Given: quadrilateral ABCD;
     AB = AD; BC = DC
   Prove: (i) BE = DE
          (ii) AE ⊥ BD

9. Given: two circles centres A and C
          intersect at B and D
   Prove: (i) ∠DAC = ∠BAC
          (ii) ∠DCA = ∠BCA

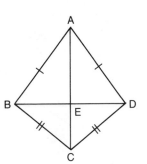

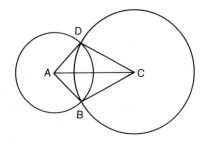

10. In quadrilateral ABCD, AD = BC and
    AB = DC. Prove that the opposite interior
    angles are equal.

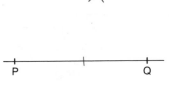

CONSTRUCTION   (SSS)

GIVEN:

Three line segments

A —————+————— B

C ———#——— D

E ———#——— F

REQUIRED:

To construct △PQR with sides
equal to AB, CD, and EF.

STRATEGY:

Copy the three segments
joining each pair at a
common endpoint.

SOLUTION:

Construct PQ = AB.

With centre P and radius
CD draw an arc.

With centre Q and radius
EF draw another arc.

Draw PR and QR.

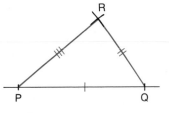

PQ = AB, PR = EF, QR = CD, and △PQR is the required triangle.

8.9 APPLICATION OF PROOF: THE SAS POSTULATE

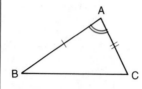
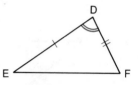

> **The SAS Postulate**
>
> If two sides and the contained angle of one triangle are respectively equal to two sides and the contained angle of another triangle, then the triangles are congruent.
>
> AB = DE
> ∠BAC = ∠EDF
> AC = DF
> △ABC ≅ △EDF

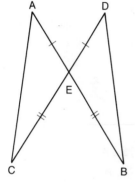

EXAMPLE 1.

GIVEN: AB and CD intersect at E; AE = DE; CE = BE

PROVE: AC = DB

PLAN: Prove that AC = DB by proving the congruence, △AEC ≅ △DEB, using SAS.
Prove angles at E equal by opposite angles.

PROOF:

Statements	Reasons
In △AEC and △DEB,	
AE = DE	given
AB and DC intersect at E	given
∠AEC = ∠DEB	OAT
EC = EB	given
△AEC ≅ △DEB	SAS
AC = DB	

EXAMPLE 2.

GIVEN: △ABC and △DCB;
AB = DC; ∠ABC = ∠DCB

PROVE: ∠BAC = ∠CDB

PLAN: Prove ∠BAC = ∠CDB by proving the congruence, △ABC ≅ △DCB, using SAS.

Since BC is a side of both triangles, BC = CB by the reflexive property.

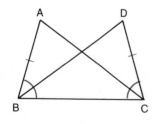

PROOF:

Statements	Reasons
In △ABC and △DCB,	
AB = DC	given
∠ABC = ∠DCB	given
BC = CB	reflexive property
△ABC ≅ △DCB	SAS
∠BAC = ∠CDB	definition of congruence

EXERCISE 8.9

A 1. Name pairs of triangles congruent by SAS.

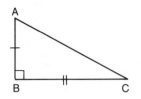

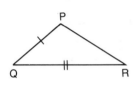

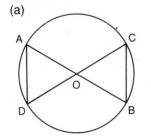

2. Prove that the triangles are congruent by naming the corresponding parts that are equal.

(a)

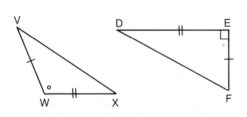

(b)

(c)

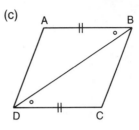

(d)

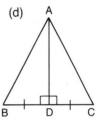

(e)

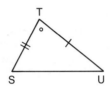

(f)

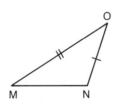

B Prove the following.

3. Given: AB and CD intersect at E;
           AE = EB; CE = ED
   Prove: (i) △ACE ≅ △BDE
          (ii) AC = BD

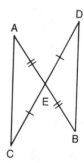

4. Given: DC ⊥ AB; AC = BC
   Prove: (i) △DAC ≅ △DBC
          (ii) DA = DB

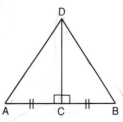

5. Given: BD bisects ∠ABC; AB = CB
   Prove: (i) △ABD ≅ △CBD
          (ii) AD = CD
          (iii) ∠ADB = ∠CDB

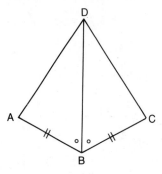

6. Given: AC and BD intersect at E;
          AE = DE; BE = CE
   Prove: AB = DC

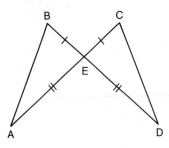

7. Given: quadrilateral ABCD;
          ∠ABD = ∠CDB; AB = CD
   Prove: AD = CB

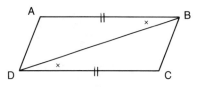

8. Given: AB = ED; BC = DC
   Prove: (i) AD = EB
          (ii) ∠CAD = ∠CEB.

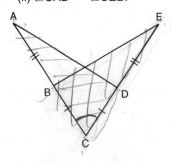

9. Given: △ABC; AB = AC; D and E are
          the midpoints of AB and AC
          respectively
   Prove: CD = BE

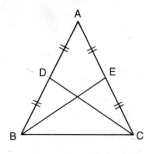

10. Given: △ABC; ∠ABC = ∠ACB;
           DB = EC
    Prove: (i) △ACD ≅ △ABE
           (ii) AD = AE

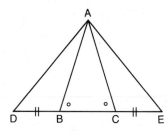

11. Given: △ABC; AB = AC;
           ∠DBC = ∠DCB
    Prove: AD bisects ∠BAC

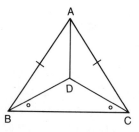

12. Prove the diagonals of a rectangle bisect
each other.

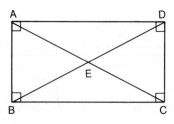

13. Given: D is the midpoint of EC;
    ∠BDE = ∠ADC; AD = BD;
    ED = CD
    Prove: (i) △AED ≅ △BCD
    (ii) AE = BC

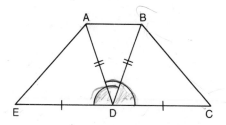

14. Given: △ABC; AB = AC;
    ∠ABC = ∠ACB;
    DB = BC = CE
    Prove: AD = AE

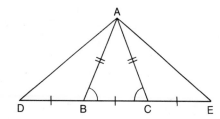

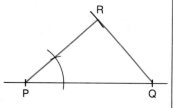

CONSTRUCTION   (SAS)

GIVEN:

Two line segments

A ——————— B

C ——————— D

and ∠LMN

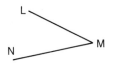

REQUIRED:

To construct △PQR with sides equal to AB and CD, and the contained angle equal to ∠LMN.

STRATEGY:

Copy one segment and construct the given angle at one endpoint. Mark off the second side.

SOLUTION:

Construct PQ = AB.

At P, construct an angle equal to ∠LMN.

With centre P and radius CD draw another arc.

Complete the triangle.

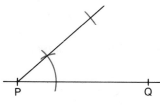

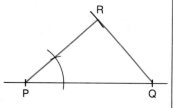

PQ = AB, PR = CD, ∠RPQ = ∠LMN, and △PQR is the required triangle.

8.10 APPLICATION OF PROOF: THE ASA POSTULATE

The ASA Postulate

If two angles and the contained side of one triangle are respectively equal to two angles and the contained side of another triangle, then the triangles are congruent.

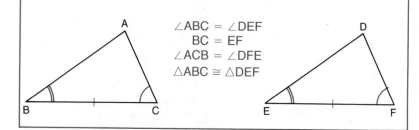

$$\angle ABC = \angle DEF$$
$$BC = EF$$
$$\angle ACB = \angle DFE$$
$$\triangle ABC \cong \triangle DEF$$

EXAMPLE 1.

GIVEN:　AB and CD intersect at E;
　　　　　AD ⊥ AB; BC ⊥ AB; AE = BE

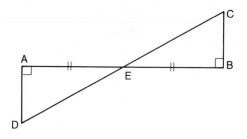

PROVE:　AD = BC

PLAN:　Prove that AD = BC by proving the congruence
　　　　　△ADE ≅ △BCE using ASA.
　　　　　Prove angles at E equal by opposite angles.

PROOF:

Statements	Reasons
In △ADE and △BCE,	
AD ⊥AE, BC ⊥ BE	given
∠DAE = ∠CBE = 90°	definition of perpendicular
AE = BE	given
AB and CD intersect at E	given
∠AED = ∠BEC	OAT
△ADE ≅ △BCE	ASA
AD = BC	definition of congruence

A corollary of a theorem or postulate is a statement which follows necessarily from the theorem or postulate.

Corollary
If any two angles and one side of one triangle are respectively equal to two angles and the corresponding side of another triangle, then the triangles are congruent.

EXAMPLE 2.

GIVEN: △ABC; ∠ABD = ∠ACD,
AD is the angle bisector of ∠BAC

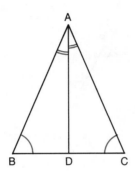

PROVE: AB = AC

PLAN: Prove that AB = AC by
proving the congruence,
△ABD ≅ △ACD, using the
corollary of ASA.
We can claim that AD = AD
by the reflexive property and
that ∠BAD = ∠CAD by the
definition of an angle bisector.

PROOF:

Statements	Reasons
In △ADB and △ADC	
∠BAD = ∠CAD	definition of an angle bisector
∠ABD = ∠ACD	given
AD = AD	reflexive property
△ABD ≅ △ACD	corollary of ASA
AB = AC	

We generalize the results to state Part II of the Isoceles Triangle Theorem.

Isosceles Triangle Theorem (ITT) Part II
If a triangle has two equal angles, then the sides opposite the equal angles are equal.

EXERCISE 8.10

A 1. Name pairs of triangles that are congruent by ASA.

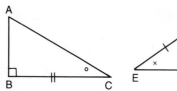

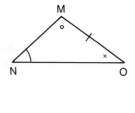

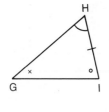

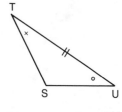

2. Prove that the triangles are congruent by naming the corresponding parts that are equal.

(a)

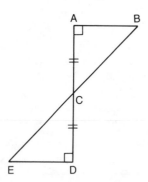

(b)

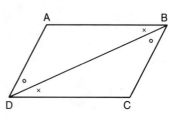

(c)

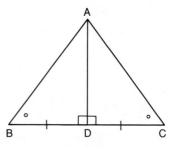

(d)

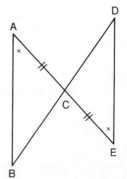

(e)

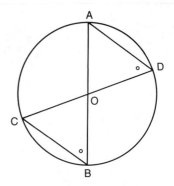

(f)

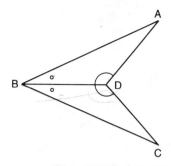

B 3. Given: AB and DC intersect at E;
∠CAE = ∠BDE; AE = DE
Prove: AC = DB

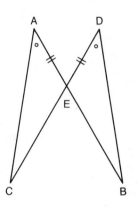

4. Given: quadrilateral ABDE;
C is on BD; AC = CE;
∠ACD = ∠ECB; ∠BAE = ∠DEA
Prove: (i) △ABC ≅ △EDC
(ii) AB = ED

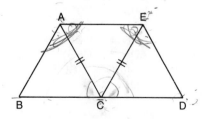

5. Given: quadrilateral ABCD,
∠ABD = ∠CDB; ∠ADB = ∠CBD
Prove: (i) AD = CB
(ii) AB = CD

6. Given: quadrilateral ABDC;
∠BAD = ∠CAD; ∠BDA = ∠CDA
Prove: (i) BD = CD
(ii) AB = AC

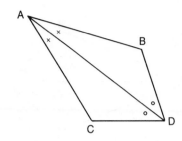

7. Given: AB ⊥ BC and DC ⊥ BC;
∠DBC = ∠ACB
Prove: AB' = DC

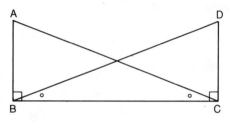

8. Given: rectangle ABCD; ∠BAC = ∠CDB
Prove: △DCB ≅ △ABC.

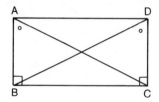

C 9. Given: △ABC; ∠ABC = ∠ACB;
CB is extended to D;
BC is extended to E;
DB = EC
Prove: AD = AE

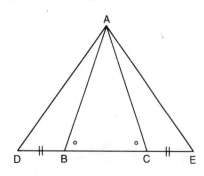

10. Given: quadrilateral ABCD;
 ∠ABC = ∠ADC;
 AC bisects ∠BCD
 Prove: BC = DC

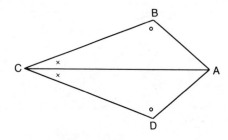

11. Prove that the bisector of the vertical angle of an isosceles triangle is the right bisector of the base.

12. Given: AB and CD bisect each other at E;
 FG passes through E
 Prove: △FED ≅ △GEC

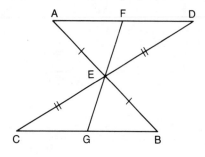

13. Given: △ABE and △ACD; AD = AE;
 DB = EC
 Prove: (i) △BDF ≅ △CEF
 (ii) BF = CF

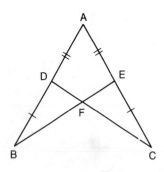

14. Given: △ABC and △DCB; AC = DB;
 ∠ACB = ∠DBC
 Prove: (i) AB = DC
 (ii) AE = DE

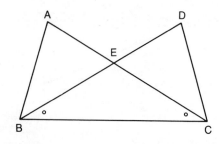

15. Given: △PBQ and △PCA; AP = PQ;
 AB ⊥ PC; ∠PAC = ∠PQB;
 Prove: △ABQ ≅ △PCA

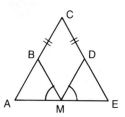

16. Given: △ACE; M is the midpoint of AE;
 CA = CE; ∠AMB = ∠EMD
 Prove: △ABM ≅ △EDM

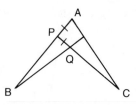

17. Given: figure ABCFED;
 ∠DBE = ∠FBE;
 ∠BED = ∠BEF;
 ∠ABD = ∠CBF;
 ∠ADB = ∠CFB;
 Prove: (i) △ABD ≅ △CBF
 (ii) AB = CB

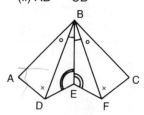

EXTRA

CONSTRUCTION   (ASA)

GIVEN:

A line segment

A ——————— B

∠DEF and ∠LMN

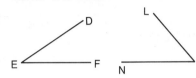

REQUIRED:

To construct △PQR with one side equal to AB, and ∠DEF and ∠LMN at each endpoint of the given segment.

STRATEGY:

Copy the segment and construct the given angles at each endpoint.

SOLUTION:

Construct PQ = AB.

At P, construct an angle equal to ∠DEF.

At Q, construct an angle equal to ∠LMN.

Complete the triangle.

  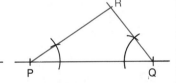

PQ = AB, ∠RPQ = ∠DEF, and ∠RQP = ∠LMN.

△PQR is the required triangle.

8.11 APPLICATION OF PROOF: THE HS RIGHT TRIANGLE POSTULATE

The HS Right Triangle Postulate

If the hypotenuse and one side of one right triangle are respectively equal to the hypotenuse and one side of another right triangle, then the triangles are congruent.

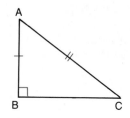

$\angle$ ABC = $\angle$DEF
AC = DF
AB = DE
$\triangle$ABC $\cong$ $\triangle$DEF

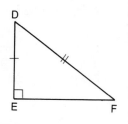

EXAMPLE.

GIVEN: $\triangle$ABC; AB = AC, AD $\perp$ BC

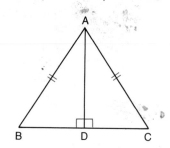

PROVE: AD bisects $\angle$BAC

PLAN: To prove that AD bisects $\angle$BAC, we must prove that $\angle$BAD = $\angle$CAD.
This is proved by proving the congruence, $\triangle$ABD $\cong$ $\triangle$ACD, using the HS postulate.
$\angle$ADB = $\angle$ADC = 90° by definition of perpendicular line segments.
AD = AD by the reflexive property.

PROOF:

Statements	Reasons
In $\triangle$ABD and $\triangle$ACD,	
AD $\perp$ BC	given
$\angle$ADB = $\angle$ADC = 90°	definition of perpendicular
AB = AC	given
AD = AD	reflexive property
$\triangle$ABD $\cong$ $\triangle$ACD	HS
$\angle$BAD = $\angle$CAD	definition of congruence
AD bisects $\angle$BAC	

EXERCISE 8.11

Prove the following deductions.

1. Given: $\angle ABC$; $AB = CB$; point D;
   DA $\perp$ BA; DC $\perp$ BC
   Prove: (i) $\triangle ABD \cong \triangle CBD$
   (ii) BD bisects $\angle ABC$

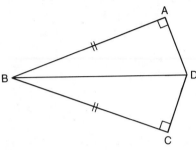

2. Given: $\triangle ABC$, BE $\perp$ AC; CD $\perp$ AB;
   BD = CE
   Prove: (i) $\triangle DBC \cong \triangle ECB$
   (ii) $\triangle ABC$ is isosceles

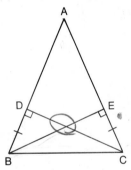

3. Given: circle centre O; M and N are
   midpoints of AB and CD
   respectively; OM $\perp$ AB;
   ON $\perp$ CD; OM = ON
   Prove: (i) AM = DN
   (ii) BM = CN
   (iii) AB = CD

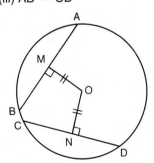

C 4. Given: quadrilateral ABCD; AB $\perp$ BC;
   DC $\perp$ BC; AC = DB
   Prove: AB = DC

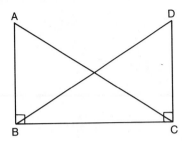

5. Given: $\triangle ABC$; $\triangle DCB$; AE = ED;
   $\angle BAC = \angle CDB = 90°$
   Prove: (i) $\triangle AEB \cong \triangle DEC$
   (ii) $\triangle ABC \cong \triangle DCB$

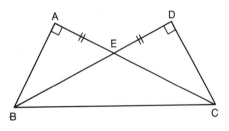

MIND BENDER

Find the missing digits in this
multiplication.

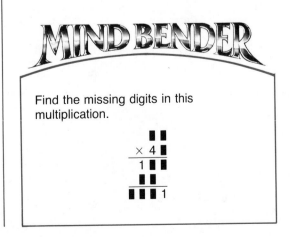

8.12 APPLICATION OF PROOF: PARALLEL LINES

Two lines are parallel if, and only if, they lie in the same plane and do not intersect. The symbol for "parallel" is ∥, so that when we mean lines ℓ_1 and ℓ_2 are parallel, we can write

$$\ell_1 \parallel \ell_2$$

$\ell_1 \parallel \ell_2$

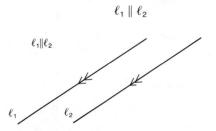

A transversal is a line, or line segment, that intersects 2 or more distinct lines (or line segments). In the figure below, t is a transversal, intersecting the lines ℓ_1 and ℓ_2 making 8 angles (a, b, c, d, e, f, g, h). We relate these angles as follows:

Alternate angles $\begin{cases} \angle c \text{ and } \angle e \\ \angle d \text{ and } \angle f \end{cases}$

Corresponding angles $\begin{cases} \angle a \text{ and } \angle e \\ \angle b \text{ and } \angle f \\ \angle c \text{ and } \angle g \\ \angle d \text{ and } \angle h \end{cases}$

Interior angles on the same side of the transversal $\begin{cases} \angle d \text{ and } \angle e \\ \angle c \text{ and } \angle f \end{cases}$

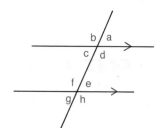

(i) c = e, d = f

(ii) b = f, a = e
     c = g, d = h

(iii) d + e = 180°
     c + f = 180°

TPT: Transversal Parallel Line Theorem—I

If a transversal meets two parallel lines, then
(i) the alternate angles are equal,
(ii) the corresponding angles are equal,
(iii) the interior angles on the same side of the transversal are supplementary.

This theorem can be remembered by thinking of the Z, F, and C patterns.

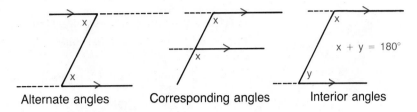

Alternate angles   Corresponding angles   Interior angles

EXAMPLE 1.

GIVEN: In quadrilateral ABCD, AB = CD, and AB ∥ DC.

PROVE: AD = CB.

PLAN: Draw diagonal BD to form triangles.
We can prove AD = CB by proving △ABD ≅ △CDB.

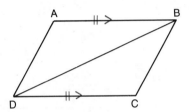

PROOF:

Statements	Reasons
In △ABD and △CDB,	
AB = CD	given
AB ∥ DC, BD is a transversal	given
∠ABD = ∠CDB	TPT
BD = DB	common
△ABD ≅ △CDB	SAS
AD = CB	

We now state and prove the converse of the Parallel Line Theorem.

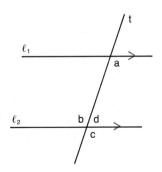

┌───┐
│   TPT: Transversal Parallel Line Theorem—II   │
│   │
│ If a transversal meets two lines making   │
│ (i) the alternate angles equal, or   │
│ (ii) the corresponding angles equal, or   │
│ (iii) the interior angles on the same side supplementary, then the │
│   lines are parallel.   │
└───┘

The method of indirect proof is another acceptable method of proof. It involves accepting as a premise a statement that is contrary to what we must prove. If a contradiction arises because of this assumption, we conclude that the assumption was false. This method was used in Chapter 1 to prove that $\sqrt{2}$ is irrational. We now use indirect proof to prove part of the Transversal Parallel Theorem.

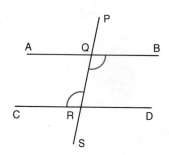

GIVEN: AB and CD with transversal PQRS;

$\angle BQR = \angle QRC$

PROVE: AB ∥ DC

PLAN: Using the method of indirect proof, we shall assume a contrary statement, that is, AB ∦ CD, where AB and CD meet at a point M. We shall then look for a contradiction in the statements that follow from this assumption.

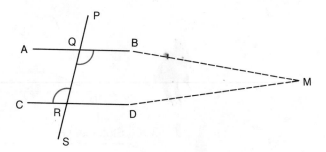

PROOF:

Statements	Reasons
Either AB ∥ CD or AB ∦ CD. We assume AB ∦ CD. Then AB and CD meet at M. In △QRM, $\angle QMR + \angle MQR + \angle QRM = 180°$ $\angle MQR = \angle QRC$ $\angle MQR + \angle QRM = 180°$	 ASTT given SAT

This contradicts our statement $\angle QRM + \angle MQR + \angle QRM = 180°$.

∴ AB ∦ CD is false and AB ∥ CD is the only other possibility.

EXAMPLE 2.

GIVEN: AB and CD intersect at E;

AE = EB; CE = ED

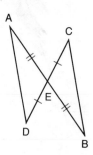

PROVE: AD ∥ CB.

PROOF:

Statements	Reasons
In △AED and △BEC,	
AE = BE	given
∠AED = ∠BEC	OAT
DE = CE	given
△AED ≅ △BEC	SAS
∠DAE = ∠CBE	
AD ∥ CB	TPT

EXERCISE 8.12

A 1. Name the alternate, corresponding, and interior angles in each of the following.

(a)

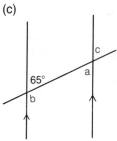

(b)

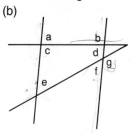

2. Find the values of a, b, and c in each of the following.

(a)

(b)

(c)

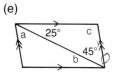

(d)

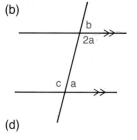

(e)

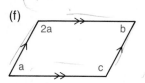

(f)

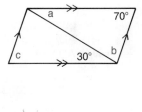

3. Find the values of x, y, and z in the following.

(a)

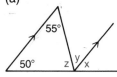

(b)

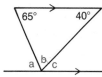

(c)

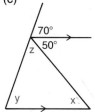

(d)

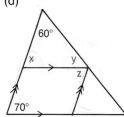

(e)

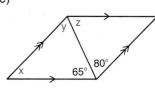

(f)

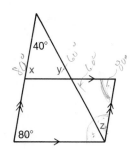

B 4. Given: AD and BC intersect at E;
AB = CD; AB ∥ CD
Prove: △AEB ≅ △DEC

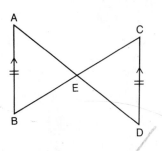

5. Given: quadrilateral ABCD; AB ∥ DC;
∠ABC = ∠DCB
Prove: (i) △BAC ≅ △CDB
(ii) ∠BCA = ∠CBD

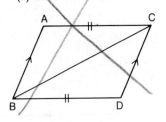

6. Given: quadrilateral ABCD;
AB ∥ DC; AD ∥ BC
Prove: (i) AB = CD
(ii) CB = AD

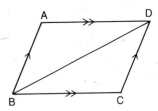

7. Given: quadrilateral ABCD; AD ∥ BC;
∠DAC = ∠BAC
Prove: AB = CB

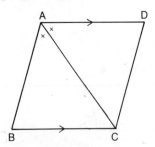

8. Given: AB ∥ CD; CD ∥ EF
Prove: AB ∥ EF

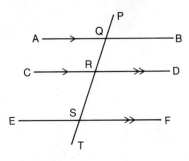

9. Given: quadrilateral ABCD;
AD ∥ BC; ∠BAD = ∠CDA
Prove: AB = DC

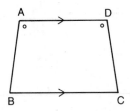

10. Use parallel lines to prove that the sum of
the angles of a triangle is 180°.

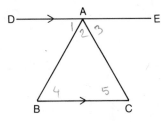

11. Given: quadrilateral ABCD; AB = CD;
AD = CB
Prove: AD ∥ BC

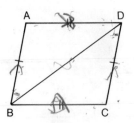

12. Given: quadrilateral ABCD; AB = AD;
    ∠ABD = ∠CBD
    Prove: AD ∥ BC

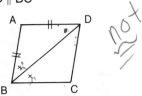

13. Given: quadrilateral ABCD; AB = DC;
    AB ∥ CD
    Prove: (i) AD = BC
    (ii) AD ∥ BC

14. Given: rhombus ABCD;
    AB = BC = CD = DA
    Prove: (i) AD ∥ BC
    (ii) AB ∥ DC

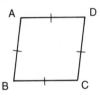

15. Given: △ABC; AC = BC;
    CE bisects the exterior ∠ACD
    Prove: AB ∥ EC

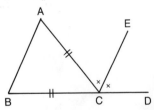

16. Given: quadrilateral ABCD; AB = DC;
    ∠ABC = ∠DCB
    Prove: AD ∥ BC

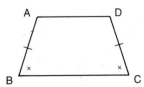

17. Given: △ABC; M and N the midpoints of
    AB and AC; MN = NO
    Prove: (i) AB ∥ OC
    (ii) MO ∥ BC

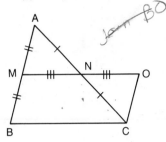

18. Given: △ABC; AM = AN; AB = AC
    Prove: MN ∥ BC

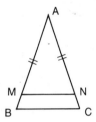

C Prove the following deductions using an
indirect proof.

19. Given: △ABC; AB ≠ AC
    Prove: ∠ABC ≠ ∠ACB

20. Given: △ABC is scalene; AD is a median
    Prove: ∠ABC ≠ ∠ACB

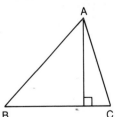

8.13 APPLICATION OF PROOF: THE PYTHAGOREAN THEOREM

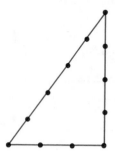

Long before the time of Pythagoras, Egyptian "harpedonaptae" or rope stretchers used a loop of rope with 12 equally spaced knots to form a right triangle with sides 3, 4, and 5 units. The right angle was used to lay out square corners and boundary markers washed out by the periodic flooding of the Nile. There are many proofs of the theorem in existence; the proof which follows dates from the twelfth century.

Pythagorean Theorem

In any right triangle, the square of the length of the hypotenuse is equal to the sum of the squares of the lengths of the other two sides.

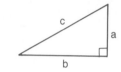

$$a^2 + b^2 = c^2$$

GIVEN: CQRS, a square with sides of length $(a + b)$;
points A, B, P, D, on CS, QC, RQ, and SR so that
$CA = QB = RP = SD = b$
$SA = CB = QP = RD = a$
$AB = c$

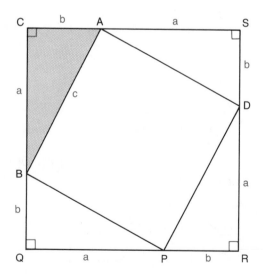

PROVE: In $\triangle ABC$, $c^2 = a^2 + b^2$.

PLAN: We must first prove that ABPD is a square by proving that AB = BP = PD = DA and that one of its angles is 90° (requiring that its three other angles are also 90°). We then use the formulas for areas of squares and triangles to establish a relationship between a, b, and c.

PROOF:

Statements	Reasons
In △ABC and △BPQ,	
AC = BQ	given
∠ACB = ∠BQP = 90°	square
CB = QP	given
△ABC ≅ △BPQ	SAS
Similarly, △ABC ≅ △PDR ≅ △DAS	
∴ AB = BP = PD = DA = c	congruency
and ∠CAB = ∠QBP	congruency
In △ABC,	
∠CAB + ∠CBA = 90°	ASTT
∠QBP + ∠CBA = 90°	
∴ ∠ABP = 90°	
ABPD is a square.	

> A quadrilateral with equal sides and a right angle is a square.

square CQRS = square ABPD + △ABC + △BPQ + △PDR + △ADS

$$(a + b)^2 = c^2 + \tfrac{1}{2}ab + \tfrac{1}{2}ab + \tfrac{1}{2}ab + \tfrac{1}{2}ab$$
$$a^2 + 2ab + b^2 = c^2 + 2ab$$
$$a^2 + b^2 = c^2$$

EXAMPLE 1. Calculate the value of x to the nearest tenth in each of the following using the Pythagorean Theorem.

(a)   (b)   (c)

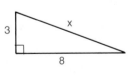

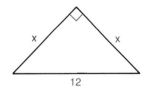

SOLUTION:

(a) $x^2 = 3^2 + 8^2$
$= 9 + 64$
$= 73$
$x = \sqrt{73}$
$\doteq 8.5$

(b) $x^2 + 9^2 = 14^2$
$x^2 + 81 = 196$
$x^2 = 115$
$x = \sqrt{115}$
$\doteq 10.7$

(c) $x^2 + x^2 = 12^2$
$2x^2 = 144$
$x^2 = 72$
$x = \sqrt{72}$
$\doteq 8.5$

The theorem has also been stated.

> In any right triangle, the area of the square on the hypotenuse is equal to the sum of the areas of the squares on the other two sides.

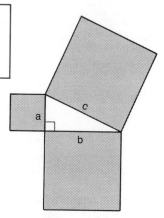

EXAMPLE 2.

GIVEN: rectangle ABCD; M in the interior

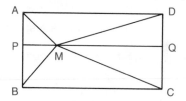

PROVE: $MA^2 + MC^2 = MB^2 + MD^2$

PLAN: Draw PMQ ∥ AD.
Treating MA, MC, MB, and MD each as a hypotenuse, use the Pythagorean Theorem to express MA^2, MC^2, MB^2 and MD^2 as the sum of the squares of the two other sides. Use these results to substitute into the left side of the required equation and to manipulate it until it equals the right side.

PROOF:

Statements	Reasons
Draw PMQ ∥ AD	
$\angle DAP = \angle APM = \angle MPB = 90°$	
$\angle ADQ = \angle DQM = \angle MQC = 90°$	
In $\triangle APM$, $MA^2 = AP^2 + MP^2$	Pythagorean Theorem
In $\triangle MQC$, $MC^2 = MQ^2 + QC^2$	Pythagorean Theorem
In $\triangle PMB$, $MB^2 = PB^2 + MP^2$	Pythagorean Theorem
In $\triangle DMQ$, $MD^2 = MQ^2 + DQ^2$	Pythagorean Theorem
$MA^2 + MC^2$	
$= AP^2 + MP^2 + MQ^2 + QC^2$	substitution
$= DQ^2 + MP^2 + MQ^2 + PB^2$	opposite sides
$= PB^2 + MP^2 + MQ^2 + DQ^2$	commutative property
$= MB^2 + MD^2$	substitution

EXERCISE 8.13

B 1. Find the value of the variable in each of the following to the nearest whole number.

(a)

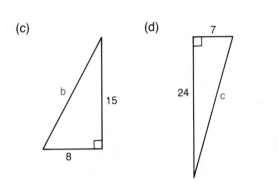

(b)

(c)

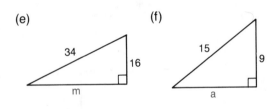

(d)

(e)

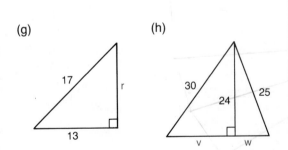

(f)

(g)

(h)

2. Find the length of the hypotenuse of a right triangle where the lengths of the other 2 sides are as follows.

(a) 6 cm, 8 cm   (b) 5 m, 12 m
(c) 8 m, 15 m   (d) 14 cm, 48 cm
(e) 30 cm, 40 cm   (f) 10 cm, 24 cm

3. Find the length of the diagonal of a rectangle 2 m by 5 m giving your answer to the nearest centimetre.

4. An isosceles triangle has sides 30 cm, 30 cm, and 20 cm. Find the altitude to the shortest side giving your answer to the nearest millimetre.

5. A rectangular field is 120 m by 300 m. What is the distance from corner to corner to the nearest metre?

6. A 2.5 m ladder leans against a wall. How far up the wall, to the nearest tenth of a metre, will the ladder reach if the foot is 1 m from the base of the wall?

7. A 5 m ladder reaches 4 m up the wall. How far is the foot of the ladder from the wall?

8. Calculate the values of a, b, c, and d in the given diagram. Leave your answers in radical form.

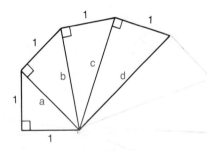

9. What is the size of the largest square timber that can be cut from a log 30 cm in diameter to the nearest centimetre?

10. Find the length of cable required to secure the sign if 20 cm are required at each end for fastening.

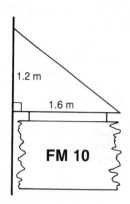

1.2 m

1.6 m

FM 10

11. Find the value of the variable in each of the following.

(a)

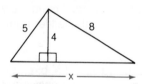

5   8
   4

x

(b)

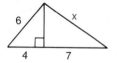

6   x

4   7

(c)

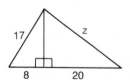

17   z

8   20

12. The inside dimensions of a crate are 45 cm by 60 cm by 180 cm. What is the length of the longest item that can be placed in the crate corner to corner?

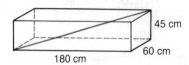

45 cm
60 cm
180 cm

13. If m, n $\in$ N and m $>$ n, then the sides of a right triangle are $m^2 + n^2$, $m^2 - n^2$, and 2mn as in the diagram.

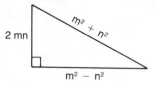

2 mn

$m^2 + n^2$

$m^2 - n^2$

Make a table with the following headings to generate Pythagorean triples.

m	n	$m^2 - n^2$	2mn	$m^2 + n^2$
2	1	3	4	5
3	1	8	6	10
3	2	5	12	13

14. Given: rectangle ABCD
Prove: $AB^2 + BC^2 + CD^2 + DA^2$
$= AC^2 + BD^2$

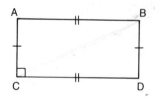

A   B

C   D

15. Given: $\triangle ABC$ and any point O in the interior; OS $\perp$ AB; OU $\perp$ BC; OT $\perp$ AC
Prove: $AS^2 + BU^2 + CT^2$
$= SB^2 + UC^2 + TA^2$

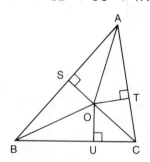

A

S

T

O

B   U   C

8.14 EXTENSIONS OF THE PYTHAGOREAN THEOREM

Prove that the area of the semi-circle on the hypotenuse is equal to the sum of the areas of the semi-circles on the other two sides.

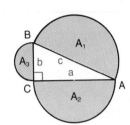

GIVEN: right triangle ABC;
$\angle ABC = 90°$

PROVE: $A_1 = A_2 + A_3$

PLAN: The radii of the circles are $\dfrac{c}{2}$, $\dfrac{a}{2}$, and $\dfrac{b}{2}$. Use the formula for the area of a semi-circle, $A = \frac{1}{2}\pi r^2$, to calculate A_1, A_2, and A_3. By substitution, show that $A_1 = A_2 + A_3$.

PROOF:

Statements	Reasons
$A = \frac{1}{2}\pi r_1{}^2$	area of a semi-circle
$A_1 = \frac{1}{2}\pi \left(\dfrac{c}{2}\right)^2$	
$\quad = \dfrac{\pi}{8}c^2$	
$A_2 + A_3 = \frac{1}{2}\pi r_2{}^2 + \frac{1}{2}\pi r_3{}^2$	area of a semi-circle
$A_2 + A_3 = \frac{1}{2}\pi \left(\dfrac{a}{2}\right)^2 + \frac{1}{2}\pi \left(\dfrac{b}{2}\right)^2$	
$\quad = \dfrac{\pi}{8}a^2 + \dfrac{\pi}{8}b^2$	
$\quad = \dfrac{\pi}{8}(a^2 + b^2)$	common factoring
$\quad = \dfrac{\pi}{8}c^2$	Pythagorean Theorem $(c^2 = a^2 + b^2)$
$\therefore A_1 = A_2 + A_3$	

EXERCISE 8.14

1. Prove that the area of the circle on the hypotenuse of a right triangle is equal to the sum of the areas of the circles on the other 2 sides.

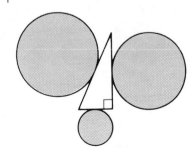

8.15 PROOF AND APPLICATION OF THE CONVERSE OF THE PYTHAGOREAN THEOREM

The converse of a statement in the form "If . . ., then . . ." is a statement formed by interchanging the "if" and "then" parts of the sentence.

We now state the converse of the Pythagorean Theorem.

> If the square of the length of one side of a triangle is equal to the sum of the squares of the lengths of the other two sides, then the angle opposite the longest side is a right angle.

EXAMPLE 1.

GIVEN: △ABC; $c^2 = a^2 + b^2$

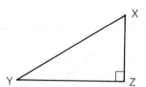

PROVE: ∠ACB = 90°

PLAN: First construct △XYZ so that
   XZ = b
   YZ = a
   ∠XZY = 90°

Show by the Pythagorean Theorem that the hypotenuse XY of △XYZ also equals c. With three pairs of corresponding sides equal, prove that the two triangles are congruent. You can then conclude that ∠ACB = ∠XZY = 90°.

PROOF:

Statements	Reasons
$XY^2 = XZ^2 + YZ^2$	Pythagorean Theorem
XZ = b and YC = a	by construction
$XY^2 = b^2 + a^2$	substitution
$= c^2$	given
XY = c	
In △ABC and △XYZ,	
AB = XY	above
BC = YZ	construction
AC = XZ	construction
∴ △ABC ≅ △XYZ	SSS
∠ACB = ∠XYZ = 90°	
∠ACB = 90°	

The theorem we have just proved is the converse of the Pythagorean theorem.

EXAMPLE 2.

GIVEN: △ABC; AB = 5; BC = 12, and AC = 13

PROVE: ∠ABC = 90°

PLAN: To prove that the triangle is a right triangle, prove that the sides satisfy the Pythagorean relationship.

PROOF:

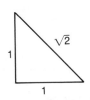

Statements	Reasons
$AC^2 = 13^2$ $= 169$	given
$AB^2 + BC^2 = 5^2 + 12^2$ $= 25 + 144$ $= 169$	given
$AC^2 = AB^2 + BC^2$	property of equality
∠ABC = 90°	converse of the Pythagorean Theorem

EXERCISE 8.15

A 1. Determine which of the following are right triangles (the figures may not be drawn to scale).

(a)

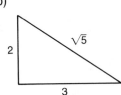

(b)

(c)

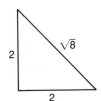

(d)

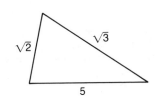

B 2. Which of the following sets of numbers can be the lengths of the sides of a right triangle?

(a) 5, 8, 10   (b) 1.25, 0.75, 1.00
(c) 30, 34, 16   (d) 24, 10, 26
(e) 1.2, 1.6, 2.0   (f) $\frac{3}{10}, \frac{2}{5}, \frac{1}{2}$

3. Find the area of each triangle with sides whose lengths are the following.

(a) 3, 4, 5   (b) 5, 12, 13   (c) 8, 15, 17
(d) 7, 24, 25   (e) 10, 6, 8   (f) 3, $\sqrt{34}$, 5

4. Given: quadrilateral ABCD; ∠ABC = 90°; AB = 12, BC = 16, CD = 25, and DA = 15 units

Prove: ∠CAD = 90°

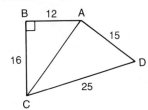

5. Given: parallelogram ABCD; AC = 10, BE = 12, and AB = 13

Prove: (i) AE ⊥ BE
(ii) ABCD is a rhombus

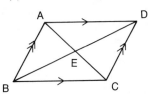

6. Given: quadrilateral ABCD; AD = 13, AB = 4, BC = 3, and CD = 12

Prove: ∠ABC = 90°

8.16 PROBLEM SOLVING

1. The latitude of Winnipeg is approximately 50°N. The latitude of Rio de Janeiro is approximately 23°S.
(a) How many degrees of latitude separate the cities?
(b) If the circumference of the earth is approximately 40 000 km, find the distance between the two cities along the earth's surface.

2. The latitude of the North Pole is 90°N and the latitude of the South Pole is 90°S.
(a) How many degrees of latitude separate the poles?
(b) Find the distance between the North Pole and the South Pole to the nearest thousand kilometres.
   (i) along the surface of the earth
   (ii) through the earth
(c) How much shorter is the distance through the centre of the earth?

3. Catherine scored 102 points in the first part of the basketball season. This was 60 points less than twice the number of points scored by Jennifer. How many points did Jennifer score?

4. A board 4 m long is cut into two pieces. One piece is 20 cm shorter than the other. How long is each piece?

5. Find three consecutive negative integers such that the sum of the greatest and twice the smallest is equal to four times the middle integer.

6. Janice has been able to divide her own age into her grandmother's age evenly for the past six years. How old are they today?

7. A printed page is 3 cm longer than it is wide. If the page is made 1.5 cm longer and the width is made 1 cm larger, the size of the printed page is increased by 17 cm². What are the original dimensions of the page?

8. When a large circular tablecloth has a strip 10 cm wide cut from around the edge, the area is reduced by 4710 cm². What is the radius of the original tablecloth?

9. A child's bank contains nickels, dimes, and quarters. There are half as many dimes as there are quarters and half as many nickels as there are dimes. What is the smallest total value of the coins in the bank?

10. There are 10 000 trees in a forest. In this forest there are twice as many spruce trees as there are pine trees. Sixty-four hundred trees are neither spruce nor pine. How many spruce trees are there?

11. Roy Tovar defeated Terry Harrison in an election for reeve of the township. A total of 6788 votes were cast. If 100 voters had switched their votes from Roy to Terry, then Terry would have won by 64 votes. How many votes did each candidate receive?

12. The total length of three cross-country ski trails is 40 km. The Yellow trail is 3 km longer than twice the length of the Blue trail, and the Red trail is 10 km shorter than twice the length of the Yellow trail. How long is each trail?

13. Tara and Joyce averaged 6 km/h walking from their house to school, and they arrived 15 min late. If they had averaged 9 km/h, they would have arrived on time. How far is it from their house to the school?

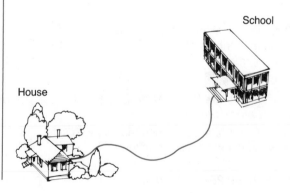

School

House

14. The Transcontinental train travels from Calgary to Thunder Bay at an average speed of 100 km/h. If the train had averaged 20 km/h less, the trip would have taken 5 h longer. How far is it by train from Calgary to Thunder Bay?

15. A rectangular sheet of tin is 40 cm longer than it is wide. Squares 15 cm by 15 cm are cut from each corner of the sheet, and the sides are folded up and soldered to make an open box with a volume of 67 500 cm³. What were the dimensions of the original sheet of tin?

16. A photograph is enlarged to 20 cm by 30 cm and framed. The frame is to include a border around the photograph equal in area to the photograph.

Find the width of the border.

17. The Andersons drove from their home to the airport, a distance of 50 km, at 60 km/h. They left for the airport 1 h prior to takeoff, but had to stop for 25 min to change a flat tire. At this point, they were still 20 km from the airport. If the speed limit for the remaining 20 km was 90 km/h, did they catch the plane?

18. Brenda and Charles have a system of walking and jogging equal distances through a course in their neighbourhood. They walk at a rate of 6 km/h and jog at a rate of 12 km/h. The total time required for them to walk and jog through the course is 2 h. How long is the course?

19. Paul can complete a job in 4 h. It takes Henry 6 h to complete the same job. How long will it take Paul and Henry to complete the job working together?

20. It takes Susan 36 h to paint an apartment. Elaine can paint the same apartment in 30 h. Elaine starts the painting alone and works for 12 h. Then Elaine and Susan paint together for 3 h. When Elaine leaves Susan completes the job working on her own. How long does it take Susan to finish the job?

PYTHAGORAS

Pythagoras was both a mystic and a scientist who lived in the sixth century B.C. He started a secret society on the south-eastern coast of what is now Italy. The members of this society (The Pythagoreans) were vegetarians whose mystical conception of numbers affected every aspect of their lives. In fact, their motto was "All is number." For example, they thought of even numbers as being female and odd numbers as being male.

Pythagoras travelled to Egypt and Babylon and probably learned of the Pythagorean Theorem from the Babylonians. But the Pythagoreans may have been the first to find a proof for the theorem.

Pythagoras is sometimes called the "Father of Mathematics" since he was one of the first to establish mathematics as a rational discipline. He is supposed to have coined the word "mathematics," meaning "that which is learned."

8.17 REVIEW EXERCISE

1. Solve for each variable.

(a)
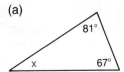

(b)
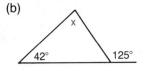

(c)
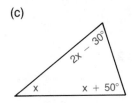

(d)
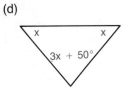

(e)
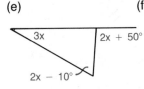

(f)
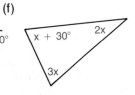

(g)
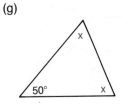

(h)
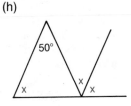

(i)
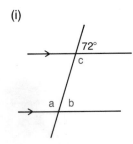

(j)
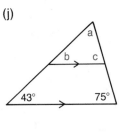

(k)
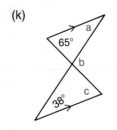

(l)
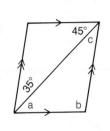

(m)
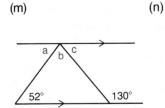

(n)
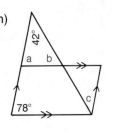

2. Find the measure of the indicated line segment in each of the following.

(a)
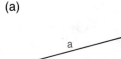

(b)
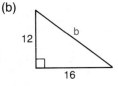

(c)
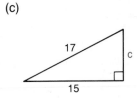

(d)
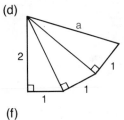

(e)
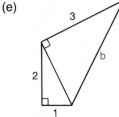

(f)
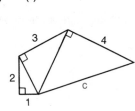

3. Given: △ABC ≅ △PQR, and
△PQR ≅ △XYZ
Prove: △ABC ≅ △XYZ

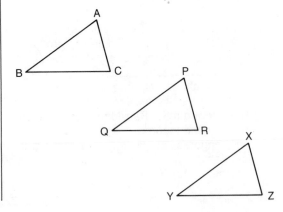

4. Determine which of the following are right triangles. (Figures may not be drawn to scale.)

(a)
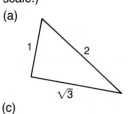

(b)
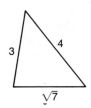

(c)
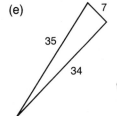

(d)
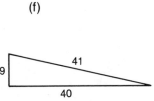

(e)
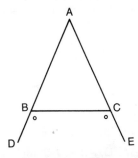

(f)
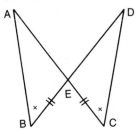

5. Given: △ABC; AB extended to D; AC extended to E; ∠DBC = ∠ECB
   Prove: △ABC is isosceles

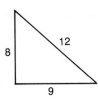

6. Given: AC and BD intersect at E; BE = CE; ∠ABE = ∠DCE
   Prove: AB = DC

7. Given: quadrilateral ABCD, AB = DC; AD = BC
   Prove: ∠BAD = ∠DCB

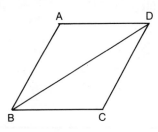

8. Given: AB and CD are chords of a circle, centre O; ∠BAO = ∠CDO; ∠AOB = ∠DOC
   Prove: AB = CD

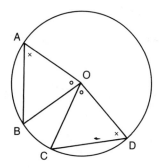

9. Given: circle with centre O; AB = BC
   Prove: ∠AOB = ∠COB

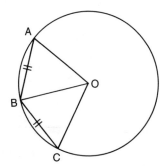

10. Given: CD, the right bisector of AB.
    Prove: CA = CB

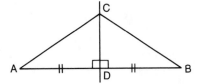

11. Given: △ABC and △DCB; AB = DC;
    ∠ABC = ∠DCB
    Prove: (i) AC = BD
    (ii) AE = DE

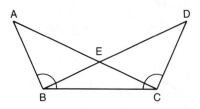

12. Given: BC is a diameter;
    BA ⊥ AC; CD ⊥ BD; AB = DC
    Prove: AC = BD

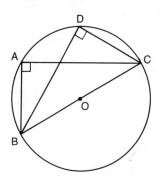

13. Given: △ABC; DF = FE;
    FD ⊥ AD; FE ⊥ AC
    Prove: AF bisects ∠BAC

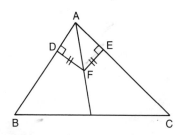

14. Given: △ABC; CE ∥ AB; AC = BC
    Prove: EC bisects the exterior ∠ACD

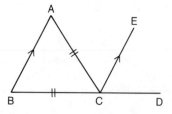

15. Given: circle centre O; radii OA, OB, and
    OC; OB bisects ∠AOC.
    Prove: AB = BC

16. Given: △ABC; MN passes through A;
    MN ∥ BC
    Prove: ∠ABC + ∠BAC + ∠ACB = 180°

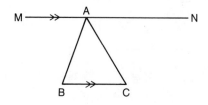

17. Given: AC and BD intersect at E;
    AE = EC; BE = ED; AB = DC
    Prove: AB ∥ DC

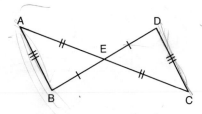

18. Given: quadrilateral ABCD;
    AB = DC; ∠ABD = ∠CDB
    Prove: ABCD is a parallelogram

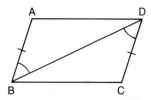

19. Given: △ABC, AB = AC; MN ∥ BC
    Prove: △AMN is isosceles

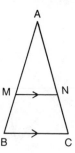

20. Given: parallelogram ABCD: P and Q on
    AD and BC; PD = BQ
    Prove: PDQB is a parallelogram

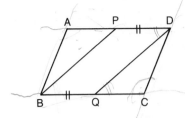

21. Given: quadrilateral ABCD; AC ⊥ BD;
    AC and BD intersect at E
    Prove: $AB^2 + CD^2 = BC^2 + DA^2$

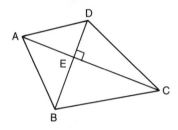

22. Prove: The median of an equilateral
    triangle is also the altitude.

23. Prove: If the altitude of a triangle bisects
    the angle at the vertex, then the
    triangle is isosceles.

24. Given: △ABC; BD ⊥ AC; BD = 15,
    AD = 12, and DC = 8
    Prove: ∠ABC = 90°

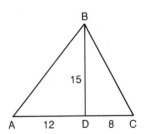

25. Prove that there is only one perpendicular
from a point to a line.

26. Prove that the bisector of the vertical
angle of an isosceles triangle bisects the
base.

27. Given: △ABC is scalene; AD is the
    altitude
    Prove: AD is not the median

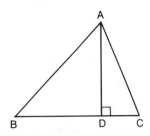

28. Prove that any point on the right bisector
of a line segment is equidistant from the
endpoints of the segment.

Given: ED is the right bisector of AB;
       P is any point on ED
Prove: PA = PB

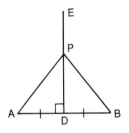

A three-ring binder and a pencil cost
$10.50. The binder costs $10.00 more
than the pencil. What is the cost of two
binders and three pencils?

8.18 CHAPTER 8 TEST

1. Solve for each variable.

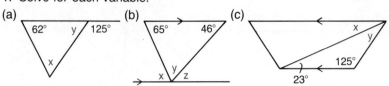

(a)　　　　　　　　(b)　　　　　　　　(c)

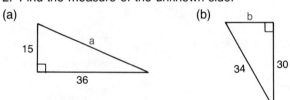

2. Find the measure of the unknown side.

(a)　　　　　　　　　　　　(b)

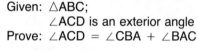

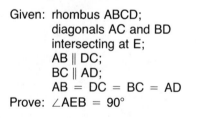

3. Prove the Exterior Angle Theorem.

Given: △ABC;
　　　　∠ACD is an exterior angle
Prove: ∠ACD = ∠CBA + ∠BAC

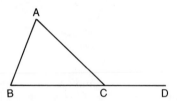

4. A rhombus is a parallelogram having four equal sides. Prove that the diagonals of a rhombus intersect at right angles.

Given: rhombus ABCD;
　　　　diagonals AC and BD
　　　　intersecting at E;
　　　　AB ∥ DC;
　　　　BC ∥ AD;
　　　　AB = DC = BC = AD
Prove: ∠AEB = 90°

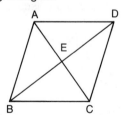

5. Given: △ABC;
　　　　DE ∥ BC;
　　　　DE = DB;
　　　Prove: ∠DBE = ∠EBC

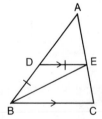

8.19 CUMULATIVE REVIEW FOR CHAPTERS 5 TO 8

1. State three ordered pairs that satisfy the following equations.

(a) $y = 3x - 7$ (b) $y = -4x + 2$

(c) $2x - 3y = 8$ (d) $5x + 4y - 6 = 0$

2. Solve the following graphically. Check your solution.

(a) $x - y = 0$ (b) $3x + 2y = 5$
    $4x - y = 3$ $5x - 2y = 3$

(c) $2x - 3y = 4$ (d) $-5x + 2y + 1 = 0$
    $4x - 6y = 5$ $3x - y - 1 = 0$

3. Classify the following systems of equations as consistent, inconsistent, or dependent.

(a) $3x - y = 2$ (b) $-3x + 2y = 5$
    $6x - 2y = 4$ $x - 5y = 6$

(c) $3x + 4y = 12$ (d) $x = y$
    $3x + 4y = 8$ $3x + 3y = 5$

4. Solve the following systems of equations.

(a) $x + y - 1 = 0$
    $x - 2y + 5 = 0$

(b) $2x + 3y = -17$
    $9x - 5y = 16$

(c) $8x - 3y = 3$
    $3x - 2y = -5$

(d) $4x - y = 10$
    $-2x + 3y = -10$

(e) $ax + by = a + b$
    $abx + aby = a^2 + b^2$

(f) $ax + by = a$
    $a^2x + b^2y = a^2$

5. Draw the graph of each of the following.

(a) $y < x + 5$
(b) $y > 2x - 3$
(c) $2x - 3y \leqslant 6$
(d) $3x - 4y \geqslant 12$
(e) $x + 3y < 6$
(f) $x > 3y$

6. Graph the following.

(a) $\{(x, y) \mid y > x + 2 \text{ and } y < -2x\}$
(b) $\{(x, y) \mid x - 2y > 8 \text{ or } 2x + y > 5\}$

7. The sum of two numbers is 132 and their difference is 16. Find the numbers.

8. The sum of three times a larger number and two times a smaller number is 242. The smaller number is 19 less than the larger number. Find the numbers.

9. There are 28 members in the school choir. The number of female voices is 24 less than 3 times the number of male voices. How many male and female voices are there in the group?

10. Three ice-cream cones and five milkshakes cost $12.20. Four ice-cream cones and 2 milkshakes cost $10.20. Find the price of an ice-cream cone and a milkshake.

11. Mario earns $11.00/h and Gisele earns $13.00/h. Together in one week they worked a total of 45 h and received $533.00. How many hours did each work?

12. An amount of money is split into two parts and invested in two different accounts. One part is invested in an account that pays interest at the rate of 5% while twice as much is invested in an account that pays 6%. The yearly interest from both accounts is $612.00. How much is invested at each rate?

13. A boat can travel upstream against the current at a rate of 16 km/h. Travelling downstream with the current, the rate is 30 km/h. Find the rate of the current, and the rate of the boat in still water.

14. Express as a single matrix.

(a) $\begin{pmatrix} 3 & 5 \\ -2 & 4 \end{pmatrix} + \begin{pmatrix} 4 & -3 \\ 3 & 0 \end{pmatrix}$

(b) $\begin{pmatrix} 4 & 6 \\ 0 & 4 \end{pmatrix} - \begin{pmatrix} -5 & 3 \\ -2 & -4 \end{pmatrix}$

(c) $\begin{pmatrix} 2 & 4 \\ 1 & 2 \\ 2 & 3 \end{pmatrix} - \begin{pmatrix} 5 & 6 \\ 3 & 4 \\ 3 & 2 \end{pmatrix}$

(d) $\begin{pmatrix} 3 & -3 \\ -3 & 3 \\ 0 & -2 \end{pmatrix} + \begin{pmatrix} 4 & -4 \\ -4 & 4 \\ -3 & 2 \end{pmatrix}$

15. Multiply the following matrices, if possible.

(a) $\begin{pmatrix} 3 & 5 \\ 1 & 3 \end{pmatrix}\begin{pmatrix} 4 & 6 \\ 4 & 3 \end{pmatrix}$

(b) $\begin{pmatrix} 1 & -4 \\ -2 & 3 \end{pmatrix}\begin{pmatrix} 2 & 5 \\ 3 & -4 \\ 4 & 1 \end{pmatrix}$

(c) $\begin{pmatrix} 1 \\ 2 \\ 3 \end{pmatrix}\begin{pmatrix} 2 & 5 \\ 3 & -4 \\ 4 & 2 \end{pmatrix}$

(d) $\begin{pmatrix} 4 & 3 \\ 5 & -2 \end{pmatrix}\begin{pmatrix} 2 \\ 4 \end{pmatrix}$

(e) $\begin{pmatrix} 3 & 5 \\ -2 & 4 \end{pmatrix}\begin{pmatrix} 7 & 3 \\ 3 & -5 \end{pmatrix}$

(f) $\begin{pmatrix} 2 & 4 \\ 3 & 1 \\ 1 & 5 \end{pmatrix}(1 \quad 2 \quad 3)$

16. Let $A = \begin{pmatrix} 2 & 3 \\ 3 & 4 \end{pmatrix}$ and $B = \begin{pmatrix} -2 & 6 \\ 3 & -2 \end{pmatrix}$.

Find.
(a) 3A   (b) −5B
(c) A + B   (d) B − A
(e) 3(A − B)   (f) AB

17. Solve for each variable.
(a) $3(x \quad y \quad z) = (12 \quad 15 \quad -6)$

(b) $4\begin{pmatrix} 0 & x \\ y & 3 \end{pmatrix} = \begin{pmatrix} 0 & 24 \\ -8 & 12 \end{pmatrix}$

(c) $2\begin{pmatrix} 3 & 4 \\ 4 & 1 \end{pmatrix} + 3\begin{pmatrix} x & 2 \\ -2 & y \end{pmatrix} = \begin{pmatrix} 12 & -12 \\ z & 5 \end{pmatrix}$

18. At a music festival, the number of firsts, seconds, and thirds for the Verdi Conservatory of Music students were listed as follows.

	First	Second	Third
Junior	4	3	6
Intermediate	5	2	8
Senior	9	5	2

5 points were awarded for a first, 4 for a second, and 3 for a third.
(a) Write the finishes and point awards as matrices.
(b) Find the total points for the school.

19. Given: AB = AD; BC = DC
      Prove: ∠BAC = ∠DAC

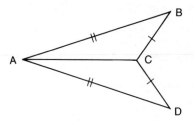

20. Given: quadrilateral ABCD;
              AD = CB; DC = BA
      Prove: ∠ADC = ∠ABC

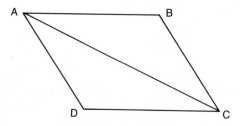

21. Given: quadrilateral ABCD;
              ∠DAC = ∠ACB;
              ∠DCA = ∠BAC
      Prove: AD = CB

22. Given: quadrilateral ABCD;
              ∠DCA = ∠BAC; DC = AB
      Prove: ∠DAC = ∠BCA

THREE~ DIMENSIONAL GEOMETRY

CHAPTER

It is the glory of geometry that from so few principles, fetched from without, it is able to accomplish so much.

Sir Isaac Newton

REVIEW AND PREVIEW TO CHAPTER 9

PERIMETER

Triangle	Square	Rectangle	Circle
$P = a + b + c$	$P = 4s$	$P = 2(\ell + w)$	$C = 2\pi r$
			$= \pi d$

EXERCISE

1. Calculate the perimeter of the following.

(a)

6 cm   7 cm
8 cm

(b)

4 cm
4 cm   4 cm
4 cm

(c)

11 m
7 m

(d)

4.5 cm
2.5 cm

(e)

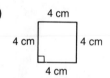

8.3 cm
4.7 cm   6.1 cm

(f)

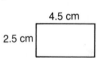

5 cm 5 cm
7 cm   7 cm
8 cm

(g)

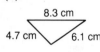

12 m
6 m
3 m
4 m   3 m

(h)

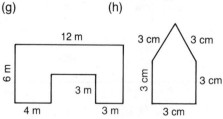

3 cm   3 cm
3 cm   3 cm
3 cm

2. Calculate the circumference to the nearest tenth.

(a)

7 m

(b)

12 m

(c)

10 cm
10 cm

(d)

50 m
100 m

(e)

10 cm

(f)

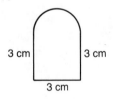

3 cm   3 cm
3 cm

AREA

Triangle

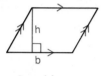

$A = \frac{1}{2}bh$

Square

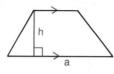

$A = s^2$

Rectangle

$A = \ell w$

Parallelogram

$A = bh$

Trapezoid

$A = \frac{1}{2}(a + b)h$

Circle

$A = \pi r^2$

EXERCISE

1. Calculate the area of each of the following to the nearest tenth.

(a)

3.2 m — 3.2 m

(b)

5.1 m — 4.3 m

(c)

5 cm

(d)

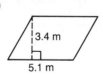
3.4 m — 5.1 m

(e)

8.1 cm
5.1 cm 6.2 cm
6.2 cm

(f)

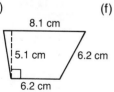
5.0 cm
6.0 cm

(g)

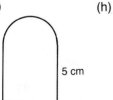
5 cm — 5 cm

(h)

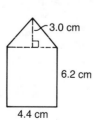
3.0 cm
6.2 cm
4.4 cm

(i)

3 m
6 m

(j)

3.1 cm   1.1 cm
1.1 cm
4.5 cm

(k)

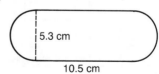
10 cm

(l)

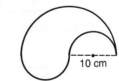
5.3 cm
10.5 cm

(m)

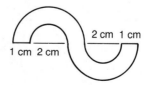
2 cm 1 cm
1 cm 2 cm

9.1 PRISMS AND PYRAMIDS

The following figures are examples of prisms.

Triangular Prism

Rectangular Prism

Pentagonal Prism

A prism is a polyhedron with a pair of congruent faces (the bases) that lie in parallel planes. All of the other faces are parallelograms. A segment between the parallel bases is called the altitude of the prism.

The following figures are examples of pyramids.

Triangular based Pyramid

Square based Pyramid

Pentagon based Pyramid

A pyramid is a polyhedron in which all faces but one have a common vertex. The base can be any polygon, while the lateral faces are triangles. A line segment from the vertex to the base, perpendicular to the base is called the altitude of the pyramid.

The surface area and volume of a right prism or right pyramid can be calculated using the following rules.

Definition	Area	Volume
Right prism	Surface area = Area of Bases + Area of Lateral Faces	$V = Bh$ where B is the area of the base and h is the altitude. For a rectangular prism $V = \ell wh$
Right pyramid	Surface area = Area of Base + Area of Lateral Faces	$V = \frac{1}{3}Bh$ where B is the area of the base and h is the altitude. For a rectangular pyramid $V = \frac{1}{3}(\ell w)h$

EXERCISE 9.1

All diagrams in this exercise involve right prisms or right pyramids.

B 1. Find the surface area of each of the following figures.

(a)

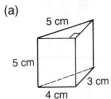

5 cm
5 cm
3 cm
4 cm

(b)

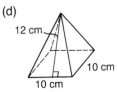

5 cm
5 cm
5 cm

(c)

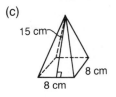

15 cm
8 cm
8 cm

(d)

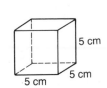

12 cm
10 cm
10 cm

2. Find the volume of each of the following figures.

(a)

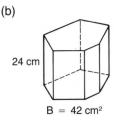

8 cm
B = 33 cm²

(b)

24 cm
B = 42 cm²

(c)

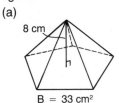

12 cm
10 cm
10 cm

(d)

10 cm
8 cm
8 cm

3. Find the surface area and volume of each of the following.

(a)

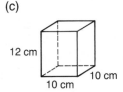

10 cm
13 cm
10 cm
12 cm
10 cm

(b)

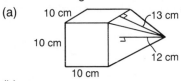

16 cm
15 cm
16 cm
17 cm
24 cm

4. (a) Find the surface area of the given right pyramid.

13 cm
10 cm
10 cm

(b) Find the third dimension of a rectangular prism with a volume of 3600 cm³, a height of 20 cm, and one side of the base 12 cm.

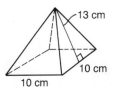

20 cm
12 cm
?

5. Find the height of a right pyramid with a square base 10 cm to a side if the pyramid is to have the same volume as a rectangular prism with dimensions 10 cm by 10 cm by 12 cm.

MICRO MATH

The following program computes surface area and volume for a rectangular prism.

NEW

```
 5 REM SURFACE AREA-VOLUME
10 INPUT "LENGTH";L
20 INPUT " WIDTH";W
30 INPUT "HEIGHT";H
40 PRINT "L","W","H","SA","VOL"
50 S = 2*(L*W+L*H+W*H)
60 V = L*W*H
70 PRINT L, W, H, S, V
80 END
```

RUN

9.2 SURFACE AREA OF A CYLINDER

If we take a cylinder and open it up as shown, the result is two circles and a rectangle.

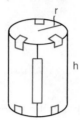

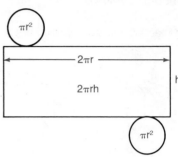

These diagrams show how to construct a right cylinder.

$E=mc^2$

The area of each of the bases is
   B.A. $= \pi r^2$

The lateral area is
   L.A. $= 2\pi rh$

The surface area of a right cylinder is

   S.A. $= \pi r^2 + \pi r^2 + 2\pi rh$
      $= 2\pi r^2 + 2\pi rh$
or S.A. $= 2\pi r(r + h)$

EXAMPLE 1.   Find the surface area of the given right cylinder to the nearest tenth.

SOLUTION:
From the diagram

   $r = 12.6 \div 2$ and $h = 21.2$
     $= 6.3$

   S.A. $= 2\pi r(r + h)$
   S.A. $= 2 \times 3.14 \times 6.3 \times (6.3 + 21.2)$
      $= 1088.01$

The surface area is 1088.0 cm².

21.2 cm

12.6 cm

EXAMPLE 2.   A right cylinder has a surface area of 12 000 cm² and a radius of 25 cm. Find the height of the cylinder to the nearest tenth.

SOLUTION:
   S.A. $= 12\ 000$ cm²
      $r = 25$ cm
   S.A. $= 2\pi r(r + h)$
   $12\ 000 = 2 \times 3.14 \times 25 \times (25 + h)$
   $12\ 000 = 3925 + 157h$
   $157h = 12\ 000 - 3925$
     $h = 51.433$

Surface Area
= 12 000 cm²

25 cm

h

The height is 51.4 cm to the nearest tenth of a centimetre.

EXERCISE 9.2

The problems in this exercise involve right cylinders.

B 1. Find the surface area of the following shapes to the nearest unit.

(a)

(b)

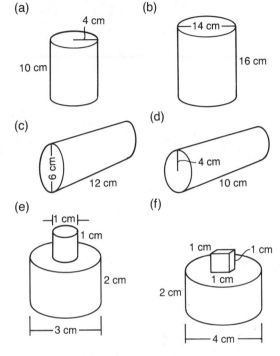

(c)

(d)

(e)

(f)

2. A cylindrical tank is 15 m high and has a base radius of 6 m. What is the surface area of this tank to the nearest tenth?

3. Two cylinders have the same radius. The height of one cylinder is twice the height of the other. What is the ratio of the surface areas of the two cylinders?

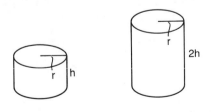

4. Two cylinders have the same height. The radius of one cylinder is twice the radius of the other. What is the ratio of the surface areas of the two cylinders?

5.

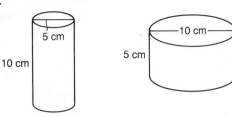

Which of the above cylinders has the larger area?

(a) Take a guess.
(b) Make an estimate.
(c) Find the difference to the nearest tenth.
(d) Construct these cylinders using paper and tape.

6. A sheet of construction paper is 10 cm by 52 cm. You wish to construct a cylinder with a height of 10 cm and a diameter of 10 cm.

(a) What is the surface area of the cylinder to the nearest whole number?
(b) What area of construction paper is left after you construct the cylinder?
(c) Construct the cylinder.

7. A cylindrical tank is to be made from stainless steel which costs about $45/m². The tank has a radius of 1.75 m and a height of 3.4 m. Find the cost of the stainless steel, to the nearest dollar, to build the tank.

8. Calculate the lateral area of a cylinder with radius 8 cm and height 10 cm to the nearest whole number.

9. A cube with sides 10 cm has a cylinder cut out of it as shown.

What is the surface area of the solid to the nearest whole number?

9.3 VOLUME OF A CYLINDER

The volume of a rectangular solid is found by multiplying the area of the base by the height.

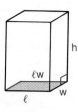

$$V = (\ell w) \times h$$
$$= \ell wh$$

The volume of a right cylinder is also found by multiplying the area of the base by the height.

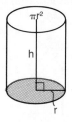

$$V = (\pi r^2) \times h$$
$$= \pi r^2 h$$

EXAMPLE 1. Find the volume of the given right cylinder to the nearest tenth.

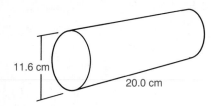

SOLUTION:
From the diagram
$$r = 11.6 \div 2 \quad \text{and} \quad h = 20.0$$
$$= 5.8$$

$$V = \pi r^2 h$$
$$V = 3.14 \times 5.8^2 \times 20.0$$
$$= 2112.592$$

The volume is 2112.6 cm³.

EXAMPLE 2. A right cylinder has a volume of 15 000 cm³ and a height of 5 cm. Find the radius of the cylinder.

SOLUTION:
$$V = 15\ 000 \text{ cm}^3 \quad \text{and} \quad h = 5 \text{ cm}$$

$$V = \pi r^2 h$$
$$15\ 000 = 3.14 \times r^2 \times 5$$
$$15\ 000 = 15.7 \times r^2$$
$$r^2 = 15\ 000 \div 15.7$$
$$r = \sqrt{15\ 000 \div 15.7}$$
$$r = 30.909772$$

$V = 15\ 000$ cm³

5 cm

The radius is 30.9 cm to the nearest tenth of a centimetre.

EXERCISE 9.3

The problems in this exercise involve right cylinders.

B 1. Find the volume of the following cylindrical shapes to the nearest unit. Use $\pi \doteq 3.14$.

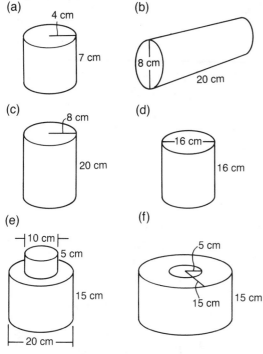

(a) 4 cm, 7 cm

(b) 8 cm, 20 cm

(c) 8 cm, 20 cm

(d) 16 cm, 16 cm

(e) 10 cm, 5 cm, 15 cm, 20 cm

(f) 5 cm, 15 cm, 15 cm

2. A cylindrical tank is 12 m high and has a base radius of 5 m. What is the volume of the tank to the nearest whole number?

3. A concrete column in the shape of a cylinder is 7 m high and 1.2 m in diameter. 1 m³ of concrete has a mass of about 275 kg. Find the mass of the column to the nearest kilogram.

4. The volume of a cylinder is 2400 cm³ and the height is 6 cm. Find the radius of the cylinder to the nearest tenth.

5. A case is packed with 12 cylindrical cans, each having a diameter of 15 cm and a height of 24 cm. Calculate the volume of the empty space in the case to the nearest whole number.

MICRO MATH

The following program calculates the surface area and volume of a cylinder.

NEW

```
10 REM CYLINDER
20 INPUT "RADIUS IS";R
30 INPUT "HEIGHT IS";H
40 S = 2*3.14*R*(R+H)
50 V = 3.14*R*R*H
60 PRINT "SURFACE AREA IS";S
70 PRINT "      VOLUME IS";V
80 END
```

RUN

EXERCISE

1. Use the program to find how the volume and surface area change when the height and radius are changed.

Height	Radius	Surface Area	Volume
10 cm	4 cm		
10 cm	8 cm		
10 cm	12 cm		
10 cm	16 cm		
10 cm	20 cm		
10 cm	5 cm		
20 cm	5 cm		
30 cm	5 cm		
40 cm	5 cm		

2. What is the effect of multiplying
(a) the radius by n on surface area and volume?
(b) the height by m on surface area and volume?
(c) the radius by n and the height by m?

9.4 SURFACE AREA OF A CONE

If we take a sector of a circle and join the radii, the result is the lateral area of a cone. This is a right circular cone since the axis is perpendicular to the circular base. The slant height of the cone is the radius of the sector that makes up the cone. We use this fact to investigate the surface area of a cone by considering a fraction of a circle with radius s.

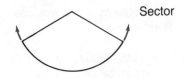
Sector

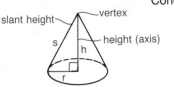
Cone

$\frac{1}{3}$ of the circle

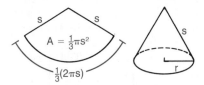

$\frac{1}{3}(2\pi s)$ is the circumference of the cone with radius r. Equate these.

$$\tfrac{1}{3}(2\pi s) = 2\pi r$$
$$\pi s = 3\pi r \qquad ①$$

The area of the sector is

$$A = \tfrac{1}{3}\pi s^2$$
$$= \tfrac{1}{3}(\pi s)s$$
$$= \tfrac{1}{3}(3\pi r)s \qquad \text{From ①.}$$
$$= \pi rs$$

The lateral area is πrs.
The area of the base is πr^2.

$\frac{1}{n}$ of the circle

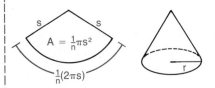

$\frac{1}{n}(2\pi s)$ is the circumference of the cone with radius r. Equate these.

$$\frac{1}{n}(2\pi s) = 2\pi r$$
$$\pi s = n\pi r$$

The area of the sector is

$$A = \frac{1}{n}\pi s^2$$
$$= \frac{1}{n}(\pi s)s$$

Substitute $n\pi r$ for πs.

$$A = \frac{1}{n}(n\pi r)s$$
$$= \pi rs$$

The lateral area is $A = \pi rs$.
The area of the base is $B = \pi r^2$.

The surface area of a right cone is

$$\text{S.A.} = \pi rs + \pi r^2$$

EXAMPLE. A right circular cone has a height of 24 cm and the radius of the base is 7 cm. Find the surface area of the cone.

SOLUTION:
First we find the slant height.

$$s^2 = h^2 + r^2$$
$$s^2 = 24^2 + 7^2$$
$$= 576 + 49$$
$$= 625$$
$$s = \sqrt{625}$$
$$= 25$$

The surface area is

$$\text{S.A.} = \pi rs + \pi r^2$$
$$\text{S.A.} = 3.14 \times 7 \times 25 + 3.14 \times 7^2$$
$$= 549.5 + 153.86$$
$$= 703.36$$

The surface area is 703.4 cm² to the nearest tenth.

EXERCISE 9.4

The following exercises involve right circular cones.

B 1. Find the surface area of each of the following conical shapes to the nearest unit. Use $\pi \doteq 3.14$.

(a)

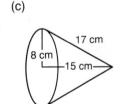

(b)

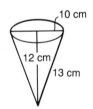

(c)

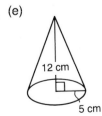

(d)

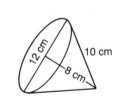

(e)

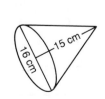

(f)

(g)

(h)

(i)

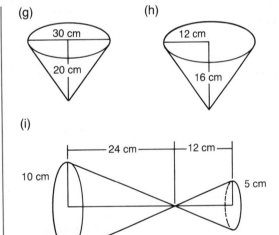

2. A silo consists of a right circular cone surmounted on a cylinder with a height of 10 m and a diameter of 4 m. The height of the conical top is 2 m. How many square metres of material are required to build the silo?

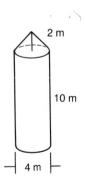

3. Find the surface area of the given top to the nearest whole number.

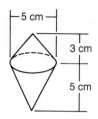

4. The following shape is formed by cutting a cone with a plane parallel to the base.

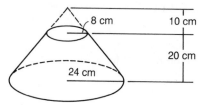

Find the total surface area of this shape to the nearest unit.

5. The shape of a cone can be traced by rotating a right triangle about one of its sides.

The sides of a right triangle are 3 cm and 4 cm. Cones are traced by rotating the triangle about these two sides as shown. Find the ratio of the surface areas of these cones.

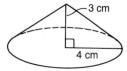

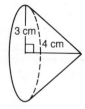

6. The following shape is formed by cutting a cone with a plane parallel to the base and inverting the tip so that it can be attached to the opening as shown.

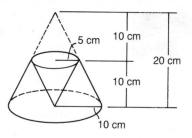

Find the surface area of this shape to the nearest unit.

EXTRA

PERIMETER OF AN ELLIPSE

If we take a loop of string and two tacks, we can draw an ellipse.

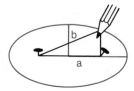

The formula for the perimeter of an ellipse is

$$P = \pi(a + b)$$

EXERCISE

1. Find the perimeter of each of the following ellipses to the nearest tenth.

(a)   (b)

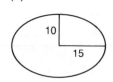

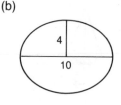

9.5 VOLUME OF A CONE

If we take a right circular cone and a right cylinder with equal radii
and height, we can find the relationship between the volume of the
cone and the volume of the cylinder. By filling the cone to the top with
sand and pouring it into the cylinder, we find that it takes three fillings
of sand from the cone to fill the cylinder. Hence the volume of the
cylinder is three times the volume of the cone.

 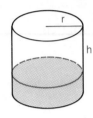 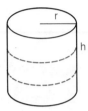

The volume of the cylinder is

$$V = \pi r^2 h$$

Since the volume of the cylinder is three times the volume of the
cone, the volume of the cone is $\frac{1}{3}$ the volume of the cylinder, and we
state the following formula.

> The volume of a cone is
>
> $$V = \frac{1}{3}\pi r^2 h$$

EXAMPLE 1. A right circular cone has a slant height of 13 cm and
the diameter of the base is 10 cm. Find the volume of the cone.

SOLUTION:
First we find the height.

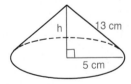

$$h^2 = s^2 - r^2$$
$$h^2 = 13^2 - 5^2$$
$$= 169 - 25$$
$$= 144$$
$$h = \sqrt{144}$$
$$= 12$$

The volume is

$$V = \frac{1}{3}\pi r^2 h$$
$$V = \frac{1}{3} \times 3.14 \times 5 \times 5 \times 12$$
$$= 314$$

The volume is 314 cm³.

EXAMPLE 2. A cylindrical tank has a height of 4.0 m and a radius of 1.5 m. Find the radius of a conical tank with the same volume and height.

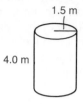
1.5 m
4.0 m

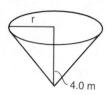
r
4.0 m

SOLUTION:
The volume of the cylinder is

$$V = \pi r^2 h$$
$$V = 3.14 \times 1.5 \times 1.5 \times 4.0$$
$$= 28.26$$

Substitute V = 28.26 and h = 4.0 in the formula.

$$V = \tfrac{1}{3}\pi r^2 h$$
$$28.26 = \tfrac{1}{3} \times 3.14 \times r^2 \times 4.0$$
$$r^2 = 6.75$$
$$r = \sqrt{6.75}$$
$$r \doteq 2.598\ 0762$$

The radius of the cone would be 2.6 m to the nearest tenth.

EXERCISE 9.5

The following problems involve right circular cones.

B 1. Find the volume of each of the following conical shapes to the nearest unit. Use π ≐ 3.14.

(a)

5 m
8 m

(b)
10 m
7 m

(c)
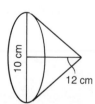
10 cm
12 cm

(d)
11 cm
6 cm

(e)
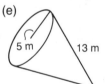
5 m
13 m

(f)
20 m
32 m

(g)

16 m
34 m

(h)
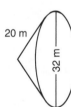
13 m
12 m

(i)
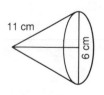
26 cm
20 cm
13 cm
10 cm

2. A sand pile is shaped like a cone as shown. Calculate the number of cubic metres of sand to the nearest unit.

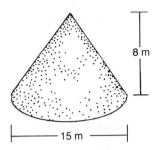

8 m

15 m

3. The tip of a lead pencil is in the shape of a cone.

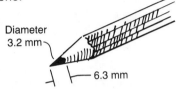

Diameter 3.2 mm

6.3 mm

Calculate the number of cubic millimetres of lead area in the sharpened tip of this pencil to the nearest tenth.

4. Calculate the volume of the shape formed by slicing the top off a cone as shown below to the nearest unit.

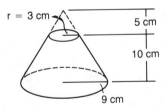

r = 3 cm

5 cm

10 cm

9 cm

5. The following solid is formed by cutting a cone with a plane parallel to the base, and then boring a cone-shaped hole into the top. Find the volume to the nearest unit.

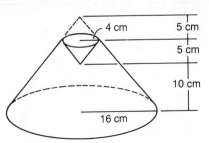

4 cm

5 cm

5 cm

10 cm

16 cm

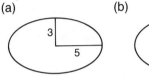

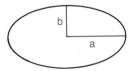

MICRO MATH

The following program calculates the surface area and volume of a cone. In order to use the program it may be necessary to use the relationship among the height, radius, and slant height of the cone:

$$h^2 = s^2 - r^2$$

NEW

```
10 REM CONE
20 INPUT "HEIGHT IS";H
30 INPUT "RADIUS IS";R
40 S = 3.14*R*SQR(H*H+R*R)+3.14*R*R
50 V = 3.14*R*R*H/3
60 PRINT "SURFACE AREA IS";S
70 PRINT "      VOLUME IS";V
80 END
```

RUN

9.6 SURFACE AREA AND VOLUME OF A SPHERE

The formula for surface area of a sphere is given below.

> For a sphere with radius r, the surface area is
> $$A = 4\pi r^2$$

The formula for the volume of a sphere is as follows.

> For a sphere with radius r, the volume is
> $$V = \tfrac{4}{3}\pi r^3$$

EXAMPLE 1. Find the surface area and volume of a sphere with a radius of 15 cm. Give your answer to the nearest cubic centimetre.

SOLUTION:

Surface Area

for r = 15

$$A = 4\pi r^2$$
$$A = 4 \times 3.14 \times 15^2$$
$$= 2826$$

The surface area is 2826 cm².

Volume

$$V = \tfrac{4}{3}\pi r^3$$
$$V = \tfrac{4}{3} \times 3.14 \times 15^3$$
$$\doteq 14\,130$$

The volume is 14 130 cm³.

EXAMPLE 2. A metal sphere with a diameter of 40 cm is packed in a cubical box. What is the volume of the unused portion of the box?

SOLUTION:

Unused Volume = Volume of Box − Volume of Sphere

Side of the box

$$s = 40$$

Volume of box

$$V = s^3$$
$$V = 40^3$$
$$= 64\,000$$

Radius of the sphere

$$r = 20$$

Volume of sphere

$$V = \tfrac{4}{3}\pi r^3$$
$$V = \tfrac{4}{3} \times 3.14 \times 20^3$$
$$\doteq 33\,493$$

Unused Volume = 64 000 − 33 493
$$= 30\,507$$

The unused volume in the box is 30 507 cm³.

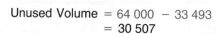

EXERCISE 9.6

For each of the following, use $\pi \doteq 3.14$.

B 1. Find the surface area of each of the following spheres to the nearest unit.

(a) (b)

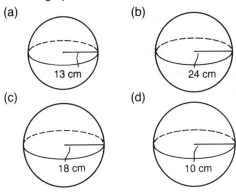

13 cm 24 cm

(c) (d)

18 cm 10 cm

2. Find the volume of each of the following spheres to the nearest unit.

(a) (b)

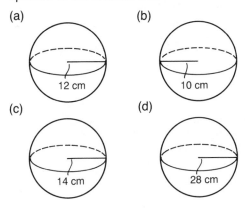

12 cm 10 cm

(c) (d)

14 cm 28 cm

3. Find the surface area and volume of each of the following to the nearest unit.

(a) (b)

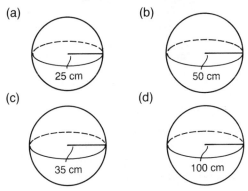

25 cm 50 cm

(c) (d)

35 cm 100 cm

4. The inside radius of a spherical metal shell is 50 cm and the thickness of the shell is 0.4 cm.

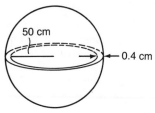

50 cm 0.4 cm

Calculate the volume of material used in the shell to the nearest unit.

5. Two racquet balls are sold in a container in the shape of a cylinder. The inside diameter of the container is 5.6 cm and the balls just fit.
(a) What is the volume occupied by one ball to the nearest tenth?
(b) What is the volume of the cylindrical container to the nearest tenth?
(c) What is the volume of the unused portion of the container?

6. The ratio of the volumes of two spheres is 27:8. What is the ratio of the radii of the two spheres?

7. The ratio of the areas of two spheres is 81:64. What is the ratio of the radii of the two spheres?

MICRO MATH

The following program calculates the surface area and volume of a sphere.

NEW

```
10 PRINT "SPHERE"
20 INPUT "RADIUS =";R
30 S=4*3.14*R*R
40 V=4/3*3.14*R*R*R
50 PRINT "SURFACE AREA =";S
60 PRINT "      VOLUME =";V
70 END
```

RUN

9.7 APPLICATIONS OF AREA AND VOLUME: PACKAGING

For the following problems, the precision of the answers should reflect that of the given data.

EXERCISE 9.7

B 1. A ball with a diameter of 12 cm is packaged in a cubical box.

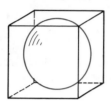

What is the area of cardboard required to make the box?

2. A racquet ball has a diameter of 5.5 cm. Racquet balls are shipped in cylindrical containers that just hold two balls. What is the surface area of the material required to make one container?

3. A spherical tank is 10 m in diameter and made of steel 1 cm thick.

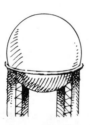

How many cubic metres of steel are required to build the tank?

4. A conical stereo speaker is shipped in a rectangular box. The diameter of the speaker is 25 cm and the height is 15 cm. Find the dimensions and surface area of the box that will just hold the speaker.

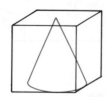

5. A square sheet of copper is 10 cm by 10 cm. A square x cm by x cm is cut from each of the 4 corners as shown. The sides are the bent upward to form an open box as shown.

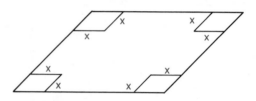

(a) Find the dimensions of the box in terms of x.
(b) Find the volume of the box in terms of x.

6. A tomato juice tin has a diameter of 10.8 cm and a height of 17.7 cm. Each case contains 12 tins in a 3 by 4 arrangement.

(a) Find the volume of 1 tin.
(b) Find the volume of 12 tins.
(c) Find the inside volume of the box.
(d) Find the unused volume in the box.
(e) Find the area of the cardboard required to make the box.

7. The silo of a barn is in the shape of a cylinder capped by a hemisphere as shown.

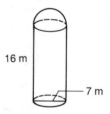

16 m

7 m

(a) Find the volume of the silo.
(b) Three cans of paint are needed to cover the hemisphere of the silo. How many cans of paint are required to paint the entire silo?

9.8 SYMMETRY

The following figures have line symmetry. Each figure coincides with its image if it is reflected about the line ℓ. ℓ is called the line of symmetry

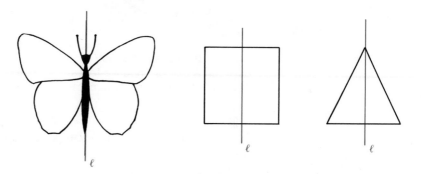

The square has 4 lines of symmetry. The square also has rotational symmetry about the centre O. If the square is rotated 90°, 180°, 270°, or 360° about the centre O, every point in the figure will match onto another point in the figure.

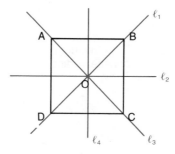

The circle can be used to show point symmetry. In a circle with centre O, the diameter AA′ is drawn. Since OA = OA′ and AA′ is a straight line segment, then A′ is symmetric to A with respect to the point O. This is true for all points on the circle. We say that the circle is symmetric about its centre.

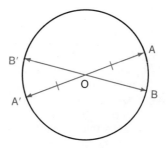

The reflection symmetry of a cube is determined by a plane.

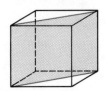

A plane that passes midway between a pair of opposite faces of a cube is a plane of symmetry.

A plane that passes through a pair of opposite edges of a cube is a plane of symmetry.

In three dimensions, we can show symmetry by considering a cube. The cube has rotational symmetry about three types of rotational axes.

The rotational axis passes through the midpoints of a pair of opposite sides.

The rotational axis passes through a pair of opposite vertices.

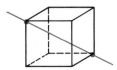

The rotational axis passes through the centres of a pair of opposite faces.

As with the circle in two dimensions, we use the sphere in three dimensions to show point symmetry. A diameter AA' of a sphere with centre O is shown. Since OA = OA' and AA' is a straight line segment, then A' is symmetric to A with respect to the point O. Since this is true for all points in the sphere, we say that the sphere has point symmetry about its centre.

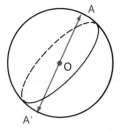

EXERCISE 9.8

1.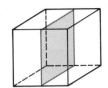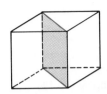

(a) How many planes of symmetry are there that pass through a pair of opposite edges?
(b) How many planes of symmetry are there that pass midway between a pair of opposite parallel faces?

2.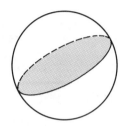

The circle formed by the intersection of a sphere and a plane containing the centre is called a great circle.

(a) How many different great circles are there in a sphere?
(b) How many different planes of symmetry are there in a sphere?

3.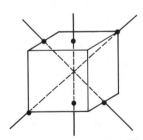

(a) How many different axes of symmetry that pass through the midpoints of opposite sides of a cube are there?
(b) How many different axes of symmetry are there that pass through the pairs of opposite vertices?
(c) How many different axes of symmetry are there that pass through the centre of opposite faces?

4. The turnstile has rotational symmetry.

(a) Make a diagram of the figure formed by the turnstile.
(b) Draw the axis of rotational symmetry on your diagram.
(c) Define the axis of rotational symmetry for a tetrahedron.
(d) How many axes of rotational symmetry are there for this figure?

5. Describe the symmetry, if any, in each of the following figures.

(a)   (b)

(c)   (d)

EXTRA

H202D is an imaginary two-dimensional person who resides on the surface of a tank of water. H202D only sees what is on the surface of the water. A ball in the shape of a sphere is lowered gently into the water until it is completely beneath the surface of the water.

Describe what H202D saw as the ball was lowered into the water.

9.9 PROBLEM SOLVING

1. The 10 members of the basketball team have a warm-up drill in which each player passes the ball to each of the other players. How many passes take place during this drill?

2. Three people, Mr. White, Ms. Brown, and Mr. Black, were all born in England. They have hair that is also white, brown, and black in colour, but none of these people's names match the colour of their hair. Ms. Brown does not have white hair. What is the colour of each person's hair?

3. AB and BC are the diagonals of two adjacent faces of a cube as shown. What is the measure of ∠ABC?

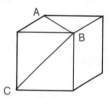

4. A stairway has 10 steps each 30 cm wide and 30 cm high. An insect starts at the bottom of the first step, and climbs straight to the top of the stairway. How far has the insect travelled when it reaches the top of the last step?

5. What is the maximum number of pieces into which a circle can be divided using 5 cuts?

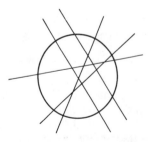

6. A pilot in a small private plane maintains a constant ground speed of 240 km/h. He travels due north for 30 min, east for 10 min, south for 45 min, and then west for 30 min. How long will it take to fly back to the starting point?

7. The ages of three people are consecutive even integers. The sum of the smallest and largest is 36. How old is each person?

8. Write the sequence of calculator keys to simplify the following.

$$1 + \cfrac{1}{2 + \cfrac{1}{3 + \cfrac{1}{4 + \cfrac{1}{5}}}}$$

9. The speed of a boat in still water is 18 km/h. It takes the boat twice as long to travel 72 km upstream in a river as it does to travel the same distance downstream. Find the rate of the current.

10. A 66 cm bicycle wheel covers a certain distance in twenty-five revolutions. How many revolutions of a 50 cm wheel will it take to cover the same distance?

11. An electronics factory produces a monochrome monitor in 20 min and a colour monitor in 30 min. If the factory plans to produce 3 monochrome for every 1 colour, what is the maximum number of each unit that can be built in a 9 h shift?

12. The sum of three different positive integers placed in increasing order is 15. The second integer is three more than the first. Find all possibilities for the three integers.

13. Janice has 300 mL of a solution of alcohol and water which is 25% alcohol. How much pure alcohol must Janice add in order to produce a 40% solution?

14. The Model 1360 computer can analyse the election results in 30 h. The Model 1500 computer can analyse the election results in 20 h. How long would it take the two computers to analyse the results if it is possible for them to interface?

15. The water tap, when turned on full, can fill the bathtub in 4 min. With the plug pulled and the bathtub draining, it took 6 min to fill the tub. How long will it take to drain the bathtub when the tap is turned off and the plug is pulled?

16. A cottage lot is to be enclosed on 3 sides by 2000 m of fencing with the fourth side left open along the river. What are the dimensions that will give the greatest area?

17. A wood-lathe operator is given three identical solid wood cubes with sides 10 cm. The operator is asked to shape the largest possible sphere, cone, and cylinder from them.

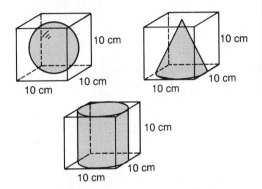

Assuming that the density of wood is the same in all three blocks, which, if any, of the following mobiles are possible using the three solids shaped by the operator.

(a)

(b)

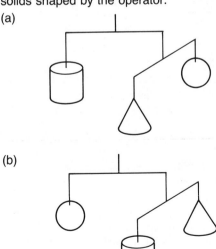

(c)

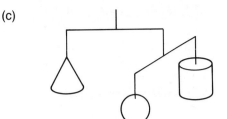

MICRO MATH

Type the following BASIC program into a computer.

NEW
```
100 REM DESIGNING A CYLINDER WITH
110 REM MINIMUM AREA FOR A GIVEN VOLUME
120 PRINT "ENTER THE VOLUME ";
130 INPUT V
140 PRINT "ENTER THE INITIAL RADIUS"
150 PRINT "(USE -1 TO QUIT)";
160 INPUT R
170 IF R=-1 THEN 280
180 PRINT "ENTER THE INCREMENT";
190 INPUT I
200 PRINT "RADIUS", "HEIGHT", "AREA"
210 FOR J=1 TO 10
220 H= V/(3.1416 * R↑2)
230 A= 2*3.1416*R*H + 2*3.1416*R↑2
240 PRINT R, H, A
250 R=R+1
260 NEXT J
270 GO TO 140
280 END
```
RUN

1. By successively guessing and checking, determine the dimensions of a cylinder having the least surface area for a volume of

(a) 1000 cm³   (b) 100 cm³   (c) 50 cm³.

Fill in the table below.

Volume (cm³)	R (cm)	H (cm)	Minimum Area (cm²)	Ratio (H/R)
1000				
100				
50				

What generalization can be made from the ratios obtained in the table above?

9.10 REVIEW EXERCISE

For each of the following, use π ≐ 3.14.

1. Find the surface area of each of the following to the nearest whole number.

(a)

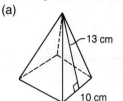

13 cm

10 cm

(b)

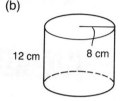

12 cm   8 cm

(c)

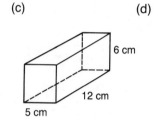

6 cm

12 cm

5 cm

(d)

15 cm

16 cm

(e)

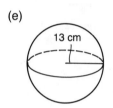

13 cm

(f)

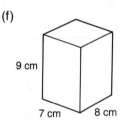

9 cm

7 cm   8 cm

2. Find the volume of each of the following to the nearest whole number.

(a)

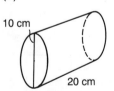

10 cm

20 cm

(b)

12 cm

10 cm

(c)

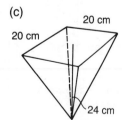

20 cm

20 cm

24 cm

(d)

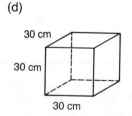

30 cm

30 cm

30 cm

(e)

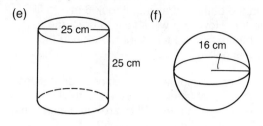

25 cm

25 cm

(f)

16 cm

3. A sphere has a radius of 4 cm and a hemisphere has a radius of 8 cm. Compare the volume of the sphere to the volume of the hemisphere using a ratio.

4. A sphere with a radius of 20 cm is inscribed in a cylinder. Find the volume of the cylinder to the nearest cubic centimetre.

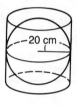

20 cm

5. The following two boxes have the same volume. Calculate the height of the taller box to the nearest tenth.

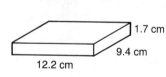

1.7 cm

12.2 cm   9.4 cm

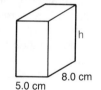

h

8.0 cm

5.0 cm

6. Find the surface area of each of the following to the nearest whole number.
(a) a sphere with a diameter of 24 cm
(b) a cone with a radius of 8 cm and a slant height of 10 cm
(c) a cylinder with a diameter of 50 cm and a height of 40 cm
(d) a square based pyramid with a slant height of 10 cm and each side of the base measuring 8 cm

7. A hollow rubber ball has an outside diameter of 5.6 cm. The thickness of the rubber in the ball is 0.3 cm. Find the amount of rubber in the ball to the nearest tenth.

8. A double cone is inscribed inside a cylinder as shown.

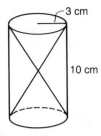

3 cm

10 cm

Calculate the amount of space in the cylinder that is not occupied by the cone to the nearest tenth.

9. A skylight is in the shape of a regular pyramid with a square base 1.8 m to a side and a slant height of 1.0 m. Find the area of glass required to make the skylight to the nearest tenth.

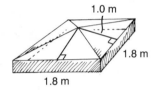

1.0 m

1.8 m

1.8 m

10. A sphere has a diameter of 30 cm. Find the height of a cylinder having the same diameter and the same volume to the nearest tenth.

30 cm

30 cm

h

11. In a right circular cone, the slant height is 16 cm. Find the height, h, of the cone that will produce the cone with the greatest volume to the nearest tenth.

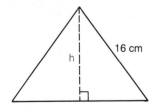

16 cm

h

12. Draw top, front, and side views for each of the following.

(a)

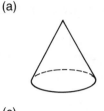

(b)

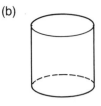

(c)

(d)

(e)

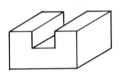

(f)

(g)

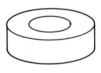

(h)

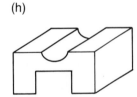

9.11 CHAPTER 9 TEST

For each of the following, use $\pi \doteq 3.14$.

1. Find the total surface area of each of the following figures to the nearest whole number.

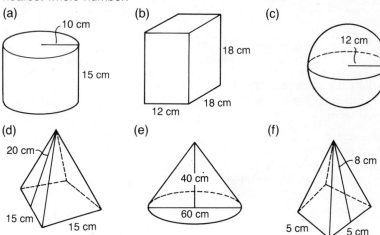

(a) 10 cm, 15 cm

(b) 18 cm, 18 cm, 12 cm

(c) 12 cm

(d) 20 cm, 15 cm, 15 cm

(e) 40 cm, 60 cm

(f) 8 cm, 5 cm, 5 cm

2. Find the volume of each of the following figures to the nearest whole number.

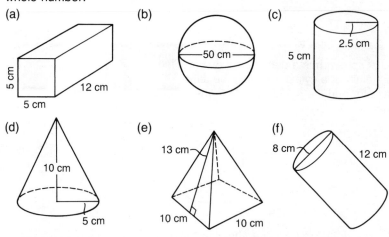

(a) 5 cm, 12 cm, 5 cm

(b) 50 cm

(c) 2.5 cm, 5 cm

(d) 10 cm, 5 cm

(e) 13 cm, 10 cm, 10 cm

(f) 8 cm, 12 cm

3. Find to the nearest whole number the volume of a cylinder that will just fit into a rectangular box 10 cm by 10 cm by 10 cm.

4. Find the surface area of a rectangular box that will hold a cone with a diameter of 10 cm and a height of 15 cm.

5. (a) Copy the figure at the right. Show all lines of rotational symmetry.
(b) Make another copy of the figure. Show all planes of reflectional symmetry.

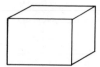

TRANSFORMATIONS

CHAPTER

10

The mathematicians, carried along on their flood of symbols, dealing apparently with purely formal truths, may still reach results of endless importance for our description of the physical universe.

Karl Pearson

LENGTH OF A LINE SEGMENT

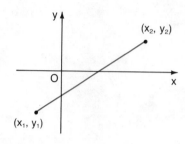

$$\ell = \sqrt{(x_2 - x_1)^2 + (y_2 - y_1)^2}$$

EXERCISE

1. Find the length of each of the following line segments.
(a) A(3, 5), B(6, 9)
(b) C(0, 0), D(5, 12)
(c) E(2, 7), F(−3, −5)
(d) G(−1, 4), H(5, −4)
(e) J(−4, −7), K(7, 4)

SLOPE OF A LINE

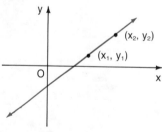

$$m = \text{slope}$$
$$= \frac{\text{rise}}{\text{run}}$$
$$m = \frac{\text{vertical change}}{\text{horizontal change}}$$
$$m = \frac{\Delta y}{\Delta x}$$
$$m = \frac{y_2 - y_1}{x_2 - x_1}$$

EXERCISE

1. Determine the slopes of the lines through the following points.
(a) A(1, 1), B(4, 3)
(b) C(0, 2), D(4, 6)
(c) E(5, 7), F(9, 11)
(d) G(0, 0), H(5, 6)
(e) K(5, 3), L(7, 3)
(f) M(−3, 4), N(5, −2)
(g) P(−3, −1), Q(−5, 7)
(h) R(2, −3), S(0, 4)

EQUATION OF A LINE

> **Linear Equation: Point-Slope Form**
>
> Given a point on the line, (x_1, y_1) and the slope of the line m, an equation of the line may be expressed as
>
> $$y - y_1 = m(x - x_1)$$

EXERCISE

1. Determine an equation of the line through the given point having the given slope. Express the equation in standard form, Ax + By + C = 0.
(a) (3, 2); m = 4
(b) (5, 7); m = 2
(c) (−5, 2); m = −3
(d) (−4, −1); m = −1
(e) (−6, −4); m = 3
(f) (4, −2); m = −6
(g) (6, 8); m = $\frac{1}{2}$
(h) (−3, 5); m = $-\frac{1}{3}$
(i) ($\frac{1}{2}$, −2); m = $-\frac{1}{2}$
(j) ($\frac{1}{4}$, $-\frac{1}{5}$); m = $\frac{2}{3}$
(k) (0.2, 0.6); m = 0.1
(l) (2.8, −3.6); m = −1.2
(m) (3, −5.7); m = 6.1
(n) (−4.1, −3.8); m = 4.6

2. Find an equation of the line through the following pairs of points. Express the equation in standard form.

(a) (2, 3) and (3, 5)
(b) (1, 4) and (3, 10)
(c) (−1, −5) and (−3, 5)
(d) (−3, −2) and (−6, 7)
(e) (−1, 0) and (3, −16)
(f) (4, 2) and (2, 1)
(g) (−5, 2) and (1, 4)
(h) (6, 4) and (−5, 4)
(i) (3, −5) and (3, 6)
(j) (2, $\frac{1}{2}$) and (3, −4)
(k) (1.5, 3) and (2.5, 7)
(l) (−0.8, −0.3) and (−1, −0.6)
(m) (−2.2, 5.4) and (−3.4, 7.2)
(n) (15.4, −47.5) and (−3.6, 0)

SIMILAR TRIANGLES

If two figures are similar,
(i) the corresponding angles are equal.
(ii) the lengths of the corresponding sides are proportional.

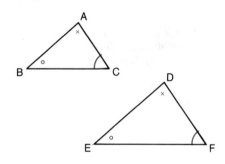

In the diagram,
△ABC ~ △DEF
  ∠A = ∠D
  ∠B = ∠E
  ∠C = ∠F

and $\dfrac{AB}{DE} = \dfrac{BC}{EF} = \dfrac{AC}{DF}$

Also,
AB : BC : AC = DE : EF : DF

EXERCISE

1. Find the values of the variables for each of the following.

(a)

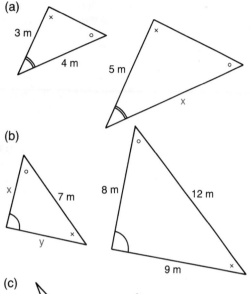

(b)

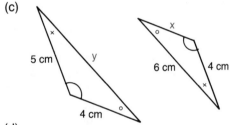

(c)

(d)

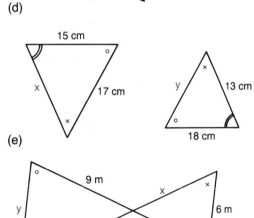

(e)

10.1 TRANSLATIONS: POINT AND LINE SEGMENT

A transformation, or mapping, is a rule for transforming, or changing, one object into another. If a transformation T maps a point P in a plane into another point P' in the same plane, then P' is called the image of P and we write

$$T : P \to P' \quad \text{or} \quad T(P) = P'$$

The transformations that we deal with in this chapter: translations, rotations, reflections, and dilatations, are all one-to-one correspondences among all the points in a plane. They are rules for associating pairs of points P and P'.

A translation is a transformation described by sliding an object a certain distance in a certain direction.

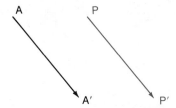

Given the translation of a point A → A', we can find the image P' of any other point P under the same translation by placing P' so that PP' = AA' and making the direction, indicated by arrows, the same.

We can describe a translation of a point in a plane using coordinates. For example, the translation which maps, or displaces, a point in the plane three units to the right and two units upwards is given by

$$(x, y) \to (x + 3, y + 2)$$

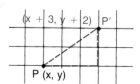

In general, a translation of a point in a plane is given by

$$(x, y) \to (x + a, y + b)$$

and moves point (x, y) a units parallel to the x-axis and b units parallel to the y-axis.

> The translation $T : (x, y) \to (x + a, y + b)$ maps the point P (x, y) into the image point P' (x + a, y + b).

The following example illustrates the translation of a line segment.

EXAMPLE. The line segment PQ has endpoints P(1, 1) and Q(4, 2).
(a) Find the images of points P' and Q' under the translation

$$(x, y) \rightarrow (x + 2, y - 3)$$

(b) Compare the slopes of PQ and P'Q'.
(c) Compare the lengths of PQ and P'Q'.

SOLUTION:

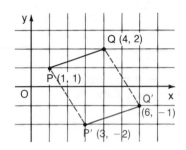

(a) $(x, y) \rightarrow (x + 2, y - 3)$
Therefore, $P(1, 1) \rightarrow P'(3, -2)$
and $\quad Q(4, 2) \rightarrow Q'(6, -1)$

(b) $\qquad m = \dfrac{y_2 - y_1}{x_2 - x_1}$

The slope of PQ is $\dfrac{1 - 2}{1 - 4} = \dfrac{1}{3}$

$$m = \dfrac{y_2 - y_1}{x_2 - x_1}$$

and the slope of P'Q' is $\dfrac{-2 - (-1)}{3 - 6} = \dfrac{1}{3}$

The slopes are equal.

(c) The distance $d = \sqrt{(x_2 - x_1)^2 + (y_2 - y_1)^2}$

$$
\begin{aligned}
PQ &= \sqrt{(1-2)^2 + (1 - 4)^2} \\
&= \sqrt{1 + 9} \\
&= \sqrt{10}
\end{aligned}
$$

$$d = \sqrt{(x_2 - x_1)^2 + (y_2 - y_1)^2}$$

and the distance $P'Q' = \sqrt{(-2 + 1)^2 + (3 - 6)^2}$
$$
\begin{aligned}
&= \sqrt{1 + 9} \\
&= \sqrt{10}
\end{aligned}
$$

The lengths of PQ and P'Q' are equal.

Notice that both the slope and the distance were unchanged under the translation. You will see from the following exercise that, in general, translations preserve distances and slopes, (and, therefore, angles). A mapping which preserves distances and angles is called a rigid motion; it maps any geometric figure into a congruent figure.

In general, for the translation, T, of a line segment defined by

$$T : PQ \rightarrow P'Q'$$

the slopes of PQ and P'Q' are equal and the distance
PQ = P'Q'. The result is that PQ is parallel to P'Q' and
PQ = P'Q'.

EXERCISE 10.1

A 1. Find the images of the following points under the translation

$$(x, y) \rightarrow (x - 5, y + 3)$$

(a) (7, 7)   (b) (3, −1)
(c) (0, 0)   (d) (5, −3)
(e) (3, 5)   (f) (2, −7)
(g) (−3, −5)   (h) (0, −5)

2. Find the images of the single point (1, −2) under the following translations.

(a) $(x, y) \rightarrow (x + 6, y + 4)$
(b) $(x, y) \rightarrow (x - 2, y + 3)$
(c) $(x, y) \rightarrow (x - 1, y - 1)$
(d) $(x, y) \rightarrow (x + 5, y - 3)$
(e) $(x, y) \rightarrow (x + 0, y + 5)$
(f) $(x, y) \rightarrow (x + 4, y + 7)$
(g) $(x, y) \rightarrow (x + 3, y - 2)$
(h) $(x, y) \rightarrow (x + 0, y - 3)$

B 3. State the value of a and b in $(x, y) \rightarrow (x + a, y + b)$ for each of the following translations.

(a) (3, 5) → (7, 8)
(b) (1, 1) → (11, 9)
(c) (−1, 4) → (4, 3)
(d) (−2, −3) → (5, 6)
(e) (−4, −5) → (−1, 4)
(f) (−7, −2) → (−5, −8)
(g) (0, −6) → (5, 0)
(h) (−4, 0) → (0, 0)
(i) (0, 0) → (−3, $\frac{1}{2}$)

4. Given the line segment AB and the translation

$$(x, y) \rightarrow (x - 3, y + 2)$$

Find the images of A′ and B′, the lengths of AB and A′B′, and the slope of the line segment and image segment. Illustrate each translation on a plane.

(a) A(3, 0) B(−1, 1)
(b) A(−1, −7) B(−2, −3)
(c) A(1, 3) B(4, 0)
(d) A(3, 6) B(1, 5)

5. Given the three points A(2, 1), B(1, 6), C(3, 5), and the translation $(x, y) \rightarrow (x + 4, y + 2)$.
(a) Graph △ABC.
(b) Find the images of A′, B′, C′ of A, B, C under this translation.
(c) Draw △A′B′C′ using the same axes as in part (a).
(d) Find the lengths AB, BC, CA, A′B′, B′C′, and C′A′.
(e) Show that △ABC ≅ △A′B′C′.
(f) Find and compare the slopes of the lines AB, BC, CA, A′B′, B′C′, and C′A′.

C 6. Given the points A(3, 4), B(5, 7), and the translation $(x, y) \rightarrow (x - 3, y + 5)$.
(a) Determine the equation of AB and the equation of A′B′.
(b) Compare the equations of AB and A′B′.

7. Draw a circle with centre the origin and a radius of 5. Select any four points on the circle and find their images under the transformation

$$(x, y) \rightarrow (x, y - 5)$$

Draw the image of the circle under this translation.

8. Points P(x, y) and Q(x, y) are mapped into the points P′ and Q′ under the translation

$$(x, y) \rightarrow (x + a, y + b)$$

Prove that the line segments PQ and P′Q′ have the same length.

9. Find the equation of the image of the line 2x + y = 5 under the translation

$$(x, y) \rightarrow (x - 1, y + 3)$$

10.2 REFLECTIONS OF POINTS

We see examples of the transformation known as reflection any time we look in a mirror, or in any other shiny surface, even a calm lake.

If you look in a mirror it appears as if the mirror-image of any object is located on the other side of the mirror at an equal distance from the mirror. It also appears as if an imaginary line joining an object to its image intersects the mirror at right angles. In other words, it appears as if the mirror is the perpendicular bisector of the line joining the object to its image.

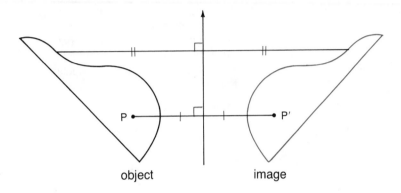

object   image

We use this as the defining property of a reflection.

> Reflection in a line m is the transformation that maps any point P into a point P' such that m is the perpendicular bisector of PP'.

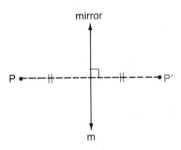

The line m is often called the mirror line because it acts like a mirror. We shall indicate mirror lines by double-ended arrows.

We shall consider reflections in the following lines.

I. The x-axis
II. The y-axis
III. The line y = x
IV. The line y = −x

EXAMPLE 1. Find the image of the point P(3, 2) under reflection in the x-axis.

SOLUTION:

Here the mirror-line is the x-axis.
If P → P' under reflection, then the
x-axis is perpendicular to PP' and so
PP' is parallel to the y-axis. This means
that the points P and P' are the same
distance from the y-axis. Therefore,
P' has the same x-coordinate at P,
namely 3. Also, P and P' must be
the same distance from the x-axis but
on opposite sides. Since the
y-coordinate of P is 2, the y-coordinate
of P' must be −2. Thus, the image of
P(3, 2) is P'(3, −2) after reflection in
the x-axis, that is (3, 2) → (3, −2).

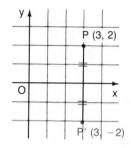

In general,

> Reflection in the x-axis maps the point P(x, y) into its
> mirror-image P'(x, −y), that is,
>
> $$T : (x, y) \rightarrow (x, -y)$$

EXAMPLE 2. Find the image of the point P(3, 2) under reflection in the y-axis.

SOLUTION:

Here the mirror-line is the y-axis
which is the perpendicular to P'P. By
reasoning as in Example 1, we see that
P and P' have the same y-coordinate,
namely 2. P' and P are the same
distance from the y-axis but on opposite
sides. The x-coordinate of P is 3, and so
the x-coordinate of P' must be −3.
Thus, P(3, 2) → P'(−3, 2).

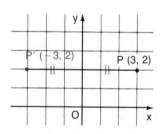

In general,

> Reflection in the y-axis maps the point P(x, y) into its
> mirror-image P'(x, y), that is,
>
> $$T : (x, y) \rightarrow (-x, y)$$

You will see from the following exercise that reflections preserve
distances. Therefore, reflections, like translations, are rigid motions.
Any figure is congruent to its mirror image.

EXAMPLE 3. Find the image of the point (6, 2) under reflection in the line y = x.

SOLUTION:
Since a reflection preserves distance PM = P'M. Also, the line y = x, the mirror of reflection, m, is the perpendicular bisector of PP'. If we draw line AP parallel to the x-axis and AP' parallel to the y-axis, we have two congruent triangles.

$$\triangle MPA \cong \triangle MP'A \text{ (SAS)}$$

Since A is on the line y = x and AP is parallel to the x-axis, the y-coordinate at P is the same as at A. Hence the coordinates of A are A(2, 2). The length of line segment PA is the difference of the x-coordinates, 6 − 2 = 4. Since PA = AP' = 4 and AP' is parallel to the y-axis, the x-coordinate is the same as in A, namely 2, and the y-coordinate is increased by 4. Thus, the coordinates of P' are (2, 6). P'(2, 6) is the image of P(6, 2) reflected in the line y = x.

The result can be generalized as follows.

A reflection in the line y = x maps the point P(x, y) into its mirror image P'(y, x) or

$$T : (x, y) \rightarrow (y, x)$$

EXAMPLE 4. Find the image of the point (6, 2) under reflection in the line y = −x.

SOLUTION:
By the reasoning in Example 3, △ MPA ≅ △MP'A. Since PA is parallel to the y-axis, the x-coordinate at P is equal to the x-coordinate at A. Because A is on the line y = −x, A has coordinates (6, −6). The length of PA is 2 − (−6) = 8. Since PA = P'A = 8 and P'A is parallel to the x-axis, the y-coordinate is unchanged and P'(6 − 8, −6) = P(−2, −6). Thus, the image of P(6, 2) under a reflection in the line y = −x is P'(−2, −6).

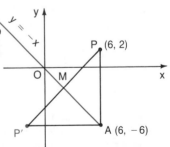

In general,

A reflection in the line y = −x maps the point P(x, y) into its mirror image P(−y, −x) or

$$T : (x, y) \rightarrow (−y, −x)$$

EXERCISE 10.2

A 1. Suppose you are standing two metres in front of a mirror.

(a) Where does your reflection appear to be?
(b) If you raise your right hand, which hand of your reflection appears to be raised?
(c) If you part your hair on the left, on which side of your reflection does the hair seem to be parted?

B 2. Write the images of the following points after reflection in the x-axis.

(a) (4, 7)   (b) (−2, 9)
(c) (6, 0)   (d) (0, −5)
(e) (−1, −1)   (f) (6, −3)
(g) (8, 1)   (h) (0, 0)

3. Write the images of the following points under reflection in the y-axis.

(a) (2, 5)   (b) (4, 3)
(c) (−8, 6)   (d) (−1, 2)
(e) (7, 11)   (f) (0, −4)
(g) (6, 0)   (h) (−1, −1)

4. Write the images of the following points under reflections in the line y = x.

(a) (3, 7)   (b) (−3, 2)
(c) (8, −6)   (d) (−1, −2)
(e) (7, 11)   (f) (4, 4)
(g) (−1, 0)   (h) (0, −7)

5. Write the images of the following points under reflection in the line y = −x.

(a) (7, 6)   (b) (0, 3)
(c) (−3, −4)   (d) (−1, 9)
(e) (−3, −3)   (f) (7, 0)
(g) (7, −5)   (h) (7, 7)

6. Under a reflection are there any points or lines which are left unchanged? Give examples from the exercises above and give an explanation for each instance.

C 7. Prove in general.

If F is reflection in the line y = x, then

$$F : (x, y) \to (y, x).$$

8. Prove in general.

If G is reflection in the line y = −x, then

$$G : (x, y) \to (−y, −x).$$

EXTRA

1. (a) A long-playing record plays for 2 min 45 s. How many times does the record turn?
(b) A long-playing record turns 150 times during a song. How long does it take for the song to play?

MIND BENDER

Identify a pattern and complete the table.

10	12	15	12	11	13	17
7	7	8	8			

10.3 REFLECTIONS OF LINE SEGMENTS

The table gives the image of point P under reflections in the x-axis, y-axis, y = x, and y = −x.

Mirror Line	P	P′
x-axis or y = 0	(x, y)	(x, −y)
y-axis or x = 0	(x, y)	(−x, y)
y = x	(x, y)	(y, x)
y = −x	(x, y)	(−y, −x)

What is the relationship of a line segment PQ and the image segment P′Q′ reflected in these special cases, that is, y = 0, x = 0, y = x, and y = −x?

EXAMPLE. The line segment PQ has endpoints P(1, 3) and Q(4, 7).
(a) Find the images of P and Q under reflection in the x-axis.
(b) Compare the slopes of PQ and P′Q′.
(c) Compare the lengths of PQ and P′Q′.

SOLUTION:
(a) $(x, y) \rightarrow (x, -y)$
Therefore, $P(1, 3) \rightarrow P'(1, -3)$
and $Q(4, 7) \rightarrow Q'(4, -7)$

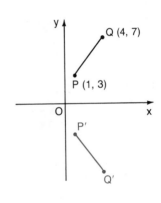

(b) Slope of PQ

$$m = \frac{y_2 - y_1}{x_2 - x_1}$$

$$m_1 = \frac{7 - 3}{4 - 1}$$

$$= \frac{4}{3}$$

Slope of P′Q′

$$m = \frac{y_2 - y_1}{x_2 - x_1}$$

$$m_2 = \frac{-7 - (-3)}{4 - 1}$$

$$= -\frac{4}{3}$$

(c) Length PQ

$$d = \sqrt{(x_2 - x_1)^2 + (y_2 - y_1)^2}$$
$$PQ = \sqrt{(4 - 1)^2 + (7 - 3)^2}$$
$$= \sqrt{9 + 16}$$
$$= \sqrt{25}$$
$$= 5$$

Length P'Q'

$$d = \sqrt{(x_2 - x_1)^2 + (y_2 - y_1)^2}$$
$$P'Q' = \sqrt{(4 - 1)^2 + (-7 - (-3))^2}$$
$$= \sqrt{9 + 16}$$
$$= \sqrt{25}$$
$$= 5$$

The lengths are equal.

We notice the following from this investigation of the reflection of a line segment in the x-axis.

For a reflection of a line segment in the x-axis
I. The length of a line segment and its image are equal.
II. The slope of the line segment and the image have the same numerical value but are opposite in sign. We call m_1 the additive inverse of m_2 or $m_1 = -m_2$.

EXERCISE 10.3

B 1. Copy the following figures and draw the reflection of each figure in the given mirror-line.

(a)

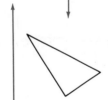

(b)

(c)

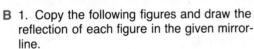

(d)

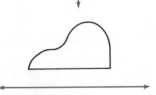

(e)

(f)

(g)

(h)

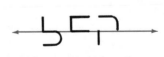

(i)

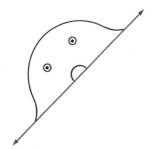

2. Find the image segment P′Q′ and the length of P′Q′ for each line segment under a reflection in the x-axis.

(a) P(3, −6), Q(−1, 0)
(b) P(2, 0), Q(−2, −1)
(c) P(−1, −3), Q(0, 0)

3. (a) Compare the lengths and the slopes of PQ and its image P′Q′ for P(1, 3), Q(4, 7) under the following reflections.
    (i) in the y-axis.
    (ii) in the line y = x.
    (iii) in the line y = −x.
(b) Generalize the results in a table.

4. Given the points A(−1, 1), B(5, 2), and C(3, 4).

(a) Graph △ABC.
(b) Find the images A′, B′, C′ of A, B, C under reflection in the x-axis.
(c) Draw △A′B′C′ using the same axes as in part (a).
(d) Find the lengths AB, BC, CA, A′B′, B′C′, and C′A′.
(e) Show that △ABC ≅ △A′B′C′.
(f) Repeat parts (b), (c), (d), and (e) for reflection in the y-axis.

5. The triangle with vertices A(−1, −1), B(6, −1), and C(6, 5) is reflected in the x-axis.

(a) Find the vertices of the image of this triangle.
(b) Find and compare the areas of the triangle and its image.

C 6. The line segment AB has endpoints A(2, 1) and B(7, 3).

(a) Find the images of A and B under reflection in the x-axis.
(b) Compare the equations of AB and A′B′.

7. Using a graph, find the image of the point (7, 2) after reflection in the following lines.
(a) x = 4
(b) y = 4

8. Find the image of the point (7, 2) after reflection in the following lines.
(a) y = x
(b) x + y = 0

9. Find the image of the point (a, b) after reflection in the line y = x.

10. The points P(a, b) and Q(c, d) are reflected in the x-axis giving the images P′ and Q′. Prove that the lengths of PQ and P′Q′ are equal.

11. The points P(a, b) and Q(c, d) are reflected in the y-axis giving the images P′ and Q′. Prove that P′Q′ = PQ.

TOP, FRONT, AND SIDE VIEWS

Draw the top, front, and side views of the following.

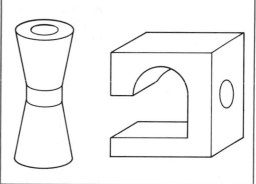

10.4 ROTATIONS OF POINTS

The word rotation has the same meaning in mathematics as it does in everyday life. We see examples of it any time we look at the wheels of a moving car or the hands of a clock.

In the figure a point P has been rotated counter-clockwise about the point C through an angle of 40° to a new position P'. P' is the image of P under the rotation. Notice that CP = CP'. C is called the centre of rotation. The angle of rotation is 40°. Note that the same result could have been achieved by a clockwise rotation of 320°. Then we would say that the angle of rotation is −320°. The convention is that a counter-clockwise rotation is positive and a clockwise rotation is negative.

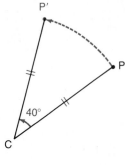

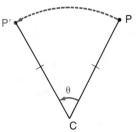

> A rotation about a point C through an angle θ is the transformation that maps any point P into a point P' such that
>
> $$\angle PCP' = \theta \quad \text{and} \quad CP = CP'.$$

If θ = 90°, then the rotation is called a quarter-turn; if θ = 180°, the rotation is called a half-turn.

We will investigate the mapping of a point P to P' under a rotation about the point (0, 0), the origin for various angles of rotation.

EXAMPLE 1. Find the image of the point P (1, 2) under a half-turn about the origin.

SOLUTION:

Since the angle of rotation for a half-turn is 180°, then ∠POP' = 180°. It follows that POP' is a straight line.

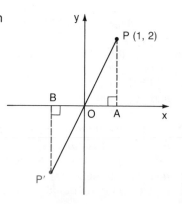

$$\therefore \angle POA = \angle P'OB \quad \text{OAT}$$
$$PO = P'O \quad \text{Definition}$$
$$\angle PAO = \angle P'BO \quad \text{Right Angles}$$
$$\therefore \triangle POA \cong \triangle P'OB \quad \text{ASA}$$
$$\therefore OA = OB$$
$$AP = BP'$$

The coordinates of the image point P' are (−1, −2).

The results of Example 1 are generalized in the following rule.

> A rotation of 180°, a half-turn, about the origin is given by
>
> $$T : (x, y) \rightarrow (-x, -y).$$

EXAMPLE 2. Find the image of P(2, 1) under a rotation of 90° (a quarter-turn) about the origin.

SOLUTION:
In a rotation of 90° about the origin, PO = P'O and ∠POP' = 90°.

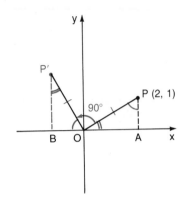

Since the sum of the angles of a triangle is 180° and BOA is a straight line, then ∠POP' = 90°. Thus,

$$∠POA + ∠OPA = 90° \quad \text{or} \quad ∠OPA = 90° - ∠POA$$

and

$$∠POA + ∠P'OB = 90° \quad \text{or} \quad ∠P'OB = 90° - ∠POA$$

$$\therefore ∠OPA = ∠P'OB$$

By the same reasoning ∠POA = ∠BP'O,
Therefore, △OPA ≅ △P'OB.

This means that the length of OA = P'B = 2.
Similarly, PA = OB = 1.

The x-coordinate of P and the y-coordinate of P' are both 2.

The y-coordinate of P and the x-coordinate of P' are opposite in sign.

Therefore, the image of P is P'(−1, 2) or

$$(2, 1) \rightarrow (-1, 2).$$

The results of Example 2 are generalized as follows.

> A rotation of 90°, a quarter-turn, about the origin is given by
>
> $$T : (x, y) \rightarrow (-y, x).$$

$$(6, 4) \rightarrow (-4, 6)$$
$$(6, -4) \rightarrow (4, 6)$$

EXERCISE 10.4

A 1. In the following diagrams P′ is the image of P under a rotation about C. In each case name two angles of rotation (counter-clockwise and clockwise).

(a)

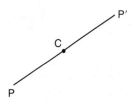

(b)

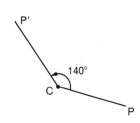

140°

(c)

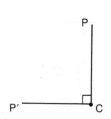

2. Name rotations which have the same effect as rotations through the following angles.

(a) 60°   (b) 10°   (c) −30°
(d) −270°   (e) 400°   (f) 100°

3. Under a rotation are there any points which are left unchanged?

4. Find the smallest positive angle of rotation which would cause the following figures to map onto themselves if C is the centre of rotation?

(a)

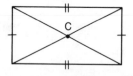

(b)

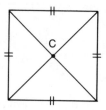

(c)

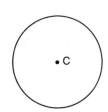

(d)

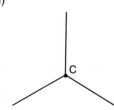

(e)

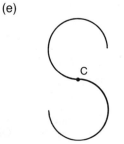

(f)

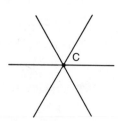

B 5. Using a method similar to that of Example 2, find the image of P(4, 2) under a rotation of 270° about the origin. Generalize your results.

6. Complete the following table in your notebook by finding the image of each given point after rotation about the origin through the given angle.

Point	Angle of Rotation			
	90°	180°	270°	−90°
A(1, 0)				
B(2, 1)				
C(3, 4)				
D(−1, 3)				
P(x, y)				

7. Give the general cases for the image of a point P(x, y) under a rotation about the origin
(a) 90°   (b) 180°   (c) 270°
(d) −90°   (e) −180°   (f) −270°

TRANSFORMATIONS IN ART

ROTATION

Escher: Circle Limit III

© M.C. Escher Heirs c/o Cordon Art — Baarn — Holland

DILATATION

Demuth: I Saw the Figure Five in Gold

The Metropolitan Museum of Art,
The Alfred Stieglitz Collection, 1949 (49.59.1)

TRANSLATION

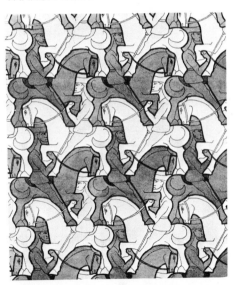

Escher: Study of Regular Division of the Plane with Horsemen

© M.C. Escher Heirs c/o Cordon Art — Baarn — Holland

10.5 ROTATIONS OF LINE SEGMENTS

The table below is a summary of our investigations of a point with centre of rotation at the origin and standard angles of rotation.

Centre of Rotation	Angle of Rotation		P	P'
Origin (0, 0)	90°	−270°	(x, y)	(−y, x)
Origin (0, 0)	180°	−180°	(x, y)	(−x, −y)
Origin (0, 0)	270°	−90°	(x, y)	(y, −x)

We will now investigate the results when a line segment PQ is rotated about the origin using these standard angles of rotation.

EXAMPLE. PQ has endpoints P(1, 2) and Q(3, 5). PQ is rotated 180° about the origin. Compare PQ and its image P′Q′ according to
(a) length.
(b) slope.

SOLUTION:

For a rotation of 180° about the origin $(x, y) \rightarrow (-x, -y)$
Therefore,

$$P(1, 2) \rightarrow P'(-1, -2)$$
$$Q(3, 5) \rightarrow Q'(-3, -5)$$

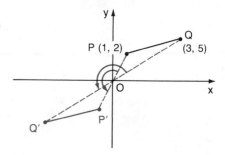

(a)
$$d = \sqrt{(x_2 - x_1)^2 + (y_2 - y_1)^2}$$
$$PQ = \sqrt{(3 - 1)^2 + (5 - 2)^2}$$
$$= \sqrt{4 + 9}$$
$$= \sqrt{13}$$

$$d = \sqrt{(x_2 - x_1)^2 + (y_2 - y_1)^2}$$
$$P'Q' = \sqrt{(-3 - (-1))^2 + (-5 - (-2))^2}$$
$$= \sqrt{4 + 9}$$
$$= \sqrt{13}$$

The lengths are equal.

(b) Slope of PQ

$$m = \frac{y_2 - y_1}{x_2 - x_1}$$
$$m_1 = \frac{5 - 2}{3 - 1}$$
$$= \frac{3}{2}$$

Slope of P'Q',

$$m = \frac{y_2 - y_1}{x_2 - x_1}$$

$$m_2 = \frac{-5 - (-2)}{-3 - (-1)}$$

$$= \frac{3}{2}$$

The slopes are equal.

We generalize the results as follows.

For a rotation of a line 180° about the origin

I. The length of a line segment and the length of its image are equal.
II. The slope of the line segment and the slope of its image are equal thus, the line segments are parallel.

EXERCISE 10.5

B 1. The endpoints of AB are A(2, −7) and B(−1, 0). AB is rotated 180° about the origin.

(a) Find the endpoints of the image A'B'.
(b) Compare the lengths of AB and A'B'.
(c) Compare the slopes of AB and A'B'.

2. The endpoints of PQ are P(1, 3) and Q(4, 7). PQ is rotated 90° about the origin.

(a) Find the endpoints of the image P'Q'.
(b) Compare the lengths and slopes of PQ and P'Q'.

3. The endpoints of DC are D(1, 0) and C(−3, −1). DC is rotated 270° about the origin.

(a) Find the endpoints of the image D'C'.
(b) Compare the lengths and slopes of DC and D'C'.
(c) Prepare a table which summarizes the results of questions 1, 2, and 3.

4. The endpoints of PQ are P(−5, −1) and Q(1, 1). PQ is rotated −90° about the origin. Compare the lengths and slopes of PQ and P'Q'.

5. The endpoints of ST are S(−3, −5) and T(0, 0). ST is rotated −270° about the origin. Compare the lengths and slopes of ST and S'T'.

6. XY has endpoints X(0, −4) and Y(3, 2). XY is rotated −180° about the origin.

(a) Compare the lengths and slopes of XY and X'Y'.
(b) Summarize your results from questions 4, 5, and 6 in a table.

7. Construct △ABC so that ∠BCA = 30°, ∠BAC = 60°, and AC = 4 cm. On the same diagram, draw the images of this triangle under rotations about C through angles of 90°, 180°, and 270°.

8. Draw an equilateral triangle ABC and on the same diagram draw the images of △ABC after rotation about C through angles of 60°, 120°, 180°, 240°, and 300°.

9. AB has endpoints A(−1, 6) and B(0, −2). AB is rotated 90° about the origin.

(a) Find the endpoints of the image A'B'.
(b) Compare the equations of AB and A'B'.

10. CD has endpoints C(−2, −4) and D(1, 1). CD is rotated −270° about the origin. Compare the equations of CD and C'D'.

10.6 SYMMETRY

Tyger! Tyger! burning bright
In the forests of the night,
What immortal hand or eye
Dare frame thy fearful symmetry?

    William Blake (1757-1827)

Artists use the word symmetry to indicate a kind of pleasing balance or harmony in painting, sculpture, architecture, or nature. The human body, a snowflake, a honeycomb, and many great works of art possess a sense of order, regularity, and balance that we call symmetry.

How can mathematics give a precise meaning to this word? There are two kinds of symmetry that we shall discuss — reflectional symmetry and rotational symmetry

The design in the figure at the right has the property that it is unchanged when reflected in m, that is, reflection in m maps the design onto itself. We say that m is a line of symmetry and that the design is symmetric about m.

> A figure is called symmetric about a line m if the figure is mapped onto itself by reflecton in m. This kind of symmetry is called reflectional symmetry (or line symmetry) and m is called the line of symmetry (or axis of symmetry).

Is it possible for a figure to have more than one line of symmetry?

EXAMPLE. How many lines of symmetry does an equilateral triangle have?

SOLUTION:
Given the equilateral triangle PQR, draw the medians PL, QM, and RN. Then $\triangle PLR \cong \triangle PLQ$ and so PL is the perpendicular bisector of QR. This means that the image of $\triangle PLQ$ after reflection in PL is $\triangle PLR$, and the image of $\triangle PLR$ is $\triangle PLQ$. Thus, $\triangle PQR$ is symmetric about the median PL. Similarly, $\triangle PQR$ is symmetric about the other two medians QM and RN. Therefore, an equilateral triangle has three lines of symmetry.

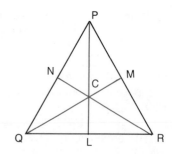

In the example, △PQR also has the property that it is unchanged when rotated about C through 120°, or 240°, or 360°. We say that △PQR has rotational symmetry of order three.

> A figure is called symmetric about a point C if the figure is mapped onto itself by a rotation with centre C. This kind of symmetry is called rotational symmetry of order n if there are n rotations which map the figure onto itself.

The human body has reflectional symmetry (perhaps imperfect), but not rotational symmetry. A snowflake possesses both types of symmetry. Most snowflakes have six lines of symmetry and also have rotational symmetry of order six.

EXERCISE 10.6

1. Which of the following figures possess reflectional symmetry or rotational symmetry? In each case state the number of lines of symmetry or the order of rotational symmetry.

(a)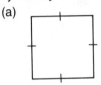

(b)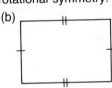

(c)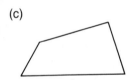

(d)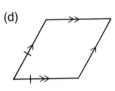

(e)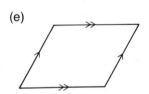

(f)

(g)

(h)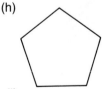

(i)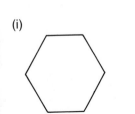

(j)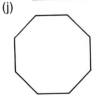

(k)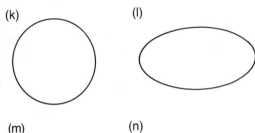

(l)

(m)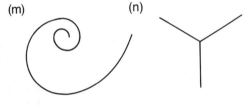

(n)

(o)

B 2. (a) List the capital letters of the alphabet which are symmetric about a vertical line.
(b) Which are symmetric about a horizontal lline?
(c) Which are symmetric about both vertical and horizontal lines?
(d) Which possess rotational symmetry?

10.7 DILATATIONS

If you wash a new pair of jeans in very hot water, they will probably shrink. We say that the jeans have undergone a dilatation because they are the same shape but smaller. If you look at some object through a microscope it appears many times enlarged. We say the object has undergone a dilatation because it appears to have the same shape but is larger. We have an example of a dilatation anytime that something is enlarged, magnified, contracted, or shrunk.

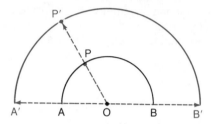

The first figure above shows a semi-circle APB with centre O and a magnified semi-circle A'P'B'. The distance OA' is twice the distance OA and OB' = 2(OB). In fact, all of the points on the larger semi-circle, such as P', were obtained by drawing a line through O and P, and then locating the point P' on it so that OP' = 2(OP). The transformation P → P' is called a dilatation by a factor of 2.

In the second figure above, however, the image semi-circle A'P'B' is smaller than the original semi-circle APB. Here OA' = $\frac{1}{2}$OA, OB' = $\frac{1}{2}$OB, and OP' = $\frac{1}{2}$OP. The transformation P → P' is called a dilatation by a factor of $\frac{1}{2}$.

> A dilatation is a transformation which maps any point P into a point P' such that OP' = kOP and O, P, and P' are collinear. The fixed point O is called the centre of the dilatation, and the number k is called the factor, (or dilatation factor, or magnification factor).

We now investigate the image P' of a point P under a dilatation with centre at the origin and dilatation factor k.

EXAMPLE 1. Find the image P' of a point P(2, 1) under a dilatation with centre O(0, 0) and dilatation factor 2.

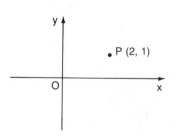

SOLUTION:

We know that OP' = 2OP. Draw line PA and P'A' perpendicular to the x-axis so that A(2, 0) and A'(x', 0). The result is two triangles which are similar, since the corresponding angles are equal: $\triangle OAP \sim \triangle OA'P'$.

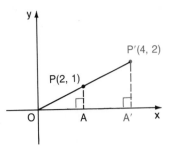

Therefore,

$$\frac{OP'}{OP} = \frac{OA'}{OA} = \frac{P'A'}{PA} = 2$$

this tells us that

$$x' = OA' = 2OA = 2x = 4$$

and

$$y' = P'A' = 2PA = 2y = 2$$

So, the coordinates of P' are (4, 2) and P(2, 1) → P'(4, 2) under a dilatation with centre (0, 0) and magnification factor 2.

In general,

> Under a dilatation with centre the origin O(0, 0) and magnification factor k,
> $$T : (x, y) \rightarrow (kx, ky)$$

Using the results above, we will investigate the effects of a dilatation of factor k and centre the origin on a line segment PQ.

EXAMPLE 2. The line segment PQ has endpoints P(2, 3) and Q(5, 1).
(a) Find the endpoints of the image P'Q' under a dilatation with centre (0, 0) and magnification factor 3.
(b) Compare the lengths of PQ and P'Q'.
(c) Compare the slopes of PQ and P'Q'.

SOLUTION:

(a) We know that (x, y) → (kx, ky) for a dilatation about the origin with factor k.

Therefore, P(2, 3) → P'(6, 9)
Q(5, 1) → Q'(15, 3)

The endpoints are P'(6, 9) and

Q'(15, 3).

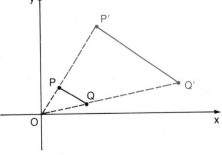

(b) The length of PQ.
$$d = \sqrt{(x_2 - x_1)^2 + (y_2 - y_1)^2}$$
$$PQ = \sqrt{(5 - 2)^2 + (1 - 3)^2}$$
$$= \sqrt{9 + 4}$$
$$= \sqrt{13}$$

The length of P'Q'
$$d = \sqrt{(x_2 - x_1)^2 + (y_2 - y_1)^2}$$
$$P'Q' = \sqrt{(15 - 6)^2 + (3 - 9)^2}$$
$$= \sqrt{81 + 36}$$
$$= \sqrt{117}$$
$$= \sqrt{9} \times \sqrt{13}$$
$$= 3\sqrt{13}$$

P'Q' is 3 times as long as PQ.

(c) The slope of PQ
$$m = \frac{y_2 - y_1}{x_2 - x_1}$$
$$m = \frac{1 - 3}{5 - 2}$$
$$= -\frac{2}{3}$$

The slope of P'Q'
$$m = \frac{y_2 - y_1}{x_2 - x_1}$$
$$m = \frac{3 - 9}{15 - 6}$$
$$= -\frac{6}{9}$$
$$= -\frac{2}{3}$$

The slopes are equal.

We generalize the results as follows.

For a dilatation whose centre is (0, 0) and factor k
I. The length of the image is k times the length of the line segment.
II. The slope of a line segment equals the slope of its image, thus, the line segments are parallel.

EXERCISE 10.7

A 1. State the images of the following points under the dilatation with centre O(0, 0) and magnification factor 3.

(a) (1, 1)   (b) (3, −1)   (c) (0, 2)

(d) (−5, −2)   (e) $(-1, \frac{1}{3})$ (f) (a, b)

2. State the images of the following points under the dilatation $(x, y) \to (\frac{1}{2}x, \frac{1}{2}y)$.

(a) (6, 2)   (b) (−2, 0)   (c) (−8, −4)

(d) (1, 9)   (e) (2, −3)   (f) (a, b)

3. State the images of the following points under the dilatation with centre O(0, 0) and factor k = −5.

(a) (1, 1) (b) (0, 6) (c) (−2, 9)

(d) (6, $\frac{4}{5}$) (e) (−7, −1) (f) (a, b)

4. Under a dilatation how many points are left unchanged? Are there any lines which are left unchanged?

3 5. Copy each of the following figures and construct their images under the dilatation with given centre O and given dilatation factor k.

(a) k = 3 (b) k = 2

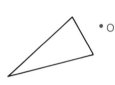

(c) k = −1 (d) k = $\frac{1}{2}$

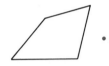

(e) k = 2 (f) k = $\frac{2}{3}$

(g) k = 3 (h) k = −2

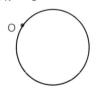

(i) k = 1

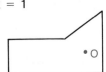

6. State the effect on the length of a line segment under a dilatation with magnification factor k if

(a) k > 1 (b) k = 1
(c) 0 < k < 1 (d) −1 < k < 0
(e) k = −1 (f) k < −1?

7. A dilatation maps A → A′, B → B′, and C → C′. If AB = 6, BC = 9, CA = 4, and A′B′ = 2, find.

(a) the dilatation factor k
(b) B′C′
(c) C′A′

C 8. Suppose that under the dilatation (x, y) → (kx, ky) the image of P(a, b) is P′ and the image of Q(c, d) is Q′. Show that

(a) P′Q′ = kPQ (b) P′Q′ ∥ PQ

9. A line segment PQ has endpoints P(1, 4) and Q(6, 1).

(a) Find the endpoints of the image P′Q′ under a dilatation with centre (0, 0) and magnification factor 3.
(b) Compare the equations of PQ and P′Q′.

10. Given the triangle A(−1, −1), B(0, 1), C(3, 2) and the dilatation with centre O(0, 0) and factor 2.

(a) Find the vertices A′, B′, C′ of the image of △ABC under the dilatation.
(b) Graph △ABC and △A′B′C′.
(c) Find and compare the lengths of the sides of the two triangles.
(d) Show that corresponding sides of the two triangles are parallel.

11. Given the triangle A(1, 1), B(6, 1), C(6, 5) and the dilatation with centre O(0, 0) and factor 3.

(a) Find the vertices A′, B′, C′ of the image triangle under the dilatation.
(b) Find and compare the lengths of the sides of the two triangles.
(c) Find the areas of △A′B′C′ and △ABC.
(d) Find the ratio of the areas of triangles A′B′C′ and ABC.

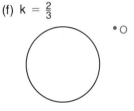

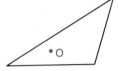

10.8 APPLICATIONS OF MATRICES TO TRANSFORMATIONS

We have explored transformations and have developed general rules by which we map a point or set of points to the image. Since these points are ordered pairs mapped to ordered pairs by a rule, we want to find a mathematical model so that these rules may be applied in an orderly fashion. Models are necessary so that computers may be programmed to perform these transformations quickly, accurately, and efficiently.

The matrix is a valuable method for organizing information that has an order. We will use matrices to define a mathematical model for the application of standard dilatations, rotations, and reflections.

Recall that a matrix is an array of numbers enclosed by parentheses. The individual numbers are the entries which are arranged in rows (horizontal) and columns (vertical). The dimension of the matrix, m × n, is the number of entries in the row, m, by the number of entries in the column n. m × n is read "m by n."

The ordered pair for P(x, y) may be written in matrix form as $\begin{pmatrix} x \\ y \end{pmatrix}$ which is a 1 × 2 matrix.

Dilatation

The rule for a dilatation with centre the origin and factor k is
$T : (x, y) \rightarrow (kx, ky)$.

EXAMPLE 1. Find a matrix representation that will map P(3, 5) into P′ under a dilatation with centre the origin and factor 4.

SOLUTION:
The coordinates of P′ are (3 × 4, 5 × 4) = (12, 20). If we express P and P′ as matrices, we have

$$\begin{pmatrix} 3 \\ 5 \end{pmatrix} \text{ and } \begin{pmatrix} 3 \times 4 \\ 5 \times 4 \end{pmatrix}$$

P′ may be derived from P by multiplying the matrix for P by the scalar 4.

$$4\begin{pmatrix} 3 \\ 5 \end{pmatrix} = \begin{pmatrix} 3 \times 4 \\ 5 \times 4 \end{pmatrix} = \begin{pmatrix} 12 \\ 20 \end{pmatrix}$$

In general,

For the dilatation with centre the origin and factor k

$$T : \begin{pmatrix} x \\ y \end{pmatrix} \rightarrow k\begin{pmatrix} x \\ y \end{pmatrix} = \begin{pmatrix} kx \\ ky \end{pmatrix}$$

REFLECTIONS

For the rules defining reflections in the x-axis, y-axis, y = x, and y = -x which map P(x, y) to P'(x', y'), the coordinates of P' maintain the magnitude of x and y. What changes is the sign, + or -, and the order in the pair. This suggests multiplication by 1 or -1 to change the sign and addition of 0 to retain the value, since 1 is the identity element for multiplication, that is, a × 1 = a, and zero is the identity element for addition, that is, a + 0 = a. If we define a matrix as a model for the rule, it would follow that the elements of the matrix would be 1, -1, or 0.

EXAMPLE 2. Find a matrix representation that will map P(3, 5) into P' under a reflection in the x-axis.

SOLUTION:

The rule for a reflection in the x-axis is T : (x, y) = (x, -y). This gives us T(3, 5) = (3, -5). We must define a matrix that leaves 3 unchanged and changes the sign of 5.

In matrix form, we have

$$T : \begin{pmatrix} 3 \\ 5 \end{pmatrix} = \begin{pmatrix} 3 \\ -5 \end{pmatrix}$$

If we let the 2 × 2 matrix below define the reflection, we want the product to give the following results.

$$\begin{pmatrix} a & b \\ c & d \end{pmatrix} \begin{pmatrix} 3 \\ 5 \end{pmatrix} = \begin{pmatrix} 3a + 5b \\ 3c + 5d \end{pmatrix} = \begin{pmatrix} 3 \\ -5 \end{pmatrix}$$

To obtain this result   a = 1,   b = 0,   c = 0, and d = -1.

$$\begin{pmatrix} 1 & 0 \\ 0 & -1 \end{pmatrix} \begin{pmatrix} 3 \\ 5 \end{pmatrix} = \begin{pmatrix} 3(1) + 5(0) \\ 3(0) + 5(-1) \end{pmatrix} = \begin{pmatrix} 3 \\ -5 \end{pmatrix}$$

For a reflection in the x-axis

$$T : \begin{pmatrix} x \\ y \end{pmatrix} \rightarrow \begin{pmatrix} 1 & 0 \\ 0 & -1 \end{pmatrix} \begin{pmatrix} x \\ y \end{pmatrix} = \begin{pmatrix} x \\ -y \end{pmatrix}$$

ROTATIONS

Similarly, rotations about the origin through angles, which are multiples of 90°, alter the sign or order of the coordinates of the image point. We may also develop matrix models for these standard rotations.

EXAMPLE 3. Find a matrix representation that will map P(2, 7) into P′ under a rotation of 90° about the origin.

SOLUTION:

The rule for a rotation about the origin, angle 90° is given by $T(x, y) = (-y, x)$. This gives us $P(2, 7) = (-7, 2)$. We must define a matrix that interchanges x and y and changes the sign of y.

In matrix form, we have

$$T : \begin{pmatrix} 2 \\ 7 \end{pmatrix} = \begin{pmatrix} -7 \\ 2 \end{pmatrix}$$

If we let the 2 × 2 matrix below define the reflection, we want the product to give the results below.

$$\begin{pmatrix} a & b \\ c & d \end{pmatrix}\begin{pmatrix} 2 \\ 7 \end{pmatrix} = \begin{pmatrix} 2a + 7b \\ 2c + 7d \end{pmatrix} = \begin{pmatrix} -7 \\ 2 \end{pmatrix}$$

To obtain this result $a = 0$, $b = -1$, $c = 1$, and $d = 0$.

$$\begin{pmatrix} 0 & -1 \\ 1 & 0 \end{pmatrix}\begin{pmatrix} 2 \\ 7 \end{pmatrix} = \begin{pmatrix} 2(0) + 7(-1) \\ 2(1) + 7(0) \end{pmatrix} = \begin{pmatrix} -7 \\ 2 \end{pmatrix}$$

For a rotation of 90° or −270° about the origin

$$T : \begin{pmatrix} x \\ y \end{pmatrix} \rightarrow \begin{pmatrix} 0 & -1 \\ 1 & 0 \end{pmatrix}\begin{pmatrix} x \\ y \end{pmatrix} = \begin{pmatrix} -y \\ x \end{pmatrix}$$

We can use a similar method to obtain matrices which rotate points about the origin through angles of 180° and 270°.

EXERCISE 10.8

B 1. Develop a matrix which defines the following transformations.

(a) a reflection in the y-axis
(b) a reflection in the line y = x
(c) a reflection in the line y = −x
(d) a rotation about the centre, angle 180°
(e) a rotation about the centre, angle 270°

2. For each of the following, use matrix representations to find the images of the line segment PQ under a reflection in the x-axis, y-axis, line y = x, and y = −x.

(a) P(0, 4) Q(−1, 2)
(b) P(1, 3) Q(−3, −4)
(c) P(8, 9) Q(12, 35)
(d) P(−3, −7) Q(−6, −3)
(e) P(0, 0) Q(−1, −1)
(f) P(1, −1) Q(−1, 0)

3. For each of the following, use matrix representations to find the images of the line segment PQ under a rotation about the origin of 90°, 180°, and 270°.

(a) P(1, 4) Q(2, −3)
(b) P(1, 0) Q(−4, −6)
(c) P(7, 2) Q(10, 35)
(d) P(−3, −2) Q(−9, −1)
(e) P(0, 0) Q(−1, −1)
(f) P(1, −1) Q(−1, 0)

4. Using a matrix representation, for the triangle A(4, 3), B(1, 0), and C(7, 2), find the image triangle A′B′C′ under a rotation of −270° about the origin.

5. Using a matrix representation, for the triangle A(1, 0), B(−8, −2), and C(7, 2), find the image triangle A′B′C′ under a dilatation with centre (0, 0) and factor −3.

TOP AND SIDE VIEWS

The drawing below is of a hockey puck with a slot carved in the side as shown.

EXERCISE

1. Draw the top view.

2. Draw a side view of the puck that does not show the slot.

3. Draw a side view of the puck showing the slot from the front.

4. Draw a side view of the puck showing the slot from the side.

5. The following are three views of an object. Make a three-dimensional drawing of the object.

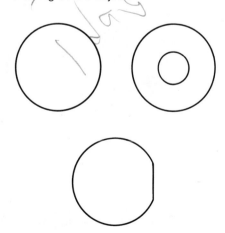

10.9 PROBLEM SOLVING

1. How many non-congruent triangles can be drawn by joining points using straight lines in the following diagram?

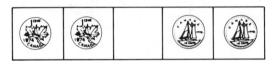

2. Two dimes and two pennies are arranged as shown.

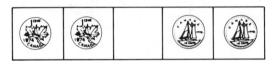

Using the rules listed below, determine the least number of moves necessary to arrange the coins so that the dimes are at the right and the pennies are at the left.

Rules:
  (i) Only one coin can be moved at a time.
  (ii) A coin can only jump over one coin at a time.
  (iii) Pennies can only move to the right, and dimes can only move to the left.
  (iv) Two coins cannot occupy the same space at the same time.

3.

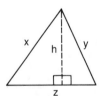

The letters x, y, z, and h stand for consecutive whole numbers. What is the area of the triangle?

4. There are approximately 800 000 words in the English language. The average person uses about 60 000 words. What percentage of the words go unused?

5. In one bag there are two red balls, in another two blue balls, and in a third a red ball and a blue ball.

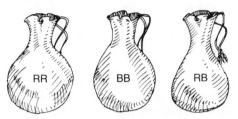

The bags are all labelled incorrectly. By taking one ball from one of the bags you can tell what is in each bag. How can you do this?

6. The diameter of the earth is about 12 600 km. The diameter of the planet Jupiter is about 142 800 km.

(a) How long would it take you to jog around the earth if you jogged at 10 km/h?
(b) How long would it take you to jog around Jupiter?
(c) The diameter of the sun is 1 392 900 km. How long would it take you to jog around the sun?
(d) The largest known star is called IRS5. It has a diameter of about 15 000 000 000 km. How long would it take you to jog around IRS5?

7. Calculate the volume of the solid.

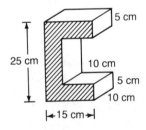

8. (a) Is it possible to draw a triangle on a grid with all sides having a negative slope?
(b) Is it possible to draw a quadrilateral on a grid with all sides having a negative slope?

9. What is the smallest positive integer by which 12 can be multiplied to obtain a perfect cube?

10. Two telephone poles stand 20 m apart. One pole is 10 m high and the other is 12 m high.

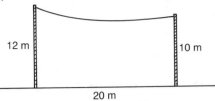

12 m   10 m

20 m

How long is the cable which extends from the top of one pole to the top of the other, assuming that 10% must be added to allow for the sag in the cable?

11. A gift shop priced a crystal plate at 30% above cost. It was later sold at a discount of 30% for $12.74. What was the profit or loss on the sale of the plate?

12. In a group of pigs and chickens, the number of legs is 28 more than twice the number of heads. How many pigs and chickens are there?

13. A ball is dropped from a height of 25 m, and bounces one-half of the distance from which it is dropped. After which bounce will the ball rise to less than 1 m?

14. A marathon runner runs 15 km south, 9 km west, 3 km north, and then heads back in a straight line to the starting point. What is the total distance covered by the runner?

15. Robert arranged his team pennants in a circle as shown in the photograph below.

Answer the following questions, assuming that the pennants are congruent triangles.

(a) What are the measures of the angles of each pennant?

(b) Find the area of one pennant if the base of the triangle is 30 cm and the height is 75.4 cm.

(c) Find the length of the other two sides of the pennant.

(d) Find the area of a circle with a radius of 76.9 cm.

(e) Find the area of a circle with a radius of 75.4 cm.

(f) Compare the total area of the pennants with the areas of the two circles calculated in (d) and (e).

(g) How would you arrange the pennants to form a parallelogram?

16. The price of Northland Mutual Fund shares rose 20% in each of the last three years. What is the total percentage increase for the three-year period?

17.

Which of the following figures can you make from the pattern above?

(a)

(b)

(c)

(d)

10.10 SOLVING ODD-ORDERED MAGIC SQUARES

Standard magic squares of odd order can be obtained by following the steps shown in the flow chart below.

The diagram below shows how the steps of the flow chart were used to construct a magic square of order 3.

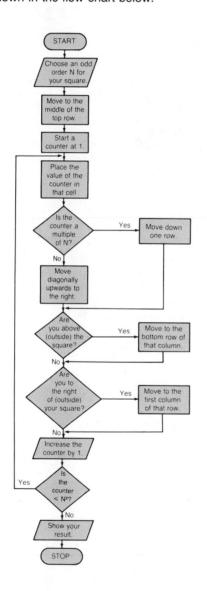

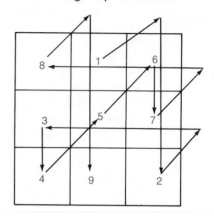

MICRO MATH

This program will construct a magic square of any odd order.

NEW

```
100 REM MAGIC SQUARE - ODD ORDER
110 PRINT "WHAT IS THE ODD ORDER";
120 INPUT N
130 DIM S(N,N)
140 R=1 : C=INT(N/2)+1
150 FOR X=1 TO N*N
160 S(R,C)=X
170 IF INT(X/N)=X/N THEN
    R=R+1:GOTO 190
180 R=R-1 : C=C+1
190 IF R<1 THEN R=N
200 IF C>N THEN C=1
210 NEXT X
220 FOR R = 1 TO N
230 FOR C = 1 TO N
240 PRINT TAB(C*5); S(R,C);
250 NEXT C
260 PRINT
270 NEXT R
280 END
```

RUN

10.11 REVIEW EXERCISE

1. For the table below, find the image P' of P

Transformation	Condition	P	P'
translation	a units ∥ x-axis, b units ∥ y-axis	(x, y)	
reflection	line of reflection, x-axis, y = 0	(x, y)	
reflection	line of reflection, y-axis, x = 0	(x, y)	
reflection	line of reflection, y = x	(x, y)	
reflection	line of reflection, y = −x	(x, y)	
rotation	origin as centre, angle 90° or −270°	(x, y)	
rotation	origin as centre, angle 180° or −180°	(x, y)	
rotation	origin as centre, angle 270° or −90°	(x, y)	
dilatation	origin as centre, factor k	(x, y)	

2. What kinds of transformations are the following?

(a) $(x, y) \rightarrow (x - 2, y + 3)$
(b) $(x, y) \rightarrow (x, -y)$
(c) $(x, y) \rightarrow (8x, 8y)$
(d) $(x, y) \rightarrow (x, y - 1)$
(e) $(x, y) \rightarrow (-x, -y)$
(f) $(x, y) \rightarrow (-x, y)$

3. State the images of the following points under the transformations

(a) reflection in the x-axis.
(b) dilatation with centre O(0, 0) and factor 3.
(c) $(x, y) \rightarrow (x + 7, y - 3)$.
(d) reflection in the y-axis.
(e) rotation through 180° about the origin.
(i)   (0, 0)   (ii)   (3, 4)

(iii) (−2, 1)
(iv) (−6, −6)
(v)   (0, 5)
(vi) (1, −1)
(vii) $(6, \frac{1}{2})$
(viii) (a, b)

4. If F is reflection in the x-axis,
T is the translation $(x, y) \rightarrow (x + 2, y - 1)$,
D is the dilatation $(x, y) \rightarrow (3x, 3y)$, and
R is rotation through 180° about the origin,
complete the table in your notebook by finding the coordinates of the images of the given points under the given transformations.

	A(−2, −2)	B(4, 6)	C(2, 8)	P(x, y)
F				
R				
T				
D				

5. Given the triangle A(1, 0), B(2, 5), C(4, 1) and the transformations

(a) reflection in the x-axis,
(b) the translation $(x, y) \rightarrow (x + 1, y + 4)$,
(c) dilatation with centre O(0, 0) and factor 3.
(i) Graph △ABC and its images under each of the transformations.
(ii) Calculate the lengths of the sides of all four triangles.

6. For each of the following figures, state the number of lines of symmetry and the order of rotational symmetry.
(a)   (b)

7. Copy the following figures and draw their reflections in the given mirror line.
(a)   (b)

10.12 CHAPTER 10 TEST

1. The line segment PQ has endpoints P(1, 2) and Q(−2, 3).
(a) Find the endpoints of the image P'Q' under the translation
$(x, y) \rightarrow (x + 3, y − 2)$.
(b) Find the length of PQ and P'Q'.

2. The line segment AB has endpoints A(−2, 4) and B(3, 3). Write
the endpoints for the image A'B' after
(a) a reflection in the x-axis.
(b) a reflection in the y-axis.
(c) a reflection in the line $y = x$.
(d) a reflection in the line $y = −x$.

3. Find the coordinates of the image of D(−2, 4) under a rotation of
90° about the origin.

4. The endpoints of ST are S(2, 2) and T(3, −1). ST is rotated 270°
about the origin.
(a) Find the endpoints of the image S'T'.
(b) Compare the slopes of ST and S'T'.

5. Line segment XY has endpoints X(−2, 0) and Y(−3, −3). Find
the endpoints of the image X'Y' under a dilatation with centre (0, 0)
and magnification factor 4.

ISOMETRIES

CHAPTER

11

Symmetry, as wide or as narrow as you may define its meaning, is one
idea by which people through the ages have tried to comprehend
and create order, beauty, and perfection.

Hermann Weyl

PARALLEL LINES AND INTERSECTING LINES

EXERCISE

1. Find the values of the variables.

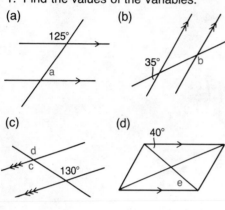

(a)

(b)

(c)

(d)

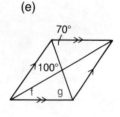

(e)

(f)

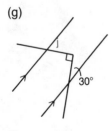

(g)

(h)

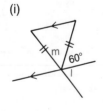

(i)

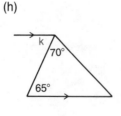

(j)

(k)

(l)

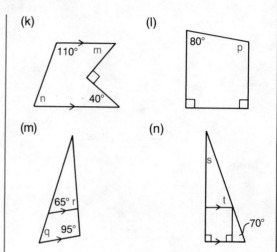

(m)

(n)

CONGRUENT TRIANGLES

EXERCISE

1. Identify pairs of congruent triangles from the following. Give the reason they are congruent.

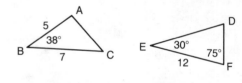

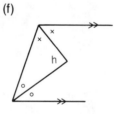

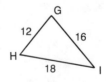

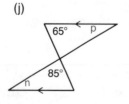

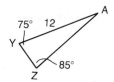

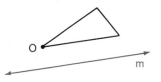

(ii)

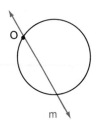

(iii)

3. A translation maps
P(1, −3) → P′(3, 4).
(a) What is the image of the point (x, y)?
(b) Find the images of the points A(3, 0), B(−1, 1), and O(0, 0) under this translation.

TRANSFORMATIONS

EXERCISE

1. State the images of the following points under the transformations
(a) reflection in line y = x.
(b) dilatation with centre the origin and factor −4.
(c) translation defined by vector [1, −3].
(d) rotation through 270° about the origin.

(i)   (0, 0)   (ii) (0, 1)
(iii) (−3, 2)   (iv) (−5, −5)
(v)   (5, 0)   (vi) (−1, 1)
(vii) (6, 4)   (viii)(a, b)

2. Copy the following figures and draw their images under
(a) dilatation with centre O and factor 2.
(b) reflection in m.
(i)

SYMMETRY

EXERCISE

1. For each of the following figures, state the number of lines of symmetry and the order of rotational symmetry.

(a)

(b)

(c)

11.1 ISOMETRIES

In Chapter 10 we investigated transformations in special cases. We found that the length of a line segment and the length of the image segment under a translation, reflection, and rotation were equal. We will now consider what occurs when a figure is transformed under these mappings.

EXAMPLE 1. Find the image of $\triangle ABC$ under the translation $T:(x, y) \rightarrow (x + 6, y - 2)$ and show that the image triangle is congruent to $\triangle ABC$.

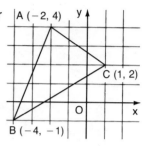

SOLUTION:
Under the given translation we have

$A(-2, 4) \rightarrow A'(-2 + 6, 4 - 2) = A'(4, 2)$
$B(-4, -1) \rightarrow B'(-4 + 6, -1 - 2) = B'(2, -3)$
$C(1, 2) \rightarrow C'(1 + 6, 2 - 2) = C'(7, 0)$

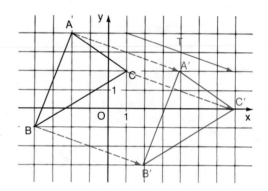

$$d = \sqrt{(x_2 - x_1)^2 + (y_2 - y_1)^2}$$

In $\triangle ABC$,

$AB = \sqrt{(-4 + 2)^2 + (-1 - 4)^2}$
$\quad\ = \sqrt{4 + 25}$
$\quad\ = \sqrt{29}$

$BC = \sqrt{(1 + 4)^2 + (2 + 1)^2}$
$\quad\ = \sqrt{25 + 9}$
$\quad\ = \sqrt{34}$

$AC = \sqrt{(1 + 2)^2 + (2 - 4)^2}$
$\quad\ = \sqrt{9 + 4}$
$\quad\ = \sqrt{13}$

In $\triangle A'B'C'$,

$A'B' = \sqrt{(2 - 4)^2 + (-3 - 2)^2}$
$\quad\quad = \sqrt{4 + 25}$
$\quad\quad = \sqrt{29}$

$B'C' = \sqrt{(7 - 2)^2 + (0 + 3)^2}$
$\quad\quad = \sqrt{25 + 9}$
$\quad\quad = \sqrt{34}$

$A'C' = \sqrt{(7 - 4)^2 + (0 - 2)^2}$
$\quad\quad = \sqrt{9 + 4}$
$\quad\quad = \sqrt{13}$

$\therefore AB = A'B'$, $BC = B'C'$, and $AC = A'C'$.
$\therefore \triangle ABC \cong \triangle A'B'C'$ (SSS)

In Example 1 we see that a translation perserves congruence, that is, $\triangle ABC \cong \triangle A'B'C'$. Under a translation, lengths of line segments and the size of angles are preserved. Any transformation which has this property is called an isometry (or rigid motion) according to the following definition.

> An isometry is a transformation
> that preserves lengths and angles.

EXAMPLE 2. Find the image $\triangle A'B'C'$ of the $\triangle ABC$ after reflection in the line m.

SOLUTION:
Draw the line through A perpendicular to m and mark the point A′ on this line such that AD = DA′. Similarly, draw the lines through B and C perpendicular to m and mark the points B′ and C′ on them such that BE = EB′ and CF = FC′. Then the image of the triangle ABC after reflection in the mirror-line m is the triangle A′B′C′.
We will now prove that $\triangle ABC$ and its image $\triangle A'B'C'$ are congruent.

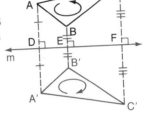

GIVEN: $\triangle A'B'C'$, the reflection image of $\triangle ABC$

PROVE: $\triangle A'B'C' \cong \triangle ABC$

PLAN: Prove the triangles congruent using SSS.

PROOF:

Statements	Reasons
AB = A′B′	reflection
BC = B′C′	reflection
AC = A′C′	reflection
$\therefore \triangle ABC \cong \triangle A'B'C'$	SSS

Notice that in Example 2, if $\triangle ABC$ is traversed counter-clockwise, then its image $\triangle A'B'C'$ is traversed clockwise. Since reflection reverses the sense of direction of a figure, we say that it is an indirect isometry.

EXAMPLE 3. Find the image of $\triangle ABC$ under a rotation of θ about B. Prove that $\triangle ABC \cong \triangle A'B'C'$.

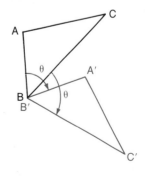

SOLUTION:

GIVEN: △ABC; △A′B′C′, ∠ABA′ = ∠CB′C′

PROVE: △ABC ≅ △A′B′C′

PLAN: Prove the triangles congruent using SAS.

PROOF:

Statements	Reasons
∠ABA′ = ∠CB′C′	given
∠ABA′ − ∠CBA′ = ∠CB′C′ − CBA′	subtraction
∠ABC = ∠A′B′C′	
AB = A′B′	rotation
CB = C′B′	rotation
∴ △ABC ≅ △A′B′C′	SAS

Since the triangles are congruent following a rotation, we say that a rotation is an isometry.

EXERCISE 11.1

B 1. Redraw the following figures on graph paper and find their images under the translations defined by the given arrows.

(a)

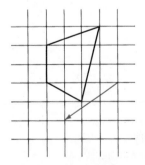

(b)

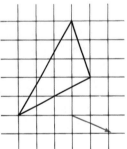

(c)

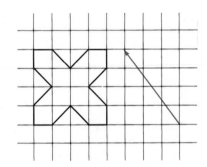

(d)

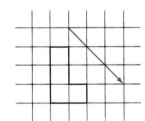

2. Copy the following figures and draw the reflection image of each in the given mirror line.

(a)

(b)

(c)

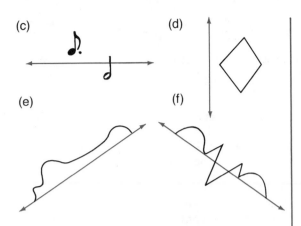

(d)

(e)

(f)

3. What transformation will map triangle 1 onto the other triangles in the figure?

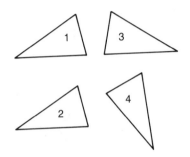

4. Given the three points R(0, 0), S(5, 1), and T(2, 4) and the translation
T : (x, y) → (x − 2, y + 1).

(a) Graph △RST.
(b) Find the images R′, S′, and T′ of R, S, and T under this translation.
(c) Draw △R′S′T′ using the same axes as in part (a).
(d) Show that △RST ≅ △R′S′T′.

5. Given the points A(−1, 1), B(5, 2), and C(3, 4).

(a) Graph △ABC.
(b) Find the images A′, B′, C′ of A, B, and C under reflection in the x-axis.
(c) Draw △A′B′C′ using the same axes as in part (a).
(d) Find the lengths of AB, BC, CA, A′B′, B′C′, and C′A′.
(e) Show that △ABC ≅ △A′B′C′.
(f) Find the reflection image △A″B″C″ of △ABC in the y-axis.
(g) Show that △ABC ≅ △A″B″C″.

6. The triangle with vertices A(−1, −1), B(6, −1), and C(6, 5) is reflected in the x-axis.

(a) Find the vertices of the image of this triangle.
(b) Find the area of the triangle and compare it to the area of its image.

7. △ABC is reflected in the line m.

(a) Find the reflection image △A′B′C′.
(b) Prove that △ABC ≅ △A′B′C′.

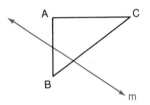

8. The triangle O(0, 0), P(2, 0), Q(2, 2) is rotated through an angle of 90° about O. Find the image △O′P′Q′.

9. In the figure below, P → P′ and Q → Q′ under a rotation about C of θ. Prove.

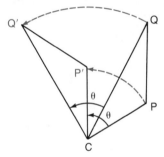

(a) △CPQ ≅ △CP′Q′
(b) PQ = P′Q′
(c) Show that this rotation is an isometry.

10.

Where is the reflection line?

11.2 COMPOSITION OF TRANSFORMATIONS

So far we have only looked at images of figures under single transformations. In this section we apply two or more transformations successively. For example, the figure shows the result of first reflecting a point P in a mirror line m, and then rotating the image point P' through 90° giving a new point P''. The reflection is described by P → P' and the rotation is written as P' → P''. The new transformation obtained by first reflecting, and then rotating is written as P → P''. It is called the composition of the two transformations. Let us call the reflection F and the rotation R. Then the composition is denoted by R ∘ F. Note that F is performed first, and then R is performed.

Does the order of F and R matter? Let us see by reversing the order and finding the transformation F ∘ R. This means that we first rotate P through 90° about C, and then reflect in m. P' obviously has different locations in the two figures, and so F ∘ R and R ∘ F are different transformations.

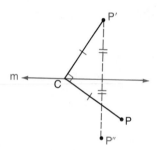

If a transformation T_1 maps P → P' and a transformation T_2 maps P' → P'', then the transformation $T_2 \circ T_1$ obtained by applying first T_1, then T_2, is called the composition of T_1 and T_2 and maps P → P''.

EXAMPLE. If T is the translation (x, y) → (x + 5, y − 3) and F is reflection in the y-axis, find the image of the point P(1, 1) under the transformations
(a) F ∘ T
(b) T ∘ F
(c) T ∘T

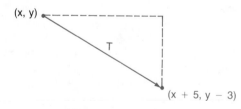

SOLUTION:
(a) Under T, (1, 1) → (6, −2) and under F, (6, −2) → (−6, −2).
Therefore, under F ∘ T, (1, 1) → (−6, −2).

(b) Under F, (1, 1) → (−1, 1) and under T, (−1, 1) → (4, −2).
Therefore, under T ∘ F, (1, 1) → (4, −2).
(c) Under T, (1, 1) → (6, −2) and under T, (6, −2) → (11, −5).
So under T ∘ T, (1, 1) → (11, 5).

In the example the transformations T ∘ F and F ∘ T had different effects on P. This reminds us to be careful of the order in applying transformations.

Now we ask you to investigate what happens when you take the composition of reflections in two lines m and ℓ. There are two cases:

(i) m ∥ ℓ
(ii) m intersects ℓ

INVESTIGATION

1. (a) Copy the following figure and draw the images of △ABC under the transformation M and L ∘ M where M is the reflection in line m and L is reflection in line ℓ.
(b) If △A″B″C″ is the image of △ABC under L ∘ M, measure the distances AA″, BB″, and CC″. Compare these distances with the distance between the lines m and ℓ.
(c) Can you identify the transformation L ∘ M?

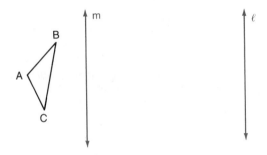

2. Let L be reflection in the x-axis, M be reflection in the line y = 4, and T be the translation (x, y) → (x, y + 8).

(a) Use a coordinate system to complete the following table in your notebook by finding the coordinates of the images of the given points under the given transformations.

	(−5, −1)	(2, 3)	(0, 6)	(x, y)
L				
L ∘ M				
T				

(b) What do you conclude from comparing the last two rows of the table?

3. (a) Copy the following figure and carefully draw the image of △ABC under the transformations M and L ∘ M. M is reflection in m and L is reflection in line ℓ.
(b) If △A″B″C″ is the image of △ABC under L ∘ M, find the distances OA, OA″, OB, OB″, OC, and OC″.
(c) Use a protractor to measure the following angles ∠BOB″ and ∠COC″. Compare the measure of these angles with ∠θ between m and ℓ.
(d) Can you identify the transformation L ∘ M?

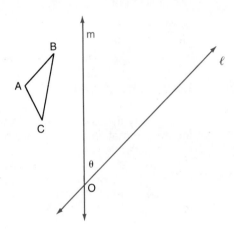

The composition of two reflections is
I. a translation if the lines of reflection are parallel, and
II. a rotation if the lines of reflection are intersecting.

EXERCISE 11.2

B 1. Copy the following figures. If L is reflection in ℓ and M is reflection in m, draw the images of these figures under L ∘ M and M ∘ L.

(a)   (b)

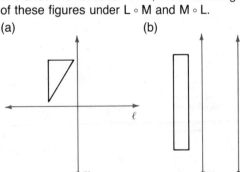

(c)   (d)

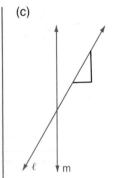

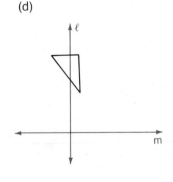

2. Given that R is rotation about C of 90° and M is reflection in m, copy the figure and draw the images of △DEF under the following transformations.

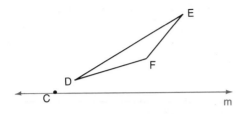

(a) R

(b) M

(c) R ∘ M

(d) M ∘ R

(e) R ∘ R

(f) M ∘ M

3. Given that L is reflection in ℓ, M is reflection in m, and R is rotation of 180° about O, copy the figure and draw the images of △OPQ under the following transformations.

(a) L ∘ M

(b) M ∘ L

(c) R

(d) M ∘ M

(e) R ∘ R

(f) R ∘ L

(g) R ∘ M

(h) L ∘ L

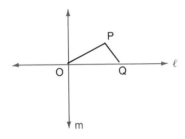

4. (a) If T is the translation defined by $(x, y) \rightarrow (x + 2, y + 1)$ and S is the translation defined by $(x, y) \rightarrow (x + 3, y + 5)$ find the images of the following points under S ∘ T.

(i) (1, 1)   (ii) (−2, 3)   (iii) (6, 4)   (iv) (x, y)

(b) If T:$(x, y) \rightarrow (x + a, y + b)$ and
S:$(x, y) \rightarrow (x + c, y + d)$,
give a formula for S ∘ T.

5. If R_θ means a rotation about C of $\theta°$, give the meaning of

(a) $R_{30} \circ R_{60}$

(b) $R_{45} \circ R_{70}$

(c) $R_\theta \circ R_\alpha$

(d) $R_{60} \circ R_{30}$

6. Given that
F is reflection in the x-axis,
G is reflection in the y-axis,
T is the translation $(x, y) \rightarrow (x − 2, y + 3)$, and
R is rotation through 180° about the origin, complete the following table in your notebook by finding the coordinates of the images of the given points under the given transformations.

	A(1, 2)	B(3, 0)	C(−2, 5)	P(x, y)
T ∘ T				
R				
F ∘ G				
G ∘ F				
T ∘ R				
R ∘ T				
T ∘ F				
F ∘ T				

7. What do you conclude by comparing parts (a), (b), and (c) of question 3 and rows R, F ∘ G, and G ∘ F of the table in question 6.

C8. Use geometry to prove the following facts which were investigated.
(a) The composition of reflections in parallel lines is a translation through a distance equal to twice the distance between the lines.
(b) The composition of reflections in lines which intersect at O is a rotation about O through an angle equal to twice the angle between the lines.

9. Suppose T is a translation, F is a reflection, and R is a rotation. Which of the following transformations are isometries? Explain.

(a) T ∘ F   (b) F ∘ R   (c) R ∘ T   (d) R ∘ F

11.3 GLIDE-REFLECTIONS

So far we have studied three types of isometries: translation, reflection, and rotation. In this section we investigate a fourth type of isometry called a glide-reflection, which is the composition of a reflection in a line and a translation parallel to the line.

INVESTIGATION

1. Let M be the reflection in the line m in the following figure and T be translation to the right through a distance 6 cm parallel to m.

(a) Copy the figure and carefully draw the images of △ABC under the transformations M, T, T ∘ M, and M ∘ T.

(b) Show that T ∘ M = M ∘ T.

This is called the glide-reflection of T and M.

(c) Let △A″B″C″ be the image of △ABC under T ∘ M. If △ABC is traversed counter-clockwise, in what direction is the image triangle △A″B″C″ traversed?

(d) Find the midpoints of the line segments AA″, BB″, and CC″. What do you notice about all of these midpoints?

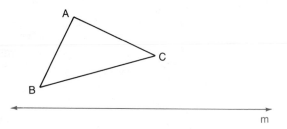

2. Let M be reflection in the y-axis and T be the translation $(x, y) \rightarrow (x, y + 3)$.

(a) Complete the following table in your notebook by finding the coordinates of the images of the given points under the given transformations.

	(−1, 2)	(5, −4)	(2, 3)	(x, y)
M				
T				
M ∘ T				
T ∘ M				

(b) What do you conclude from comparing the last two rows of the table?

(c) Find the midpoints of the line segments joining the given points to their images under the glide-reflection.

On what line do these midpoints lie?

3. (a) Copy the figure and draw the image of △ABC under the composition $M_1 \circ M_2 \circ M_3$ where M_1, M_2, and M_3 are reflections in the lines m_1, m_2, and m_3.
(b) What type of transformation is $M_1 \circ M_2 \circ M_3$?

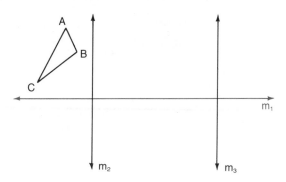

EXERCISE 11.3

B 1. In the figure △ABC is reflected onto △A'B'C' with respect to the parallel lines ℓ and m, and the transversal t.

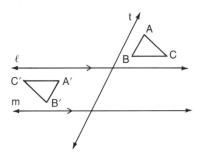

(a) Prove △ABC ≅ △A'B'C'.
(b) Show that the result is a glide-reflection.

2. The image of △PQR following reflection in line ℓ is △P'Q'R'. The image of △P'Q'R' reflected over line m is △P"Q"R".

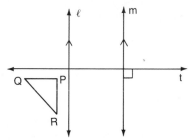

(a) Find △P'''Q'''R''', the image of △PQR, by reflecting △P"Q"R" over line t where t ⊥ m.
(b) Draw PP''' to intersect line t at O. Prove PO = P'''O.

3. (a) Find the image of △ABC following reflection over lines m and n followed by reflection in line p.

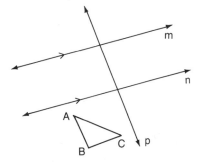

(b) Find the image of △ABC following reflection in line p followed by reflection in lines m and n.
(c) Compare the glide-reflection images in (a) and (b).

4. Given the figure ABCD with vertices A(1, 3), B(4, 5), C(6, 2), and D(4, 4), the reflection R in the x-axis, and a translation T : $(x, y) \rightarrow (x + 5, y - 4)$.
(a) Find the image A"B"C"D" under the composition R ∘ T.
(b) Illustrate the two transformations of the composition R ∘ T on a graph.
(c) Find the image A'''B'''C'''D''' of A"B"C"D" following reflection in the line y = 5.
(d) Determine whether the transformation that matches ABCD onto A'''B'''C'''D''' is a glide-reflection.

11.4 SUMMARY OF ISOMETRIES

An isometry is a transformation which preserves lengths and angles. It maps any geometric figure into a congruent figure. Translations, reflections, and rotations are all isometries. Since a glide-reflection is the composition of a reflection and a translation, it follows that a glide-reflection is also an isometry. In fact, it can be shown that these four transformations are the only isometries.

Direct Isometries

Translations and rotations are called direct isometries because they preserve not only lengths and angles, but the sense of the figure as well. If △ABC is traversed counter-clockwise, then its image under a translation and rotation is traversed counter-clockwise as well.

Translation T
T: △ABC → △A′B′C′

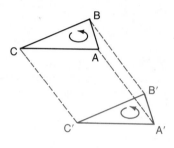

Rotation R
R: △ABC → △A′B′C′

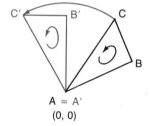

Indirect Isometries

Reflections and glide-reflections are called indirect isometries because they perserve lengths and angles, but the sense of the figure is changed. If △ABC is traversed counter-clockwise, then its image under a reflection or glide-reflection is traversed clockwise.

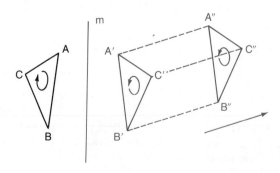

Composition of Isometries

The composition of two reflections is a translation if the lines of reflection are parallel and a rotation if the lines of reflection are intersecting. A glide-reflection is the composition of three reflections.

> Every isometry is the composition of at most three reflections. An odd number of reflections gives an indirect isometry and an even number of reflections gives a direct isometry.

A single reflection is an indirect isometry.

Two reflections in parallel lines produce a translation which is a direct isometry.

Two reflections in intersecting lines produce a rotation which is a direct isometry.

Three reflections produce a glide-reflection which is an indirect isometry.

EXERCISE 11.4

B 1. Complete the table below for

$T : (x, y) \rightarrow (x + a, y + b)$

$S : (x, y) \rightarrow (-x, y)$

$R : (x, y) \rightarrow (-y, x)$

$Q : (x, y) \rightarrow (x, -y)$

Isometry	Type of Transformation	Direct or Indirect	Coordinates of Image
T			
S			
R			
Q			
S ∘ Q			
Q ∘ S ∘ Q			

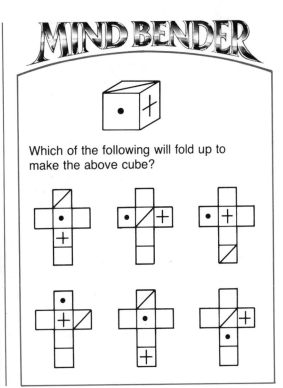

MIND BENDER

Which of the following will fold up to make the above cube?

11.5 PROBLEM SOLVING

1. A palindromic number is one that reads the same from right to left or from left to right. For example, 34 843 is a palindromic number.
(a) How many two-digit palindromic numbers are there?
(b) How many three-digit palindromic numbers are there?

2. Terry has four scuba-diving books. How many different ways can they be arranged on a shelf?

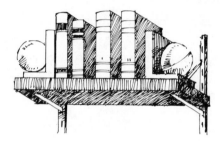

3. At the Equator, the radius of the earth is about 6300 km.
(a) What length of yellow ribbon would you need to wrap the earth at the Equator?
(b) How much more yellow ribbon would you need if you raised the ribbon one metre above the Equator?

4. Three people are sitting in a row of three seats on an airplane. How many ways can the three people be seated?

5. Each edge of the cube below is 2 m long.

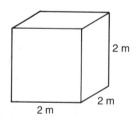

2 m

2 m

2 m

(a) How many line segments of different lengths can be drawn by joining two vertices of the cube?
(b) Determine the length of each of the lines.

6. The following are the products of five-digit numbers. The factors contain each of the digits 0, 1, 2, 3, 4, 5, 6, 7, 8, and 9 exactly once.

$$12\ 345 \times 56\ 890 = 838\ 102\ 050$$
$$24\ 680 \times 13\ 579 = 337\ 573\ 940$$
$$78\ 256 \times 10\ 493 = 821\ 140\ 208$$

Using each of the digits from 0 to 9 once, find the two five-digit numbers with the greatest product.

7. Pete has two watches. One does not run at all. The other runs, but loses one hour per day. Which watch shows the correct time the most often?

8. What is the next year that the square of someone's age will equal the year?

9. Calculate the volume and surface area of the solid.

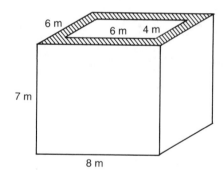

6 m

6 m   4 m

7 m

8 m

10. On three geography tests Marcia earned marks of 81, 87, and 64. What mark will she need on the next test to have an average of 80?

11. Three adults and three children found themselves at a river bank. The only way to cross the river was in a rowboat so small that it could carry only 1 adult and 2 children at a time. How could all six people cross the river?

12. Divide 25 in two parts so that the first part is 5 less than twice the second part.

13. Calculate the perimeter of the figure.

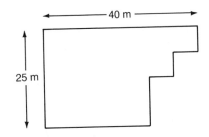

14. Twenty fence posts are spaced 17 m apart. What is the distance from the first post to the last post?

15. A room measures 6.2 m by 4.4 m and is 3.6 m high. There are three windows in the room, each measuring 1.2 m by 1.6 m. The door measures 1.2 m by 2.3 m. How much paint is needed to paint the walls of the room if 1 L of paint covers 6 m²?

16. Find the sum of

1 + 2 + 3 + 4 + ··· + 22 + 23 + 24 + 25

by determining a pattern.

17. Make an assumption and determine the next three numbers.
(a) 7, 12, 9, 14, 11, 16, ■, ■, ■.
(b) 1, 2, 3, 5, 8, 13, 21, ■, ■, ■.
(c) 2, 5, 7, 12, ■, ■, ■, ...
(d) 8, 3, 11, ■, ■, ■, ...
(e) ?, ?, 11, 18, 29, ■, ■, ■, ...
(f) ?, ?, ?, 25, ■, ■, ■, ...

18. Marilyn drove 12 km across town at 30 km/h, and then returned by the same route at 40 km/h. Find the average speed for the round trip to the nearest tenth.

19. Laura has been hired to replace the wood trim around the windows of an office building with aluminium trim. The office has 256 windows.

    30 windows measure 1 m by 1.5 m
    90 windows measure 1.5 m by 2 m
    80 windows measure 1.5 m by 2.6 m
    56 windows measure 2.0 m by 3.2 m

(a) What is the total length of trim needed?

(b) It takes Laura about one hour and fifteen minutes to remove the old trim from a window and to cut and install the new trim. If she charges $4.60/m for the aluminium trim and $26.70/h for her time, how much will it cost to change the trim?

20. The Trans-Canada Highway is 7826 km long.

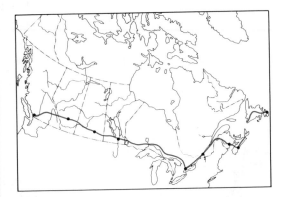

(a) How many steps would you take to walk across Canada?
(b) If you walked at your normal pace, how long would it take you to walk across Canada if you did not stop to eat or rest?

21.

Which of the following figures can you make from the pattern above?

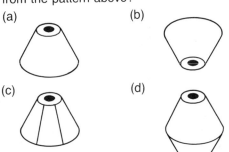

(a)   (b)

(c)   (d)

11.6 TRANSFORMATIONS IN MUSIC

Mathematical Name	Musical Name	Example	Object (Melody)	Image (Transformed Melody)
translation	transposition	The Beatles *I Want You* *(She's So Heavy)*		
reflection in x-axis	inversion	Bach *The Art of the Fugue*		
dilatation (k > 1)	augmentation	Shostakovich *Fifth Symphony*		

11.7 REVIEW EXERCISE

1. Given the triangle A(1, 0), B(2, 5), C(4, 1) and the transformations

(a) reflection in the x-axis.
(b) the translation $(x, y) \rightarrow (x + 1, y + 4)$.
(c) dilatation with centre O(0, 0) and factor 3.
(i) Graph △ABC and its images under each of the transformations.
(ii) Calculate the lengths of the sides of all four triangles.

2. Copy the following figures. If L is reflection in ℓ and M is reflection in m, draw the images of these figures under the transformations L, M, L ∘ M, and M ∘ L.

(a)

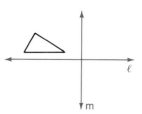

(b)

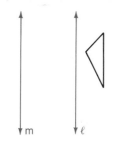

(c)

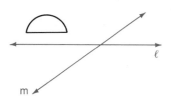

(d)

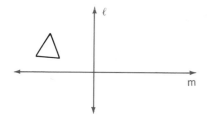

3. If F is reflection in the x-axis,
T is the translation $(x, y) \rightarrow (x + 2, y - 1)$.
D is the dilatation $(x, y) \rightarrow (\frac{1}{2}x, \frac{1}{2}y)$, and
R is rotation through 180° about the origin, complete the table in your notebook by finding the coordinates of the images of the given points under the given transformations.

	A(−2, −2)	B(4, 6)	C(2, 8)	P(x, y)
F				
R				
T				
D				
T ∘ D				
D ∘ T				
F ∘ R				
D ∘ F				
F ∘ D				
D ∘ D				
D ∘ R				
F ∘ T				

4. T, U, and R are reflections in lines t, u, and r respectively. t ∥ r and u intersects both t and r. Complete the table below for each transformation.

Isometry	Type of Transformation	Direct or Indirect
T		
T ∘ U		
U ∘ T		
T ∘ R		
R ∘ U		

11.8 CHAPTER 11 TEST

1. Copy △ABC and find the reflection image in the given mirror line.

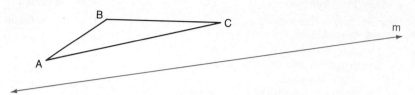

2. Given △ABC with vertices A(−3, 5), B(6, 2) and C(0, −2), find the image △A′B′C′ under reflection in the x-axis.

3. (a) Given △PQR with vertices P(0, 5), Q(−5, −5), and R(−5, 0), find the image △P″Q″R″ under reflection in the y-axis followed by reflection in the x-axis.
(b) What single transformation is equivalent to the translations described above in part (a)?

4. Given △LMN with vertices L(2, 5), M(6, 9), and N(7, 0), find the image L′M′N′ under a rotation of 90°.

5. If T is the translation (x, y) → (x + 6, y − 3) and X is reflection in the x-axis, find the image of the point P(3, 5) under the transformations.
(a) T ∘ X
(b) X ∘ T
(c) T ∘ T

6. Copy the following diagram. Find the image triangle A″B″C″ of △ABC following reflection in the parallel lines m and n, followed by reflection in the transversal t.

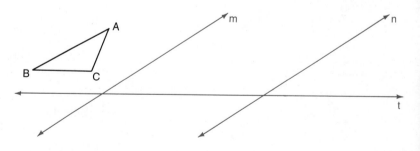

7. Identify the following isometries as direct or indirect.
(a) T : (x, y) → (x + a, y + b)
(b) U : (x, y) → (x, −y)
(c) V : (x, y) → (−x, y)
(d) W : (x, y) → (−y, −x)

VECTORS

CHAPTER

12

Algebra is generous, she often gives more than is asked of her.

D'Alembert

REVIEW AND PREVIEW TO CHAPTER 12

USING A PROTRACTOR

EXERCISE

1. Measure the indicated angles with a protractor.

(a)

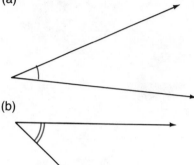

(b)

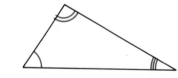

(c)

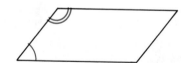

(d)

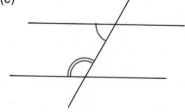

(e)

CONSTRUCTING PARALLELOGRAMS

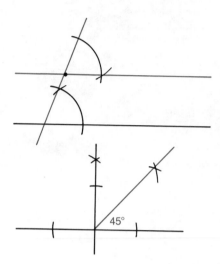

EXERCISE

1. Construct the following parallelograms using only ruler and compass.

(a) parallelogram ABCD; AB = 3 cm, BC = 5 cm, ∠ABC = 45°

(b) parallelogram PQRS; PQ = 2.5 cm, QR = 7 cm, ∠QRS = 135°

(c) parallelogram STUV; ST = 4 cm, TU = 10 cm, ∠UVS = 45°

(d) parallelogram JKLM; JK = AB, KL = PQ, ∠JKL = ∠XYZ

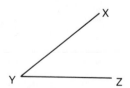

(e) parallelogram EFGH; EF = ST,
EH = XY, ∠EFG = ∠ABC

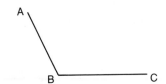

THE LENGTH OF A LINE SEGMENT

EXERCISE

1. For the segments HI, GF, DA, BC, and DE on the graph, find.
(a) Δx
(b) Δy
(c) the length of the segment

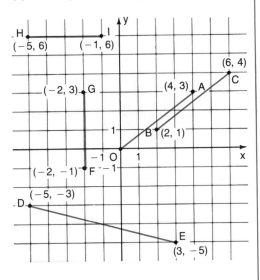

2. Find the length of the line segments joining
(a) $(-5, 0)$ and $(8, 0)$.
(b) $(0, -7)$ and $(0, 15)$.
(c) $(5, 3)$ and $(2, 3)$.
(d) $(-6, 4)$ and $(-6, -5)$.

SCALE DRAWINGS — THE RULE OF THREE

EXERCISE

1. If 1 cm on a blueprint represents 2 m, calculate the length represented by each of the following.
(a) 2 cm
(b) 5 cm
(c) 2.5 cm
(d) 7.5 cm

2. The scale of a map is such that a distance of 50 km is represented by 1 cm on the map. How far apart on the map will two cities be if the actual distance between them is given as follows.
(a) 100 km
(b) 275 km
(c) 425 km
(d) 75 km

3. In a family portrait, the 1.6 m tall mother measures 8 cm. Find the height on the portrait of each other member of the family if their actual heights are as follows.
(a) father; 1.9 m
(b) daughter: 1.4 m
(c) son; 1.2 m

Determine the pattern. Find the missing number.

21	9	5	25
18	7	6	
5	16	11	10
7	14	10	11
5	3	2	6

12.1 DIRECTED LINE SEGMENTS

We have studied mathematical objects such as numbers, geometric figures, and systems. In this chapter we shall study mathematical objects that can be represented by either an ordered pair, or a line segment with direction indicated.

Directed line segments can be used to represent displacements. If an object moves 3 units to the right and 4 units up, its displacement can be represented by the directed line segment $\overrightarrow{AB}$ as in the figure at the right. The length of the line segment, AB, is 5 units (using the Pythagorean Theorem). This displacement can also be represented by the ordered pair [3, 4]. Note that we shall use square brackets to signify a displacement and the round brackets to locate a point. In a coordinate system, a displacement from (1, 2) to (5, 7) is represented by [4, 5].

$$[5 - 1, 7 - 2] = [4, 5]$$

[3, −2] represents a directed line segment which has a displacement of "three units to the right and two units down." In the figure at the right, the displacement is shown with the initial points O(0, 0), A(1, 3), B(−2, 3), and C(−4, 1). The displacement [3, −2] originates from four different points to produce four different terminal points.

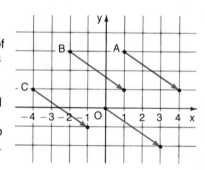

Displacements can be represented geometrically by directed line segments and algebraically by ordered pairs with square brackets, [a, b], where a and b are the components of the displacement.

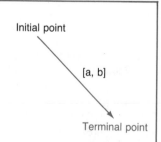

Initial point

[a, b]

Terminal point

Directed line segments can also be used to represent velocities, since velocities can be described in terms of magnitude and direction. In a geometric representation, the magnitude of the segment represents the magnitude of the velocity.

If an object is moving due north at a velocity of 2 m/s, its velocity can be described by any one of the directed line segments at the right. Each of these can be represented algebraically by the ordered pair [0, 2]. We note that for vertical directed line segments, the first component of the ordered pair is zero.

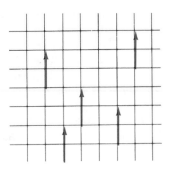

When larger quantities are involved, we use a scale diagram. In the diagram at the right, the scale shows that 1 unit represents 10 km/h. The velocity of a car travelling due east at 50 km/h can be represented by any one of the directed line segments shown. Algebraically, they are represented by the ordered pair [50, 0]. We note that for horizontal directed line segments, the second component of the ordered pair is zero.

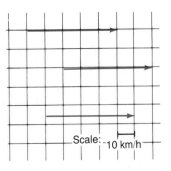

Scale: 10 km/h

In the two previous examples, the velocities were represented geometrically by either vertical or horizontal directed line segments. The directed line segment at the right represents the velocity of an object moving in the direction of the arrow. The velocity can be represented algebraically by the ordered pair [30, 40]. By the Pythagorean Theorem, we calculate that the magnitude of the velocity is 50 km/h.

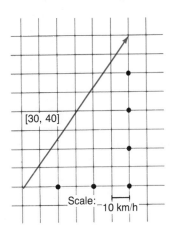

[30, 40]

Scale: 10 km/h

EXERCISE 12.1

A 1. Which of the following statements can be represented by directed line segments?

(a) Marilyn is sixteen years old.
(b) The winds are north-west at 40 km/h.
(c) The basketball team has four wins.
(d) The radius of the circle is 10 cm.
(e) The plane flew from Ottawa to Vancouver.
(f) The automated door will open if a force of 10 N(newtons) is applied downwards on the electronic door-mat.

2. Express each of the following displacements in the form [a, b].

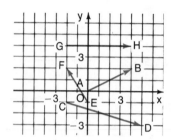

(a) $\overrightarrow{AB}$ (b) $\overrightarrow{CD}$
(c) $\overrightarrow{EF}$ (d) $\overrightarrow{GH}$

3. Find the terminal points determined by the displacement [2, 5] for each of the initial points.

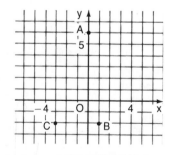

(a) O(0, 0)   (b) A(0, 6)
(c) B(1, −2)   (d) C(−3, −2)

4. Find the displacement determined by the initial point (3, 2) for each of the terminal points.

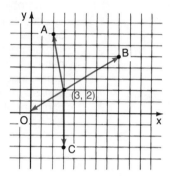

(a) O(0, 0)   (b) A(2, 7)
(c) B(8, 5)   (d) C(3, −3)

B 5. Make a diagram to show each of the following displacements as a directed line segment and label

(a) the initial point,
(b) the terminal point,
(c) the displacement as an ordered pair, [a, b].
(i) O(0, 0) to A(3, 6)
(ii) B(−2, 5) to C(10, 8)
(iii) D(−4, 0) to E(6, −3)
(iv) F(2, 1) to G(5, −4)
(v) G(5, −4) to H(2, 1)

6. Find the terminal points of the directed line segments representing the displacement [4, 3] for each of the initial points.

(a) A(2, 5)
(b) B(−4, −3)
(c) C(0, −2)
(d) D(3, 8)
(e) E(−5, −2)

7. Each of the following pairs of points describes a displacement. Make a diagram and determine which are the same displacement.

(a) from (0, 0) to (3, 4)
(b) from (−3, 4) to (1, 7)
(c) from (7, 0) to (11, 3)

(d) from (6, 3) to (10, 5)
(e) from (5, 1) to (1, −2)
(f) from (−4, 3) to (0, 0)

C 8. Choosing any initial point, plot the following displacements on squared paper and find a single displacement equivalent to each.

(a) [3, 2] followed by [2, 7]
(b) [5, 4] followed by [−2, 3]
(c) [6, 4] followed by [−2, −5]
(d) [4, 3] followed by [4, 3]

9. Find the lengths of the directed line segments indicated by the following displacements.

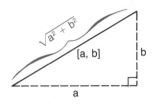

(a) [−4, 3]
(b) [5, 12]
(c) [−5, −12]
(d) [8, −15]
(e) [−7, 24]
(f) [−15, −8]
(g) [−6, 8]
(h) [−3, −4]

10. Find the initial points of the directed line segments representing the displacement [5, 2] for each of the following terminal points.

(a) R(9, 8)
(b) S(−3, 6)
(c) T(−1, −2)
(d) U(7, −4)
(e) O(0, 0)

11. Find the initial points of the directed line segments representing the displacement [−3, −2] for each of the following terminal points.

(a) D(5, 5)
(b) E(−3, 7)
(c) F(−4, −5)
(d) G(6, −2)
(e) K(−1, 1)

TOPOLOGY

Topology is a special kind of geometry that studies the properties of figures that remain unchanged no matter how the figures are twisted, bent, or stretched. Topology is sometimes called "the mathematics of distortion."

In plane geometry, the following figures are different. Each has its own name.

Square   Circle   Rectangle   Pentagon

To a topologist the above figures are all alike. They are all "simple closed curves."

A simple closed curve is a curve in which you can start at any point and move around the curve, passing through every point only once before returning to the starting point.

The above figures are also topologically equivalent. Figures are topologically equivalent if they can be turned into the same shape without disconnecting or connecting any points.

EXERCISE

1. Print all the capital letters. Which ones are topologically equivalent to a straight line?

2. Which are topologically equivalent to

3. Which are topologically equivalent to

4. It is possible to take off a vest without removing your jacket. Try it. To a topologist this means that the vest was never inside the jacket.

12.2 VECTORS

Mathematical objects that have both magnitude and direction, and can be represented by ordered pairs or by directed line segments, are called vectors. The vector A to B shown in the figure below can be represented geometrically by the directed line segment $\overrightarrow{AB}$ or algebraically by the ordered pair [4, 5]. The geometric vector $\overrightarrow{AB}$ can also be represented simply by $\vec{v}$.

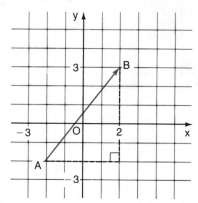

The figure below shows the vector [4, 5] represented geometrically by selecting several initial points. While each geometric vector in the figure has a different initial point, each can be represented by the same ordered pair [4, 5]. The magnitude or length of each vector is

$$\sqrt{4^2 + 5^2} = \sqrt{41}$$

and each has the same slope, $\frac{5}{4}$.

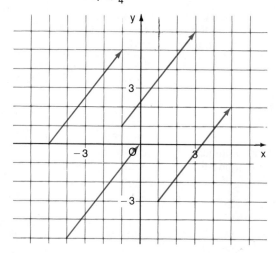

If $\vec{v} = [a, b]$, then the magnitude of $\vec{v}$ is $|\vec{v}| = \sqrt{a^2 + b^2}$.

Vectors with the same magnitude and direction can be represented by the same pair and are called equal vectors.

EXERCISE 12.2

A 1. (a) State the algebraic vectors represented by $\overrightarrow{AB}$, $\overrightarrow{CD}$, $\overrightarrow{EF}$, $\overrightarrow{GH}$, and $\overrightarrow{KL}$.
(b) Name the vectors in (a) that are equal vectors.

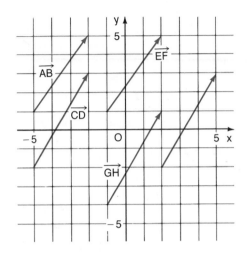

B 2. Draw 3 geometric vectors representing each of the following algebraic vectors.
(a) [3, 6]
(b) [4, −3]
(c) [0, −4]
(d) [2, 2]
(e) [−3, −5]

3. Plot the points A(2, 4), B(7, 2), C(−3, −6), D(5, −1), and find the algebraic vectors represented by $\overrightarrow{AB}$, $\overrightarrow{BA}$, $\overrightarrow{BC}$, $\overrightarrow{CD}$, $\overrightarrow{DA}$, $\overrightarrow{AC}$, and $\overrightarrow{DB}$.

4. (a) Plot the points P(−1, 3), Q(−3, −5), R(8, 1), S(10, 9), and draw the vectors represented by $\overrightarrow{PQ}$, $\overrightarrow{QR}$, $\overrightarrow{SR}$, and $\overrightarrow{PS}$. Identify figure PQRS.
(b) Find the algebraic vectors represented by $\overrightarrow{PQ}$, $\overrightarrow{QR}$, $\overrightarrow{SR}$, and $\overrightarrow{PS}$.

5. If A(−2, 5), B(3, 2), and C(1, 6) are three points in the plane, make a diagram and find the coordinates of point D so that $\overrightarrow{AB}$ and $\overrightarrow{CD}$ are equal vectors.

6. Given points A(2, 7), B(3, 1), and C(−2, 0), find the following.
(a) The coordinates of D so that $\overrightarrow{AB}$ and $\overrightarrow{CD}$ are equal vectors.
(b) The coordinates of point E so that $\overrightarrow{AC} = \overrightarrow{BE}$.

7. Given points P(−5, 5), Q(9, 2) and R(4, −7),
(a) Find the coordinates of point S so that PQRS is a parallelogram.
(b) Verify that PQRS is a parallelogram by showing that $\overrightarrow{PQ} = \overrightarrow{SR}$.
(c) Verify that PQRS is a parallelogram by showing that $\overrightarrow{RQ} = \overrightarrow{SP}$.
(d) Is it necessary to show both $\overrightarrow{PQ} = \overrightarrow{SR}$ and $\overrightarrow{RQ} = \overrightarrow{SP}$ in order to verify that PQRS is a parallelogram?

8. (a) Complete the following table.

Initial Point	Terminal Point	[a, b]	Magnitude $\sqrt{a^2 + b^2}$	Slope $\dfrac{b}{a}$
A(2, 4)	B(3, 6)			
C(2, 7)	D(5, 3)			
E(−2, 1)	F(0, 5)			
G(3, −2)	H(6, −6)			
I(−4, −3)	J(−3, −1)			
K(0, −5)	L(1, −3)			
M(0, 2)	N(3, −2)			
P(5, 3)	Q(4, 1)			

(b) Name vectors from part (a) that are equal vectors. Note: When two vectors have the same magnitude and the same slope they are not equal unless they can be represented by the same ordered pair.

9. If [5, 3], [5, b], and [a, 3] are equal vectors,
(a) State the numerical values of a and b.
(b) If [a, b] = [c, d], how are the numbers a, b, c, and d related?
(c) If a = c and b = d, how are [a, b] and [c, d] related?

In general,

> Two vectors [a, b] and [c, d] are equal if, and only if, a = c and b = d.

C 10. Three aircraft are flying north-east at 125 kn, 150 kn, and 200 kn respectively. Using a suitable scale, draw vectors to show the flight paths of the aircraft.

(a) How are the 3 vectors related?
(b) How do they differ?
(c) How would you change the vector of the first aircraft so that it has the same vector as the second aircraft?

11. (a) Using a suitable scale, draw the vectors to represent a flight path 200 nautical miles north followed by 400 nautical miles west.
(b) Draw the vector to show the resulting displacement from the starting point to the terminal point of the flight.
(c) Measure the length of this new vector and the angle it makes with the horizontal vector.

12. A man rows a boat at the rate of 5 kn in a direction directly across a river. The river has a current of 12 kn.

(a) Using a suitable scale, make a vector diagram to show the actual direction of his travel.
(b) Find his actual speed
    (i) by measurement.
    (ii) by calculation.

13. Express the following as vectors in the form [a, b].

(a) 500 km north
(b) 100 km east
(c) 200 km in a direction 120° west of north

14. (a) Draw a geometric vector $\overrightarrow{PQ}$ with magnitude 10 units at an angle of 30° to the horizontal measured counter-clockwise. Draw $\overrightarrow{QR}$ with magnitude 5 units and direction 90° to the horizontal measured clockwise.
(b) Find the direction of $\overrightarrow{PR}$ and the approximate magnitude.

15. A plane flies east for one hour at a speed of 800 km/h. There is a wind blowing from the south at a speed of 200 km/h.
(a) Use a suitable scale and make a vector diagram to show the actual path of the plane.
(b) Find the actual speed of the plane
    (i) by measurement.
    (ii) by calculation.

16. A rescue helicopter left home base and flew north for one hour at a speed of 50 km/h. It turned and flew west at a speed of 50 km/h for two hours. Then it turned again and flew south for one hour at a speed of 100 km/h.
(a) Use a scale diagram and draw the flight path of the helicopter, assuming that there is no wind.
(b) Determine how far the helicopter is away from home base
    (i) by measurement.
    (ii) by calculation.
(c) How long will it take the helicopter to fly directly to home base at a speed of 50 km/h?

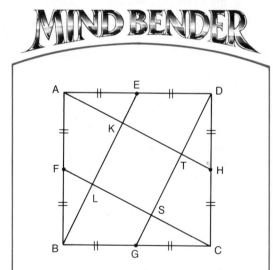

Each side of the square ABCD is 10 cm long. E, F, G, H are the midpoints of the sides.

Calculate the area of square KLST.

12.3 ADDITION OF VECTORS

When we add two vectors, the result is another vector called the resultant. In this section we will add vectors — algebraically and geometrically.

EXAMPLE 1.   An aircraft flies 200 km east from A to B, then continues another 400 km to C. Find the resultant.

SOLUTION:

Algebraically

$$\overrightarrow{AB} = [200, 0]$$
$$\overrightarrow{BC} = [400, 0]$$
$$\overrightarrow{AB} + \overrightarrow{BC} = [200, 0] + [400, 0]$$
$$= [600, 0]$$
$$\overrightarrow{AB} + \overrightarrow{BC} = \overrightarrow{AC}$$

$\overrightarrow{AC}$ is the resultant.

Geometrically

$\overrightarrow{AB}$ $\overrightarrow{BC}$

A   B   C

EXAMPLE 2.   A man walks 200 m south from P to Q, then north 500 m to R. Find the resultant.

SOLUTION:

Algebraically

$$\overrightarrow{PQ} = [0, -200]$$
$$\overrightarrow{QR} = [0, 500]$$
$$\overrightarrow{PQ} + \overrightarrow{QR} = [0, -200] + [0, 500]$$
$$= [0, 300]$$
$$\overrightarrow{PQ} + \overrightarrow{QR} = \overrightarrow{PR}$$

$\overrightarrow{PR}$ is the resultant.

Geometrically

R

$\overrightarrow{QR}$

P

$\overrightarrow{PQ}$

Q

EXAMPLE 3.   A ship sails according to the vector $\overrightarrow{AB} = [4, 2]$ followed by the vector $\overrightarrow{BC} = [1, 3]$. Find the resultant.

SOLUTION:

Algebraically

$$\overrightarrow{AB} = [4, 2]$$
$$\overrightarrow{BC} = [1, 3]$$
$$\overrightarrow{AB} + \overrightarrow{BC} = [4, 2] + [1, 3]$$
$$= [5, 5]$$
$$\overrightarrow{AC} = [5, 5]$$

$\overrightarrow{AC}$ is the resultant.

Geometrically

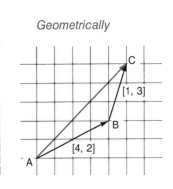

In general, vectors can be added	
I. Algebraically	II. Geometrically
[a, b] + [c, d] = [a + c, b + d] by adding the respective first components and second components.	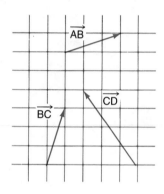 by arranging the vectors so that we can join the initial point of the second vector to the terminal point of the first vector.

EXAMPLE 4. If $\overrightarrow{AB} = [4, 1]$, $\overrightarrow{BC} = [1, 3]$, and $\overrightarrow{CD} = [-3, 4]$, find the resultant $\overrightarrow{AB} + \overrightarrow{BC} + \overrightarrow{CD}$.

SOLUTION:

Algebraically

$\overrightarrow{AB} + \overrightarrow{BC} + \overrightarrow{CD}$
$= [4, 1] + [1, 3] + [-3, 4]$
$= [4 + 1 - 3, 1 + 3 + 4]$
$= [2, 8]$

The resultant is $\overrightarrow{AD} = [2, 8]$.

Geometrically

We first arrange the vectors joining the initial point of one vector to the terminal point of another.

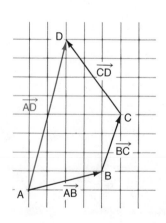

EXERCISE 12.3

A 1. Add the following vectors algebraically.
(a) [2, 3] + [5, 7]
(b) [−5, 4] + [6, 3]
(c) [−2, −5] + [5, 4]
(d) [3, −5] + [4, 2]
(e) [−3, −4] + [−2, −3]
(f) [4, 7] + [3, 6]
(g) [5, 2] + [−5, −2]
(h) [10, 3] + [−10, −3]
(i) [0, 0] + [3, 6]
(j) [2, 5] + [3, 12] + [−5, −8]

2. Find [x, y] for each of the following.
(a) [x, y] + [2, −5] = [0, 0]
(b) [3, −4] + [x, y] = [3, 4]
(c) [x, y] + [−2, 5] = [−2, 5]
(d) [4, 7] + [−2, 3] = [x, y]
(e) [5, −2] + [x, y] = [4, −3]
(f) [x, y] + [x, y] = [4, 10]

B 3. Using a suitable scale, add the following vectors geometrically.
(a) 5 km east followed by 12 km north
(b) 30 km north followed by 15 km west
(c) 10 km north-west followed by 3 km west
(d) 10 km east, 5 km north, 7 km north.

4. Find the following sums geometrically using a vector diagram.
(a) [2, 3] + [5, 2]
(b) [5, 1] + [4, 3]
(c) [3, −4] + [2, 6]
(d) [−5, 3] + [4, −2]
(e) [3, 6] + [−2, −6]
(f) [−2, −3] + [−4, 4]
(g) [3, −2] + [2, −3] + [−4, 8]
(h) [4, −5] + [0, 4] + [−4, 5] + [3, 0]

5. (a) Find [3, 7] + [−1, −4] and identify the result of adding two vectors.
(b) Find [a, b] + [c, d] and identify the result of adding any two vectors.
(c) Is the sum of two vectors always a vector? Name the property.

6. Simplify the left side and right side separately and insert the proper sign, = or ≠.
(a) [−5, 4] + [3, −6] ■ [3, −6] + [−5, 4]

(b) [a, b] + [c, d] ■ [c, d] + [a, b]
(c) ([3, 5] + [4, −2]) + [−5, 6]
   ■ [3, 5] + ([4, −2] + [−5, 6])
(d) ([a, b] + [c, d]) + [e, f]
   ■ [a, b] + ([c, d] + [e, f])

7. (a) Find the sums.
   (i) [3, 2] + [0, 0]
   (ii) [0, 0] + [−2, −6]
   (iii) [−4, 3] + [0, 0]
   (iv) [0, 0] + [−2, −4]
(b) Add.
   (i) [a, b] + [0, 0]
   (ii) [0, 0] + [a, b]
(c) Find values of x and y so that
   (i) [a, b] + [x, y] = [a, b]
   (ii) [x, y] + [a, b] = [a, b]
(d) What is the zero vector?

> The zero vector is $\vec{v}$ = [0, 0].

8. Find values of x and y so that
(a) [3, 4] + [x, y] = [0, 0]
(b) [x, y] + [3, 11] = [0, 0]
(c) [−5, 3] + [x, y] = [0, 0]
(d) [−4, −7] + [x, y] = [0, 0]
(e) [a, b] + [x, y] = [0, 0]
(f) [x, y] + [a, b] = [0, 0]

> The inverse or negative of [a, b] is [−a, −b],
>
> [a, b] + [−a, −b] = [0, 0]

9. (a) Make a diagram to show $\vec{a}$ = [3, 4] and its negative, both having the same initial point.
(b) Repeat part (a) for $\vec{b}$ = [0, 5] and $\vec{c}$ = [−3, 5].
(c) From your diagrams in (a) and (b) state how a vector and its negative are
   (i) similar
   (ii) different

12.4 TRIANGLE AND PARALLELOGRAM LAWS OF ADDITION

In the previous section we added vectors algebraically and geometrically. When we add the geometric vectors $\overrightarrow{AB}$ and $\overrightarrow{BC}$, by joining the initial point of $\overrightarrow{BC}$ to the terminal point of $\overrightarrow{AB}$, we form $\triangle ABC$ with the resultant $\overrightarrow{AC}$.

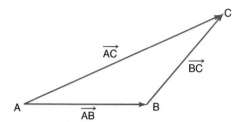

This method of adding two vectors permits us to state the Triangle Law.

The Triangle Law

$\overrightarrow{AB} + \overrightarrow{BC} = \overrightarrow{AC}$ if the three vectors can be arranged to form the sides of a triangle, $\triangle ABC$.

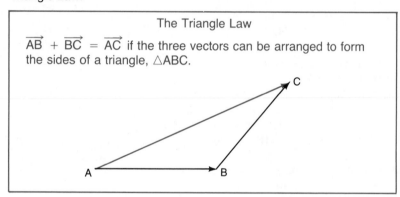

Equivalent to the Triangle Law, we can also add vectors geometrically using the Parallelogram Law by arranging the two given vectors so that they have the same initial point.

The Parallelogram Law

$\overrightarrow{AD} + \overrightarrow{AB} = \overrightarrow{AC}$ if the three vectors can be arranged so that the vectors $\overrightarrow{AD}$ and $\overrightarrow{AB}$ have the same initial point and AC is the diagonal of the parallelogram determined by $\overrightarrow{AD}$ and $\overrightarrow{AB}$.

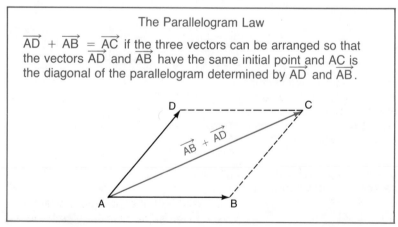

EXAMPLE. Add the following pairs of vectors using
(a) the Triangle Law
(b) the Parallelogram Law

(i)

(ii)

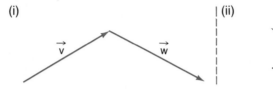

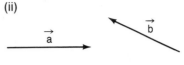

SOLUTION:

(a) Use the Triangle Law.

We first arrange the vectors with the initial point of the second on the terminal point of the first.

(i)

(ii)

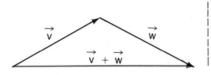

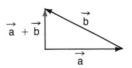

Then we draw the resultant from the initial point of the first vector to the terminal point of the second vector.

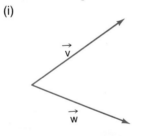

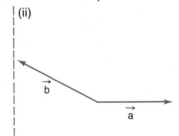

(b) Use the Parallelogram Law.

We first arrange the vectors to have the same initial point.

(i)

(ii)

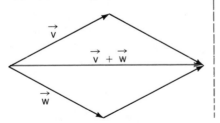

The resultant is found by completing the parallelogram and drawing the appropriate diagonal.

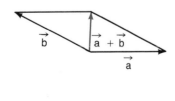

Note that both the Triangle Law and the Parallelogram Law produced the same resultant vectors in each case.

EXERCISE 12.4

B 1. Express $\vec{v}$ as the sum of two other vectors.

(a)

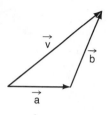

(b)

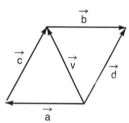

(c)

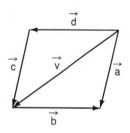

2. Name a single vector equal to $\vec{a} + \vec{b}$ in the following parallelograms.

(a)

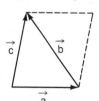

(b)

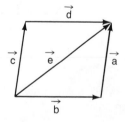

(c)

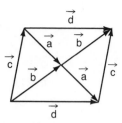

(d)

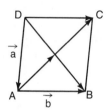

(e)

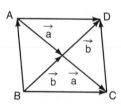

(f)

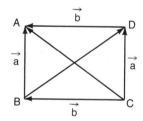

3. Name a single vector equal to
(a) $\overrightarrow{AB} + \overrightarrow{BC}$.
(b) $\overrightarrow{BC} + \overrightarrow{CD}$.
(c) $\overrightarrow{AB} + \overrightarrow{BC} + \overrightarrow{CD}$.

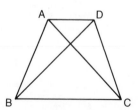

4. Use a vector diagram to find the sum of the following.

(a)

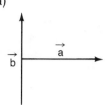

(b)

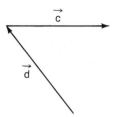

(c)

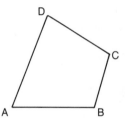

(d)

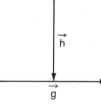

5. In quadrilateral ABCD show that $\overrightarrow{AB} + \overrightarrow{BC} = \overrightarrow{AD} + \overrightarrow{DC}$.

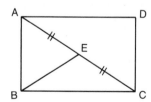

6. In parallelogram ABCD, E is the midpoint of AC. Redraw the diagram inserting arrowheads, then express each of the following as a single vector.

(a) $\overrightarrow{AB} + \overrightarrow{BE}$
(b) $\overrightarrow{CE} + \overrightarrow{EA}$
(c) $\overrightarrow{DA} + \overrightarrow{CD}$
(d) $\overrightarrow{BC} + \overrightarrow{EB}$
(e) $\overrightarrow{BC} + \overrightarrow{AB}$
(f) $\overrightarrow{CE} + \overrightarrow{EB}$

7. ABCDE is a pentagon. Redraw the figure inserting appropriate arrowheads and diagonals to express each of the following as a single vector.

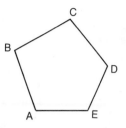

(a) $\overrightarrow{AB} + \overrightarrow{BC}$
(b) $(\overrightarrow{AB} + \overrightarrow{BC}) + \overrightarrow{CD}$
(c) $\overrightarrow{CD} + \overrightarrow{DE}$
(d) $\overrightarrow{BC} + (\overrightarrow{CD} + \overrightarrow{DE})$
(e) $(\overrightarrow{AB} + \overrightarrow{BC}) + (\overrightarrow{CD} + \overrightarrow{DE})$

8. Add the following vectors using scale diagrams.

(a)

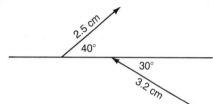

(b)

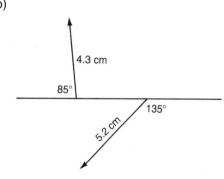

(c)

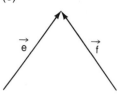

12.5 MULTIPLICATION OF A VECTOR BY A SCALAR

We have represented vectors as directed line segments or as ordered pairs with square brackets, [a, b]. When working with vectors, we also use real numbers which we shall call scalars. While a vector has both magnitude and direction, a scalar has only magnitude.

Consider two vectors $\vec{a}$ = [3, 4] and $\vec{b}$ = [6, 8]. Both $\vec{a}$ and $\vec{b}$ have the same direction, but $|\vec{a}|$ = 5 and $|\vec{b}|$ = 10, so that the magnitude of $\vec{b}$ is twice the magnitude of $\vec{a}$. We can express this as

$$\vec{b} = 2\vec{a}$$

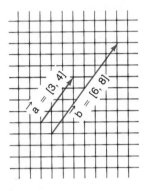

When we write

$$\vec{c} = 5\vec{a}$$

we mean that $\vec{c}$ has the same direction but five times the magnitude of $\vec{a}$.

Using $\vec{a}$ and $\vec{b}$, above, we can also find a meaning for multiplication of an algebraic vector by a scalar.

$$
\begin{aligned}
2\vec{a} &= \vec{a} + \vec{a} &\qquad \vec{b} &= [6, 8]\\
&= [3, 4] + [3, 4]\\
&= [6, 8]
\end{aligned}
$$

We get the same result by the following method

$$
\begin{aligned}
2[3, 4] &= 2[3, 4]\\
&= [2 \times 3, 2 \times 4]\\
&= [6, 8]
\end{aligned}
$$

which suggests the following rule.

If $\vec{v}$ = [a, b], then $k\vec{v}$ = k[a, b] = [ka, kb].

Note that while the vectors [3, 4] and [−3, −4] have the same magnitude, 5, and the same slope, $\frac{4}{3}$, they are not equal vectors because they have opposite direction.

EXERCISE 12.5

A 1. Express all vectors as a scalar multiple of $\vec{a}$.

(a)

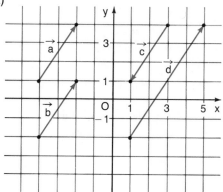

(b)

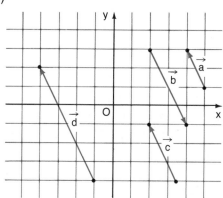

(c)

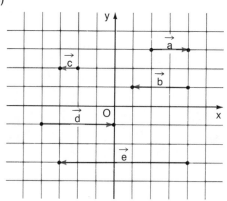

B 2. State each of the following in the form [a, b].

(a) 3[2, 5]   (b) 3[6, −2]   (c) $\frac{1}{2}$[4, 8]

(d) −3[−2, −3]   (e) $\frac{2}{3}$[−3, 6]   (f) 2[0, 0]

(g) 3[0, −2]   (h) −$\frac{1}{2}$[4, −16]   (i) 5[2, 4]

3. Simplify and express your answer in the form [a, b].

(a) 2[2, 3] + 3[2, 1]

(b) 2[−1, 5] + [4, −3]

(c) $\frac{1}{2}$[0, 6] + $\frac{2}{3}$[3, 6]

(d) $\frac{1}{4}$[0, 4] + $\frac{1}{3}$[3, 9]

(e) (−2)[2, 5] + (−3)[2, −1]

(f) 3([2, 3] + [4, −2])

(g) 5([2, 3] + 2[1, −2])

(h) 5([3, 2] + (−3)[1, 2])

4. If $\vec{a}$ = [2x, 3y] and $\vec{b}$ = [3x, −2y], find.

(a) $4\vec{a} + 2\vec{b}$ (b) $3\vec{a} + \vec{b}$

(c) $4(\vec{a} + \vec{b})$ (d) $3(\vec{a} + 2\vec{b})$

5. Make a diagram to verify that

(a) $3\vec{a} + 2\vec{a} = (3 + 2)\vec{a}$ for $\vec{a}$ = [3, −2]

(b) $-2(\vec{a} + \vec{b}) = (-2)\vec{a} + (-2)\vec{b}$

for $\vec{a}$ = [−3, 5] and $\vec{b}$ = [−2, −3]

6. Find the missing coordinates.

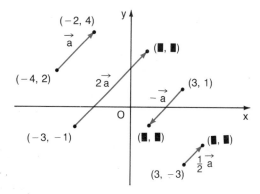

C 7. Use a scale diagram to write a vector with length 10 and inclination of 70° in the form [a, b].

12.6 SUBTRACTION OF VECTORS

In working with real numbers, we subtract by adding the negative. For example,

$$8 - (-3) = 8 + (+3)$$
$$= 11$$

$$9 - (+11) = 9 + (-11)$$
$$= -2$$

We also subtract a vector by adding its negative. For example, we subtract $[4, -7]$ by adding $[-4, 7]$. Recall that the negative of a vector has the same magnitude as the original vector but opposite direction.

EXAMPLE 1. Simplify. $[7, 5] - [4, -3]$

SOLUTION:

$$[7, 5] - [4, -3] = [7, 5] + [-4, 3]$$
$$= [3, 8]$$

This result may be generalized to

$$[a, b] - [c, d] = [a, b] + [-c, -d]$$
$$= [a - c, b - d]$$

EXAMPLE 2. Given $\vec{a} = [3, -5]$ and $\vec{b} = [-2, -6]$, find $\vec{a} - \vec{b}$
(a) algebraically,
(b) geometrically.

SOLUTION:

(a) $\vec{a} - \vec{b} = [3, -5] - [-2, -6]$
$\qquad = [3, -5] + [2, 6]$
$\qquad = [3 + 2, -5 + 6]$
$\qquad = [5, 1]$

> To subtract a vector, we add its opposite
> $$\vec{a} - \vec{b} = \vec{a} + (-\vec{b})$$

(b) Step 1.

Draw $\vec{a} = [3, -5]$ and $\vec{b} = [-2, -6]$.

Step 2.

Draw $-\vec{b} = [2, 6]$.

Step 3.

Draw the resultant $\vec{a} - \vec{b} = [5, 1]$.

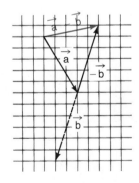

EXERCISE 12.6

A 1. Simplify and express your answers in the form [a, b].

(a) [5, 2] − [4, 0]

(b) [7, −5] − [−2, −4]

(c) [−3, −4] − [−5, −6]

(d) [6, 9] − [−6, −9]

(e) [4, 5] − [4, 5]

(f) [0, 0] − [4, −7]

(g) [3x, 2b] − [x, b]

(h) [5a, −2b] − [3a, 2b]

(i) [4a, 3b] − [7a, −3b]

(j) [p, q] − [m, n]

2. Express $\vec{a} - \vec{b}$ as a single vector in the following parallelograms.

(a)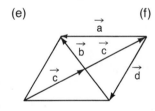

(b)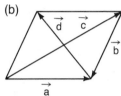

(c)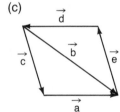

(d)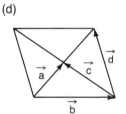

(e)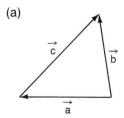

(f)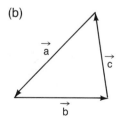

3. Express each vector in terms of the other two.

(a)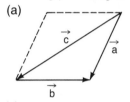

(b)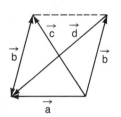

B 4. Simplify and express your answer in the form [a, b].

(a) 3[5, −2] − 7[1, −1]

(b) 4[6, −3] − 2[5, 4]

(c) $\frac{1}{2}$[−6, 4] − $\frac{1}{4}$[−4, 8]

(d) 5$\left[\frac{3}{5}, \frac{1}{5}\right]$ − 4[6, −1]

(e) −2[4, −1] − 3[1, −2]

(f) −5([6, −3] − [−2, 5])

(g) 3(−2[1, 5] − 4[−1, −1])

(h) 4[2, 7] − [2, 7]

5. If $\vec{v}$ = [x, y], find $\vec{v} - \vec{v}$.

6. Express in the form [a, b].

(a) [5, 7] − [2, 4]

(b) [−3, 12] − [2, −7]

(c) 3[4, −7] − 2[1, 5]

(d) 4[3, 6] − [7, 4]

(e) [2, 7] − 3[−1, 4]

(f) [3, −7] − 4[0, 2]

(g) 3[2, −5] − 3[−5, 2]

(h) [7, −2] − [2, 5] − [−3, −3]

(i) 2[4, 1] − 3[1, −2] + 4[2, 7]

(j) 3[−7, −1] − 2[−1, −7] − $\frac{1}{2}$[4, −6]

7. Given parallelogram ABCD, redraw the figure inserting arrowheads and find the following.

(a) $\overrightarrow{AB} - \overrightarrow{BC}$

(b) $\overrightarrow{AB} - \overrightarrow{AE}$

(c) $\overrightarrow{BC} - \overrightarrow{EC}$

(d) $\overrightarrow{AE} - \overrightarrow{EB}$

(e) $\overrightarrow{AE} - \overrightarrow{AE}$

(f) $\overrightarrow{BE} - \overrightarrow{EB}$

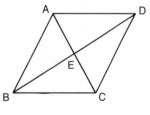

8. Name a single vector equal to

(a) $\overrightarrow{AB} - \overrightarrow{CB}$

(b) $\overrightarrow{BC} - \overrightarrow{DC}$

(c) $(\overrightarrow{AB} + \overrightarrow{BC}) - \overrightarrow{DC}$

(d) $\overrightarrow{BA} - (\overrightarrow{BC} + \overrightarrow{CD})$

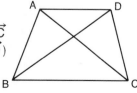

12.7 GEOMETRY WITH VECTORS

In this section we shall apply some of the vector properties we have studied to geometrical problems.

Summary of Geometric Properties of Vectors
I. Equality: $\overrightarrow{AB} = \overrightarrow{CD}$ 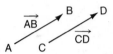 $\overrightarrow{AB}$ and $\overrightarrow{CD}$ have the same magnitude and direction.
II. Multiplication by Scalar: 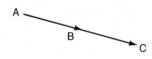 If $\overrightarrow{AB} = \overrightarrow{BC}$, then $\overrightarrow{AC} = 2\overrightarrow{AB} = 2\overrightarrow{BC}$ and $\overrightarrow{AB} = \overrightarrow{BC} = \frac{1}{2}\overrightarrow{AC}$.
III. Negative: 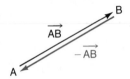 The negative of a vector is a vector with the same magnitude as, but opposite direction to, a given vector.
IV. Addition: 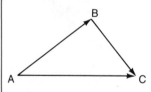 $\overrightarrow{AC} = \overrightarrow{AB} + \overrightarrow{BC}$ $\overrightarrow{AC}$ is the resultant of $\overrightarrow{AB} + \overrightarrow{BC}$ when the initial point of $\overrightarrow{BC}$ coincides with the terminal point of $\overrightarrow{AB}$.
V. Subtraction: 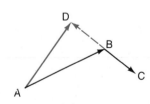 $\overrightarrow{AB} - \overrightarrow{BC} = \overrightarrow{AB} + (-\overrightarrow{BC})$ $= \overrightarrow{AB} + \overrightarrow{BD}$ $= \overrightarrow{AD}$ where $\overrightarrow{BD} = -\overrightarrow{BC}$. To subtract a vector, we add its negative.

EXAMPLE 1. M and N are the midpoints of AD and BC respectively in parallelogram ABCD. Show that AN is equal to and parallel to MC (that is, show that $\overrightarrow{AN} = \overrightarrow{MC}$).

SOLUTION:

$$\overrightarrow{AN} = \overrightarrow{AB} + \overrightarrow{BN}$$
$$= \overrightarrow{DC} + \tfrac{1}{2}\overrightarrow{BC}$$
$$= \overrightarrow{DC} + \tfrac{1}{2}\overrightarrow{AD}$$
$$= \overrightarrow{DC} + \overrightarrow{MD}$$
$$= \overrightarrow{MC}$$

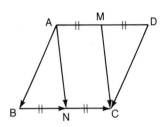

∴ AN = MC and AN ∥ MC

EXAMPLE 2. Point M is the midpoint of the diagonal PR of parallelogram PQRS. Prove that QM = MS.

SOLUTION:

In parallelogram PQRS,

$\overrightarrow{QP} = \overrightarrow{RS}$, $\overrightarrow{PS} = \overrightarrow{QR}$, and

$\overrightarrow{PM} = \overrightarrow{MR} = \tfrac{1}{2}\overrightarrow{PR}$ (midpoint).

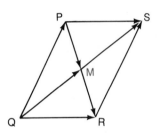

$$\overrightarrow{QM} = \overrightarrow{QP} + \overrightarrow{PM}$$
$$= \overrightarrow{RS} + \overrightarrow{MR}$$
$$= \overrightarrow{MS}$$

∴ QM = MS

EXAMPLE 3. In quadrilateral ABCD, AB = CD and AB ∥ CD. Prove that AD = BC and AD ∥ BC.

SOLUTION:

Join AC.

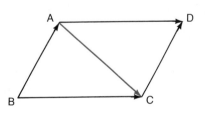

$$\overrightarrow{BC} = \overrightarrow{BA} + \overrightarrow{AC}$$
$$= \overrightarrow{CD} + \overrightarrow{AC}$$
$$= \overrightarrow{AC} + \overrightarrow{CD}$$
$$= \overrightarrow{AD}$$

∴ AD = BC and AD ∥ BC.

EXERCISE 12.7

A 1. Express each vector in terms of the other two.

(a)

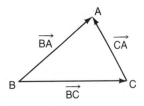

(b)

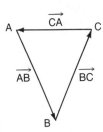

(c)

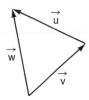

B 2. In parallelogram PQRS,
$\overrightarrow{PQ} = \vec{x}$, $\overrightarrow{QR} = \vec{y}$, and $\overrightarrow{PR} = \vec{z}$

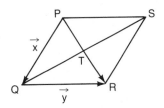

Express each of the following in terms of $\vec{x}$, $\vec{y}$, and $\vec{z}$.

(a) $\overrightarrow{SR}$ (b) $\overrightarrow{PS}$
(c) $\overrightarrow{QP}$ (d) $\overrightarrow{PR}$
(e) $\overrightarrow{RS}$ (f) $\overrightarrow{QS}$
(g) $\overrightarrow{SQ}$ (h) $\overrightarrow{PT} + \overrightarrow{TR}$
(i) $\overrightarrow{PT}$ (j) $\overrightarrow{PQ} + \overrightarrow{QR}$
(k) $\overrightarrow{QT} + \overrightarrow{TS}$ (l) $\overrightarrow{QT}$
(m) $\overrightarrow{TS}$ (n) $\overrightarrow{ST}$

3. D is the midpoint of $\overrightarrow{BC}$ in $\triangle ABC$. Make a vector diagram and find $\overrightarrow{AD}$ in terms of $\overrightarrow{AB}$ and $\overrightarrow{BC}$.

4. Show that in figure ABCD,
$\overrightarrow{BA} - \overrightarrow{BC} = \overrightarrow{CD} - \overrightarrow{AD}$.

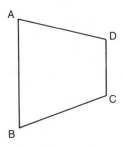

5. ABCD is any quadrilateral with P, Q, R, and S the midpoints of AB, BC, CD, and DA respectively. Use vectors.
(a) Prove $\overrightarrow{PQ} = \overrightarrow{SR}$.
(b) Identify PQRS.
(c) Check your answer to (b) using PS and QR.
(d) Identify the figure formed by joining the midpoints of a quadrilateral.

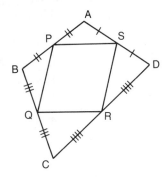

6. M and N are the midpoints of the sides AB and AC in $\triangle ABC$ as shown.

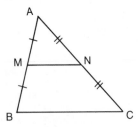

(a) Prove $\overrightarrow{MN} = \frac{1}{2}\overrightarrow{BC}$.

(b) Make a general statement concerning the line joining midpoints of two sides of a triangle and the third side.

(c) Check this statement using P, the midpoint of BC, and either M and N.

7. In △PQR, S and T are points on PQ and PR such that $ST = \frac{1}{2}QR$ and ST is parallel to QR (that is, $\overrightarrow{ST} = \frac{1}{2}\overrightarrow{QR}$).

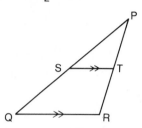

(a) Use vectors to show that PS = SQ.

(b) Show that PT = TR.

(c) How does a line segment parallel to and equal to one-half of the base of a triangle divide the other two sides?

8. X is the midpoint of PR and QS in quadrilateral PQRS.

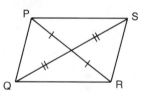

(a) Show that PS = QR and that PQ = SR.

(b) Prove PQRS is a parallelogram.

(c) Make a general statement concerning the above.

9. In △ABC, D is the midpoint of BC.

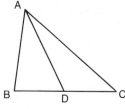

Make a vector diagram and prove that $\overrightarrow{AD} = \frac{1}{2}(\overrightarrow{AB} + \overrightarrow{AC})$.

10. In △ABC, $AM = \frac{1}{3}AB$ and $AN = \frac{1}{3}AC$.

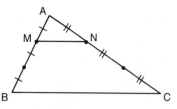

Make a vector diagram and prove that $MN = \frac{1}{3}BC$ and MN ∥ BC.

11. In trapezoid ABCD, AD ∥ BC, AP = PB, and DQ = QC.

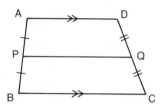

Prove that $PQ = \frac{1}{2}(AD + BC)$.

12.8 PROBLEM SOLVING WITH VECTORS

In the diagram at the right, the vector $\overrightarrow{OA}$ can be represented by the ordered pair [1, 1]. This representation describes the vector in terms of its horizontal and vertical components.

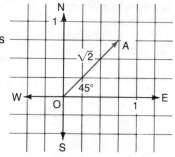

A vector can also be described in terms of its direction and magnitude. The magnitude of $\overrightarrow{OA}$ is 2, and the angle it makes with the vertical is 45°. Using compass directions we can represent $\overrightarrow{OA}$ as follows.

$$\overrightarrow{OA} = (45°, 2)$$

This is called the polar representation of a vector, where the first number of the ordered pair is the bearing (or direction) and the second number is the magnitude.

Our problem solving model suggests that drawing a diagram is sometimes a useful planning strategy.

In this section we shall solve problems using vectors with scale drawings. It is often convenient to choose a scale relating the given magnitudes to centimetres.

EXAMPLE 1. Using a suitable scale, make a vector diagram for each of the following.

(a) 30 m/s west
(b) 620 N force downwards
(c) 125 km south-west

SOLUTION:

(a) Scale: 10 m/s → 1 cm
        1 m/s → 0.1 cm
        30 m/s → 3 cm

$$\xleftarrow{\hspace{3cm}} \overset{\text{30 m/s}}{}$$

(270°, 30)

Direction: west requires arrowhead pointing left.

(b) Scale: 500 N → 1 cm
        1 N → $\frac{1}{500}$ cm
        620 N → $620 \times \frac{1}{500} = 1.24$ cm

620 N

Direction: arrowhead pointing down.

(c) Scale: 100 km → 1 cm
        1 km → 0.01 cm
        125 cm → $125 \times 0.01 = 1.25$ cm

125 m

(225°, 125)

Direction: south-west requires arrowhead pointing downwards to the left.

EXAMPLE 2. A ship sails 300 km north and 125 km west, then develops engine trouble. Find the distance and direction in which a rescue ship must sail to go directly to the first ship if both ships leave from the same point.

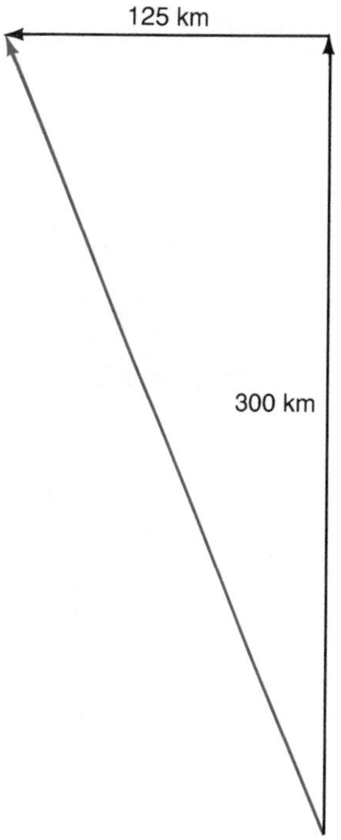

SOLUTION:

We solve the problem using an accurate construction. Let $\vec{R}$ represent the course of the rescue ship.

Scale: 30 km → 1 cm
125 km → 4.2 cm
300 km → 10 cm

SOLVE

The length of the resultant in the drawing is 10.8 cm (by measurement) so that the real magnitude of $\vec{R}$ is 325 km and using a protractor the angle is measured and found to be approximately 23°. Hence

ANSWER
$$\vec{R} = (337°, 325)$$

(Diagram, upper right: a triangle with "125 km" labeled across the top, "300 km" labeled down the right side.)

READ

EXAMPLE 3. A pilot wishes to fly his aircraft, according to the vector (90°, 350), where the velocity, 350, is in knots. A 65 kn north wind causes the pilot to alter his course. Make a vector diagram and find the course the pilot must set.

PLAN

SOLUTION:

The pilot must set a course $\vec{c}$ which is the sum of the two vectors (90°, 350) and the opposition to the wind.

Note that a north wind blows from the north, and the vector representing opposition to this wind has the same magnitude but opposite direction.

Scale: 30 kn → 1 cm
350 kn → 11.7 cm
65 kn → 2.2 cm

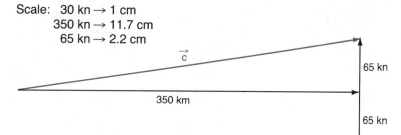

$\vec{c}$

350 km

65 kn

65 kn

SOLVE

The length of the resultant in the drawing is 11.9 cm (by measurement) so that the real magnitude of $\vec{c}$ is 356 kn and using a protractor the angle is measured and found to be approximately 11°.
Hence

ANSWER
$$\vec{c} = (79°, 356).$$

EXAMPLE 4. The bearing from Winnipeg to Prince Albert is 302°. If there is a 35 kn west wind and the cruising speed of the aircraft is 180 kn find
(i) the course that must be set to fly from Winnipeg to Prince Albert
(ii) the ground speed.

PLAN

SOLUTION:
Scale: 18 kn → 1 cm
       180 kn → 10 cm
        35 kn → 1.94 cm

$\overrightarrow{WE}$ represents the wind. The line WA gives the direction to Prince Albert.

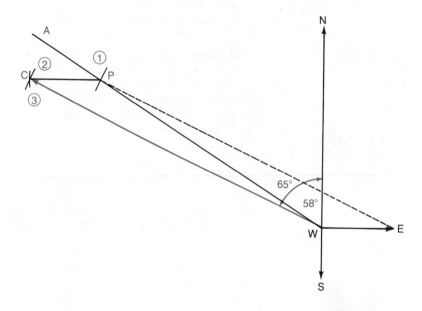

With compasses, radius 10 cm (180 kn) and centres E and W draw arcs ① and ② respectively. Arc ① cuts WA at P.

With centre P and radius WE, draw arc ③ to cut arc ② at C. WC represents the required course. Using a protractor, ∠NWC is measured and found to be 65°.

SOLVE

Hence the required course is (295°, 180). The length of WP is 8.1 cm (by measurement) so that the real magnitude of $\overrightarrow{WP}$ is 145 kn.

ANSWER

The ground speed is 145 kn.

EXERCISE 12.8

A 1. Name the following vectors in polar form.

(a) (b)

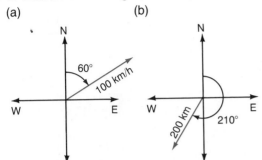

(c) (d)

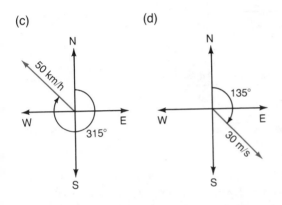

2. What is the length of the line segment representing the following quantities using the scale: 5 km = 2 cm?

(a) 10 km east
(b) 15 km left
(c) 7.5 km south
(d) 12.5 km north
(e) 4 km south-east
(f) 9 km north-west

B 3. Using a suitable scale, draw each of the following vectors.

(a) (180°, 20)
(b) (110°, 75)
(c) (285°, 150)
(d) (135°, 300)
(e) (315°, 450)

4. A ship sails 300 km north, then 500 km east. Make a vector diagram to find the direct course that will reach the same position.

5. A ship sails 500 km north, then 1200 km west and develops engine trouble. Make a vector diagram and find the course that a rescue ship would sail.

6. A small motorboat with a speed of 20 kn in still water is driven across a river with a current of 5 kn. Find the actual direction and velocity of the boat if the captain does not compensate for the current.

7. A plane travels north with an air speed of 400 kn. Find the ground speed and direction if there is a 40 kn east wind.

8. An airliner is heading east at 600 kn and encounters a 75 kn north wind. Find the resultant velocity and the true direction.

9. A pleasure craft is speeding across a river at 25 kn. Find the actual speed and direction if the current is 5 kn.

10. A pilot sets a course according to the vector (270°, 400), relative to the ground. Find the true ground velocity and direction if the flight is affected by a 45 kn south wind.

11. A plane flies 300 km east, then 200 km north. In what direction and how far should the aircraft fly to return to its home field?

12. In what direction should a pilot set his course if he wants to fly south at 300 kn and there is a 50 kn west wind?

13. A pilot wishes to fly at 400 kn towards the west and there is a 35 kn south wind. Find the course she must set and the air speed.

14. What course must a pilot set to fly north if his air speed is 350 kn and there is a 50 kn west wind? What is the ground speed?

15. A pilot wishes to fly her aircraft directly east. What course must she set and what is her ground speed if there is a 50 kn north wind and the aircraft cruises at 300 kn?

12.9 VECTORS IN THREE DIMENSIONS

Vectors may also have applications in space where magnitude and direction are involved.

In two dimensions, the direction of a vector [x, y] was described in terms of a horizontal component x and a vertical component y. In three dimensions, the direction of a vector must be described in terms of three components.

In the rectangular prism below, if O is the origin, the point C may be reached by travelling 4 units along OA, 3 units along AB, and then 2 units along BC.

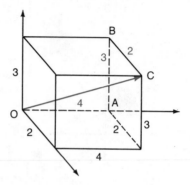

The vector $\overrightarrow{OC}$ is represented by the ordered triplet [4, 3, 2]. It is important to note the order of these components. Use the following diagram as a memory aid.

$\overrightarrow{OM}$ = [a, b, c]

where a is the x-component,
b is the y-component,
and c is the z-component.

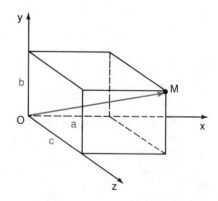

EXAMPLE 1. Describe the vector $\vec{v}$ as an ordered triplet.

(a)

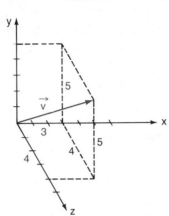

(b)

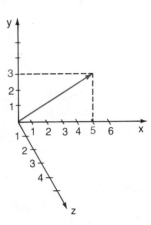

SOLUTION:

(a) $\vec{v} = [3, 5, 4]$
     ↑ ↑, ↑
     x y z

(b) $\vec{v} = [5, 3, 0]$
     ↑ ↑ ↑
     x y z

EXAMPLE 2. A fly starts at the corner O of the room, then walks 4 m along the edge OA, 3 m up AB, and 2 m along the edge BC. A second fly flies directly from O to C.

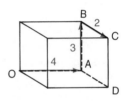

(a) Represent the three successive paths $\overrightarrow{OA}$, $\overrightarrow{AB}$, and $\overrightarrow{BC}$ of the first fly as ordered triplets.

(b) Represent the flight path $\overrightarrow{OC}$ of the second fly as an ordered triplet.

(c) What distance did the second fly travel?

SOLUTION:

(a) First path: 4 units in a x-direction only,
                   $\overrightarrow{OA} = [4, 0, 0]$

    Second path: 3 units in a y-direction only,
                   $\overrightarrow{AB} = [0, 3, 0]$

    Third path: 2 units in a z-direction only,
                   $\overrightarrow{BC} = [0, 0, 2]$

(b) The flight path of the second fly is represented by the vector $\overrightarrow{OC} = [4, 3, 2]$.

$$[4, 3, 2] = [4, 0, 0] + [0, 3, 0] + [0, 0, 2]$$

(c) The flight distance of the second fly is equal to the magnitude of vector $\overrightarrow{OC}$.

$|\overrightarrow{OC}|$ is found by using the Pythagorean Theorem twice.

(i) In △OAD, ∠OAD = 90°.

$$|\overrightarrow{OD}|^2 = |\overrightarrow{OA}|^2 + |\overrightarrow{AD}|^2$$

$$|\overrightarrow{OD}| = \sqrt{|\overrightarrow{OA}|^2 + |\overrightarrow{AD}|^2}$$
$$= \sqrt{4^2 + 3^2}$$
$$= 5$$

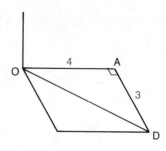

(ii) In △ODC, ∠ODC = 90°.

$$|\overrightarrow{OC}| = \sqrt{|\overrightarrow{OD}|^2 + |\overrightarrow{DC}|^2}$$
$$= \sqrt{5^2 + 2^2}$$
$$= \sqrt{29}$$
$$\doteq 5.4 \text{ to the nearest tenth of a metre}$$

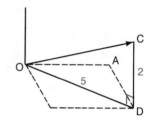

The second fly travelled approximately 5.4 m.

In the solution (c) above, we used

$$|\overrightarrow{OC}| = \sqrt{|\overrightarrow{OD}|^2 + |\overrightarrow{DC}|^2} \quad \text{and} \quad |\overrightarrow{OD}|^2 = |\overrightarrow{OA}|^2 + |\overrightarrow{AD}|^2$$

Substitute the second expression into the first.

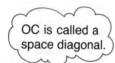

OC is called a space diagonal.

$$|\overrightarrow{OC}| = \sqrt{|\overrightarrow{OA}|^2 + |\overrightarrow{AD}|^2 + |\overrightarrow{DC}|^2}$$

Now substitute the appropriate values.

$$|\overrightarrow{OC}| = \sqrt{4^2 + 3^2 + 2^2}$$
$$= \sqrt{29}$$
$$\doteq 5.4$$

We generalize the result as follows.

> If $\vec{v} = [a, b, c]$, then $|\vec{v}| = \sqrt{a^2 + b^2 + c^2}$.

EXAMPLE 3. Find the magnitude of the following vectors.
(a) $\vec{u} = [3, 4, 12]$ (b) $\vec{v} = [8, 15, 0]$

SOLUTION:
(a) $|\vec{u}| = \sqrt{3^2 + 4^2 + 12^2}$ (b) $|\vec{v}| = \sqrt{8^2 + 15^2 + 0^2}$
$\quad\quad = \sqrt{169}$ $\quad\quad = \sqrt{289}$
$\quad\quad = 13$ $\quad\quad = 17$

EXERCISE 12.9

A 1. Express each vector as an ordered triplet.

(a)

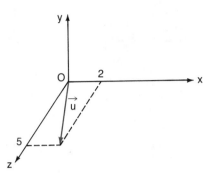

(b)

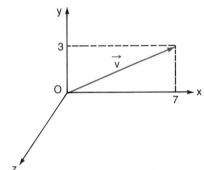

(c)

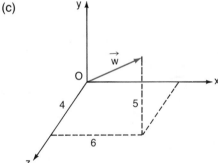

(d)

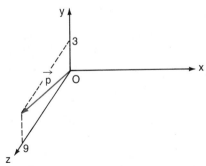

B 2. Find the magnitude of each of the following vectors to the nearest tenth.

(a) $\vec{a} = [1, 2, 3]$
(b) $\vec{b} = [7, 24, 0]$
(c) $\vec{c} = [0, 5, 12]$
(d) $\vec{d} = [5, 7, 4]$
(e) $\vec{e} = [3, 2, 1]$

3. A room in the shape of a cube has dimensions 3 m by 3 m by 3 m. Find to the nearest tenth of a metre the length of the space diagonal.

4. A 4 m post stands at one corner of a rectangular garden plot. A guy wire attached to the top of the post is anchored at the opposite corner of the garden plot. The plot measures 5 m by 6 m. Find the length of the guy wire to the nearest tenth of a metre.

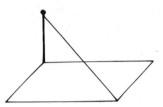

5. A man wishes to send his 1.7 m fishing rod to his granddaughter. The courier will not accept a parcel if any one dimension exceeds 1 m. The man decides to try a box with dimensions 1 m by 1 m by 1 m. Will the fishing rod fit?

Continue each pattern.

1, 4, 7, 10, 13, ...
1, 1, 2, 3, 5, 8, ...
1, 3, 9, 27, 81, ...
1, 4, 9, 16, 25, ...

12.10 PROBLEM SOLVING

1. The school board has put out a tender to have identification numbers painted on the student lockers in your school. Calculate a reasonable bid for the job, taking into account such things as

(a) the number of lockers,
(b) the materials needed,
(c) the time required.

2. A rectangular box has a total surface area of 1980 cm².

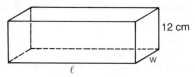

The height of the box is 12 cm. The length of the box is twice the width. What are the dimensions of the box?

3. The diagrams illustrate how a cross can be cut into four congruent pieces using straight lines.

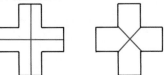

Can you find 2 other ways?

4. Place the numbers 1, 2, 3, 4, 5, 6, 7, 8, and 9 into groups so that the sum of the numbers in each group is 15.

5. Six arrows hit this target. The score was exactly 100. Where did the arrows land?

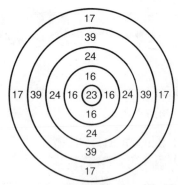

6. Calculate the surface area of the solid.

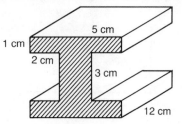

7. The frustum of a cone is shown in the diagram. Calculate the volume of the frustum to the nearest tenth.

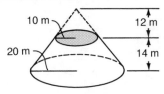

8. Place the numbers from 1 to 14 in the circles so that the sum along each row is 30.

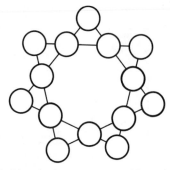

9. Six identical squares are placed side by side to form a rectangle.

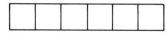

The perimeter of the rectangle is 686 m. What is the area of each square?

10. If the area of square C is 16 and the perimeter of square B is 28, find the perimeter of square A.

11. The sum of five consecutive integers is always evenly divisible by a one-digit number. What is the number?

12. A row of coins is arranged as follows: 1 penny, 3 dimes, 5 pennies, 7 dimes, and so on. What is the fiftieth coin in the row?

13. Find an odd number between 11 and 25 that is divisible by 3, but is not divisible by 5.

14. Place the digits from 1 to 8 in the boxes so that no two consecutive numbers are in boxes that touch at a point or a side.

15. The second hand of a clock is 14 cm long. Through how many centimetres will the endpoint of the second hand move in one day?

16. When the diameter of a circle was increased, the area of the circle was increased by 100%. By what percentage was the radius increased?

17. Each triangle inside the large triangle was drawn by joining the midpoints of the sides. What is the perimeter of the smallest triangle?

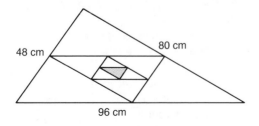

48 cm   80 cm

96 cm

18.

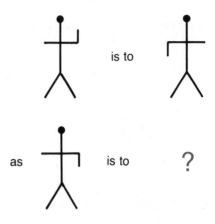

is to

as   is to   ?

MIND BENDER

Place each of the digits from 0 to 9 in the spaces to make the addition correct.

▪▪▪
+ ▪▪▪
▪▪▪▪

What is the smallest triangle whose sides are consecutive integers and whose area is exactly divisible by 2?

Determine the pattern. Find the missing number.

38	47	29	73
24	28	18	21
48	25	▨	36
68	55	78	49

12.11 REVIEW EXERCISE

1. Find the terminal point determined by the vector [2, −3] if the initial point is as follows.
(a) (5, 2) (b) (2, −3)
(c) (0, 0) (d) (−3, 2)

2. Simplify.
(a) 3[2, 5] + 2[3, −1]
(b) 2[−4, 3] + 3[4, −5]
(c) 4[1, −2] − [3, −2]
(d) 3[−2, 5] − 2[4, 3]

3. Find the magnitude of the following vectors.
(a) [4, 3] (b) [3, −4]
(c) [5, −12] (d) [−8, 15]
(e) [11, −7] (f) [−5, −7]
(g) [−15, 8] (h) [m, n]
(i) [1, 3, 10] (j) [9, 12, 8]
(k) [12, 16, 21] (l) [7, 5, 3]
(m) [p, q, r] (n) [3, −4, −12]

4. Express the following vectors in polar form (bearing, magnitude).
(a) [200, 0] (b) [0, −100]
(c) [−150, 0] (d) [0, 200]
(e) [10, 10] (f) [5, −5]
(g) [−3, −3] (h) [−7, 7]

5. Name equal vectors if ABCD is a parallelogram.

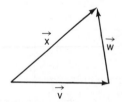

6. Name a single vector equal to $\vec{v} + \vec{w}$.
(a)

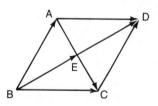

(b)

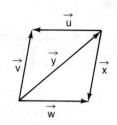

(c)

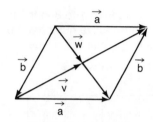

7. If $\vec{x} = [4, 2]$, $\vec{y} = [-1, 5]$, and $\vec{z} = [4, -3]$, find.
(a) $3\vec{x}$ (b) $\vec{x} + \vec{z}$
(c) $4\vec{x} + 3\vec{y}$ (d) $\vec{x} - \vec{y}$
(e) $|\vec{x}|$ (f) $|\vec{x} + \vec{y}|$
(g) $|\vec{x}| + |\vec{y}|$ (h) $-(3\vec{x} + 2\vec{y} - \vec{z})$

8. If $\vec{x} = [4, 7]$, $\vec{y} = [-2, 6]$, and $\vec{z} = [0, -3]$, find.
(a) $\vec{x} + \vec{y} + \vec{z}$ (b) $3\vec{x} + 2\vec{z}$
(c) $\vec{x} - (\vec{y} + \vec{z})$ (d) $\vec{x} - \vec{y} + \vec{z}$
(e) $|\vec{x}| + |\vec{y}| + |\vec{z}|$ (f) $|\vec{x} + \vec{y} + \vec{z}|$

9. Given the points O(0, 0), A(4, 2), B(7, 5), C(2, 0), D(−6, 1).
(a) Show $\overrightarrow{OA}$, $\overrightarrow{AB}$, $\overrightarrow{BC}$, $\overrightarrow{CD}$, and $\overrightarrow{OD}$.
(b) Express $\overrightarrow{OA}$, $\overrightarrow{AB}$, $\overrightarrow{BC}$, $\overrightarrow{CD}$, and $\overrightarrow{OD}$ in the form [a, b].

10. Given $\overrightarrow{TP} = [4, 2]$, $\overrightarrow{PQ} = [4, 2]$, $\overrightarrow{QR} = [7, 5]$, $\overrightarrow{RS} = [2, 0]$, and $\overrightarrow{ST} = [-6, 1]$.
(a) Show the addition
$\overrightarrow{TP} + \overrightarrow{PQ} + \overrightarrow{QR} + \overrightarrow{RS} + \overrightarrow{ST}$
on squared paper.
(b) State the coordinates of P, Q, R, and S if the coordinates of T are (−2, 4).

11. Given the points A(4, 2), B(7, 3), C(−3, 0), and D(0, 1), determine which of $\overrightarrow{AB}$, $\overrightarrow{CD}$, $\overrightarrow{BA}$, and $\overrightarrow{DC}$ are equal vectors.

12. Find to the nearest tenth the length of the space diagonal of a room whose dimensions are

(a) 3 m by 5 m by 2 m
(b) 6 m by 4 m by 3 m
(c) 9 m by 10 m by 4 m

13. Use a scale drawing to find the direction and magnitude of

$$\overrightarrow{AB} + \overrightarrow{BC}$$

if $\overrightarrow{AB} = (30°, 25)$ and $\overrightarrow{BC} = (300°, 6)$.

14. Given three points $A(-2, -2)$, $B(0, 3)$, and $C(8, 5)$.
(a) Find the coordinates of point D by means of a diagram so that $\overrightarrow{AB} = \overrightarrow{DC}$.
(b) Express $\overrightarrow{AB}$, $\overrightarrow{BC}$, $\overrightarrow{AD}$, and $\overrightarrow{DC}$, in the form [a, b].
(c) Identify figure ABCD.

15. (a) Make a diagram to show

$$(-3)[4, -2] = [-12, 6].$$

(b) Find x and y so that $[4, -2] = 2[x, y]$.

16. An aircraft flies east at 250 kn relative to the ground and encounters a north wind of 40 kn. Make vector diagrams and find

(a) the ground speed and direction if the pilot does not adjust the course to account for the wind
(b) the course the pilot should set to maintain the heading at 250 kn east

17. In quadrilateral ABCD, $\overrightarrow{AB} = \overrightarrow{DC}$.
(a) Show that $\overrightarrow{AD} = \overrightarrow{BC}$ and make a general conclusion.
(b) Identify figure ABCD.

18. P and Q are the midpoints of AD and BC respectively in parallelogram ABCD.
(a) Make a vector diagram.
(b) Show that

   (i) ABQP
   (ii) PQCD
   (iii) AQCP
   (iv) PBDQ

are parallelograms.

19. A basketball court is 26 m by 14 m. If the hoop is 3 m from the floor, how far is it from one corner of the court to the point where the hoop at the opposite end of the court is fastened to the backboard?

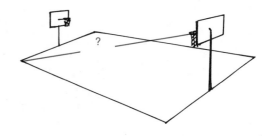

20. Use a vector diagram to find $\vec{a} - \vec{b}$ in each of the following.

(a)   (b)

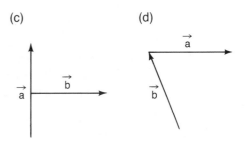

(c)   (d)

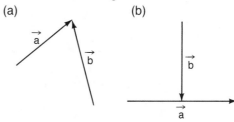

The year 1961 reads the same upside down. What is the next year that will read the same upside down?

12.12 CHAPTER 12 TEST

1. Find the terminal point of the vector $[-3, 4]$ if the initial point is as follows.

(a) $(3, -2)$ (b) $(-2, -1)$

2. Find the length of each of the following vectors.

(a) $[5, -12]$

(b) $[0, 3]$

(c) $[3, 4, 12]$

3. In the parallelogram, name a single vector equal to

(a) $\vec{b} - \vec{a}$

(b) $\vec{a} + \vec{b}$

(c) $\vec{c} + \vec{d}$

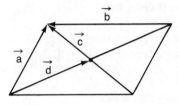

4. If $\vec{a} = [3, -2]$ and $\vec{b} = [-4, -3]$, find.

(a) $2\vec{a}$ (b) $\vec{a} + \vec{b}$ (c) $\vec{a} - \vec{b}$

(d) $3\vec{a} - \vec{b}$ (e) $\vec{a} - 2\vec{b}$ (f) $2(\vec{a} - \vec{b})$

5. Express the following vectors in polar form (bearing, magnitude).

(a) $[0, 3]$ (b) $[-2, 0]$

(c) $[2, 2]$ (d) $[1, -1]$

6. Find to the nearest tenth of a metre the length of the space diagonals of the following rectangular rooms.

(a) 3 m by 5 m by 3 m   (b) 7 m by 8 m by 2 m

7. A boat is sailing 40 kn due east while the current is moving at 25 kn due north.

(a) Draw a vector diagram to scale.

(b) Determine the actual velocity of the boat.

(c) Determine the actual direction of the boat.

8. A squirrel and a sparrow both start at the same corner of a tennis court. The squirrel runs along the edge to the centre, along the net to the other side, then runs up the post. The sparrow flies directly to the top of the same post. The tennis court measures 24 m by 11 m and the net posts are 1 m high.

(a) How far did the squirrel run?

(b) How far did the sparrow fly?

STATISTICS AND PROBABILITY

CHAPTER

13

We see . . . that the theory of probabilities is at bottom only common sense reduced to calculations; it makes us appreciate with exactitude what reasonable minds feel by a sort of instinct, often without being able to account for it.

Pierre Laplace

PERCENT

EXERCISE

1. Express each of the following as
(a) common fractions.
(b) decimals.

(i)   25%   (ii)   75%
(iii) $33\frac{1}{3}$%   (iv)   10%
(v)   65%   (vi)   120%
(vii) 85%   (viii) 225%
(ix)   5%   (x)   1.5%
(xi)   10.5%   (xii) $66\frac{2}{3}$%
(xiii) $12\frac{1}{2}$%   (xiv) 37.5%
(xv)   62.5%   (xvi) 112.5%

2. Express each of the following as a percent.

(a) $\frac{2}{5}$ (b) $\frac{3}{4}$

(c) $\frac{7}{10}$ (d) $\frac{3}{20}$

(e) $\frac{3}{50}$ (f) 0.25

(g) 1.75   (h) 0.575
(i) 0.345   (j) 2.025
(k) 0.625   (l) $\frac{1}{8}$

(m) $\frac{3}{8}$ (n) $1\frac{1}{4}$

(o) $3\frac{7}{8}$ (p) $1\frac{5}{8}$

3. Evaluate.
(a) 5% of 20
(b) 18% of 24
(c) 9% of 82
(d) 125% of 600
(e) 12% of 12
(f) 5% of 3.75
(g) $12\frac{1}{2}$% of 64
(h) 62.5% of 88.8
(i) 28% of 50
(j) 45% of 1400
(k) $1\frac{1}{2}$% of 240

(l) $\frac{1}{3}$% of 330
(m) $6\frac{1}{2}$% of 1800
(n) $16\frac{2}{3}$% of 6600
(o) $32\frac{1}{2}$% of 1000
(p) 0.5% of 2500

4. How many students were absent from a school of 1450 with an absentee rate of 8%?

5. How much would you pay for a car listing at $8225 with a 17% fleet discount?

6. How much is a used car worth today if it cost $5680 when new and if it depreciated at a rate of 30% per annum for the past three years?

7. How much would you charge for a pump, which costs you $250, to make a 35% profit?

8. Find the rate of percent.
(a) What percent of 24 is 9?
(b) 6 is what percent of 35?
(c) 24 is what percent of 18?
(d) What percent is 12 of 36?
(e) What percent is 13 of 65?
(f) What percent of 18 is 30?

9. An athletic supply store sold 940 baseball uniforms, 1340 hockey uniforms, and 850 football uniforms last year. This year, the store expects to sell 5% more baseball uniforms, 10% more hockey uniforms, and 4% more football uniforms. How many more uniforms does the company expect to sell this year?

FRACTIONS

EXERCISE

1. Add.

(a) $\frac{5}{8} + \frac{3}{4}$ (b) $\frac{5}{6} + \frac{1}{3}$

(c) $\frac{4}{9} + \frac{2}{3}$ (d) $\frac{3}{7} + \frac{5}{8}$

(e) $\frac{4}{11} + \frac{2}{3}$ (f) $\frac{4}{7} + \frac{3}{5}$

(g) $\frac{1}{3} + \frac{5}{8}$ (h) $\frac{4}{9} + \frac{2}{5}$

(i) $\frac{3}{8} + \frac{1}{2}$ (j) $\frac{5}{7} + \frac{3}{4}$

(k) $\frac{1}{8} + \frac{1}{3}$ (l) $\frac{5}{13} + \frac{2}{3}$

2. Multiply.

(a) $\frac{2}{3} \times \frac{1}{5}$ (b) $\frac{7}{8} \times \frac{5}{9}$

(c) $\frac{1}{6} \times \frac{5}{8}$ (d) $\frac{3}{4} \times \frac{8}{9}$

(e) $\frac{1}{7} \times \frac{21}{25}$ (f) $\frac{4}{7} \times \frac{21}{44}$

(g) $\frac{4}{9} \times \frac{3}{5}$ (h) $\frac{5}{12} \times \frac{6}{11}$

(i) $\frac{8}{15} \times \frac{12}{13}$ (j) $\frac{15}{28} \times \frac{7}{10}$

(k) $\frac{5}{9} \times \frac{3}{8}$ (l) $\frac{4}{17} \times \frac{17}{20}$

3. Simplify the following.

(a) $\frac{1}{4} \times \frac{4}{7} + \frac{3}{7} \times \frac{2}{3}$

(b) $\frac{2}{5} \times \frac{10}{11} + \frac{6}{11} \times \frac{5}{6}$

(c) $\frac{9}{10} \times \frac{5}{6} + \frac{3}{4} \times \frac{8}{9}$

(d) $\frac{4}{9} \times \frac{3}{8} + \frac{4}{3} \times \frac{1}{2}$

(e) $\frac{5}{6} + \frac{4}{15} \times \frac{5}{8} + \frac{2}{3}$

(f) $\frac{3}{5} + \frac{5}{6} \times \frac{2}{25} - \frac{1}{3}$

(g) $\frac{5}{12} + \frac{2}{3} \times \frac{3}{4} - \frac{7}{12}$

(h) $\frac{4}{7} + \frac{3}{5} \times \frac{10}{21} + \frac{1}{2}$

(i) $\frac{3}{4}(\frac{1}{3} + \frac{1}{2})$

(j) $\frac{5}{6}(\frac{2}{5} + \frac{3}{4})$

(k) $\frac{4}{5}(\frac{1}{3} + 3)$

(l) $\frac{3}{4}(\frac{2}{5} + \frac{1}{3})$

WORKING WITH TABLES

EXERCISE

1. Find the grand total by adding both vertical and horizontal totals.
Can you add two-digit numbers in one pass?

(a)

2.5	5.8	3.4	0.7	2.3	
4.7	9.0	9.6	5.1	1.7	
3.8	3.6	4.8	2.8	6.2	
5.2	5.1	1.5	3.4	5.3	
7.3	1.3	2.6	1.7	9.7	

(b)

3.4	4.6	0.4	2.3	3.9	
5.2	7.9	5.2	0.0	5.4	
7.6	1.4	0.7	5.4	7.6	
1.3	3.7	1.3	1.6	2.8	
2.5	5.8	4.7	2.8	1.1	

(c)

4.2	7.1	6.2	3.2	3.1	
3.7	4.8	3.9	1.7	5.2	
1.6	5.7	5.8	2.5	4.6	
5.8	3.2	4.6	8.1	8.1	
2.1	1.5	1.4	6.2	7.4	

(d)

5.1	6.1	2.1	6.4	2.2	
3.7	2.4	8.7	8.6	4.2	
2.8	2.3	6.1	2.2	3.8	
8.0	3.3	3.7	6.9	1.7	
3.0	9.4	5.6	2.3	1.8	

13.1 SAMPLING AND SURVEYING

Statistics is the science of collecting, organizing, and interpreting collections of facts or numbers called data.

To determine public reaction to a new program, pollsters find it impractical to survey every viewer. They select a small group, called a sample, and ask these people for their reaction. Their comments are used to generalize for all television viewers. Hence we say that a sample is a small group of individuals (or objects) selected to stand for a larger group called the population.

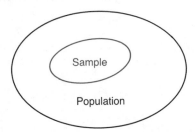

In this section we will investigate some procedures that are used in designing polls, questionnaires, and experiments.

I. Structure of the Sample

In a random sample, the sample intentionally has no structure. The people or objects in the sample are selected at random from the entire population.

In a stratified sample, the structure of the sample is similar to that of the population; the sample resembles a cross-section or a scaled-down version of the population in which certain classes and categories are represented proportionally. For example, in a survey of the Canadian public, a stratified sample would include proportionate numbers from each region of the country. Within each region, proportionate numbers might be selected according to such classifications as social and economic status, occupation, marital status, age, sex, or any other classification that might significantly affect the results of the survey.

EXAMPLE 1. A marketing firm wishes to study the reaction of the adults in a city to a car commercial. If 55% of the city's adults are between the ages of 18 and 35, 35% between 36 and 50, and 10% are older than 50, how many of each age group should be included in a stratified sample of 700?

SOLUTION:
The number of adults to be selected in each age group are:
(i)   18 to 35: 55% of 700 = 385
(ii) 36 to 50: 35% of 700 = 245
(iii)   > 50: 10% of 700 = 70

II. Randomness

In both random and stratified sampling, the selection methods must ensure that the items within a sample group are selected at random.

Some popular methods are
(i) using a computer to select names at random;
(ii) picking names from a telephone, city, or school directory (provided that the entire survey population is included in the directory).

EXAMPLE 2. A mid-morning radio talk show wishes to investigate the number of people in the listening area who are unemployed. The pollsters record the status of the people who call in. Is this a valid random method of selection for this type of survey?

SOLUTION:
Most of the employed would be at work and not listening to the radio. The majority of callers would likely be unemployed. This is not a valid random selection method.

III. Sample Size

A large sample gives more reliable results than a small one. However, a large sample is time-consuming and costly. In some cases, a sample is not even recommended and the entire population must be surveyed. A company that manufactures lightbulbs may want to test 2% of its lightbulbs, while a car manufacturer would want to test every car that is produced.

To determine the size of the sample, we consider the following:
  (i) margin of error
  (ii) size of the population
  (iii) cost of the survey

IV. Data Gathering Methods

To obtain information about a population some of the most popular methods are
  (i) questionnaires by mail, in newspapers, accompanying a product at the time of purchase
  (ii) personal interviews
  (iii) telephone surveys
  (iv) tests and measurements

EXERCISE 13.1

A 1. State the reason why a sample is used rather than the entire population in each of the following.

(a) The Buck Shot Ammunition Company tests one bullet in every two hundred by actual firing.

(b) The East Bay Exploration Company tests ore samples to determine the value of the ore body.

(c) The Pacer Poll Company is commissioned to determine the popularity of the president of the United States.

(d) The Maison Bleu Cheese Company employs a cheese taster to determine the quality of the cheese.

(e) The Fish and Game Association tags wild geese to determine their migratory habits.

B 2. The Sure Jump Parachute Company tests every chute before shipping. List three other examples where it is necessary to test the entire population rather than use a sample.

3. Give an example of a problem that could arise when

(a) the sample is too small.

(b) the sample is too large.

(c) the members of the sample are not selected at random.

4. Discuss the validity of the following sampling techniques.

(a) A survey dealing with the problems of the unemployed was conducted on a 747 jet bound for the Bahamas.

(b) The whole school was surveyed regarding this year's graduation plans.

(c) An ammunition company tested the bullets it produced by firing every one.

(d) A company that produces 10 000 lightbulbs per week tests the first 200 lightbulbs off the assembly line Monday morning to check the quality of bulbs for that week.

(e) A newspaper wishes to know what percentage of people who read their newspaper read the sports section. The ad inviting people to respond is printed in the sports section.

(f) A shoe company wishes to introduce a new line of running shoes. To determine the percentage of its production to be devoted to each shoe size, it takes a sample of shoe sizes of thousands of people.

(g) In a poll to predict the Canadian Prime Minister to be elected in an up-coming election.

    (i) 10 000 eligible voters are interviewed in British Columbia

    (ii) 10 000 school children are interviewed across the country

    (iii) 100 eligible voters are interviewed across the country.

5. Describe how you would conduct a survey to determine the number of two-car families in your town or city.

6. Describe the sampling techniques you would use to estimate the following.

(a) the trees in a forest

(b) the number of pennies in a jar

(c) the number of people in a crowd at St. Peter's square

(d) the number of stitches in a metre of fabric

(e) the number of bacteria in a glass of water

7. At Lakefield Secondary School 45% of the student population are boys. In a survey to determine the theme of the next spirit day, how many boys and how many girls should be interviewed in a stratified sample of 200?

8. Conduct a survey in your class to determine the number of radios in each home.

9. Conduct a survey in your class to determine the number of hours the television is on during a week day.

10. Using an appropriate sampling method, conduct a survey in your school to determine the number of students who

(a) attended the last school dance.

(b) attended a particular sporting event.

(c) saw a particular television program.

(d) take a bus to school.

(e) play tennis.

13.2 REACTION TIME: EMPIRICAL DATA

When an object falls freely to the earth, it accelerates at a rate of 983.217 cm/s. Substituting this value in the formula $d = \frac{1}{2}t^2$ gives a formula for the distance, d cm, that an object falls in a time, t s.

$$d = 491.609t^2$$

Solving this equation for t,

$$t = 0.045\sqrt{d}$$

A person's reaction time can be measured by using a 30 cm ruler and then calculating with the formula above.

Hold a 30 cm ruler vertically with the lower end just at the opening between your thumb and forefinger. Release the ruler. As the ruler drops, catch it between your thumb and the forefinger. Read the amount of drop from the ruler and calculate the reaction time.

EXERCISE 13.2

1. (a) Perform the experiment on a number of subjects and complete the following table.

Drop d	Reaction Time t

(b) What is the average person's reaction time?

2. The reaction time for your feet is the same as for your hands. How far will your car travel until you begin to stop if you are driving at 80 km/h? Use your reaction time as determined in the experiment above.

MICRO MATH

The following program computes the reaction time when you enter the amount of drop from the experiment above.

NEW

```
10 PRINT "REACTION TIME"
20 PRINT "AMOUNT OF DROP"
30 INPUT D
40 T = .045*SQR(D)
50 PRINT "REACTION TIME IN SECONDS: ";T
60 PRINT "ANOTHER VALUE? Y OR N"
70 INPUT Z$
80 IF Z$ = "Y" THEN 20
90 END

REACTION TIME
AMOUNT OF DROP?
? 18.3
REACTION TIME IN SECONDS: .1925032
ANOTHER VALUE? Y OR N
? Y
AMOUNT OF DROP?
? 12.5
REACTION TIME IN SECONDS: .159099
ANOTHER VALUE? Y OR N
?
```

RUN

13.3 PREDICTING FROM SAMPLES

Predicting involves making statements about an entire population from data obtained from a sample of the population.

EXAMPLE 1. Five college students decided to try to predict the results of an upcoming election of a student council. Each student asked 50 eligible voters as to how they might vote in the upcoming election. Each opinion was registered in the tally column as a stroke (/). After 50 strokes the results were totalled. The following is Gail's completed tally sheet.

	Tally	Number
Candidate A		10
Candidate B		18
Candidate C		15
Undecided		7

The data gathered by the students were summarized as follows.

	Gail	Bob	Theo	Chris	Beth	Totals
Candidate A	10	9	10	7	6	42
Candidate B	18	11	13	9	19	70
Candidate C	15	24	19	26	20	104
Undecided	7	6	8	8	5	34

(a) If there are 3000 eligible voters and 85% usually vote, how many votes can be expected?
(b) Predict the minimum number of votes for each candidate. Round off to the nearest whole number.
(c) What is the undecided vote?
(d) If the election is one week away, who has a chance of defeating candidate C?

SOLUTION:

(a) $\frac{85}{100} \times 3000 = 2550$

2550 votes are expected.

(b) Candidate A: $\frac{42}{250} \times 2550 = 428$ (to the nearest whole number)

Candidate B: $\frac{70}{250} \times 2550 = 714$

Candidate C: $\frac{104}{250} \times 2550 = 1061$ (to the nearest whole number)

(c) Undecided: $\frac{34}{250} \times 2550 = 347$ (to the nearest whole number)

(d) If B can capture the undecided vote B can win the election.

Some sampling methods involve taking a sample and counting or weighing the objects within it, and then projecting the results over the entire population. If you had to estimate the number of beans in a 10 kg bag, knowing how many there are in a 200 g container would give you a fair idea of the number of beans in the bag. Another method to determine the mass of the entire bag would be to determine the mass of a sample of 100 beans, then calculate.

$$\text{Estimated Number of Beans} = \frac{\text{Mass of Bag}}{\text{Mass of Sample}} \times \text{Number in Sample}$$

To estimate the number of trees in a forest, count the number of trees in a sample area 100 m by 100 m, then apply the results over the entire forest area.

EXAMPLE 2. A 100 m by 100 m sample area of a forest contained 400 spruce trees. Estimate the number of spruce trees in a forest with an area of 24 km².

SOLUTION:
Area of sample = 100 m × 100 m
           = 10 000 m²

Area of forest = 24 km²
           = 24 × 1 000 000 m²
           = 24 000 000 m²

Estimated number of spruce trees in the forest
     $\frac{24\ 000\ 000}{10\ 000} \times 400 = 960\ 000$

Can you think of a better sampling procedure for Example 2 using a stratified sample?

EXERCISE 13.3

B 1. A bag contains 200 marbles; some are white, and some are black. Twenty are drawn, of which 6 are white and 14 are black. How many marbles in the bag do you expect were
(a) white?
(b) black?

2. In order to estimate the fish population of a pond, a game warden caught 200 fish, tagged them, and then returned them to the pond. A week later the warden caught 200 fish and found that 40 of them were tagged. What is the estimated fish population of the pond?

3. A manufacturer of computer diskettes found that out of the 200 diskettes checked in one week, 13 were defective.

(a) If the manufacturer produces 3000 diskettes per week, how many would you expect to be defective that week?
(b) If you bought a box of 10 diskettes from that week's shipment, how many defective ones would you expect to find in your box? (Round off to nearest integer.)

4. In an experiment testing a suspicious die, the data contained from 200 rolls are as follows.

Face	Frequency
1	25
2	43
3	32
4	34
5	31
6	35

How many times would you expect each face number to occur if the die is to be rolled 9000 times in its lifetime?

5. Choose a sample paragraph from a novel and count off the first 100 words. Count the number of letters in each word and record your results on a tally sheet. Use the same tally sheet to record another 100 word sample.

Length of Word	Tally	Number	% of Total
1 letter			
2 letters			
3 letters			
4 letters			
5 letters			
6 letters			
7 letters			
8 letters			
9 letters			
10 or more			

(a) According to your sample, what length of word is most common?
(b) Out of 5000 words in the novel, how many would you predict to have
    (i) 2 letters?
    (ii) 3 letters?
    (iii) 4 letters?
(c) Conduct a similar survey using a newspaper as a source for words. Compare these results to the novel results. Can you account for any difference?

Use $+$, $-$, $\times$, $\div$, and ( ) to make a true statement.

6 2 2 = 5 7 4

7 5 6 1 = 4 3 3 1

4 2 7 3 = 4 1 6 6

3 4 1 5 = 2 4 2 2

10 6 1 = 5 3 10

1 1 1 1 = 2 2 2 2

6 3 4 = 2 3 0

5 2 3 = 2 5 3

3 7 5 = 1 8 2

13.4 USING VENN DIAGRAMS TO SORT DATA

It is sometimes helpful to organize data in diagrams called Venn diagrams

EXAMPLE. The community college conducted a survey of the high school backgrounds of its first-year students. A sample of 100 students was taken and data was collected.

30 took art   19 took music and French
46 took music   11 took art and French
57 took French   8 took art, music, and French
15 took art and music

(a) How many students
    (i) did not take art, music, or French?
    (ii) took French only?
    (iii) took music and art with no French?
(b) If there are 1300 first-year students, how many would you expect
    (i) did not take art, music, or French?
    (ii) took French only?
    (iii) took music and art with no French?

SOLUTION:
(a) The data can be sorted using a Venn Diagram.
(i) Number of students who did not take art, music, or French is

$$100 - (12 + 7 + 8 + 3 + 11 + 20 + 35) = 100 - 96$$
$$= 4$$

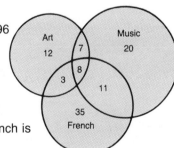

(ii) Number of students who took French only is

$$57 - (8 + 3 + 11) = 57 - 22$$
$$= 35$$

(iii) Number of students who took music and art with no French is

$$15 - 8 = 7$$

(b)		Number in Sample	Fraction of Sample	Prediction for First-year Students
	(i) No art, music, or French	4	$\frac{4}{100} = \frac{1}{25}$	$\frac{1}{25} \times 1300 = 52$
	(ii) French only	35	$\frac{35}{100} = \frac{7}{20}$	$\frac{7}{20} = 1300 = 455$
	(iii) Music and art with no French	7	$\frac{7}{100}$	$\frac{7}{100} \times 1300 = 91$

13.5 FREQUENCY DISTRIBUTION: TABLES AND GRAPHS

When presented with a large mass of data it is convenient to express the information in a frequency table. The frequencies obtained in the table can then be used to give a more visual representation of the distribution by means of a graph.

The following example involves discrete data. Discrete data are obtained by counting, there are no fractions and each value is exact. Bar graphs are often used to represent this type of data.

EXAMPLE 1. Toss four coins 50 times and record the number of heads which turn up on each toss. Tabulate the results in a frequency table and construct a bar graph.

SOLUTION:
Construct a table showing the possible numbers of heads. Perform the experiment and tally the results.

Frequency Table for the Number of Heads in Tossing Four Coins		
Number of Heads	Tally	Frequency
0	ǀ	1
1	₩₩ ₩₩ ₩₩ ǀǀǀ	18
2	₩₩ ₩₩ ₩₩ ₩₩	20
3	₩₩ ǀǀ	7
4	ǀǀǀǀ	4

To make a bar graph showing this information:
(i)   draw and label the horizontal axis;
(ii) draw and label the vertical axis using an appropriate scale so that the highest frequency can be graphed;
(iii) draw the bars so that all have the same width.

Number of Heads Obtained by Tossing Four Coins

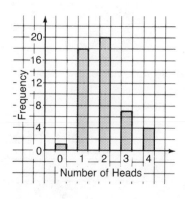

Continuous data are obtained by measuring. The values obtained
are approximate, the precision limited by the measuring instrument
used. In placing the values in a frequency table, we must set class
intervals to group the data. If our measures are to the nearest unit,
then the class boundaries will be the half unit. For example, if we
measure the heights of students to the nearest centimetre and the
class interval of 3 cm is from 160 cm to 163 cm, then students with
heights between 159.5 cm and 163.5 cm would fall in this class;
therefore, the class boundaries are 159.5 cm and 163.5 cm.

A histogram is a vertical bar graph on which the class boundaries
are marked along the horizontal axis and the frequency on the vertical
axis. Each bar represents the number of cases in the class interval.

EXAMPLE 2. Following is a table of masses in kilograms for
50 grade ten students.

$$
\begin{array}{cccccccccc}
48 & 61 & 55 & 56 & 52 & 58 & 55 & 52 & 57 & 51 \\
59 & 55 & 54 & 55 & 54 & 58 & 54 & 56 & 52 & 54 \\
56 & 56 & 51 & 48 & 51 & 60 & 53 & 59 & 57 & 53 \\
55 & 56 & 54 & 57 & 53 & 49 & 54 & 50 & 50 & 58 \\
57 & 51 & 56 & 51 & 55 & 53 & 53 & 55 & 56 & 53
\end{array}
$$

Tabulate the results in a frequency table.

SOLUTION:
The lowest value is 48 and the highest is 61. Using class intervals of
2 kg, we obtain class limits as shown in the table below. From these
we obtain class boundaries which are half-way between succeeding
limits.

Masses of Grade 10 Students			
Class Limits	Class Boundaries	Tally	Frequency
48–49	47.5–49.5	|||	3
50–51	49.5–51.5	︱︱︱︱ ||	7
52–53	51.5–53.5	︱︱︱︱ ||||	9
54–55	53.5–55.5	︱︱︱︱ ︱︱︱︱ |||	13
56–57	55.5–57.5	︱︱︱︱ ︱︱︱︱ |	11
58–59	57.5–59.5	︱︱︱︱	5
60–61	59.5–61.5	||	2

A histogram is constructed using the class boundaries and the frequency for each class. The widths of the bars correspond to the class intervals. The graph has a title and the axes are clearly labelled.

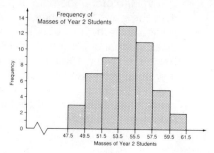

If we join the mid-value of each succeeding class we have another form of the graph called a frequency polygon.

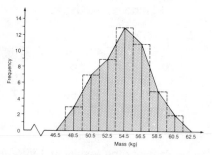

If the group of students was expanded to include all grade ten students, we could estimate that it would more closely reflect the properties of the whole group if the graph was drawn as a smooth curve.

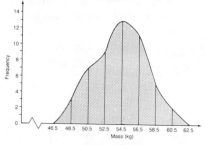

There are many frequency distributions whose graphs are bell shaped curves. We call such a graph a normal curve and the frequency distribution a normal distribution.

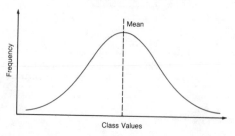

EXERCISE 13.5

1. A pair of dice was rolled 50 times to obtain the discrete data shown below.

9	6	6	9	6
4	10	7	9	7
6	9	6	11	4
4	6	3	4	10
8	7	10	9	3
2	6	5	3	8
8	11	11	8	7
5	12	9	6	11
4	8	8	7	7
7	7	10	11	6

(a) Construct a frequency distribution table.
(b) Draw a bar graph.

2. Construct a frequency distribution table for the following set of golf scores, using the classes 70–71, 72–73, 74–75, ... , 88–89.

75	78	70	82	88	79	78	77
89	78	77	78	82	71	82	81
81	76	84	79	76	81	79	83
79	85	74	80	81	73	74	82
73	83	79	79	74	85	77	85
84	77	83	78	81	80	79	78
79	83	81	88	72	78	81	80
72	78	79	74	84	75	77	82

3. Draw a histogram to illustrate the following data. Weekly earnings of students ages 13-17 from part-time work.

Earnings ($)	Frequency
0–10	7
10–20	9
20–30	10
30–40	9
40–50	8
50–60	6
60–70	4
70–80	2
80–90	1
90–100	1

4. The following table contains the number of basketball free throws sunk by 70 students, each taking 100 throws.

60	58	56	61	63	79	58
57	68	41	75	71	69	65
85	58	54	51	61	64	84
79	83	72	61	43	58	42
63	69	92	71	62	50	38
73	65	76	61	73	78	79
42	71	47	45	63	74	39
81	61	75	87	94	46	52
48	59	69	48	21	39	65
75	84	91	32	54	61	73

(a) Make a frequency distribution table using a class interval of 5.
(b) Draw a histogram.

5. A company is considering buying local movie theatres. In order to analyze the movie going habits of a population, the following data were collected.

Number of Movies Attended in the Past Two Years	Frequency
0–4	51
5–9	87
10–14	131
15–19	96
20–24	68
25–29	37
30–34	19
35–39	8
40 and over	3

(a) Prepare a histogram to display the data.
(b) Draw the frequency polygon.
(c) What conclusions concerning the data can you draw from the histogram?

13.6 MEASURES OF CENTRAL TENDENCY

In the previous section we grouped data into classes, then drew graphs of the frequency distributions to provide a "picture" to assist in the analysis. Statisticians are able to describe further a mass of data by indicating a centre of the distribution called a measure of central tendency. The three measures of central tendency are the mode, median, and mean. In this section you will learn how to find these and also when their use is meaningful.

I. MODE

The mode is the value that occurs most frequently in the data. In the following list of numbers:

$$1, 1, 2, 2, 2, 3, 3, 3, 3, 3, 4, 4, 4, 5, 5, 5, 6, 6, 7$$

the mode is 3. The use of the mode is limited to cases such as the manager of a shoe store determining how many pairs of shoes of each size to stock. The sales of the most popular sizes would determine how many of each size should be ordered.

II. MEDIAN

The median is the mid-value of a group in which all values have been ranked. Knowing the median enables one to tell whether any value is in the top-half or bottom-half of the group. To find the median of any group of n values, we first arrange the values according to rank then
    (i) select the mid-value if n is odd,
    (ii) find the average of the two mid-values if n is even.

If there are n values in the group, the median is located in the $\dfrac{n + 1}{2}$ position when the data is arranged according to rank. The median is shown in the following groups of ranked data.

(i) n is odd

$$9 \; 9 \; 10 \; 11 \; 12 \quad 13 \quad 14 \; 16 \; 17 \; 19 \; 20$$

The position of the median is calculated as follows:

$$\frac{11 + 1}{2} = 6$$

In the sixth position, the median is 13.

(ii) n is even

$$4 \; 9 \; 9 \; 10 \; 11 \; 11 \; 12 \bigcirc 14 \; 15 \; 16 \; 19 \; 20 \; 21 \; 22$$

The position of the median is calculated as follows:

$$\frac{14 + 1}{2} = 7\tfrac{1}{2}$$

The median is the average of the 7th and 8th values.

$$\frac{12 + 14}{2} = 13 \text{ is the median.}$$

III. MEAN

The arithmetic mean is found by dividing the sum of all values in a group by the number of values in the group. For example, if Tim Horvath, a basketball player, scored 22, 35, 47, 28, 25, and 35 points in 6 games, then his mean score is

$$\frac{22 + 35 + 47 + 28 + 25 + 35}{6} = \frac{192}{6}$$
$$= 32$$

We could now say that Tim "averaged" 32 points per game.

For a set of values $x_1, x_2, x_3, \ldots, x_n$, the mean is

$$\bar{x} = \frac{x_1 + x_2 + x_3 + \cdots + x_n}{n}$$

EXAMPLE 1. When a firm first went into production ten years ago, it paid the following annual salaries.

1 President at $75 000

1 Vice President at $62 000

1 Secretary Treasurer at $56 000

3 Accountants at $40 000

7 Salespeople at $30 000

8 Support staff at $16 000

Find.
(a) the median salary
(b) the mean salary

SOLUTION:
(a) There were 21 people on the payroll, hence the median salary is in the $\dfrac{21 + 1}{2} = 11$th position.

The median salary is $30 000.

(b) $\bar{x} = \dfrac{x_1 + x_2 + x_3 + \cdots + x_n}{n}$

$\bar{x} = \dfrac{75\,000 + 62\,000 + 56\,000 + \cdots + 16\,000 + 16\,000}{21}$

$= \dfrac{651\,000}{21}$

$= 31\,000$

75 000
62 000
56 000
40 000
40 000
40 000
30 000
30 000
30 000
30 000
30 000
30 000
30 000
16 000
16 000
16 000
16 000
16 000
16 000
16 000
16 000

$E=mc^2$

For large masses of data, we can use the following method:

x_i	f	$f \times x_i$
75 000	1	75 000
62 000	1	62 000
56 000	1	56 000
40 000	3	120 000
30 000	7	210 000
16 000	8	128 000
Total	21	651 000

$$\bar{x} = \frac{651\ 000}{21}$$

$$= 31\ 000$$

The mean salary was $31 000.

In the example, we found the median to be $30 000, the mean to be $31 000, and we see that the mode is $16 000. Which is the better statistic to indicate the level of salary that was paid by the company?

EXAMPLE 2. During a chocolate bar sale competition, two classes were very close and each group had its own reason for feeling it was the winner. The number of chocolate bars sold by each student is given in the table.

Class A		Class B	
35	22	33	24
34	20	31	24
30	20	29	23
30	20	29	23
28	20	27	20
26	19	25	19
26	18	25	19
25	16	25	16
22	16	25	16
		24	7

For each class, find
(a) the mode.
(b) the median.
(c) the mean.

SOLUTION:

Class A	Class B

Class A

(a) The mode is 20.

(b) The median is the average of the 9th and 10th values.

$$\frac{22 + 22}{2} = 22$$

The median is 22.

(c) The mean is

$$\bar{x} = \frac{16 + 16 + 18 + \cdots + 34 + 35}{18}$$

$$= \frac{427}{18}$$

$$\doteq 23.7$$

Class B

(a) The mode is 25.

(b) The median is the average of the 10th and 11th values.

$$\frac{24 + 24}{2} = 24$$

The median is 24.

(c) The mean is

$$\bar{x} = \frac{7 + 16 + 16 + \cdots + 31 + 33}{20}$$

$$= \frac{464}{20}$$

$$= 23.2$$

The results of Example 2 are summarized in the following table.

Class	Total	Mode	Median	Mean
A	427	20	22	23.7
B	464	25	24	23.2

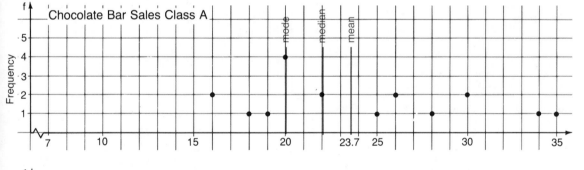

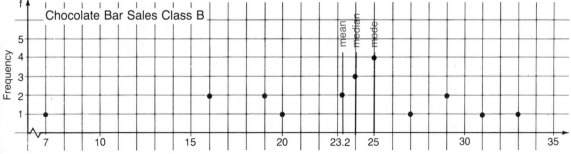

Which figure would you use to determine the winner?

EXERCISE 13.6

A 1. State the measure of central tendency that best describes the following.

(a) level of salary paid by a company
(b) shoe sizes to be kept in stock
(c) the mass of an offensive line on a football team
(d) the number of cubic metres per hectare of corn
(e) a set of class marks
(f) the helmet size of a hockey team
(g) the rainfall in a certain area

B 2. Order each of the following sets of data, then find the mode(s), median, and mean correct to one decimal place.

(a) 71 26 35 69 53 26 70 33 61
(b) 3 13 20 20 11 18 12 7 5
(c) 5 5 5 4 4 3 7 2
(d) 8 12 7 15 19 7 9 8 8 11
(e) 3 3 3 5 6 2 4 2 4 5 4 7 8

3. The following table gives the bulb life in hours of overhead projector bulbs. Find the mode, median, and mean.

Time (h)	8	9	10	11	12	13	14	15	16
Frequency	1	0	0	1	3	5	6	8	9

Time (h)	17	18	19	20	21	22	23	24	25
Frequency	12	7	4	8	6	5	3	1	2

4. In the first eight months of the fiscal year, the salaries paid to Astro employees were as follows:

1 President at $80 000
2 Vice-Presidents at $65 000
1 Secretary Treasurer at $50 000
1 Controller at $45 000
3 Managers at $40 000
14 Salespeople at $31 000
10 Support staff at $17 000
2 Receptionists at $13 000

Find
(a) the mode.
(b) the median.
(c) the mean.

5. The following is a set of marks on a college entrance examination.

(a) Make a frequency table.
(b) State the mode.
(c) Find the median.
(d) Calculate the mean.

43	61	51	51	71	65	62	86
77	51	64	56	30	56	85	68
60	55	41	72	57	63	68	65
41	62	80	46	54	60	45	61
49	48	53	66	69	84	51	69
74	60	61	58	53	75	88	40
81	83	71	51	65	71	62	48
80	80	55	53	71	51	66	52
60	56	65	48	67	66	82	54
87	77	75	77	70	68	41	56
59	72	58	61	79	46	57	61
85	68	65	60	66	64	40	57
70	76	84	53	62	88	78	67
93	61	61	74	70	52	57	70
62	80	72	50	65	51	92	69

6. The weekly closing prices for one year of stock for Bank of Nova Scotia were as follows:

$55.50	$56.75	$57.25	$56.75
$56.25	$55.75	$55.75	$54.75
$54.75	$54.50	$53.00	$54.00
$55.00	$55.50	$55.75	$54.25
$53.00	$54.50	$55.25	$56.25
$57.75	$58.00	$57.50	$56.75
$55.00	$54.00	$54.00	$53.75
$53.00	$54.25	$55.50	$55.75
$57.00	$57.75	$58.00	$57.50
$58.25	$58.00	$58.50	$58.25
$58.75	$59.25	$59.00	$59.25
$58.75	$59.50	$60.00	$59.75
$60.25	$59.50	$60.00	$59.25

Find the
(a) mode,
(b) median, and
(c) mean for the stock.

7. The following is a list of 500 numbers from 00 to 99 as chosen randomly by a computer.

20	43	15	55	64	41	83	70	11	49	94	04	56	49	72	67	47	77	87	18
80	17	62	68	02	04	69	74	10	21	28	48	52	03	13	47	23	34	45	82
71	49	96	11	93	32	88	44	35	18	92	41	94	91	31	11	18	85	76	13
03	85	50	57	96	25	24	01	94	89	20	56	44	12	10	81	42	78	16	84
35	22	09	27	22	27	12	17	47	29	96	14	08	12	84	28	53	09	47	18
77	06	07	93	29	37	36	13	03	86	56	87	49	88	39	75	61	26	06	85
88	36	29	78	26	01	31	62	22	57	83	97	73	86	07	93	26	25	75	08
77	57	09	52	74	16	81	85	14	87	12	16	42	05	74	04	57	53	90	58
04	66	31	39	82	29	20	55	36	75	27	65	64	90	75	80	13	07	35	58
78	11	30	09	08	36	32	92	00	67	62	17	99	38	92	43	03	34	44	79
59	88	91	85	63	85	53	70	63	60	02	94	56	97	62	65	87	30	02	43
55	44	46	39	06	73	66	10	36	01	82	66	94	63	67	67	75	44	43	23
26	76	82	91	45	46	05	83	79	87	85	57	23	84	43	22	25	70	51	39
82	31	32	16	41	01	56	12	99	64	06	38	02	55	74	52	48	57	61	64
82	06	80	33	03	85	52	69	57	30	50	31	41	24	94	28	01	01	58	20
36	47	62	15	90	96	79	75	62	31	30	07	99	87	88	72	96	50	74	78
02	52	61	85	12	79	69	02	74	64	72	89	85	93	90	56	91	99	96	60
90	67	11	13	27	32	08	73	01	77	08	49	58	37	84	01	95	96	56	39
59	89	98	22	46	01	30	58	04	65	25	08	29	66	05	81	69	38	41	36
19	66	55	83	28	84	20	81	91	76	56	39	57	77	37	16	20	72	83	23
30	93	67	19	82	27	11	12	23	07	86	62	50	18	15	79	10	94	68	22
00	19	69	01	67	28	88	74	07	05	49	51	68	84	22	92	46	51	30	05
89	39	44	51	93	32	86	38	04	66	29	27	21	24	94	25	89	40	52	94
06	00	27	41	19	38	89	27	24	37	61	61	68	33	14	02	48	09	71	60
11	00	02	93	54	91	31	12	24	16	29	76	18	58	17	94	82	54	69	25

The following problems may be done with either the top-half, the bottom-half, or the entire list of 500 numbers.

(a) Select a random sample of 50 numbers.
(b) Construct a frequency table for your sample using a class interval of 10 and a frequency polygon.
(c) Find the mean, median, and mode of your sample.

(d) Construct a frequency table (with a class interval of 10) and a frequency polygon for this population.
(e) How well do the results of your sample compare with those of the population where the mean is 48.43, the median is 49, and the modes are 1 and 94?

upper limit

$$\sum_{i=1}^{n}$$

lower limit

EXTRA

13.7 SIGMA NOTATION

The $\sum$ symbol is commonly used to express a sum of terms into a more concise expression. It is called the summation or sigma symbol.

Rather than write $x_1 + x_2 + x_3 + x_4 + \cdots + x_n$, we can write $\sum_{i=1}^{n} x_i$, which represents the sum of all terms obtained by substituting the values from 1 to n into the variable i of the expression x_i.

In sigma notation, the formula for the mean can be written as follows:

$$\bar{x} = \frac{x_1 + x_2 + x_3 + \cdots + x_n}{n} = \frac{1}{n} \sum_{i=1}^{n} x_i$$

EXAMPLE 1. Express the following in sigma notation.
(a) $1 + 2 + 3 + 4 + 5$
(b) $1^2 + 2^2 + 3^2 + 4^2 + \cdots + n^2$
(c) the sum of the cubes of the natural numbers from 1 to 20

SOLUTION:

(a) $1 + 2 + 3 + 4 + 5 = \sum_{i=1}^{5} i$

> The sum of the squares of the natural numbers.

(b) $1^2 + 2^2 + 3^2 + 4^2 + \cdots + n^2 = \sum_{i=1}^{n} i^2$

(c) $1^3 + 2^3 + 3^3 + \cdots + 20^3 = \sum_{i=1}^{n} i^3$

EXAMPLE 2. Express the following in expanded form, $x_1 + x_2 + x_3 + \cdots + x_n$, then evaluate.

(a) $\sum_{i=4}^{9} i$
(b) $\sum_{i=1}^{5} (i + 3)^2$

SOLUTION:
(a) Substitute the values 4, 5, 6, 7, 8, and 9 into the variable i, then combine the results into one sum.

$$\sum_{i=4}^{9} = 4 + 5 + 6 + 7 + 8 + 9$$
$$= 39$$

(b) Substitute the values 1, 2, 3, 4, and 5 into the variable i of the expression $(i + 3)^2$, then combine the results into one sum.

$$\sum_{i=1}^{5} (i + 3)^2 = (1 + 3)^2 + (2 + 3)^2 + (3 + 3)^2 + (4 + 3)^2 + (5 + 3)^2$$
$$= 4^2 + 5^2 + 6^2 + 7^2 + 8^2$$
$$= 16 + 25 + 36 + 49 + 64$$
$$= 190$$

In BASIC, expressions involving sigma notation can often be evaluated using a "FOR ... NEXT" loop. The following program evaluates the expression $\sum_{i=10}^{20} i$, which represents the sum of the natural numbers from 10 to 20.

NEW

```
10 REM SUM 10 TO 20
20 FOR I=10 TO 20
30 S=S+I
40 NEXT I
50 PRINT "THE SUM IS";S
60 END
```

The FOR ... NEXT loop.

RUN

Line 20, the first line of the loop, identifies the variable I of the expression to be summed, and also identifies both lower and upper limits of the summation. The value of the expression I is added to the cumulative sum, S, in line 30.

EXAMPLE 3. Write a BASIC program to evaluate the expression

$$\sum_{i=10}^{20} (i + 5)^2.$$

SOLUTION:
Since both limits are the same as in the previous program, the only change is in the algebraic expression to be summed. Hence the change to line 30 is as follows:

```
30 S=S+(I+5)↑2
```

EXERCISE 13.7

1. Express each of the following in sigma notation.
(a) $3 + 4 + 5 + 6 + 7$
(b) $2^2 + 3^2 + 4^2 + 5^2$
(c) $5^3 + 6^3 + 7^3 + 8^3 + 9^3$
(d) $(1 + 5)^2 + (2 + 5)^2 + (3 + 5)^2 + (4 + 5)^2$
(e) $(2 \times 1) + (2 \times 2) + (2 \times 3) + (2 \times 4) + (2 \times 5)$
(f) the sum of the natural numbers from 50 to 60
(g) the sum of the perfect squares from 1 to 100

2. Express in expanded form and evaluate.
(a) $\sum_{i=1}^{5} i$ (b) $\sum_{i=3}^{9} (i + 2)$
(c) $\sum_{i=1}^{5} (i + 1)^3$ (d) $\sum_{i=3}^{6} (i - 2)^2$
(e) $\sum_{i=1}^{10} (2i - 1)$ (f) $\sum_{i=5}^{10} (2i)$

3. Write BASIC programs to evaluate the expressions in question 2.

13.8 MEASURES OF DISPERSION

In the previous section we studied the measures of central tendency of data. The mean or median might not tell someone everything they want to know about a set of data. It is possible for two sets of data to have the same mean or median and yet differ greatly in their dispersion, or spread.

One measure of dispersion is the range. The range of a set of data is found by subtracting the smallest number from the largest. The range is very sensitive to extreme values as shown in the table of fielding errors. By including the second baseman with 33 errors the range is increased from 18 to 30.

Major League Baseball Fielding Errors in One Season			
Second Baseman		Third Baseman	
33	12	22	14
21	11	18	11
18	11	16	11
18	11	16	11
16	10	15	10
15	9	15	10
14	8	14	9
13	7	13	8
13	7	13	8
13	5	13	6
12	4	14	6
12	4	14	5
12	3	14	4

The range is determined by two numbers and unfortunately it does not tell us how the other numbers vary. Are the numbers evenly spread out or do they concentrate about the mean? To determine this we use another measure of dispersion called the standard deviation

$$R_{SB} = 33 - 3$$
$$= 30$$

$$R_{TB} = 22 - 4$$
$$= 18$$

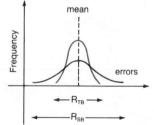

EXAMPLE 1. Find the standard deviation of the fielding errors by second basemen found in the table below.

SOLUTION:
To determine the standard deviation of a set of numbers we find, in order
(i) the mean of the numbers,
(ii) the difference between each number and the mean,
(iii) the square of each difference,
(iv) the mean of the squares,
(v) the square root of the mean of the squares.

The number that results is the standard deviation.

Errors x_i	Differences $(x_i - \bar{x})$	Squares $(x_i - \bar{x})^2$
33	21	441
21	9	81
18	6	36
18	6	36
16	4	16
15	3	9
14	2	4
13	1	1
13	1	1
13	1	1
12	0	0
12	0	0
12	0	0
12	0	0
11	−1	1
11	−1	1
11	−1	1
10	−2	4
9	−3	9
8	−4	16
7	−5	25
7	−5	25
5	−7	49
4	−8	64
4	−8	64
3	−9	81

Sum = 312

$$\bar{x} = \frac{312}{26}$$
$$= 12$$

Sum = 966

$$\text{Mean} = \frac{966}{26}$$
$$\doteq 37.2$$
$$\text{S.D.} = \sqrt{37.2}$$
$$\doteq 6.1$$

The five steps may be abbreviated in the formula

$$S.D. = \sqrt{\frac{(x_1 - \bar{x})^2 + (x_2 - \bar{x})^2 + \cdots + (x_n - \bar{x})^2}{n}}$$

In sigma notation, the formula can be written as,

$$S.D. = \sqrt{\frac{\sum_{i=1}^{n} (x_i - \bar{x})^2}{n}}$$

It can be shown that another formula for standard deviation is

$\bar{x}^2$ is not part of the summation.

$$S.D. = \sqrt{\frac{1}{n} \sum_{i=1}^{n} x_i^2 - \bar{x}^2}$$

The standard deviation becomes meaningful when the frequency distribution has a normal curve as its graph. When this is true, then 68% of the population will lie within one standard deviation of the mean and 95% of the population will always be within two standard deviations of the mean. Almost all (99.7%) of the population will lie within three standard deviations of the mean.

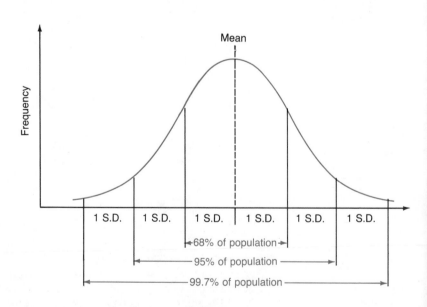

In order to facilitate calculations the distribution is simplified as follows.

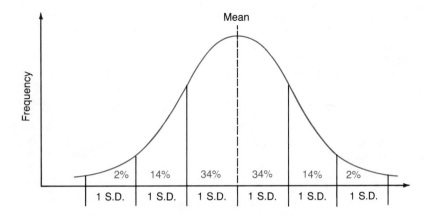

EXAMPLE 2. A football coach graphed the masses of his players and found that the data was distributed normally. The mean was 100 kg and the standard deviation 10 kg.

(a) What percent of the players have masses between 90 kg and 110 kg?

(b) What percent of the players have masses between 80 kg and 120 kg?

(c) What percent of the players have masses between 100 kg and 120 kg?

SOLUTION:
Draw a normal curve.

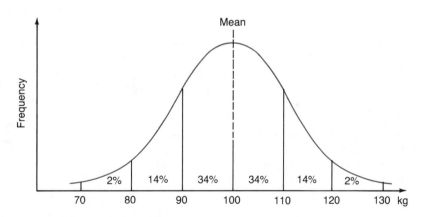

The standard deviation is 10, so 34% of the players have masses between 100 kg and 110 kg. Similarly, we can place the remaining masses and percents on the horizontal axis.

(a) 68% of the players have masses between 90 kg and 110 kg.

(b) 96% of the players have masses between 80 kg and 120 kg.

(c) 48% of the players have masses between 100 kg and 120 kg.

EXERCISE 13.8

A 1. State the range of each of the following.
   (a) 3, 5, 9, 14, 15, 22, 27
   (b) 8, 6, 24, 37, 81, 43
   (c) 58, 147, 318, 72, 14, 281
   (d) 185, 35, 167, 48, 93
   (e) 66, 78, 44, 75, 94

B 2. A local hospital finds that the average stay for maternity cases is 5 d with a standard deviation of 1 d. Assuming a normal distribution,
   (a) what percent of mothers stay in the hospital between 4 and 5 d?
   (b) what percent of the mothers stay in the hospital between 3 and 6 d?
   (c) what percent of the mothers stay less than 6 d?

3. The quality controller at a pharmaceutical company finds that the mean number of vitamin pills in a bottle is 100 with a standard deviation of 1. Assuming a normal distribution,
   (a) what percent of the bottles contain more than 101 pills?
   (b) what percent of the bottles contain between 98 and 102 pills?
   (c) what percent of the bottles contain less than 99 pills?

4. A factory ordered 1000 light bulbs from the Brite-Lite Company. The company claimed that the mean life of the bulbs was 800 h with a standard deviation of 100 h. Assuming a normal distribution,
   (a) what percent of the bulbs will last between 700 h and 900 h?
   (b) what percent of the bulbs will last longer than 600 h?
   (c) how many bulbs could be expected to last over 900 h?
   (d) how many bulbs will last longer than 1000 h?

5. The personnel manager of a factory employing 2000 people found that the average term of employment was 22 a with a standard deviation of 7 a. Assuming normal distribution,

(a) what percentage of the employees will work more than 15 a?
(b) how many employees will work between 15 and 29 a?
(c) how many people will work less than 8 a?
(d) how many employees will work longer than 29 a?

6. The Acme Paper Company makes rolls of paper towels. The mean length of each roll is 50 m with a standard deviation of 2 m. A grocery store ordered 500 rolls. Assuming a normal distribution,
   (a) what percent of the rolls will have lengths between 44 m and 48 m?
   (b) how many rolls will be longer than 52 m?
   (c) how many rolls will be shorter than 52 m?

7. The Department of Health conducted a dental survey of 6000 sixteen year old high school students to determine the extent of tooth decay. It was found that the mean number of teeth per student affected by decay was 8 with a standard deviation of 2. Assuming a normal distribution,
   (a) what percent of the students has less than 6 teeth affected by decay?
   (b) how many students had more than 10 teeth affected by decay?
   (c) how many students had between 6 and 12 teeth affected by decay?
   (d) what factors could contribute to bias in this survey?

8. A basketball coach measured the heights of the players on the team and found them to be
   172 cm, 176 cm, 176 cm, 178 cm, 180 cm, 180 cm, 181 cm, 181 cm, 182 cm, 184 cm
   Find the range, mean, and standard deviation of this set of data.

9. The quality controller removes 20 bags of potato chips at random from the production line and finds the masses to be
   46 g, 46 g, 47 g, 47 g, 48 g, 48 g, 48 g, 50 g, 50 g, 50 g, 50 g, 50 g, 51 g, 51 g, 52 g, 52 g, 52 g, 53 g, 54 g, and 55 g.
   Find the range, mean, and standard deviation of this sample.

10. The quality controller at a candy factory finds that the mean mass of the Krunchy Nut chocolate bar is 60 g with a standard deviation of 2 g. The company produces 3000 bars per day. Assuming a normal distribution,

(a) what percent of the bars will have masses between 58 g and 64 g?

(b) on one day, how many bars will have a mass over 62 g?

(c) on one day, how many bars will have masses between 54 g and 60 g?

(d) what steps should be taken if the standard deviation increases to 10 g?

C 11. Fifteen fans were surveyed to determine the number of home games they attended throughout the season. The results were 6, 7, 8, 8, 10, 11, 11, 11, 13, 14, 14, 15, 16, 17, and 19.

(a) Calculate the mean, $\bar{x}$.

(b) Complete the table below.

x_i	$x_i - \bar{x}$	$(x_i - \bar{x})^2$	x_i^2
6			
7			
8			
8			
10			
11			
11			
11			
13			
14			
14			
15			
16			
17			
19			

Totals $\displaystyle\sum_{i=1}^{15} x_i$ $\displaystyle\sum_{i=1}^{15}(x_i - \bar{x})^2$ $\displaystyle\sum_{i=1}^{15} x_i^2$

(c) Using the results of the third column calculate the standard deviation with the formula

$$S.D. = \sqrt{\frac{\sum_{i=1}^{n}(x_i - \bar{x})^2}{n}}$$

(d) Using the results of the fourth column calculate the standard deviation with the formula

$$S.D. = \sqrt{\frac{1}{n}\sum_{i=1}^{n} x_i^2 - \bar{x}^2}$$

MICRO MATH

This BASIC program will calculate the mean and standard deviation for a set of numbers input by the user.

NEW

```
100 REM MEAN AND STANDARD DEVIATION
110 N = 0
120 STERMS = 0
130 SSQUARES = 0
140 PRINT "INPUT DATA (USE 999 TO
    END INPUT)"
150 PRINT "ENTER AT LEAST TWO NUMBERS."
160 INPUT TERM
170 IF TERM = 999 THEN GOTO 220
180 N = N + 1
190 STERMS = STERMS + TERM
200 SSQUARES = SSQUARES + TERM*TERM
210 GOTO 160
220 IF N<2 THEN GOTO 270
230 MEAN = STERMS/N
240 SDEV = SQR(SSQUARES/N-MEAN*MEAN)
250 PRINT "THE MEAN IS"; MEAN
260 PRINT "THE STAND. DEV. IS"; SDEV
270 END
```

RUN

13.9 BASIC TERMS OF PROBABILITY

Girolamo Cardano

Probability theory has long been associated with games of chance. The first book on the subject was written by the Italian mathematician Girolamo Cardano (1501–1576) who supported himself as a professional gambler for several years. Later, the French mathematicians Blaise Pascal (1623–1662) and Pierre Fermat (1601–1665) founded the modern development of probability theory with their correspondence on games played with dice and coins.

Blaise Pascal

When we toss a coin, we can expect to obtain a head or a tail. The actual result is called an outcome. If it is a fair coin, we say that the two outcomes are equally likely.

In attempting to predict the outcome of a single coin toss, we would expect that there is one chance in two of obtaining a head and one chance in two of obtaining a tail. We say that the probability of a head is $\frac{1}{2}$ and that the probability of a tail is $\frac{1}{2}$. We simplify this by writing

$$P(\text{head}) = \tfrac{1}{2} \quad \text{and} \quad P(\text{tail}) = \tfrac{1}{2}$$

These are called theoretical probabilities. We realize that in an actual experiment, if a coin is tossed 100 times, the results may be slightly imbalanced.

EXAMPLE 1. Express each of the following statements as a simplified probability.
(a) There is one chance in 6 of obtaining a 3 when tossing a die.
(b) There is a 20% chance of rain.
(c) There is a 50/50 chance of winning the game.

SOLUTION:
(a) The probability of obtaining a 3 is

$$P(3) = \tfrac{1}{6}$$

(b) There are 20 chances out of 100 that it will rain.

$$P(\text{rain}) = \tfrac{20}{100}$$
$$= \tfrac{1}{5}$$

(c) There is one chance in two of winning the game.

$$P(\text{win}) = \tfrac{1}{2}$$

In our experiment of tossing a coin, the two outcomes of obtaining a head (H) or a tail (T) can be listed in a set S called the sample space.

$$S = \{H, T\}$$

A sample space is a set of all possible outcomes.

EXAMPLE 2. A die is tossed. List the sample space.

SOLUTION:
There are 6 possible outcomes. If a die is fair, then all the numbers have the same chance of turning up. We say that these events are equally likely.

The sample space is

$$S = \left\{ \boxdot , \because , \therefore , \vdots\vdots , \because\cdot , \vdots\vdots\vdots \right\}$$

or $S = \{1, 2, 3, 4, 5, 6\}$.

An event is a subset of the sample space.

EXAMPLE 3. A die is tossed. List the outcomes which make up the following events and the probability of each event.
(a) the event E of obtaining an even number
(b) the event A of obtaining a number greater than 4
(c) the event B of obtaining a number less than 1
(d) the event C of obtaining a number greater than 0

SOLUTION:
(a) E = {2, 4, 6}

If the die is fair, the outcomes of obtaining one of sides 1, 2, 3, 4, 5, or 6 are equally likely. Since there are 3 chances in 6 of obtaining an even number,

$$P(E) = \tfrac{3}{6}$$
$$= \tfrac{1}{2}$$

(b) A = {5, 6}

Since the outcomes are equally likely, there are 2 chances in 6 of obtaining a number greater than 4.

$$P(A) = \tfrac{2}{6}$$
$$= \tfrac{1}{3}$$

(c) Since none of the outcomes involve a number less than 1,
B = { } or B = ϕ.

Since there are 0 chances in 6 of obtaining a number less than 1,

$$P(B) = \frac{0}{6}$$
$$= 0$$

(d) C = {1, 2, 3, 4, 5, 6}

Since there are 6 chances in 6 of obtaining a number greater than 0,

$$P(C) = \frac{6}{6}$$
$$= 1$$

We generalize the results of the previous example as follows.

(a) The probability of an event is a number between 0 and 1, inclusive.

$$0 \leqslant P(\text{event}) \leqslant 1$$

(b) The probability of an impossible event is 0.

(c) The probability of a certainty is 1.

(d) In general, if a sample space consists of N equally likely outcomes and if S of those outcomes are considered successful or favourable for an event E, then

$$\frac{\text{probability of}}{\text{an event E}} = \frac{\text{number of successful outcomes}}{\text{total number of possible outcomes}}$$

$$P(E) = \frac{S}{N}$$

Many of the examples and questions in this chapter make reference to a standard deck of cards. A standard deck of 52 cards contains 13 clubs, 13 diamonds, 13 hearts, and 13 spades. Each suit has an ace, king, queen, jack, 10, 9, 8, 7, 6, 5, 4, 3, and 2. Drawing a card at random means that each card has an equally likely chance of being drawn.

EXAMPLE 4. If a card is drawn at random from a standard deck of 52 cards, what is the probability that the card will be
(a) a king?
(b) a heart?

SOLUTION:
The outcomes of the sample space are equally likely.

(a) Let K be the event of obtaining a king. The sample space contains 52 different outcomes. Since there are 4 kings, four of these outcomes are considered "successful."

N = 52   and   S = 4

$$P(K) = \frac{S}{N}$$
$$= \frac{4}{52}$$
$$= \frac{1}{13}$$

The probability of obtaining a king is $\frac{1}{13}$.

(b) Let H be the event of obtaining a heart. There are 52 equally likely outcomes in the sample space. Since there are 13 hearts, then there are 13 "successful" outcomes. The probability of obtaining a heart is

$$P(H) = \frac{S}{N}$$
$$= \frac{13}{52}$$
$$= \frac{1}{4}$$

In some cases it may be possible to list the outcomes of a sample space and yet not know the individual probability of each outcome. These probabilities may sometimes be obtained in an experiment.

> A probability obtained from data collected in an experiment is called an experimental probability.

EXAMPLE 5. A thumbtack is dropped. What is the probability that it falls pointing up?

SOLUTION:
If a thumbtack is dropped, there are two possible outcomes:
(i) the tack points up,
(ii) the tack points down.

The sample space is S = {up, down}.

To investigate the experimental probability of each outcome, we conduct an experiment where a thumbtack is dropped a number of times and we record the data.

Suppose that the data from one such experiment were as follows.

Number of "tosses" : 100
Number of "up"   : 56
Number of "down"   : 44

The experimental probabilities are summarized as follows.

$$P(up) = \frac{56}{100} \qquad P(down) = \frac{44}{100}$$
$$= \frac{11}{25} \qquad\qquad\qquad = \frac{14}{25}$$

EXERCISE 13.9

A 1. Express each of the following in a simplified probability.

(a) There is a 60% chance that I will get a job this summer.
(b) There is a chance in a million that I will win the lottery.
(c) The player scores on 15% of his shots.
(d) There is a 50/50 chance that I will make the team.
(e) One of every 10 males is colour-blind.
(f) 5% of the light bulbs in the shipment were defective.

2. List the sample space of each of the following experiments.

(a) tossing a coin
(b) tossing a six-sided die
(c) dropping a piece of buttered toast
(d) picking a name from a hat if William's, Debbie's, Craig's, and Nicole's names are in the hat.

B 3. A fair die is tossed. What is the probability of obtaining

(a) a 2?
(b) an odd number?
(c) a number divisible by 3?
(d) a 7?
(e) a natural number?

4. A book has pages numbered from 1 to 100. The book is open.
What is the probability that it is open at

(a) page 57?
(b) an even-numbered page?
(c) a page number divisible by 5?

5. One thousand tickets were sold for a raffle. What is the probability that

(a) Joyce will win if she bought one ticket?
(b) Katie will win if she bought 10 tickets?
(c) Andrew will win if he did not buy a ticket?
(d) George will win if he bought all of the tickets?

6. A card is drawn from a standard deck of 52 cards. What is the probability that it is

(a) a 5 of clubs?
(b) a spade?

(c) an ace?
(d) a red card?
(e) a face card (ace, king, queen, or jack)?

7. A box contains 3 red marbles, 4 black marbles, and 5 white marbles. You are to pick one marble at random.

(a) How many possible outcomes are there?
(b) If you hope to pick a red marble, how many possible outcomes are successes?
(c) What is the probability of picking a red marble?
(d) What is the probability of picking a black marble?
(e) What is the probability of picking a marble which is not red?

8. There are 12 boys and 18 girls in a mathematics class. The teacher chooses one student at random to answer a question.

(a) What is the probability that a girl is chosen?
(b) What is the probability that a boy is chosen?

9. In an experiment, a lawn dart was thrown 100 times. It was found that the dart penetrated well enough to remain upright 75 times. What is the experimental probability that a throw is successful?

10. (a) When tossing a coin, what is the theoretical probability of tossing a head?
(b) Toss a coin 100 times and record the data as shown in the table below.

Frequency Table		
Outcome	Tally	Frequency
Heads		
Tails		
Total		

What was your experimental probability of tossing a head?

13.10 RANDOM NUMBERS

Pick a random number from 0 to 9. Copy the table below and mark a tally in the corresponding row.

Digit	Tally	Frequency
0		
1		
2		
3		
4		
5		
6		
7		
8		
9		

Now continue to pick 99 completely random digits. The task sounds relatively simple. But are your numbers really random? How can you be sure? There are several tests for randomness. One of the tests is based on the fact that for a large sample of random digits, each digit has an equal probability of occurring; hence each digit should occur approximately 10% of the time. Are you still convinced of the randomness of your numbers?

EXERCISE 13.10

1. Generate a set of 100 random digits using one of the following methods. Complete a frequency table as above, and discuss the randomness of your sample.

(a) Using a standard deck of cards, remove the jacks, queens, and kings. Treat the tens as zeros and the aces as ones. Pick a card, record it, then return it to the deck. Repeat 99 more times.
(b) Number ten ping-pong balls with the digits 0 to 9. Place them in a box. Pull out one ball at a time, record the digit, and then return it to the box. Repeat 99 more times.
(c) Write a BASIC program to generate 100 random digits.

```
NEW
10 REM RANDOM NUMBERS
20 FOR I=1 TO 100
30 N=RND(0)
40 PRINT INT (10*N);
50 NEXT I
60 END

RUN
```

The RND function in line 30 may differ from one computer model to another. One of the following might be more appropriate for your computer.

```
30 N=RND

30 N=RND(-1)

30 N=RND(9)
```

2. Given a set of 100 truly random digits from 0 to 9,

(a) what would you expect the mean to be?
(b) what would you expect the mode(s) to be?
(c) what would you expect the median to be?
(d) what is the probability that the last number of the list is a 3?
(e) how many times would you expect the digit 0 to occur?

13.11 TREE DIAGRAMS

We sometimes use a tree diagram to list the outcomes that make up a sample space. When a single die is rolled, the six equally likely outcomes can be illustrated in the following tree diagram.

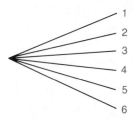

Depending on the experiment, the tree diagram may have more levels of branches. There is a level of branches for each experiment.

EXAMPLE.   A game consists of rolling a die and tossing a penny. Use a tree diagram to list the sample space.

SOLUTION:

(1, H) represents the event of obtaining a 1 in the die roll and a head in the coin toss.

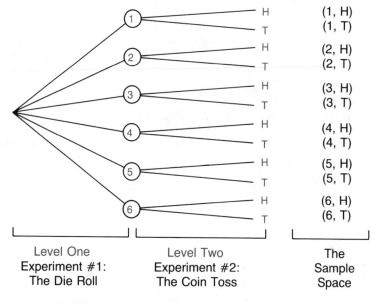

The possible outcomes of the sample space are listed by following all possible paths from beginning to end. The sample space is

{(1, H), (1, T), (2, H), (2, T), (3, H), (3, T), (4, H), (4, T), (5, H), (5, T), (6, H), (6, T)}

The number of branches in the last level equals the number of elements in the sample space.

We observe that there are 6 branches in level one. For each of these, there are two branches in level 2. The total number of outcomes is

$$6 \times 2 = 12$$

Since all of the outcomes of the die roll in level one are equally likely and all of the outcomes of the coin toss in level two are also equally likely, then all 12 final outcomes of the sample space are equally likely.

The probability of rolling a 3 and tossing a head is

$$P(3, H) = \frac{20}{100}$$

The three outcomes (2, H), (4, H), and (6, H) correspond to the event of rolling an even number and tossing a head. The probability of such an event where there are 3 "successful" outcomes of 12 equally likely ones is

$$P(\text{even, head}) = \frac{S}{N}$$

$$= \frac{3}{12}$$

$$= \frac{1}{4}$$

EXERCISE 13.11

B 1. A nickel and a dime were tossed together.

(a) Show a two-level tree diagram in which the outcomes of the nickel are displayed in the first level.

(b) How many possible outcomes are there?

(c) Show a two-level diagram in which the outcomes of the dime are displayed in the first level.

(d) How many possible outcomes are there?

2. Michelle has her left hand in a bag containing one red, one blue, and one green ball. Her right hand is in a bag containing a white and a black ball. She draws one ball from each bag. Use a tree diagram to list the sample space.

3. A young married couple plan to have two children. Show all possible outcomes in a tree diagram.

4. Three coins are tossed, a nickel, a dime, and a quarter. Use a three-level tree diagram to list the sample space.

5. A team plays three play-off games in one week. Assuming that no ties are possible, use a tree diagram to list the sample space.

6. A die is rolled three times. How many outcomes does the sample space contain?

7. Two full decks, one blue and one red, of 52 playing cards are placed on a table. One card is drawn. How many outcomes are there in the sample space?

8. A tetrahedron with congruent faces has its faces numbered from 1 to 4.

(a) Use a tree diagram to list the sample space of an experiment in which the tetrahedron is rolled
   (i) once
   (ii) twice
   (iii) three times.

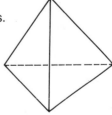

(b) How many outcomes are possible if it is rolled 7 times?

13.12 PROBABILITY FORMULAS

We shall use the results of the following example to establish the relationship between the probability that an event will occur and the probability that it will not occur.

EXAMPLE 1. A game is played by rolling a die. You win if the die shows 1 or 2. What is the probability of winning? Of losing?

SOLUTION:

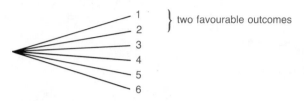

two favourable outcomes

There are six equally likely outcomes. Two of them result in a win for you and the remaining four result in a loss.

$$P \text{ (winning)} = \frac{2}{6} \qquad\qquad P \text{ (losing)} = \frac{4}{6}$$
$$= \frac{1}{3} \qquad\qquad\qquad\qquad = \frac{2}{3}$$

Notice that the sum of the probabilities in Example 1 is 1. This always happens when we calculate the probabilities of the occurrence and non-occurrence of an event.

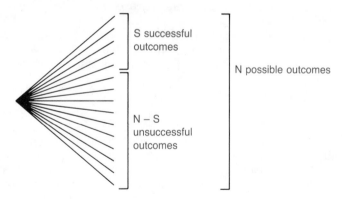

S successful outcomes

N − S unsuccessful outcomes

N possible outcomes

The probability of a successful outcome is $p = \dfrac{S}{N}$ and the probability of an unsuccessful outcome is $q = \dfrac{N - S}{N}$. Adding, we get

$$p + q = \frac{S}{N} + \frac{N - S}{N}$$
$$= \frac{S + (N - S)}{N}$$
$$= \frac{N}{N}$$
$$= 1$$

Thus, p + q = 1.

If p is the probability that an event will occur, then $0 \leq p \leq 1$.

If q is the probability that the event will not occur, then p + q = 1.

If p = 1, the event is a certainty.

If p = 0, the event is impossible. The closer p is to 1, the more likely the event. The closer p is to 0, the less likely the event.

If we flip a coin and roll a die the events are independent because the outcome of the coin has no effect on the outcome of the die.

Two events are called independent if neither has an influence on the other.

EXAMPLE 2. A game consists of tossing a penny and rolling a die. You win if the penny shows tails and the die shows 5. What is your probability of winning?

SOLUTION:
The tree diagram involves two independent events.

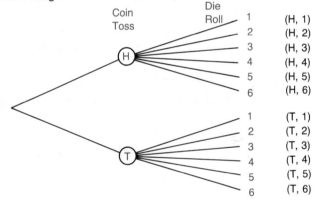

The sample space {(H,1), (H,2), (H,3), (H,4), (H,5), (H,6), (T,1), (T,2), (T,3), (T,4), (T,5), (T,6)} consists of twelve equally likely outcomes. Only one of the outcomes is (T, 5). Thus, N = 12 and S = 1.

$$P \text{ (winning)} = \frac{1}{12}$$

Notice that this probability is the product of the individual probabilities of the two events.

$$P(\text{tails}) = \frac{1}{2} \qquad\qquad P(5) = \frac{1}{6}$$

The probability of both events happening is

$$P(\text{winning}) = \frac{1}{2} \times \frac{1}{6}$$

$$= \frac{1}{12}$$

The reason for multiplying the probabilities is seen in the tree diagram. There are six small branches on each of the two main branches and so there are twelve possible outcomes.

We generalize the results as follows.

> Suppose that two events are independent of each other. If p_1 is the probability that the first event will occur and p_2 is the probability that the second event will occur, then the probability that both events will occur is the product $p = p_1 p_2$.

EXAMPLE 3. (a) A card is dealt from a standard 52 card deck. Then it is replaced, the deck is shuffled, and another card is dealt. What is the probability that both cards are spades?
(b) If the first card is not replaced, what is the probability that both cards are spades?

SOLUTION:
(a) Since there are 13 spades in the deck,

$$P \text{ (spades)} = p_1$$
$$= \frac{13}{52}$$
$$= \frac{1}{4}$$

Since the card is replaced and the deck is shuffled, the second deal is independent of the first. Again, the probability of dealing a spade is

$$p_2 = \frac{1}{4}$$

Thus, the probability that both cards are spades is

$$p_1 p_2 = \frac{1}{4} \times \frac{1}{4}$$
$$= \frac{1}{16}$$

(b) As in part (a), P(spades) $p_1 = \frac{1}{4}$.

If the first card is a spade, there are 12 spades left in the deck. The probability that the second card is a spade is

$$p_2 = \frac{12}{51}$$
$$= \frac{4}{17}$$

The probability that both cards are spades is

$$p_1 p_2 = \frac{1}{4} \times \frac{4}{17}$$
$$= \frac{1}{17}$$

Notice that if the first event has occurred before the second event and we know its outcome, then we can use the outcome of the first event as one of the conditions in calculating the probability of the second event.

EXERCISE 13.12

B 1. A coin is tossed twice. Draw a tree diagram to illustrate the sample space and calculate the following probabilities.
(a) both heads
(b) both tails
(c) one head, one tail

2. A deck of playing cards is shuffled and a card is dealt. Find the probability that the card is
(a) a club.
(b) not a club.
(c) an ace.
(d) not an ace.
(e) black (a club or a spade).
(f) a red king.
(g) the 5 of hearts.

3. A deck of cards numbered from 1 to 100 is shuffled and a card is drawn at random. What is the probability that the number on the card
(a) is odd?
(b) ends in a 7?
(c) is divisible by 4?

4. Two dice are rolled.
(a) Draw a tree diagram to illustrate the sample space.
(b) List the sample space of possible sums.
(c) Find the probabilities of rolling a sum of 1, 2, 3, 4, 5, 6, 7, 8, 9, 10, 11, and 12.
(d) Find the probability of getting 9 or more.
(e) Find the probability that the numbers on both dice are even.

5. Three dice are rolled. Find the probability that the total is
(a) 2.
(b) 3.
(c) 5.

6. For families with three children, find the probabilities of the following, assuming that it is equally likely for a child to be a boy or a girl.
(a) all the children are girls
(b) two children are girls and one is a boy
(c) at least one child is a boy

7. Four coins are tossed. What is the probability of
(a) 2 heads and 2 tails?
(b) 3 heads and a tail?
(c) at least 2 heads?

8. A card is dealt from a deck of playing cards and is replaced. The deck is shuffled and another card is dealt. What are the probabilities of the following events?
(a) both cards are red
(b) the first card is red and the second is black
(c) one card is red and the other is black
(d) the first is clubs and the second is hearts
(e) the king of hearts is dealt twice
(f) the same card is dealt twice

9. There is a 3% chance that a new lightbulb will be defective. What is the probability that all the lightbulbs in the next package that you buy will be defective if there are
(a) 2 bulbs in the package?
(b) 4 bulbs in the package?
(c) 6 bulbs in the package?

10. In the preceding problem,
(a) what percentage of the bulbs are not defective?
(b) what is the probability that in a package of two bulbs neither are defective?

11. In a round-robin playoff involving three teams A, B, and C, games must not end in a tie. The probability that A will beat B is $\frac{3}{5}$, that A will beat C is $\frac{2}{5}$, and that B will beat C is $\frac{2}{5}$.
(a) Find the probability that

    (i) B will beat A.
    (ii) C will beat A.
    (iii) C will beat B.
    (iv) A wins both of its games.
    (v) B wins both of its games.
    (vi) C wins both of its games.

(b) Which team has the best chance of winning the round-robin?

13.13 PROBLEM SOLVING

1. Place the numbers from 1 to 16 in the circles so that the sum along each row is 34.

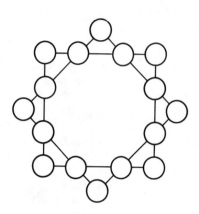

2. If $\dfrac{a}{b} = \dfrac{2}{3}$, $\dfrac{b}{c} = -\dfrac{3}{5}$, and $\dfrac{c}{d} = -\dfrac{5}{6}$ find $\dfrac{a}{d}$.

3. Develop a method of adding both columns of numbers at the same time, using your calculator.

```
    65        205
    52        217
    38         68
    74        134
    85        490
  + 67      + 307
```

4. Place the digits 0, 1, 2, 3, 5, 6, and 8 in the boxes to make the statement true.

■■ × 4■ = ■■■■

5. Sam and Carl ran a 100 m dash and Sam won by 10 m. Carl and David ran a 100 m dash and Carl won by 10 m. If Sam and David run a 100 m dash at the same rate as before, by how many metres will Sam win?

6. How many triangles are there in the following figure?

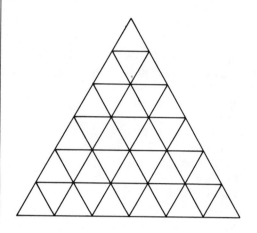

7. How many squares are there in the following figure?

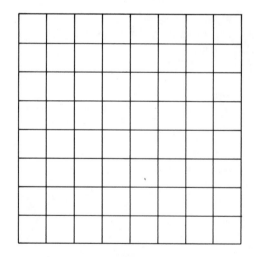

8. The number 31 is a prime number. If you drop the ones digit, we get the number 3, which is also a prime number. Numbers with this property are called prime primes. Find all of the two-digit prime primes.

9. Mary and Hank start jogging towards each other from opposite ends of the neighbourhood. After 1.5 min they pass each other going in opposite directions.

(a) How many minutes after starting do they pass each other for the second time?
(b) How long is their route if they both jog in "five minute kilometres"?
(c) What assumptions have to be made to complete parts (a) and (b)?

10. Six pennies are arranged in two rows.

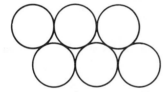

Move three pennies to form a circle according to the following rules.
    (i) Move only one penny each time.
    (ii) While moving a penny, you must not disturb any other penny.
    (iii) Do not move a penny by picking it up.
    (iv) After each move, the penny moved must touch at least two other pennies.

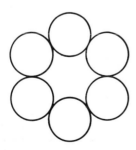

11. (a) Determine the pattern.

$$\frac{1+2}{3} = \blacksquare$$

$$\frac{1+2+3}{4} = \blacksquare$$

$$\frac{1+2+3+4}{5} = \blacksquare$$

$$\frac{1+2+3+4+5}{6} = \blacksquare$$

(b) Evaluate.

$$\frac{1+2+3+\cdots+16+17+18}{19}$$

(c) Find a formula for the nth term in the pattern.

$$\frac{1+2+3+\cdots+(n-2)+(n-1)}{n}$$

Determine the pattern. Find the missing number.

53	21	18
15	2	8
36	54	25
18	20	

13.14 THE BIRTHDAY PARADOX

Sometimes our intuition leads us to believe that some events are far more or less probable then they actually are. Such events are called mathematical paradoxes

Of all probability calculations, one of the most difficult to believe is the one mathematicians call the "Birthday Paradox."

EXAMPLE. If there are 23 students in your classroom, what is the probability that two students were born on the same day of the same month?

SOLUTION:
We consider the reverse situation where no matches occur. Take any two students. The probability that their birthdates do not match is $\frac{364}{365}$.

The probability that a third student's birthdate will miss both of these is $\frac{363}{365}$.

The probability that a fourth student's birthdate will miss all three of these is $\frac{362}{365}$.

Continue these calculations until you reach the twenty-third student.

The probability that each of these independent events will occur is the product

$$\underbrace{\frac{364}{365} \times \frac{363}{365} \times \frac{362}{365} \times \cdots \times \frac{343}{365}}_{\text{22 factors}} \doteq \frac{49}{100}$$

Since the probability of no match is approximately $\frac{49}{100}$, then the probability of a match is

$$1 - \frac{49}{100} = \frac{51}{100}$$

The chances are better than even!

The following BASIC program will calculate the probability that two people will have the same birthdate in a group of any given size.

NEW

```
10 REM THE BIRTHDAY PARADOX
20 INPUT "HOW MANY PEOPLE?"; N
30 PRODUCT=1
40 FOR I=1 TO N-1
50 P=(365-I)/365
60 PRODUCT=PRODUCT * P
70 NEXT I
80 PMATCH=1-PRODUCT
90 PRINT "THE PROBABILITY OF AT
   LEAST ONE MATCH AMONG"
100 PRINT N; "PEOPLE IS"; PMATCH
110 END
```

RUN

13.15 REVIEW EXERCISE

1. The quality control division of a bar soap manufacturing company selects 40 bars of soap at random from every batch of 10 000.

The masses in grams of 40 such soap bars are as follows.

```
138 136 135 137 135 136 136 134
133 132 137 134 133 135 136 133
137 136 138 137 136 138 137 137
137 135 136 134 134 136 136 135
136 136 135 134 134 135 135 136
```

(a) Prepare a frequency distribution table.
(b) Determine the range.
(c) Draw a histogram.
(d) State the mode(s).
(e) Find the median.
(f) Calculate the mean.
(g) Find the standard deviation.

2. A box contains 5 blue marbles, 6 yellow marbles, and 9 green marbles. Find the probability of picking at random a marble which is

(a) blue.
(b) not blue.
(c) yellow.
(d) not yellow.
(e) green.
(f) not green.

3. If two dice are rolled, what is the probability of getting

(a) 4 or less?
(b) a 7 or an 11?
(c) an even number?

4. A card is drawn from a shuffled deck of playing cards. Find the probability that the card is

(a) a diamond.
(b) the jack of diamonds.
(c) not a diamond.
(d) not a jack.
(e) a face card.
(f) a king or queen.

5. Four dice are rolled. Find the probability that the total is

(a) 4.
(b) 5 or less.
(c) 6 or more.
(d) 24.

6. The federal government bought 10 000 Mark X tires from the BMA Tire Co. The company claims that the Mark X has a mean life of 150 000 km with a standard deviation of 15 000 km. Assuming normal distribution,

(a) what percent of the tires will last between 135 000 km and 180 000 km?
(b) what percent of the tires will wear out in less than 120 000 km?
(c) how many of the tires will last more than 165 000 km?
(d) how many tires will last less than 135 000 km?

7. The City of Blind Canyon did a traffic survey on the street where the high school was located in order to determine whether or not a traffic light should be installed. After clocking 1000 vehicles it was found that the mean speed was 45 km/h with a standard deviation of 4 km/h. Assuming normal distribution,

(a) what percent of the cars were travelling faster than 41 km/h?
(b) how many vehicles were travelling less than 49 km/h?
(c) how many vehicles were travelling between 45 km/h and 53 km/h?

The day before yesterday I was 22 years old. Next year I will turn 25. When is my birthday?

13.16 CHAPTER 13 TEST

1. A coin is tossed twice.
(a) Draw a tree diagram to illustrate the sample space.
(b) What is the probability of obtaining
   (i) two heads?
   (ii) exactly one head?
   (iii) at least one head?

2. A card is drawn from a deck of 52 cards. What is the probability of obtaining

(a) a red card?
(b) a club?
(c) a jack?
(d) a jack of clubs?

3. Jill has applied to two employers for a summer job. The probability that employer A offers her the job is $\frac{2}{5}$ and the probability that employer B offers her a job is $\frac{2}{3}$. What is the probability that

(a) A will not offer her a job?
(b) B will not offer her a job?
(c) A and B will both offer her a job?
(d) Neither A nor B will offer her a job?

4. A company found that in a sample of 150 computer chips, 8 were defective. How many defective ones can be expected among the 750 from which the sample was taken?

5. The list at the right gives the number of goals scored by Wayne Gretzky in each game of one NHL season.
(a) Complete a frequency table showing the number of 0, 1, 2, 3, 4, and 5 goal games he had.
(b) Draw a bar graph.
(c) Find the mean, median, and mode(s).

1	0	2	4	1	0	0	1	3	0
0	3	1	1	2	0	1	0	1	0
2	0	0	1	2	1	0	1	0	1
4	1	1	1	0	3	2	2	1	2
0	0	2	3	1	0	1	1	5	0
1	2	0	1	0	1	2	1	3	0
2	0	2	0	2	1	1	0	0	1
3	1	0	0	1	0	1	2	4	1

6. The data for the heights of 50 students are given at the right.
(a) Construct a frequency table using class intervals of 3 cm.
(b) Draw a histogram.
(c) Draw a frequency polygon.
(d) Find the mean and median.
(e) Find the standard deviation.

Heights of 50 Students (to nearest centimetre)				
150	157	162	168	150
157	162	168	151	157
163	169	152	158	164
170	152	158	164	172
153	159	164	172	153
159	165	175	154	160
165	176	155	160	166
179	155	160	166	180
155	161	167	184	156
161	167	156	161	167

13.17 CUMULATIVE REVIEW FOR CHAPTERS 9 TO 13

1. Find the total surface area of each of the following figures to the nearest integer. Use $\pi = 3.14$.

(a)

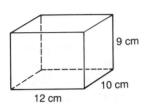

9 cm
10 cm
12 cm

(b)

6 cm
20 cm

(c)

80 cm

(d)

40 cm
20 cm

(e)

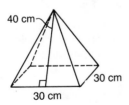

40 cm
30 cm
30 cm

(f)

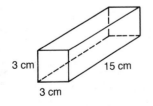

3 cm
15 cm
3 cm

2. Find the volume of each of the following figures to the nearest integer. Use $\pi = 3.14$.

(a)

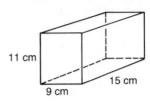

11 cm
9 cm
15 cm

(b)

60 cm

(c)

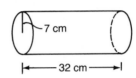

7 cm
32 cm

(d)

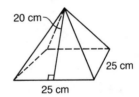

20 cm
25 cm
25 cm

3. The line segment ST has endpoints S(3, 4) and T(-2, 1). Write the endpoints for the image S'T' after
(a) a reflection in the x-axis.
(b) a reflection in the y-axis.
(c) a reflection in the line y = x.
(d) a reflection in the line y = $-$x.

4. The line segment PQ has endpoints P(4, 5) and Q(2, 1).
(a) Find the image P'Q' under the translation (x, y) → (x + 2, y − 3).
(b) Find the length of PQ and P'Q'.

5. Find the coordinates of the image of M($-$3, 5) under a rotation of 180° about the origin.

6. The line segment AB has endpoints A(5, 7) and B(−3, −4). Find the endpoints of the image A′B′ under a dilatation with centre (0, 0) and magnification factor 3.

7. For each figure state the number of lines of symmetry and the order of rotational symmetry.

(a)

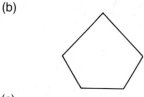

(b)

(c)

(d)

8. Given △RST with vertices R(1, 3), S(−4, 2) and T(5, 6), find the image △R′S′T′ under a reflection in the y-axis.

9. Given △ABC with vertices A(5, 1), B(2, 6), and C(4, −3), find the image △A′B′C′ under a reflection in the x-axis followed by a reflection in the y-axis.

10. If Y is a reflection in the x-axis and T is the translation (x, y) → (x + 2, y − 5), find the image of point P(2, 4) under the following transformations.
(a) T ∘ T
(b) Y ∘ T
(c) T ∘ Y

11. Find the terminal point of the vector [−5, 6] if the initial point is
(a) (2, 1)
(b) (−4, −7)

12. If $\vec{a}$ = [2, −3] and $\vec{b}$ = [−5, −1], find.
(a) $2\vec{b}$
(b) $\vec{a} + \vec{b}$
(c) $\vec{a} - \vec{b}$

13. A plane is flying at 300 kn due west relative to the ground. It encounters a south wind of 50 kn. Draw vector diagrams and find
(a) the ground speed and direction if the pilot does not adjust the course to account for the wind.
(b) the course the pilot should set to maintain a heading of due west at 300 kn.

14. The golf scores of fifty players entered in a tournament are shown below.

73 75 76 71 76 79 72 75 73 72
72 76 70 78 74 74 73 72 75 73
71 73 74 73 76 70 71 77 74 71
75 72 74 75 76 73 72 73 77 72
73 74 73 75 70 71 74 72 73 74

(a) Prepare a frequency distribution table.
(b) Determine the range.
(c) Draw a histogram.
(d) Find the median.
(e) Calculate the mean.

15. Find the range, mean, and standard deviation of the following set of data.

30, 32, 36, 34, 30
31, 33, 30, 31, 33

16. A bag contains six red marbles, five blue marbles, and seven white marbles. Find the probability of picking at random a marble that is

(a) white.
(b) not white.
(c) blue.
(d) not blue.
(e) white or blue.
(f) black.

Table I SQUARES AND SQUARE ROOTS

n	n^2	$\sqrt{n}$	$\sqrt{10n}$	n	n^2	$\sqrt{n}$	$\sqrt{10n}$
1.0	1.00	1.000	3.162	**5.5**	30.25	2.345	7.416
1.1	1.21	1.049	3.317	**5.6**	31.36	2.366	7.483
1.2	1.44	1.095	3.464	**5.7**	32.49	2.387	7.550
1.3	1.69	1.140	3.606	**5.8**	33.64	2.408	7.616
1.4	1.96	1.183	3.742	**5.9**	34.81	2.429	7.681
1.5	2.25	1.225	3.873	**6.0**	36.00	2.449	7.746
1.6	2.56	1.265	4.000	**6.1**	37.21	2.470	7.810
1.7	2.89	1.304	4.123	**6.2**	38.44	2.490	7.874
1.8	3.24	1.342	4.243	**6.3**	39.69	2.510	7.937
1.9	3.61	1.378	4.359	**6.4**	40.96	2.530	8.000
2.0	4.00	1.414	4.472	**6.5**	42.25	2.550	8.062
2.1	4.41	1.449	4.583	**6.6**	43.56	2.569	8.124
2.2	4.84	1.483	4.690	**6.7**	44.89	2.588	8.185
2.3	5.29	1.517	4.796	**6.8**	46.24	2.608	8.246
2.4	5.76	1.549	4.899	**6.9**	47.61	2.627	8.307
2.5	6.25	1.581	5.000	**7.0**	49.00	2.646	8.367
2.6	6.76	1.612	5.099	**7.1**	50.41	2.665	8.426
2.7	7.29	1.643	5.196	**7.2**	51.84	2.683	8.485
2.8	7.84	1.673	5.292	**7.3**	53.29	2.702	8.544
2.9	8.41	1.703	5.385	**7.4**	54.76	2.720	8.602
3.0	9.00	1.732	5.477	**7.5**	56.25	2.739	8.660
3.1	9.61	1.761	5.568	**7.6**	57.76	2.757	8.718
3.2	10.24	1.789	5.657	**7.7**	59.29	2.775	8.775
3.3	10.89	1.817	5.745	**7.8**	60.84	2.793	8.832
3.4	11.56	1.844	5.831	**7.9**	62.41	2.811	8.888
3.5	12.25	1.871	5.916	**8.0**	64.00	2.828	8.944
3.6	12.96	1.897	6.000	**8.1**	65.61	2.846	9.000
3.7	13.69	1.924	6.083	**8.2**	67.24	2.864	9.055
3.8	14.44	1.949	6.164	**8.3**	68.89	2.881	9.110
3.9	15.21	1.975	6.245	**8.4**	70.56	2.898	9.165
4.0	16.00	2.000	6.325	**8.5**	72.25	2.915	9.220
4.1	16.81	2.025	6.403	**8.6**	73.96	2.933	9.274
4.2	17.64	2.049	6.481	**8.7**	75.69	2.950	9.327
4.3	18.49	2.074	6.557	**8.8**	77.44	2.966	9.381
4.4	19.36	2.098	6.633	**8.9**	79.21	2.983	9.434
4.5	20.25	2.121	6.708	**9.0**	81.00	3.000	9.487
4.6	21.16	2.145	6.782	**9.1**	82.81	3.017	9.539
4.7	22.09	2.168	6.856	**9.2**	84.64	3.033	9.592
4.8	23.04	2.191	6.928	**9.3**	86.49	3.050	9.644
4.9	24.01	2.214	7.000	**9.4**	88.36	3.066	9.695
5.0	25.00	2.236	7.071	**9.5**	90.25	3.082	9.747
5.1	26.01	2.258	7.141	**9.6**	92.16	3.098	9.798
5.2	27.04	2.280	7.211	**9.7**	94.09	3.114	9.849
5.3	28.09	2.302	7.280	**9.8**	96.04	3.130	9.899
5.4	29.16	2.324	7.348	**9.9**	98.01	3.146	9.950
5.5	30.25	2.354	7.416	**10**	100.00	3.162	10.000

ANSWERS

REVIEW AND PREVIEW TO CHAPTER 1

ROUNDING

1. (a) 30   (b) 130   (c) 3280   (d) 180
2. (a) 14.2   (b) 213.2   (c) 147.5   (d) 0.3
3. (a) 3.12   (b) 5.14   (c) 63.22   (d) 143.19
4. (a) 51.6   (b) 36.7   (c) 2.9   (d) 98.3
    (e) 91.7   (f) 2.0   (g) 3.0   (h) 165.3
5. (a) 0.5   (b) 0.25   (c) 0.75   (d) 0.2   (e) 0.6
    (f) 0.375   (g) 0.625   (h) 2.125   (i) 3.8   (j) 4.875
6. (a) $\frac{7}{20}$ (b) $\frac{3}{4}$ (c) $\frac{21}{50}$ (d) $\frac{611}{1000}$ (e) $\frac{21}{40}$ (f) $\frac{37}{1000}$

LE SYSTÈME INTERNATIONAL D'UNITÉS: SI

1. (a) 0.3 m   (b) 4 L   (c) 100 g   (d) 750 m
    (e) 0.5 m   (f) 15 000 m   (g) 300 L   (h) 70 g
    (i) 0.21 m   (j) 0.5 L   (k) 250 g   (l) 2300 m
    (m) 4.2 m   (n) 325 m   (o) 1200 L   (p) 6.5 g
2. (a) 2000 cm, 150 m, 15 km   (b) 9990 mg, 112.3 g, 1.1 kg   (c) 5000 mL, 25.8 L, 2 kL
    (d) 0.5 m, 7 dm, 0.01 km   (e) 100 mg, 1 g, $\frac{1}{100}$ kg
3. (a) 6 L for $5.75   (b) 500 mL for $0.44   (c) 1 kg for $3.29   (d) 1 kg for $2.99

KNOW YOUR CALCULATOR

7. (a) (i) 256   (ii) 3125   (iii) 2401   (b) (i) 8   (ii) 10   (iii) 16
8. (a) 19   (b) 30   (c) 52   (d) 4
    (e) 33   (f) 180   (g) 6.0625   (h) 22.09
9. (a) $1.61   (b) $0.32   (c) $1.32   (d) $8.89
    (e) $2.09   (f) $307.48   (g) $0.03   (h) $1666.40

SETS

1. (a) T   (b) T   (c) T   (d) T
    (e) F   (f) F   (g) T   (h) T
2. (a) {1, 2, 3, 5, 7}   (b) {1, 2, 3, 5, 6}   (c) {1, 2, 3, 5, 6, 7}
    (d) {3}   (e) {1, 2}   (f) {5}
3. (i) (a)   (ii) (d)   (iii) (b)   (iv) (c)
    (v) (b)   (vi) (c)   (vii) (a)   (viii) (a)

EXERCISE 1.1

1. (a) Q   (b) $\overline{Q}$ (c) Q   (d) $\overline{Q}$ (e) $\overline{Q}$ (f) Q
2. (a) 205, 3   (b) 204, 3   (c) 542, 3   (d) 3427, 4
    (e) 2, 1   (f) 25, 2   (g) 36, 2   (h) 122, 3
    (i) 012, 3   (j) 12, 2   (k) 1, 1   (l) 2473, 4
3. (a) 0.75   (b) 0.625   (c) 0.5625   (d) 1.75   (e) 1.375
    (f) 0.156 25   (g) 0.82   (h) $0.\overline{27}$ (i) $1.\overline{36}$ (j) $0.7\overline{3}$
    (k) 0.53   (l) $0.\overline{53}$ (m) $0.\overline{1}$ (n) $0.\overline{4}$ (o) $1.\overline{09}$
4. (a) $\frac{5}{8}$ (b) $\frac{183}{250}$ (c) $\frac{321}{100}$ (d) $\frac{93}{20}$ (e) $\frac{8}{11}$ (f) $\frac{7}{9}$
    (g) $\frac{215}{999}$ (h) $\frac{3014}{9999}$ (i) $\frac{17}{45}$ (j) $\frac{27}{110}$ (k) $\frac{599}{1980}$ (l) $\frac{649}{900}$
    (m) $\frac{322}{99}$ (n) $\frac{4071}{999}$ (o) $\frac{23\ 435}{3330}$ (p) $\frac{70\ 368}{9999}$
5. (a) $\frac{1}{3}$ (b) $\frac{1}{12}$ (c) $\frac{1}{9}$ (d) $\frac{1}{11}$ (e) $\frac{1}{9}$ (f) $\frac{2}{15}$

6. (a) $\frac{1}{2}$ (b) $\frac{3}{10}$ (c) $\frac{3}{5}$ (d) 1

7. (b) $4.\overline{36}$ and $4.3\overline{63}$ are equal.

8. (a) 4   (b) 5   (c) 6   (d) 12
   (e) 16   (f) 30   (g) 42   (h) 70
        (b) $\frac{2}{9}$

9. (a) $\frac{1}{9}$

EXERCISE 1.2

1. (a) rational   (b) rational   (c) irrational   (d) rational   (e) rational
   (f) rational   (g) rational   (h) rational   (i) rational   (j) rational

2. (a), (d), (e), (i), (j), (k)

3. (a) (i) 12   (ii) 64   (iii) 20   (iv) 3
   (b) (i) 3.3   (ii) 8.6   (iii) 9.9   (iv) 2.1
   (c) (i) 7.42   (ii) 2.55   (iii) 13.86   (iv) 2.81

EXERCISE 1.3

1. (a) Q   (b) N   (c) $\overline{Q}$ (d) Q   (e) Q
   (f) $\overline{Q}$ (g) Q   (h) Q   (i) $\overline{Q}$ (j) N
   (k) Q   (l) Q   (m) Q   (n) Q   (o) $\overline{Q}$

2. (a) $\{x \in R \mid x > -2\}$ (b) $\{x \in R \mid x \leq 3\}$ (c) $\{x \in R \mid -1 \leq x < 3\}$
   (d) $\{x \in R \mid x < -2$ or $x \geq 2\}$ (e) $\{x \in R \mid x < 0$ or $x > 4\}$ (f) $\{x \in R \mid -3 < x \leq 1\}$

EXERCISE 1.4

1. (a) $\{0.45, 0.5, 0.65\}$ (b) $\{-2, -1, 0, 3, 4\}$ (c) $\{-\frac{1}{2}, \frac{1}{2}, \frac{2}{3}, 1\}$ (d) $\{-5, -4, -2, 0, 1\}$

2. (a) $\{0.75, 0.33, 0.28, 0.2\}$ (b) $\{5, 1, 0, -2, -3\}$ (c) $\{3, \frac{2}{3}, 0, -\frac{1}{3}, -2\}$ (d) $\{2, 1, 0, -2, -3\}$

3. (a) $x > 4$ (b) $x < 5$ (c) $x < 0$ (d) $x < -3$ (e) $x > 4$ (f) $x < 3$
   (g) $x < -2$ (h) $x > -2$ (i) $x < -3$ (j) $x < 6$ (k) $x < -6$ (l) $x > -4$

4. (a) 3.5   (b) -1 (c) -4 (d) 42.5   (e) 2.55   (f) -2.65
   (g) -3.45 (h) 2.8   (i) $\frac{5}{12}$ (j) $-\frac{7}{24}$ (k) $\frac{23}{32}$ (l) $-\frac{1}{4}$

5. (a) 7.22, 7.221 234 56 ...   (b) $-0.271\,46$, $-0.271\,461\,611\,611\,1$ ...
   (c) 4.274, 4.274 142 43 ...

EXERCISE 1.5

1. (a) 4   (b) 7   (c) 9   (d) 10   (e) 11
   (f) $\frac{2}{3}$ (g) $\frac{6}{5}$ (h) $\frac{8}{9}$ (i) $\frac{6}{7}$

2. (a) $\sqrt{6}$ (b) $\sqrt{66}$ (c) $\sqrt{15}$ (d) $\sqrt{35}$ (e) $\sqrt{77}$
   (f) $\sqrt{30}$ (g) $\sqrt{42}$ (h) $\sqrt{22}$ (i) $\sqrt{143}$ (j) $\sqrt{85}$

3. (a) $6\sqrt{10}$ (b) $5\sqrt{21}$ (c) $4\sqrt{15}$ (d) $42\sqrt{10}$ (e) $6\sqrt{30}$
   (f) $8\sqrt{35}$ (g) $12\sqrt{10}$ (h) $6\sqrt{6}$ (i) $15\sqrt{6}$ (j) $8\sqrt{21}$

4. (a) $2\sqrt{3}$ (b) $3\sqrt{2}$ (c) $2\sqrt{5}$ (d) $4\sqrt{2}$ (e) $3\sqrt{5}$ (f) $5\sqrt{3}$
   (g) $5\sqrt{2}$ (h) 32   (i) $6\sqrt{2}$ (j) $2\sqrt{17}$ (k) $10\sqrt{2}$ (l) $2\sqrt{6}$

5. (a) 2.83   (b) 5.66   (c) 4.90   (d) 7.07   (e) 6.32   (f) 5.20

6. (a) $\sqrt{12}$ (b) $\sqrt{50}$ (c) $\sqrt{45}$ (d) $\sqrt{75}$ (e) $\sqrt{99}$ (f) $\sqrt{250}$
   (g) $\sqrt{300}$ (h) $\sqrt{28}$ (i) $\sqrt{200}$ (j) $\sqrt{126}$ (k) $\sqrt{252}$ (l) $\sqrt{242}$

7. (a) $2\sqrt{3}$ (b) $2\sqrt{15}$ (c) $7\sqrt{2}$ (d) $3\sqrt{2}$ (e) $5\sqrt{3}$ (f) $5\sqrt{10}$
   (g) $2\sqrt{15}$ (h) $15\sqrt{6}$ (i) $10\sqrt{30}$ (j) $70\sqrt{2}$ (k) $30\sqrt{5}$ (l) 36
   (m) 6   (n) $5\sqrt{6}$ (o) 30   (p) 36   (q) $90\sqrt{3}$ (r) 144

EXERCISE 1.6

1. (a) $8\sqrt{2}$ (b) $3\sqrt{3}$ (c) $13\sqrt{11}$ (d) $7\sqrt{5}$ (e) $9\sqrt{13}$
   (f) $5\sqrt{5}$ (g) $6\sqrt{2}$ (h) $7\sqrt{3}$ (i) $6\sqrt{2}$ (j) $18\sqrt{3}$
   (k) $2\sqrt{7}$ (l) $\sqrt{2}$ (m) $11\sqrt{2}$ (n) $8\sqrt{3}$
2. (a) $2\sqrt{2} + 9\sqrt{11}$ (b) $14\sqrt{13} - 3\sqrt{7}$ (c) $10\sqrt{3} + 2\sqrt{2}$ (d) $4\sqrt{7} - \sqrt{11}$
   (e) $3\sqrt{5} + \sqrt{7}$ (f) $6\sqrt{3}$ (g) $8\sqrt{10} - 7$ (h) $16 - 11\sqrt{11}$
3. (a) $4\sqrt{3} + 3$ (b) $10\sqrt{3} + 5$ (c) $11 + \sqrt{5}$
   (d) $7\sqrt{5} + 5\sqrt{3}$ (e) $\sqrt{7}$ (f) $2\sqrt{2} - 11$
4. (a) $5\sqrt{3}$ (b) $\sqrt{2}$ (c) $9\sqrt{2}$ (d) $2\sqrt{2}$ (e) $5\sqrt{2}$
   (f) $\sqrt{3}$ (g) $11\sqrt{2}$ (h) $2\sqrt{3}$ (i) $2\sqrt{6} - 4\sqrt{2}$ (j) $4\sqrt{2}$
5. (a) $3\sqrt{x}$ (b) $4\sqrt{a}$ (c) $21\sqrt{x}$ (d) $2\sqrt{a}$ (e) $2\sqrt{2x}$ (f) 0

EXERCISE 1.7

1. (a) $2\sqrt{3} + 10$ (b) $42 - 28\sqrt{3}$ (c) $5\sqrt{2} + 5\sqrt{6}$ (d) $3\sqrt{2} - 2\sqrt{22}$
   (e) $7\sqrt{7}$ (f) $2\sqrt{3} + 3\sqrt{6}$ (g) $2\sqrt{10} + 2\sqrt{5}$ (h) $3\sqrt{33} + 6\sqrt{3}$
2. (a) $2\sqrt{10} - 8\sqrt{15}$ (b) $3\sqrt{10} - 12\sqrt{3}$ (c) $10\sqrt{15} + 30\sqrt{10}$
   (d) $81\sqrt{5} + 18\sqrt{6}$ (e) $6\sqrt{26} - 15\sqrt{39}$
3. (a) $\sqrt{2} + 2\sqrt{6} + \sqrt{10}$ (b) $2\sqrt{6} + 2\sqrt{15} + 2\sqrt{33}$ (c) $6\sqrt{10} + 9\sqrt{15} + 12\sqrt{35}$

EXERCISE 1.8

1. (a) $\sqrt{2}$ (b) $\sqrt{6}$ (c) $9\sqrt{3}$ (d) 2
   (e) $\sqrt{3}$ (f) 6 (g) 5 (h) 15
2. (a) $\dfrac{\sqrt{15}}{3}$ (b) $\sqrt{2}$ (c) $\dfrac{\sqrt{30}}{4}$ (d) $\dfrac{2\sqrt{14}}{5}$
   (e) $\dfrac{\sqrt{21}}{2}$ (f) $\dfrac{\sqrt{15}}{5}$ (g) $\dfrac{3\sqrt{14}}{8}$ (h) $\sqrt{2}$

EXERCISE 1.10

1. (a) 6.7 (b) 11.3 (c) 5.4 (d) 11.8
   (e) 18.6 (f) 7.8 (g) 0.2 (h) 0.1
2. (a) 2.6 (b) 1.4 (c) 2.4 (d) 47.4 (e) 44.7 (f) 3.5
   (g) 3.6 (h) 6.7 (i) 4.5 (j) 4.4 (k) 1.3 (l) 0.8
3. (a) 1.2 (b) 1.9 (c) 1.1 (d) 1.3 (e) 0.4 (f) 1.2
   (g) 1.4 (h) 1.1 (i) 6.2 (j) 1.5 (k) 0.8 (l) 6.6
4. (a) 6.7 (b) 9.8 (c) 11.5
5. 4.6 m 6. 7.8 m 7. 5.3 cm 8. 46.6 cm 9. (a) 9 s (b) 2 s
10. (a) 2 s (b) 5 s. (c) 3 s
11. (a) 71.2 km/h (b) 65.6 km/h (c) 50.7 km/h
12. 5.8 km 13. 31.9 km 14. 9.9 cm 15. 8.6 cm 16. 4.2 cm 17. 28.4 m
18. 12.2 km 19. 15.5 km 20. 9 m
21. (a) 36 m² (b) 358 m² (c) 1180 m² (d) 24 m²
22. 6.9 cm 23. 9.5 cm 24. 1.8 m 25. 8.8 m

EXERCISE 1.11

1. (a) 2^3 (b) $(-3)^3$ (c) 7^2 (d) 10^2 (e) 6^2
   (f) $(-5)^3$ (g) 12^2 (h) 17^2 (i) 6^3 (j) 20^2
2. (a) 4 (b) -1 (c) 9 (d) -125 (e) 1 (f) -27

3. (a) 30 km = 300 hm = 3000 dam = 30 000 m   (b) 200 kg = 2000 hg = 20 000 dag = 200 000 g
4. (a) 2^4, 4^2 (b) 5^4, 25^2 (c) 2^6, 8^2, 4^3 (d) 6^4, 36^2 (e) 4^4, 16^2, 2^8 (f) 2^9, 8^3
5. (a) 8   (b) 9   (c) -24 (d) -54 (e) 27   (f) 1
   (g) 1   (h) 7   (i) -35 (j) 0
6. (a) 16.0 m^2 (b) 28.3 m^2 (c) 84.8 cm^2
7. (a) 384 cm^2, 512 cm^3 (b) 5024 cm^2, 33 493 cm^3
   (c) 352 cm^2, 503 cm^3 (d) 417 cm^2, 565 cm^3
8. 3 800 000 km^2 9. (a) 21.5 cm^2 (b) 30.9 mm^2 (c) 16.0 cm^2
10. 8.4 cm^3 11. 50.3 cm^2

EXERCISE 1.12

1. (a) x^8 (b) a^{12} (c) b^3 (d) m^6 (e) a^5b^5 (f) a^3b^4
2. (a) a^4 (b) b (c) n^9 (d) x^3 (e) a^4 (f) x
3. (a) x^8 (b) a^9 (c) a^6b^3 (d) x^5y^{15} (e) $a^5b^5c^5$ (f) b^{24}
   (g) $8x^9$ (h) $a^{15}b^6$ (i) $9a^{10}$ (j) $27x^3y^6$ (k) $125a^{24}$ (l) $64x^6y^3z^3$
4. (a) $\dfrac{x^5}{y^5}$ (b) $\dfrac{a^4}{9}$ (c) $\dfrac{x^6}{y^3}$ (d) $\dfrac{a^4}{b^{20}}$
   (e) $\dfrac{9x^2}{y^2}$ (f) $\dfrac{8x^6}{w^3}$ (g) $\dfrac{25a^4}{4b^6}$ (h) $\dfrac{9a^2}{b^6}$
5. (a) $15a^9$ (b) $-8x^5$ (c) $6a^3b^5$ (d) $10x^4$ (e) $15m^2n$ (f) $12x^5$
   (g) $30y^4$ (h) $-6a^8$ (i) $-14x^8$
6. (a) $4a^2$ (b) $3xy^4$ (c) a (d) $8m$ (e) -5 (f) $9b^2$
   (g) $7q$ (h) -3 (i) $-3x^9y$
7. (a) $-8a^9$ (b) $9x^6$ (c) $9x^4$ (d) $36a^{14}b^2$
   (e) $\dfrac{a^{15}b^3}{c^{12}}$ (f) $2a^4$ (g) $-64x^6y^{18}$ (h) $\dfrac{x^3}{27}$
8. (a) $16x^{11}$ (b) $2b^3$ (c) $3x^5y^{13}$ (d) $-4m^6$ (e) $-8xy$ (f) $-4m^4n^2$

EXERCISE 1.13

1. (a) x^{-2} (b) a^7 (c) y^4 (d) b^{-4}
   (e) a^8 (f) x (g) 1   (h) 1
2. (a) x^5 (b) b^{-3} (c) a^{-3} (d) x^{-5}
   (e) m^{-5} (f) n^7 (g) 0   (h) m^{-4}
3. (a) 1   (b) $\frac{1}{2}$ (c) 1   (d) $\frac{1}{10}$
   (e) $\frac{1}{9}$ (f) 1   (g) $\frac{1}{16}$ (h) $\frac{1}{8}$
4. (a) $15x^3$ (b) a^5b^{-3} (c) 6   (d) x^2 (e) $9m^{-2}$ (f) $15a^{-6}$
   (g) m^7 (h) $8a^{15}b^{-9}$ (i) x^5y^2 (j) $35x^4y^{-2}$ (k) $7m^{-2}n^{-2}$ (l) 15
5. (a) a^2 (b) $3x^{-5}$ (c) $4b^{-10}$ (d) $m^{-3}n$ (e) 1   (f) $3a^2b^{-2}$
   (g) b^4 (h) y^{-4} (i) $16x^{-4}$ (j) x^7 (k) $16b^8$ (l) $\frac{1}{2}a^{-14}$
6. (a) $1\frac{1}{5}$ (b) $\frac{7}{12}$ (c) $\frac{1}{25}$ (d) $\frac{1}{4}$ (e) 2   (f) 4
   (g) 1   (h) $\frac{9}{20}$ (i) 10   (j) $\frac{1}{100}$ (k) 9   (l) $\frac{1}{100}$

EXERCISE 1.14

3. 2^6 or 64   4. 6   5. 1024
6. (a) 26   (b) 6   (c) 12   (d) 8   (e) 0
7. (a) 8   (b) 10
8. (a) 12   (b) 8   (c) 3   (d) 11   (e) 4
9. 20 m   10. 19   11. 3

1.15 REVIEW EXERCISE

1. (a) 0.875   (b) $0.\overline{384\ 615}$ (c) $0.\overline{2}$ (d) $0.7\overline{2}$ (e) $0.\overline{230\ 769}$ (f) $0.\overline{7}$

2. (a) $\frac{9}{11}$ (b) $\frac{2}{15}$ (c) $\frac{235}{999}$ (d) $\frac{67}{495}$

5. (a) $\{-0.25,\ 0,\ 0.3,\ 0.54,\ 1.3\}$ (b) $\{1.3,\ 0.54,\ 0.3,\ 0,\ -0.25\}$

6. (a) 3.5, 3.512 345 6 ...   (b) 2.56, 2.561 661 666 1 ...
  (c) 3.123, 3.123 456 ...

7. (a) $\sqrt{18}$ (b) $\sqrt{175}$ (c) $\sqrt{44}$ (d) $\sqrt{98}$ (e) $\sqrt{125}$ (f) $\sqrt{52}$

8. (a) $4\sqrt{2}$ (b) $5\sqrt{3}$ (c) $12\sqrt{2}$ (d) $11\sqrt{2}$ (e) $7\sqrt{3}$ (f) $6\sqrt{3}$

9. (a) $30\sqrt{2}$ (b) $36\sqrt{2}$ (c) $40\sqrt{3}$ (d) $42\sqrt{2}$ (e) $48\sqrt{2}$
  (f) $18\sqrt{10}$ (g) $\frac{\sqrt{2}}{12}$ (h) $6\sqrt{7}$ (i) $\sqrt{6}$ (j) 3

10. (a) $\sqrt{6} - 5\sqrt{3}$ (b) $6\sqrt{6} - 10\sqrt{2}$ (c) $2\sqrt{15} - \sqrt{10}$
   (d) $4 + 2\sqrt{2}$ (e) $15\sqrt{2} - 5\sqrt{6}$ (f) $6 + 6\sqrt{2}$

11. (a) $\sqrt{6}$ (b) $\sqrt{5}$ (c) 1   (d) $\sqrt{7}$ (e) 10   (f) $\frac{2}{3}$

12. (a) $2\sqrt{2}$ (b) $4\sqrt{3}$ (c) $8\sqrt{2}$ (d) $2\sqrt{10}$
   (e) $15\sqrt{6}$ (f) $\sqrt{5}$ (g) $10\sqrt{7}$

13. (a) $4\sqrt{3} + 8\sqrt{2}$ (b) $12\sqrt{3} + 6\sqrt{2}$ (c) $14\sqrt{2} - 4\sqrt{3}$ (d) $30\sqrt{5}$ (e) $18\sqrt{2} + 8$

14. (a) $\frac{3\sqrt{2}}{2}$ (b) $\sqrt{10}$ (c) $\sqrt{21}$ (d) $\frac{2\sqrt{6}}{3}$
   (e) $\frac{3\sqrt{2}}{2}$ (f) $\sqrt{2}$ (g) $\frac{2\sqrt{15}}{5}$ (h) $\sqrt{6}$

15. (a) 1.3   (b) 3.1   (c) 1.7   (d) 3.7   (e) 1.6   (f) 8.8

16. 6.6 m   17. 37.0 km   18. 2.8 cm

19. (a) $15a^7$ (b) $28y^3$ (c) a^7b^4 (d) $-12x^8$ (e) $35a^8$ (f) $-15a^2$
   (g) $7a^8b$ (h) $-15a^3b^5$ (i) $45a^2$ (j) $-20x^2y^3$ (k) $15a^{\,9}$ (l) $-18a^5b$

20. (a) $3b^2$ (b) $5x^6$ (c) $9b^5$ (d) $3y^2$ (e) $4x^7$ (f) $-2a$
   (g) $9b^2$ (h) $6x^5$ (i) $5a^2$ (j) $17y^4$ (k) $-8w^5$ (l) $a^{-5}b^3$

21. (a) $5x^4$ (b) $15a^4$ (c) x^6y^{10} (d) $3x^2$
   (e) $4x^3$ (f) $72x^7$ (g) $25a^2$ (h) $5mn^{-1}$

22. (a) 125   (b) 81   (c) 32   (d) 1   (e) $\frac{1}{2}$ (f) $\frac{1}{3}$
   (g) 1   (h) $\frac{1}{10}$ (i) $\frac{1}{4}$ (j) $\frac{8}{27}$ (k) 9   (l) 5
   (m) 1   (n) $\frac{1}{2}$ (o) $\frac{1}{9}$ (p) 4   (q) $1\frac{1}{3}$ (r) $1\frac{1}{2}$

1.16 CHAPTER 1 TEST

		Decimal	Period	Length
1. (a)	(i)	$0.\overline{1}$	1	1
	(ii)	$0.\overline{285\ 714}$	285 714	6

(b) $\frac{23}{99}$

3. 3.125 70 $\in$ Q, 3.125 707 16 ... $\in \overline{Q}$ (provided that 3.125 707 16 ... continues without repetition)

4. (a) $5\sqrt{5}$ (b) $\sqrt{63}$

5. (a) $6\sqrt{35}$ (b) 144   (c) $15\sqrt{6} - 20\sqrt{2}$ (d) 3

6. (a) $3\sqrt{7} - 7\sqrt{2}$ (b) $7\sqrt{3}$ 7. 8.6 m

8. (a) $6x^2y^5$ (b) $-21a^3b^4$ (c) $\frac{4}{3}a^2c^2$ (d) $4x^2$ (e) $4x^4y^{\,4}$ (f) $-a^2b^{\,1}$

9. (a) 1   (b) $\frac{9}{4}$ (c) $\frac{8}{15}$ (d) -3

REVIEW AND PREVIEW TO CHAPTER 2

OPERATIONS WITH INTEGERS

1. (a) -3 (b) 5   (c) -8 (d) 1
  (e) -1 (f) -4 (g) -10 (h) -2

2. (a) -2 (b) 12   (c) -15 (d) 18
  (e) -4 (f) -2 (g) 2   (h) -4

ORDER OF OPERATIONS

1. (a) 26   (b) 37   (c) 6   (d) 37   (e) 1   (f) 8
    (g) 4   (h) 2   (i) 6   (j) 1   (k) 49

SUBSTITUTION

1. (a) 16   (b) 72   (c) 38   (d) -2
    (e) 29   (f) -3 (g) -2 (h) -26
    (i) -20 (j) -8 (k) -60 (l) -5
    (m) -18 (n) 17   (o) 0   (p) 576
2. (a) -25 (b) -19 (c) 18   (d) -24
    (e) -2 (f) 14   (g) -6 (h) 15
    (i) 84   (j) 8   (k) 8   (l) 16
    (m) -14 (n) -3 (o) -2 (p) -5

THE RULE OF THREE

1. 187.5 km   2. $500.80   3. 33   4. 29.76 g   5. 1239 MJ
6. 32.69   7. $32.40   8. 7 365 000 km   9. 303.3 g   10. 3060 m

CALCULATOR MATH

1. (a) 2461   (b) 49   (c) 5   (d) 11
    (e) 9.819 805   (f) 36   (g) 5.5   (h) 31.45

EXERCISE 2.1

1. (a) $5x + 9y$ (b) $11x^2 + 13x$ (c) $27xy + 3w$ (d) $7x - y$
2. (a) $9w - 12x - 4y$ (b) $5m^2 + 2m - 6$ (c) $2x^2 + 19x + 12$
3. (a) $3x + y$ (b) $2x^2 + 4x - 9$ (c) $3x^2 - 6x + 5$ (d) $-y^2 - 5y + 2$
4. (a) $3x + 3y$ (b) $4w + 9x + 4y$ (c) $7x^2 - 9x - 4$
5. (a) $x^3 + x + 9$ (b) $x^2 - 5x + 2$ (c) $y^3 + 6y^2 - 3y + 2$
6. (a) $-x - y - 3$ (b) $-8x^2 - 2xy + 7y^2$ (c) $13x^3 - 3x^2 + 3y^2 - 13y^3$
7. (a) $x^2 - 6y$ (b) $2x^2 - 4xy + 3y^2$

EXERCISE 2.2

1. (a) $2a + 2b$ (b) $3x - 3y$ (c) $6a - 15b$ (d) $10x + 15y$
    (e) $7p + 7q - 7r$ (f) $-6c + 3d$ (g) $-a - b$ (h) $-4a + 2b - 2c$
2. (a) $2x^2 - 10xy$ (b) $6a^2 - 15ab$ (c) $-20ap - 12aq$ (d) $10x^3 - 4x^2y$
    (e) $6c^4 - 12c^3d$ (f) $2x^2y + 4xy^2$ (g) $6x^3y + 15x^2y^2$ (h) $20x^2y^2 - 10xy^4$
3. (a) $6x^3 + 4x^2y + 10x^2$ (b) $x^2y - 2xy^2 + 5xy$ (c) $6a^2b - 21ab^2 - 27ab$
    (d) $3x^3y - 6x^2y^2 + 9x^2y$ (e) $2a^2bc - 3ab^2c + abc^2$ (f) $27a^2b^2 - 6ab^3 + 12a^2b^3$
4. (a) $5x + 22$ (b) $8m + 18$ (c) -14 (d) $2y - 6$
    (e) $5x - 11$ (f) $4m - 20$ (g) $5x - 4y - 42$ (h) -6
    (i) $3x^2 - 19x + 30$ (j) $2x^2 - 16x + 6$

EXERCISE 2.3

1. (a) $x^2 + 5x + 6$ (b) $x^2 + 5x + 6$
2. (a) $x^2 + 3x + 2$ (b) $x^2 + 5x + 6$ (c) $x^2 + 6x + 8$ (d) $x^2 - 4x + 3$
    (e) $x^2 + 2x - 15$ (f) $x^2 + x - 2$ (g) $y^2 - 9y + 20$ (h) $t^2 + 15t + 56$
    (i) $m^2 + 5m - 36$ (j) $n^2 - 11n + 18$ (k) $x^2 + x - 56$ (l) $y^2 - 6y - 7$
    (m) $x^2 + 13x + 42$ (n) $t^2 - 14t + 45$ (o) $m^2 - 17m + 66$ (p) $w^2 - 16$
3. (a) $2x^2 + 13x + 15$ (b) $6x^2 + 29x + 28$ (c) $14y^2 + 31y - 10$
    (d) $6m^2 - 17m + 5$ (e) $12m^2 - 24m + 9$ (f) $9x^2 + 30x + 25$
    (g) $4x^2 - 25$ (h) $8t^2 + 26t + 21$ (i) $25t^2 - 60t + 36$
    (j) $49t^2 + 56t + 16$ (k) $12x^2 - 17xy + 6y^2$ (l) $20m^2 + 3mn - 2n^2$
    (m) $9x^2 + 30xy + 25y^2$ (n) $-3x^2 + 5xy + 28y^2$ (o) $49 - 64t^2$

(p) $28x^2 - 55xy - 18y^2$
(s) $12x^4 - 11x^3 + 2x^2$
(v) $5x^8 - 21x^4 + 18$
(q) $72x^2 + 107xy + 30y^2$
(t) $-x^4 + 5x^3y - 4x^2y^2$
(w) $-8x^2 + 26xy - 21y^2$
(r) $56m^2 - 19mn - 15n^2$
(u) $4t^4 - 28t^2 + 49$

4. (a) $2x^2 + 20x + 33$
(d) $60t - 210$
(g) $70m^2 + 66m - 33$
(j) $-3x^2 - 48x - 67$
(b) $5x^2 + 27x + 46$
(e) $5m^2 + 4m + 29$
(h) $-5x^2 - 60x - 17$
(k) $-84w^2 - 12w + 99$
(c) $-m^2 - 15m + 22$
(f) $-10x^2 + 83x + 2$
(i) $-40t^2 + 49t + 16$

5. $2x^2 - 5x - 12$
6. $9x^2 - 12x + 4$

7. (a) $11 + 6\sqrt{3}$
(e) $37 - 6\sqrt{14}$
(b) $11 + 3\sqrt{15}$
(f) $-9 - 8\sqrt{10}$
(c) $4 + \sqrt{6}$
(g) $16 - 8\sqrt{21}$
(d) $24 - 5\sqrt{5}$
(h) $18 - \sqrt{5}$

8. (a) $x^3 + 3x^2 + 3x + 2$
(c) $6x^3 - x^2 - 16x - 5$
(e) $x^4 + x^3 - 8x^2 - 9x + 5$
(g) $x^4 + 9x^3 + 13x^2 - 34x - 24$
(b) $2x^3 - x^2 - 14x - 12$
(d) $3m^3 - 13m^2 + 6n + 8$
(f) $6m^4 - 5m^3 + m^2 - 4m + 2$
(h) $2w^2 - 15x^2 - 12y^2 + 7wx + 29xy - 2wy$

9. (a) $4x^3 - 12x^2 - 31x + 60$
(b) $x^4 - 6x^3 + 7x^2 + 6x + 1$

(c) $x^2 - \dfrac{1}{x^2}$
(d) $-x^2 + x + 5$

(e) $w^2 + x^2 + y^2 + z^2 + 2wx + 2wy + 2wz + 2xy + 2xz + 2yz$

EXERCISE 2.4

1. (a) $x^2 + 6x + 9$
(e) $y^2 + 4y + 4$
(i) $y^2 + 2y + 1$
(m) $x^2 + 24x + 144$
(b) $x^2 - 4x + 4$
(f) $m^2 - 14m + 49$
(j) $x^2 - 18x + 81$
(n) $x^2 - 12x + 36$
(c) $x^2 + 10x + 25$
(g) $t^2 - 25$
(k) $x^2 + 20x + 100$
(o) $y^2 - 1$
(d) $x^2 - 16$
(h) $x^2 - 36$
(l) $x^2 - 49$
(p) $a^2 - b^2$

2. (a) $9x^2 - 25$
(e) $25x^2 - y^2$
(i) $16 - 9m^2$
(b) $4x^2 + 28x + 49$
(f) $a^2 + 4ab + 4b^2$
(j) $36 + 84x + 49x^2$
(c) $16x^2 + 40x + 25$
(g) $a^2b^2 - 4$
(d) $4x^2 - 12xy + 9y^2$
(h) $x^4 - 8x^2 + 16$

3. (a) 2704
(e) 10 201
(b) 1575
(f) 891
(c) 9025
(g) 6889
(d) 5041
(h) -2484

4. (a) $x^2 + 10x + 16$
(d) $5x^2 - y^2$
(b) $-3x^2 + 4x - 1$
(e) $3a^2 - 16ab + 9b^2$
(c) $4a^2 - 25ab + 49b^2$
(f) $-4c^2$

5. (a) $2x^2 - 6x + 29$
(d) $-x^2 + 12x - 29$
(b) $x^2 - 32$
(e) $-8x^2 - 12x$
(c) $2x^2 + 10x + 1$
(f) $82x^2 - 40x + 6$

6. (a) $5 + 2\sqrt{6}$
(e) $22 + 12\sqrt{2}$
(i) 18
(b) $7 - 2\sqrt{10}$
(f) $278 - 160\sqrt{3}$
(j) 8
(c) $9 - 6\sqrt{2}$
(g) 1
(k) -5
(d) $13 - 2\sqrt{42}$
(h) -1
(l) 28

7. (a) 8091
(b) 9975
(c) 2496
(d) 1479

EXERCISE 2.5

1. (a) $2 - \sqrt{3}$
(e) $10 + 5\sqrt{3}$
(b) $\sqrt{5} - 2$
(f) $2\sqrt{26} - 10$
(c) $-\sqrt{15} - 4$
(d) $3\sqrt{2} + 3$

2. (a) $3 - 2\sqrt{2}$
(b) $5 + 2\sqrt{6}$
(c) $7 - 4\sqrt{3}$
(d) $18 + 8\sqrt{5}$

3. (a) $\sqrt{3} - \sqrt{2}$
(b) $\sqrt{6} - \sqrt{5}$
(c) $\dfrac{\sqrt{5} + \sqrt{3}}{2}$
(d) $\sqrt{5} - \sqrt{2}$

EXERCISE 2.6

1. (a) $2(x + 3)$
(f) $2(x^2 - 41)$
(b) $5(y - 2)$
(g) $2t(w + 2x - 3y)$
(c) $3(x + 2)$
(h) $ab(3x - y - 2z)$
(d) $7(w - 1)$

2. (a) $5x(5x^2 + 2x + 3)$
(c) $9(4x^5 - y^3)$
(e) $3m(3m^2 - 2mt + t^2)$
(h) $11y(2x - y + 3w)$
(j) $7rst(1 - 2rs)$
(l) $10m^5n^3(2mn - 3n^2 + 4m^2 - 1)$
(b) $y^2(y^3 - y^2 + y - 1)$
(d) $4x(3y + w - 2z)$
(f) $7xy(z - 2 + 3t)$
(i) $4mn(9n - 6m + 7)$
(k) $9rs^2(2rs - 1 - 3r^2)$
(n) $4x^5y^4(10y^3 - 8x^2y^2 - 7x^3 - 9x^2y)$

3. (a) $(x + y)(3m + 2)$ (b) $(y - 1)(3x + 2)$
   (c) $(m + 3)(9x - 2)$ (d) $(m + n)(5y + t)$
   (e) $(x - 2)(5w - 3t)$ (f) $(x + 5)(2t + 1)$
   (g) $(t - 4)(4mn - 1)$

EXERCISE 2.7

1. (a) $x + 4$ (b) $x + 2$ (c) $x - 3$ (d) $m + 3$ (e) $y - 2$
   (f) $t + 4$ (g) $s - 4$ (h) $w + 5$ (i) $n - 5$ (j) $x - 7$
2. (a) $(x + 5)(x + 2)$ (b) $(m + 6)(m + 2)$ (c) $(n + 4)(n + 2)$ (d) $(w - 5)(w - 2)$
   (e) $(x - 5)(x - 4)$ (g) $(r - 6)(r + 5)$ (h) $(m + 7)(m - 6)$ (i) $(n + 9)(n + 2)$
   (j) $(x + 10)(x + 2)$ (l) $(s + 8)(s - 2)$ (m) $(y - 7)(y + 5)$ (n) $(x + 8)(x - 5)$
   (o) $(t + 8)(t + 9)$ (q) $(r - 10)(r - 8)$ (r) $(m - 3)^2$ (s) $(y + 5)^2$
   (t) $(x + 9)(x - 7)$ (v) $(x - 10)^2$ (w) $(m - 10)(m + 2)$ (x) $(n + 12)(n - 2)$
                                                (c) $(m - 11)(m + 7)$ (d) $5(x - 5)(x - 2)$
3. (a) $2(x + 1)^2$ (b) $3(w + 3)(w + 1)$ (g) $3(x^2 + x + 1)$ (h) $2(x - 9)(x - 5)$
   (e) $(n + 11)(n + 5)$ (f) $(w - 10)(w - 3)$ (k) $(8 - x)(2 + x)$ (l) $2(x^2 - 3x + 5)$
   (i) $2(w + 7)^2$ (j) $(5 - m)(7 - m)$
   (m) $4(x - 6)^2$ (n) $(m + 14)(m - 3)$

EXERCISE 2.8

1. (a) $2, 5$ (b) $2, 3$ (c) $-3, -4$ (f) $3, 6$
   (g) $10, -3$ (h) $-4, -4$ (i) $4, -5$ (j) $7, -2$
2. (a) $(2x + 1)(3x + 5)$ (b) $(2w + 3)(w + 1)$ (c) $(3x - 2)(2x - 1)$ (d) $(m + 6)(4m + 3)$
   (e) $(w - 2)(3w - 4)$ (f) $(5t - 2)(3t + 1)$ (g) $(m + 2)(2m - 5)$ (h) $(4x + 1)(x + 6)$
   (i) $(3n - 2)(2n - 3)$ (j) $(3x - 2)(x - 7)$
3. (a) $(t + 7)(4t + 3)$ (b) $(3m + 4)(2m - 1)$ (c) $(2x + 5)(x + 6)$ (d) $(3x + 1)^2$
   (e) $(4m - 3)(m + 6)$ (f) $(2x - 5)(3x - 2)$ (g) $(5x + 2)(2x + 5)$ (h) $(2t - 7)(3t + 2)$

EXERCISE 2.9

1. (a) $(x - 4)(x + 4)$ (b) $(m + 3)^2$ (c) $(r - 5)^2$ (d) $(m - 7)(m + 7)$
   (e) $(t - 4)^2$ (f) $(x - 6)(x + 6)$ (g) $(x + 7)^2$ (h) $(m - 2)^2$
   (i) $(w + 10)^2$ (j) $(y - 1)^2$ (k) $(x - 8)(x + 8)$ (l) $(n + 9)^2$
   (m) $(s + 8)^2$ (n) $(r - 3)^2$ (o) $(x - 12)(x + 12)$ (p) $(3 - y)(3 + y)$
2. (a) $(2x - 5)(2x + 5)$ (b) $(2x + 1)^2$ (c) $(3x - 1)^2$ (e) $(4m - 1)^2$
   (f) $(10t - 7)(10t + 7)$ (g) $(2w - 3)^2$ (h) $(5s + 4)^2$ (i) $(3 - 7y)(3 + 7y)$
   (j) $(2 - 5x)^2$ (k) $(7y + 3)^2$ (l) $(1 - 7m)^2$ (n) $(2r + 7)^2$
3. (a) $9(x - 2)(x + 2)$ (b) $(x - 4)(x + 2)$ (c) $(3x + 2)(2x - 5)$
   (d) $3t(mn - 2m^2 - 3n)$ (e) $(4x + 1)^2$ (f) $2(x - 4)(x + 3)$
   (g) $(x - 2)(5m - 4)$
4. (a) $4(m + 5)(m - 3)$ (b) $2(2 - 3x)(2 + 3x)$ (c) $m(n + 6)(n + 3)$
   (d) $(5y - 4)(3y - 2)$ (e) $(6x + 5)^2$ (f) $(x + y)(2x + 2y - m)$
   (g) $7m^2n^5(7 - 4mn - 2m^4n^2)$ (h) $(4x + 7)(2x + 5)$

EXERCISE 2.10

1. (a) $2y, x \neq 0$ (b) $2, m, n \neq 0$ (c) $7x, x \neq 0$
   (d) $5n^2, m \neq 0$ (e) $-5xy, x \neq 0$ (f) $-6x^4, x \neq 0$
   (g) $-9x^2yz^3, x, y, z \neq 0$ (h) $3s, r, s \neq 0$ (i) $-5x^4, x, y \neq 0$
   (j) $-6m^3n^5, m, n \neq 0$ (k) $12x^2y^3, x, y, z \neq 0$ (l) $t, r, s, t \neq 0$
2. (a) $x + 2y$ (b) $x - 3y$ (c) $4x - 6, x \neq 0$
   (d) $-2x^3 + 3x, x \neq 0$ (e) $3x^3y - 4xy^2 - 1, x, y \neq 0$ (f) $4x^2y^3 - y^5 + 2xy^3, x \neq 0$

EXERCISE 2.11

1. (a) $\frac{4}{y}$, x, y ≠ 0

   (d) $\frac{a}{2b}$, a, b ≠ 0

   (g) $\frac{1}{x + 1}$, x ≠ −1, −3

   (j) $\frac{x - 4}{x + 2}$, x ≠ 0, −2

2. (a) $\frac{1}{2(x - 2)}$, x ≠ 0, 2

   (d) $\frac{x - 2}{x + 3}$, x ≠ −3, 0

3. (a) $\frac{2x + 3y}{x(x + 4)}$, x ≠ 0, −4

   (c) $\frac{1}{x - 2}$, x ≠ 2

   (b) $\frac{3}{4x}$, x ≠ 0

   (e) $\frac{4ab}{9c}$, c ≠ 0

   (h) $\frac{x}{x - 7}$, x ≠ 0, 7

   (k) $\frac{2}{x - 1}$, x ≠ 1

   (b) $\frac{x}{x + 3}$, x ≠ 0, −3

   (e) $\frac{4}{9}$, x ≠ 3

   (b) $\frac{1}{x - 3}$, x ≠ −3, 3

   (d) $\frac{x + 4}{x + 5}$, x ≠ −5, −3

   (c) $\frac{6}{x}$, x ≠ 0

   (f) $\frac{2}{x + 1}$, x ≠ 0, −1

   (i) 2(x − 9), x ≠ 0

   (l) b, a ≠ 0, −1, c ≠ 0

   (c) $\frac{x - 2}{3x}$, x ≠ 0

   (f) 6, x ≠ −6

EXERCISE 2.12

1. (a) 2

   (g) $\frac{x^2}{y^2}$

   (m) $\frac{x + 3}{x - 5}$

2. (a) $3x^2$

3. (a) 2x

4. (a) 1

   (b) $\frac{3}{4}$

   (h) $\frac{5x}{y}$

   (n) $\frac{x + y}{x - y}$

   (b) $\frac{x^2y^4}{6}$

   (b) 6x

   (b) $\frac{t}{t + 1}$

   (c) $\frac{5}{18}$

   (i) $\frac{5}{7}$

   (o) $\frac{x + y}{x - y}$

   (c) $\frac{3m}{4}$

   (c) 2t(x − 3)

   (c) $\frac{w + 5}{w - 6}$

   (d) $\frac{7}{5t}$

   (j) $\frac{1}{7}$

   (p) $\frac{x + 3}{x + 1}$

   (d) $\frac{4ry}{3}$

   (d) $\frac{2x(x + 2)}{5}$

   (d) $\frac{4}{x - 7}$

   (e) $\frac{2x}{y}$

   (k) y^2

   (e) $\frac{6xy^2}{mn}$

   (e) $\frac{n^2}{2m}$

   (e) $\frac{10}{x - 6}$

   (f) 28

   (l) $\frac{y}{x}$

   (f) $\frac{6}{y}$

   (f) $\frac{1}{2x^2}$

EXERCISE 2.13

1. (a) 40   (b) 200   (c) 180   (d) 1050   (e) 180   (f) 140
2. (a) $60x^4$ (b) $12x^2y^2$ (c) $6m^2n^2$ (d) $150x^3y^2$ (e) 18abc   (f) $120a^2b^2$
3. (a) (x − 1)(x − 4)   (b) (x + 1)(x + 2)(x − 3)
   (c) (x + 3)(x + 4)(x + 5)   (d) x(x + 1)(x − 1)
   (e) 6(x − 3)   (f) (x + 1)(x + 5)(x − 3)
   (g) (m + 1)(m − 2)(m − 3)(m − 5)   (h) 3(x + 4)(x + 7)(x − 8)
   (i) x(x + 5)(x − 4)(x − 5)

EXERCISE 2.14

1. (a) $1\frac{2}{7}$

   (e) $\frac{x + y}{2}$

2. (a) $\frac{17}{20}$

   (e) $\frac{m - 17}{12}$

   (b) $\frac{6}{11}$

   (f) $\frac{4x - 1}{5}$

   (b) $2\frac{7}{24}$

   (f) $\frac{12 - x - 13y}{12}$

   (c) $\frac{11}{x}$

   (g) $\frac{5}{x + 1}$

   (c) $\frac{5x}{12}$

   (g) $\frac{37x - 1}{14}$

   (d) $\frac{8}{m}$

   (h) $\frac{m - n}{x - 3}$

   (d) $\frac{16x + 11y}{6}$

   (h) $\frac{8t - 13}{24}$

3. (a) $\dfrac{11}{6x}$ (b) $-\dfrac{1}{20x}$ (c) $\dfrac{26x - 9}{12x^2}$ (d) $\dfrac{2t^2 - 3st + 4s^2}{s^2t^2}$

(e) $\dfrac{4xy + 2x - y + 3}{xy}$ (f) $\dfrac{x^2 + 4x - 1}{x}$ (g) $\dfrac{y^2 + 3y - 2}{y}$ (h) $\dfrac{x + 1 + xy}{x}$

4. (a) $\dfrac{5x + 7}{(x + 1)(x + 2)}$ (b) $\dfrac{5m - 5}{(m - 4)(m + 1)}$ (c) $\dfrac{x + 22}{(x - 3)(x + 2)}$ (d) $\dfrac{x - 5}{2(x + 1)}$

(e) $\dfrac{23x + 18}{5(x + 1)}$ (f) $\dfrac{2x^2 - 2x - 2}{x(x - 2)}$ (g) $\dfrac{4x^2 + x - 23}{(x + 3)(x - 2)}$ (h) $\dfrac{4x^2 - 6}{(x + 1)(x - 1)}$

EXERCISE 2.15

1. (a) 5 (b) 2 (c) −6 (d) 1
   (e) 5 (f) 3 (g) −4 (h) 2
2. (a) 3 (b) 1 (c) 2 (d) 3
3. (a) 6.4 (b) 5.0 (c) 4.24 (d) 5.0 (e) 5.4 (f) 2.0
4. (a) −10 (b) 4 (c) 7 (d) 14 (e) 22 (f) 20
   (g) −2 (h) 2 (i) 2 (j) 4 (k) −16 (l) −3
   (m) 5 (n) −3 (o) 2 (p) 3 (q) 9
5. (a) 1.0 (b) 0.6 (c) 5.0 (d) −1.13 (e) 7.636 (f) 4.968
6. (a) 1.398 (b) 3.286

EXERCISE 2.16

1. (a) 8 (b) 15 (c) $1\frac{2}{3}$ (d) $10\frac{2}{3}$

2. (a) 2 (b) $\frac{1}{8}$ (c) $\frac{5}{6}$ (d) $\frac{1}{2}$

3. (a) 19 (b) 0 (c) $2\frac{1}{4}$ (d) $-2\frac{1}{4}$ (e) $8\frac{1}{2}$

(f) $7\frac{1}{2}$ (g) −2 (h) −5 (i) 9 (j) $-\frac{2}{5}$

4. (a) $-\frac{1}{3}$ (b) $1\frac{1}{5}$ (c) 2 (d) 3

5. (a) $\frac{2}{5}$ (b) 4 (c) 3 (d) $-2\frac{2}{5}$

6. (a) −7 (b) −2 (c) −2 (d) −10

7. (a) 11 (b) 7 (c) −4

EXERCISE 2.17

1. (a) x + 3 (b) 2x (c) x − 5
   (d) 3x (e) 2x + 3 (f) x + 1, x + 2, x + 3
   (g) 2x, 2x + 2, 2x + 4 (h) x + 5 2. 21, 22, 23
3. 14, 16, 18 4. 23, 25, 27 5. 53
6. 15 7. 8, 16 8. 15, 10
9. 7 nickels, 5 dimes, 3 quarters 10. 75 mL and 125 mL 11. 90 km/h
12. 80 km 13. 350 km 14. 60 km/h
15. 5 h 16. 22 cm by 30 cm

EXERCISE 2.18

1. (a) $x = \dfrac{b}{a}$ (b) $x = \dfrac{d}{2c}$ (c) $x = \dfrac{2}{a + b}$ (d) $x = \dfrac{b - 2}{a}$ (e) $x = \dfrac{2b}{a}$ (f) $x = \dfrac{5}{3 + a}$

2. (a) $x = \dfrac{4}{b} + a, b \neq 0$ (b) $x = \dfrac{a - 2}{4b}, b \neq 0$

(c) $x = \dfrac{10}{3} + a$ (d) $x = \dfrac{5}{2 - a}, a \neq 2$

$x = \dfrac{5}{a + b + c}, a + b + c \neq 0$

(f) $x = c - b, x = -b, c \neq 0$

(g) $x = \dfrac{a + b}{c}, c \neq 0, x \neq 0$

(h) $x = \dfrac{2c}{a + b}, a \neq -b$

3. (a) $\ell = \dfrac{A}{w}, w = \dfrac{A}{\ell}$

(b) $\ell = \dfrac{P}{2} - w, w = \dfrac{P}{2} - \ell$

(c) $r = \dfrac{C}{2\pi}$

(d) $h = \dfrac{V}{\pi r^2}$

(e) $\ell = \dfrac{V}{wh}, w = \dfrac{V}{\ell h}, h = \dfrac{V}{\ell w}$

(f) $u = v - at, a = \dfrac{v - u}{t}, t = \dfrac{v - u}{a}$

(g) $a = \dfrac{2s}{t^2}$

(h) $p = \dfrac{I}{rt}, r = \dfrac{I}{pt}, t = \dfrac{I}{pr}$

4. (a) $a = \dfrac{2A}{h} - b$

(b) $n = \dfrac{t - a}{d} + 1$

(c) $r = \dfrac{S - a}{S}$

EXERCISE 2.19

1. (a) $x > 2$ (b) $a < 11$ (c) $x < 4$ (d) $x \geqslant 5$
   (e) $x \leqslant 4$ (f) $x \leqslant 4$ (g) $x < -2$ (h) $x \geqslant -2$
2. (a) $x < 6$ (b) $x \leqslant 9$ (c) $x \leqslant -6$ (d) $x > 8$
   (e) $x > 7$ (f) $m \geqslant 40$ (g) $b \geqslant -4$ (h) $x \leqslant 11$
3. (a) $x < -3$ (b) $x \geqslant 7$ (c) $m \leqslant -3$ (d) $x > -7$
   (e) $a \leqslant -11$ (f) $x \leqslant 2$ (g) $x \geqslant 5$
4. (a) $c \leqslant 6$ (b) $x > 1$ (c) $a \geqslant 12$ (d) $b \geqslant 6$
   (e) $x \leqslant 11$ (f) $a < -4$ (g) $x > \dfrac{5}{4}$ (h) $x \geqslant -3$
5. (a) $a \leqslant 2.5$ (b) $x > -2$ (c) $x \leqslant 2.5$ (d) $x > 2$ (e) $x \leqslant 4.5$ (f) $x \geqslant -2.5$

EXERCISE 2.20

1. 24 cm   2. 1250 cm³   3. 676 cm²   4. 320 m
5. 77.5 m by 77.5 m   6. 2 cans   7. 411 cm   8. 80 m²
9. 2π m   10. 10 tubes   11. 23 km   12. 10 m   13. 1160 m³   14. 130 m²

2.21 REVIEW EXERCISE

1. (a) $3x + 2xy - 4y$ (b) $-7x^2 - 2x - 1$ (c) $-2x^2 + 5x + 1$
   (d) $-5 + 7x - x^2$ (e) $-x^2y + 4x^3 - 5xy^2$ (f) $x^3 + x^2 + 14x - 5$
2. (a) $-x - 16$ (b) $2x^2 + 2x - 12$ (c) $x^2 + 4x + 1$ (d) $x^2 - y^2$
   (e) $x - 29$ (f) $x^2 - 13x + 40$ (g) $3m^2 - 2m - 36$ (h) $w^2 + 15w - 82$
   (i) $4x^2 + 2x - 17$ (j) $11x^2 + 83x + 24$ (k) $8t^2 + 32t + 28$ (l) $-38x^2 + 79x - 47$
3. (a) $3mn(1 - 3m - 4n)$ (b) $(x - 6)(x + 5)$
   (c) $(x - 9)(x + 9)$ (d) $(x + 4)^2$
   (e) $(6t - 7)(6t + 7)$ (f) $(m - 7)(5x - 3)$
   (g) $2(x - 6)(x + 10)$ (h) $(x - 7)^2$
   (i) $3x(3xy - 1 + 4y^2)$ (j) $(10m - 11)(10m + 11)$
   (k) $(2m + 7)^2$ (l) $(5x - 2)^2$
   (m) $x(m - n)(5x - 2)$ (n) $3(x - 4)(x + 4)$
4. (a) $\dfrac{1}{2x - 3}, x \neq \frac{3}{2}, 0$ (b) $\dfrac{x - 5}{3}, y \neq 0$ (c) $6, x \neq 5$
   (d) $\dfrac{1}{x + 7}, x \neq -7, 7$ (e) $\dfrac{1}{x + 2}, x \neq -2, -3$ (f) $\dfrac{x - 5}{x + 5}, x \neq -5$
5. (a) $10mnx^2y$ (b) $\dfrac{9t^3xy^2w}{4}$ (c) $\dfrac{4}{x}$
   (d) $x - 2$ (e) x (f) $\dfrac{2}{(x - 3)(x - 2)}$

6. (a) $\frac{3}{7}$ (b) $\frac{17x}{15}$ (c) $\frac{17x + 2}{12}$

(d) $\frac{-10m - 21}{18}$ (e) $\frac{-2x^2 + 15x + 5}{6x^3}$ (f) $\frac{7x + 1}{(x + 1)(x - 1)}$

7. (a) -7 (b) 1   (c) 5   (d) 2   (e) $-\frac{3}{8}$

(f) 1.25   (g) -6 (h) -4 (i) 2

8. (a) $\ell = \frac{A}{w}$ (b) $r = \frac{I}{pt}$ (c) $l = \frac{V}{R}$ (d) $h = \frac{3V}{\pi r^2}$ (e) $t = \frac{d}{v}$ (f) $h = \frac{2A}{a + b}$

9. 31, 32, 33   10. 462, 498   11. 21 quarters, 42 dimes   12. 480 km

13. (a) $x < 2$ (b) $x \geq -1$ (c) $x \leq -4$ (d) $x \geq 1$

(e) $x \leq 1$ (f) $x < \frac{2}{7}$ (g) $x > 2.5$ (h) $x \leq 1$

14. 36.6 cm   15. 112 cm   16. 368 cm

2.22 CHAPTER 2 TEST

1. (a) $-x^2 + 4x - 10$ (b) $-xy + 2y^2$ 2. (a) $-4x - 3y$ (b) $3c^2 + 15cd + 19d^2$
3. (a) $2ab(2a - 1 + 4b^2)$ (b) $(2x - 3)(2x + 3)$ (d) $(2x - 5)^2$
   (e) $2(x - 11)(x + 11)$ (f) $(x + 3)(2x - 3)$

4. (a) $\frac{1}{3 - 4x}$, $x \neq \frac{3}{4}, 0$ (b) $\frac{2x}{x - 2}$, $x \neq 2, 8$

(c) $2a^4b^3$, $a \neq 0, b \neq 0$ (d) $\frac{3}{2x - 3}$, $x \neq \frac{3}{2}, 5, -5$

5. (a) $74x - 15$ (b) $21x + 16$ 6. (a) 2   (b) 9   (c) 4   (d) $-\frac{35}{12}$

7. (a) $x \geq -5$ (b) $x < 5$ (c) $x \leq 3$ (d) $x \leq \frac{1}{2}$ 8. 7.1 cm

REVIEW AND PREVIEW TO CHAPTER 3

TABLES OF VALUES

1. (a) $y = 2$ (b) $y = 5$ (c) $n = -11$ (d) $n = 6$
   $x = 3.7$ $x = 5.4$ $m = -8.6$ $m = 4.9$
   $x = 13$ $x = 1$ $n = 2$ $n = -3$
   $x = 8.6$ $x = 1.7$ $m = -2.5$ $m = -4.9$
   (e) $y = 16$ (f) $y = -17$ (g) $y = 7$ (h) $y = 4$
   $y = -11.9$ $y = -31.8$ $y = 6.5$ $y = -12$
   $y = -29$ $y = 17$ $y = 9$ $y = -16$
   $y = 13.6$ $y = -8.4$ $y = 15$ $y = -38$

SUBSTITUTION

1. (a) $x = 4$ (b) $y = -9$ (c) $x = 1800$ (d) $y = -300$
2. (a) $s = 93.6$ (b) $t = 1.1$ (c) $s = -52.6$ (d) $t = -0.5$
3. (a) $m = 630$ (b) $n = 0.11$ (c) $m = 2.21$ (d) $n = 142.86$
4. (a) $x = -3.6$ (b) $y = 0.06$ (c) $x = -0.24$ (d) $y = -40$
5. (a) $c = -1008$ (b) $d = -0.42$ (c) $c = 32.256$ (d) $d = 0.08$
6. (a) 10.5   (b) 16.8   (c) 4.0   (d) 6.0

EXERCISE 3.2

1. (b) $\{1, 2, 3, 4, \ldots 50\}$ (c) $\{6, 12, 18, 24, \ldots 300\}$
   (d) 25 teams need 150 players   (f) $(20, 120), (31, 186), (40, 240)$
2. (a) Domain: $\{5, 7, 8\}$, Range: $\{6, 12, 41\}$ (b) Domain: $\{-3, 0, 3, 5\}$, Range: $\{-7, 6, 11, 20\}$
   (c) Domain: $\{2, 5\}$, Range: $\{7\}$ (d) Domain: $\{-6\}$, Range: $\{3, 8, 14\}$
   (e) Domain: $\{a, c, e, g\}$, Range: $\{b, d, f, h\}$ (f) Domain: $\{3, 4, 7, 15\}$, Range: $\{11\}$

3. (a) (1, 400), (2, 800), (9, 3600), $(13\frac{1}{2}, 5400)$, (20, 8000)
   (b) He ran 2400 m in 6 min.
   (c) (8, 3200), (7, 2800), (11, 4400)
   (d) He ran 2000 m in 5 min; he ran 1000 m in 25 min; no meaning.
4. (b) {(1, 1), (2, 2), (3, 4), (4, 8), (5, 16), (6, 32), (7, 64), (8, 128), (9, 256), (10, 512) (11, 1024), (12, 2048), (13, 4096), (14, 8192)}
   (c) Domain: {1, 2, 3, ... 14}   (d) Range: {1, 2, 4, ... 8192}
5. (b) {(3, 0), (4, 2), (5, 5), (6, 9), (7, 14), (8, 20)}   (c) Domain: {3, 4, 5, 6, 7, 8}
   (d) Range: {0, 2, 5, 9, 14, 20}   (f) $\dfrac{n(n-3)}{2}$
6. Domain: {B, I, N, G, O}, Range: {1, 2, 3, ... 75}
7. (b) {(0, 1), (1, 2), (2, 4), (3, 7), (4, 11), (5, 16)}   (c) {0, 1, 2, 3, 4, 5}
   (d) {1, 2, 4, 7, 11, 16}   (e) There are no partial cuts.
   (f) 22

EXERCISE 3.6

1. (a) k = 0.6, x = 0.6y   (b) 63
2. (a) k = 2.5, m = 2.5n   (b) 175
3. (a) k = 3, r = 3t   (b) 13
4. (a) k = $\frac{2}{3}$, c = $\frac{2}{3}$d   (b) 142.5
5. (a) k = 52, w = 52t   (b) 884   (c) 25 min
6. (a) k = 0.75   (b) 225 cm   (c) 200 cm
7. (a) k = 4.9, p = 4.9m   (b) $40.18   (c) 7 kg
8. (a) k = 42.5, c = 42.5t   (b) $318.75   (c) 3.5 h

EXERCISE 3.7

1. (b) $1000   (c) c = 200n + 1000   (d) $15 000
2. (b) $2000   (c) c = 5n + 2000   (d) $152 000
3. (a) c = 0.05n + 75 (b) $2575
4. (a) c = 200n + 500 (b) $2700
5. (a) c = 10n + 125   (b) $325   (c) $1.25   6. (b) 2.5 h

EXERCISE 3.8

1. 1, 64, and 729   2. 101   3. (a) 137.2 m^2 (b) 205.8 m^3
4. 17   5. 22, 4; 6, 20; 10, 16; 2, 24; 18, 8; 12, 14
6. 25.12 cm   7. 75   8. 729   9. 30%
10. (a) 26   (b) 182   11. 1 + 9 + 25 + 81 = 116
12. 4 kg   13. $\frac{1}{65}$
14. (a) (1, 120), (2, 60), (3, 40), (4, 30), (5, 24), (6, 20), (8, 15), (10, 12)   (b) (10, 12)
15. $9\frac{1}{3}$ min   16. 8 : 50   17. $65\frac{5}{11}$ km/h   18. 22.5%
19. 48 L   20. 9.9 cm   21. 20   22. 15
23. $\dfrac{11x}{20}, \dfrac{13x}{24}, \dfrac{11x}{21}, \dfrac{12x}{23}, \dfrac{11x}{24}$ 24. None

3.9 REVIEW EXERCISE

2. (b) 2.5 cm
3. (a) Domain: {3, −2, −1, 0}, Range: {4, 9, 7, 8}   (b) Domain: {2, 4, 6, 8}, Range: {0, 4, 8, 10}
   (c) Domain: {1}, Range: {−2, −1, 0, 1}   (d) Domain: {3, 2, 1}, Range: {−2}
8. (a) k = $\frac{4}{3}$, x = $\frac{4}{3}$y   (b) 200
9. (a) k = 6.7, c = 6.7 m   (b) $358.45   (c) 60 kg

10. (b) $3000   (c) c = 7m + 3000   (d) $40 100

3.10 CHAPTER 3 TEST

1. (a) {(1, 8), (2, 16), (3, 24), (4, 32)}   (b) Domain: {1, 2, 3, 4},   (c) Range: {8, 16, 24, 32}
4. (a) k = 2.8, c = 2.8a   (b) $26.60   (c) 13 kg

REVIEW AND PREVIEW TO CHAPTER 4

THE PYTHAGOREAN THEOREM

1. (a) a = 10   (b) a = 17   (c) c = 12   (d) b = 12
   (e) b = 6.9   (f) a = 9.2   (g) b = 32   (h) c = 48
2. (a) x = 16.9   (b) x = 4.9   (c) x = 5   (d) x = 2

FORMULAS AND EQUATIONS

1. (a) $\ell = \dfrac{A}{w}, w = \dfrac{A}{\ell}$ (b) $p = \dfrac{I}{rt}, t = \dfrac{I}{pr}$ (c) $r = \dfrac{C}{2\pi}$

   (d) $\ell = \dfrac{V}{wh}, w = \dfrac{V}{\ell h}$ (e) $S = \dfrac{D}{T}, T = \dfrac{D}{S}$ (f) $h = \dfrac{2A}{b}, b = \dfrac{2A}{h}$

   (g) $\ell = \dfrac{P - 2w}{2}, w = \dfrac{P - 2\ell}{2}$ (h) $h = \dfrac{2A}{(a + b)}, b = \dfrac{2A - ha}{h}$

2. (a) y = 7 − x   (b) y = x − 9   (c) $y = \dfrac{-x}{2} + 3$

   (d) $y = \dfrac{-2x + 8}{3}$ (e) $y = \dfrac{2x}{5} - 2$ (f) $y = \dfrac{-4x}{5} + 4$

EXERCISE 4.1

2. (a) $\frac{2}{3}$ (b) 1   (c) 1   (d) $\frac{6}{5}$

   (e) 0   (f) $-\frac{3}{4}$ (g) −4   (h) $-\frac{7}{2}$

3. (a) $-\frac{10}{9}$ (b) 0   (c) no slope   (d) 1

   (e) no slope   (f) −1   (g) −4   (h) $\frac{6}{5}$

   (i) $-\frac{35}{57}$ (j) no slope   (k) −2.4   (l) 0.35

   (m) 0.26   (n) 4.6

4. (a) 3   (b) −1   (c) $-\frac{2}{3}$ (d) $\frac{5}{3}$

   (e) $\frac{1}{3}$ (f) 2   (g) 2   (h) −3

5. (a) y = 8   (b) y = −8   (c) y = −3   (d) x = 2
6. x = 1   7. Answers vary

EXERCISE 4.2

1. (a) 5x + 3y − 7 = 0   (b) 3x − 2y + 4 = 0   (c) 4x + 5y − 3 = 0
   (d) 7x + 3y + 2 = 0   (e) 3x + 5y − 2 = 0   (f) 7x − 2y + 3 = 0
   (g) 4x − 3y + 5 = 0   (h) 3x − 4y = 0   (i) 2x + 7 = 0
   (j) −4y + 3 = 0   (k) 4x − 3y + 2 = 0   (l) 2x − y − 7 = 0
2. (a) 4x − y − 10 = 0   (b) 2x − y − 3 = 0   (c) 3x + y + 13 = 0
   (d) x + y + 5 = 0   (e) 3x − y + 14 = 0   (f) 6x + y − 22 = 0
   (g) x − 2y + 10 = 0   (h) x + 3y − 12 = 0   (i) 2x + 4y + 7 = 0
   (j) 20x − 30y − 11 = 0
3. (a) 2x − y = 0   (b) 6x − y + 3 = 0   (c) 2x + y − 2 = 0

(d) $3x + y + 13 = 0$ (e) $3x - y + 1 = 0$ (f) $x - 2y - 6 = 0$
(g) $x + 2y + 4 = 0$ (h) $x - 3y - 14 = 0$ (i) $0.1x + y - 0.36 = 0$
4. $2x - y - 10 = 0$
5. $3x + y + 2 = 0$
6. (a) $4x - y + 26 = 0$ (b) $y = 6$ (c) $x = -5$
7. $y = 0$ 8. $x = 0$ 9. $2x - y + 12 = 0$
10. $x - y + 2 = 0$ 11. $x - y = 0$ 12. $x - y + (b - a) = 0$

EXERCISE 4.3

	A	B	C	Description
1. (a)	2	0	3	vertical
(b)	0	3	5	horizontal
(c)	1	1	0	through the origin
(d)	2	0	-7	vertical
(e)	5	-4	0	through the origin
(f)	1	0	0	vertical line through the origin
(g)	0	1	0	horizontal line through the origin

2. (a) $C = 0$ (b) $B = 0$ (C) $A = 0$ (d) $A = 0, C = 0$
3. (a) $2x - y - 1 = 0$ (b) $3x - y + 1 = 0$ (c) $5x + y + 10 = 0$
(d) $2x + y + 8 = 0$ (e) $4x + y + 4 = 0$ (f) $x - 2y = 0$
(g) $x - 3y + 11 = 0$ (h) $y - 4 = 0$ (i) $x - 3 = 0$
(j) $9x + 2y - 19 = 0$ (k) $4x - y - 3 = 0$ (l) $3x - 2y + 1.8 = 0$
(m) $3x + 2y - 4.2 = 0$ (n) $5x + 2y + 18 = 0$
4. $4x - y + 18 = 0$ 5. $3x + 4y - 8 = 0$ 6. $4x - 5y - 20 = 0$
7. $5x - y - 5 = 0$ 8. $bx + ay - ab = 0$

EXERCISE 4.4

1. (a) $x = 3, y = 2$ (b) $x = 3, y = 4$ (c) $x = 3, y = 9$
(d) $x = 8, y = 2$ (e) $x = 2, y = -5$ (f) $x = 3, y = -7$
(g) $x = -5, y = 4$ (h) $x = -5, y = 3$ (i) $x = 2, y = 7$
(j) $x = -3, y = 8$ (k) $x = 2, y = -8$ (l) $x = 4, y = 12$
2. (a) $x = 5, y = 4$ (b) $x = 4, y = -3$ (c) $x = 2, y = 4$
(d) $x = 3, y = 5$ (e) $x = -7, y = 7$ (f) $x = -2, y = -5$
(g) $x = 7, y = 2$ (h) $x = -6, y = 2$
3. (a) $x = 2, y = -6$ (b) $x = 2, y = 4$ (c) $x = -3, y = -3$
(d) $x = -4, y = 2$ (e) $x = 3, y = 1$ (f) $x = 2, y = 3$
(g) $x = 12, y = -6$ (h) $x = -3, y = 8$
4. (a) $x = \frac{3}{2}$ (b) $y = -3$ (c) $x = 3, -3, y = -9$
(d) $x = 2, -2, y = -8$ (e) $x = 5, -5, y = 5, -5$ (f) $x = 2, -2, y = 3, -3$
5. $y = n, n \neq 0$ 6. $x = n, n \neq 0$
7. (a) $y = -\frac{1}{2}x + 2$ (b) $y = \frac{3}{5}x - 3$ (c) $y = 3$

EXERCISE 4.5

1. (a) $m = 4, b = 6$ (b) $m = 1, b = -4$ (c) $m = -2, b = -3$
(d) $m = -7, b = 4$ (e) $m = \frac{1}{2}, b = -6$ (f) $m = -\frac{2}{3}, b = 7$
(g) $m = 3, b = -7$ (h) $m = -2, b = 6$ (i) $m = 0, b = 5$
(j) no slope, no y-intercept   (k) $m = 0, b = -2$ (l) no slope, no y-intercept
(m) $m = -3, b = 2$ (n) $m = 2, b = 0$
2. (a) $y = 2x + 3$ (b) $y = 4x - 2$ (c) $y = -2x - 4$
(d) $y = 3$ (e) $y = -x$ (f) $y = -\frac{1}{2}x - 2$

(g) $y = 0.2x + 1.7$

(h) $y = -1.5x - 4.6$

(i) $y = -\frac{4}{5}x$

(j) $y = -\frac{1}{5}$

(k) $y = 15.3x - 45.6$

3. (a) (iv) (b) (v) (c) (vi) (d) (iii) (e) (i) (f) (ii)

4. (a) $m = -\frac{2}{3}, b = \frac{8}{3}$ (b) $m = \frac{3}{2}, b = -\frac{5}{2}$ (c) $m = -\frac{5}{2}, b = -2$

(d) $m = -\frac{2}{5}, b = 0$ (e) $m = \frac{7}{3}, b = \frac{2}{3}$ (f) $m = \frac{7}{2}, b = 2$

(g) $m = 0, b = \frac{7}{2}$ (h) no slope, no y-intercept (i) $m = -6, b = 8$

(j) $m = 4, b = -0.4$ (k) $m = -0.8, b = 0.4$ (l) $m = -12, b = 0$

6. (i) parallel lines (ii) $m = 2$ (iii) Parallel lines have equal slopes.

7. (b) $90°$ (c) (i) -1 (ii) -1 (iii) -1

(d) The product of the slope of perpendicular lines is -1.

EXERCISE 4.6

1. (i) (c) (ii) (b) (iii) (a) (iv) (b)
(v) (c) (vi) (b) (vii) (a) (viii) (c)
(ix) (b) (x) (a) (xi) (c) (xii) (c)
(xiii) (b) (xiv) (c) (xv) (c) (xvi) (b)

2. (i) $2, -\frac{1}{2}$ (ii) $3, -\frac{1}{3}$ (iii) $-3, \frac{1}{3}$ (iv) $-1, 1$

(v) $\frac{1}{2}, -2$ (vi) $-\frac{2}{3}, \frac{3}{2}$ (vii) $-\frac{3}{4}, \frac{4}{3}$ (viii) $\frac{5}{4}, -\frac{4}{5}$

(ix) $-7, \frac{1}{7}$ (x) $3, -\frac{1}{3}$ (xi) $-3, \frac{1}{3}$ (xii) $-\frac{5}{2}, \frac{2}{5}$

(xiii) $\frac{5}{4}, -\frac{4}{5}$ (xiv) $3, -\frac{1}{3}$ (xv) $\frac{5}{7}, -\frac{7}{5}$ (xvi) $-\frac{3}{2}, \frac{2}{3}$

3. $2x - y + 8 = 0$ 4. $2x + y + 7 = 0$ 5. $x + 2y - 7 = 0$
6. $3x - 4y + 18 = 0$ 7. (b) $3x + 4y - 20 = 0$ (c) $x + 2y = 0$

EXERCISE 4.7

1. (a) 2150 (b) 1700 (c) 220
(d) the cost per meal (e) 350, room rent
2. (a) $22.5°C$ (b) 3.2 h (c) 10, initial water temperature
3. (a) 2200 (b) 450 (c) 2500
(d) the cost of the lunch per person (e) 1000, cost of band
4. (a) 20 L (b) 100 L (c) 500 km
(d) 70 L (e) litres per kilometre
5. (a) 2046 m (b) 4 s 6. (a) 69.0 m/s (b) 3.5 s

EXERCISE 4.9

1. (a) m (b) b (c) m (d) a (e) b
2. (a) $y = mx + 5$ (b) $y = b$ (c) $y = m(x - 4) + 5$
(d) $y = -3x + b$ (e) $x = a$ (f) $y = mx$
3. (a) $y = \frac{3}{2}x + \frac{5}{2}$ (b) $y = \frac{1}{2}x + \frac{3}{2}$ (c) $y = -x + 16$ (d) $y = -\frac{2}{5}x + \frac{4}{5}$ (e) $y = \frac{2}{3}x - 6$

EXERCISE 4.10

1. (a) 5 (b) 6 (c) 11 (d) 11 (e) 7 (f) 17
(g) 15 (h) 10 (i) 8 (j) 1 (k) 4 (l) 3.2
2. (a) $\sqrt{58}$ (b) $\sqrt{89}$ (c) $\sqrt{34}$ (d) $\sqrt{234}$ (e) $\sqrt{265}$ (f) $\sqrt{85}$
(g) $5\sqrt{10}$ (h) $\sqrt{113}$ (i) $\sqrt{17}$ (j) $\sqrt{8}$ (k) $\sqrt{5}$ (l) $\sqrt{89}$
(m) 2.6 (n) $\sqrt{49.46}$
3. $AB = 2\sqrt{13}, BC = \sqrt{29}, AC = \sqrt{97}$ 4. $AC = \sqrt{202}, BD = 3\sqrt{10}$
5. $AC = \sqrt{41}, BC = \sqrt{41}$ 6. 5

EXERCISE 4.11

1. (a) (4, 4) (b) (2, 6) (c) (6.5, −2) (d) (−1, 1.5)
   (e) (4.5, 0) (f) (0, 3) (g) (1, 3.4) (h) $(1, -\frac{5}{2})$

2. (a) (5, 1) (b) (3, 2) (c) (2, −3) (d) $(5, 3\frac{1}{2})$
   (e) $(-\frac{1}{2}, -5)$ (f) $(1, -\frac{3}{2})$ (g) (1, 3) (h) (1, 5)

EXERCISE 4.13

1. (a), (b), (d), (e) (h) 2. (a), (b), (d)
3. (a) 12 (b) 7 (c) 4 (d) 1 (e) 14 (f) −7
   (g) −9 (h) 2 (i) −15
4. (a) 2 (b) 10 (c) 6 (d) 9 (e) 4 (f) 1
   (g) −9 (e) −14 (i) −2
5. (a) Yes (b) No 6. No
7. (b) Domain: {1, 2, 3, 4, 5}, Range: {−1, 1, 3, 5, 7} (c) Yes
8. (b) Domain: {−2, −1, 0, 1, 2}, Range: {2, 3, 6} (c) Yes
9. (b) Domain: {0, 1, 2, 3, 4}, Range: {4, 7, 10, 13, 16} (c) Yes
10. (b) Yes
11. (a) {(0, −4), (1, 1), (2, 6), (3, 11), (4, 16)}
    (b) Domain: {0, 1, 2, 3, 4}, Range: {−4, 1, 6, 11, 16} (c) Yes
12. (a) {(0, 3), (2, 4), (4, 5), (6, 6)} (b) Yes
13. (a) {(−2, 4), (−1, −2), (0, −4), (1, −2), (2, 4)} (b) Yes
14. {(0, 0), (0, 1), (0, 2), (0, 3), (1, 0), (1, 1), (1, 2), (1, 3), (2, 0), (2, 1), (2, 2), (2, 3), (3, 0), (3, 1), (3, 2), (3, 3), (4, 0), (4, 1), (4, 2), (4, 3)}. Not a function.
15. {(4, −2), (1, −1), (0, 0), (1, 1), (4, 2)}. Not a function.

EXERCISE 4.14

1. (a) 7 (b) 11 (c) −5 (d) 3 (e) 43 (f) −25
   (g) −397 (h) 203 (i) 27 (j) −17 (k) 4a + 3 (l) 4b + 3
2. (a) 1 (b) 16 (c) −14 (d) −5 (e) 25 (f) −35
   (g) −26 (h) 55 (i) −17 (j) 3m − 5 (k) 3t − 5 (l) 3a² − 5
3. (a) 4 (b) −8 (c) 5 (d) 0 (e) 13 (f) 4
   (g) −7 (h) −11 (i) 13 (j) $\frac{1}{4}$ (k) 6 (l) 0
4. (a) 8, (2, 8) (b) 13, (−3, 13) (c) 40, (6, 40) (d) 8, (−2, 8)
5. (a) −3, (2, −3) (b) −6, (−4, −6) (c) −1, (6, −1) (d) $\frac{1}{2}$, $(9, \frac{1}{2})$
6. (a) 5 (b) 5 (c) 25 (d) 7
7. (a) 9 (b) 25 (c) 0 (d) 9
8. (a) 6 (b) 18 (c) −24 (d) −23
9. (a) 18 (b) 14 (c) 1 (d) 20
10. (a) 39 (b) 7 (c) 78 (d) 35
11. (a) −13 (b) 1 (c) 5 (d) −9 (e) 2 (f) −19
12. (a) 16 (b) 6 (c) 4 (d) 18
13. (a) 2 (b) 7 (c) −5 14. −1, 2

EXERCISE 4.15

1. Fill the five litre container and pour water into the three litre container until it is full. Empty the three litre container and pour the remaining 2 L of water from the five litre container into the three litre container. Then refill the five litre container and pour water into the three litre container until it is full. This leaves 4 L of water in the five litre container.
2. (a) 400 m (b) 500 m (c) 550 m (d) 575 m 3. 01:00 4. No
5. 12 6. (a) 20 s (b) 1 min 7. 6

8. $0 = 4 - 4 - 4 + 4$, $1 = 4 - 4 + 4 \div 4$
   $2 = 4 \div 4 + 4 \div 4$, $4 = (4 - 4) \times 4 + 4$
   $5 = (4 \times 4 + 4) \div 4$, $6 = (4 + 4) \div 4 + 4$
   $7 = 4 - 4 \div 4 + 4$, $8 = 4 \times 4 - 4 - 4$
   $9 = 4 + 4 + 4 \div 4$, $12 = (4 - (4 \div 4)) \times 4$

9. (a) 17   (b) 21

10. $22 + 23 = 45$,
    $14 + 15 + 16 = 45$,
    $7 + 8 + 9 + 10 + 11 = 45$,
    $5 + 6 + 7 + 8 + 9 + 10 = 45$

11. 3

12. $40 + 41 = 81$,
    $26 + 27 + 28 = 81$,
    $11 + 12 + 13 + 14 + 15 + 16 = 81$,
    $5 + 6 + 7 + 8 + 9 + 10 + 11 + 12 + 13 = 81$

13. Celsius — 33.3, 46.7, 60; Exinor — 65, 72.5, 95

14. 27 min

15. 24 and 48   16. 9   17. 13   18. 125   19. 15   20. (c)

4.16 REVIEW EXERCISE

1. (a) $m = 7, b = 6$ (b) $m = -3, b = 14$ (c) $m = 4, b = -7$ (d) $m = \frac{1}{3}, b = -4$

   (e) $m = -2, b = \frac{7}{2}$ (f) no slope, no y-intercept   (g) $m = 0, b = -4$

   (h) $m = \frac{3}{5}, b = -\frac{9}{5}$ (i) $m = \frac{4}{7}, b = \frac{11}{7}$ (j) $m = \frac{2}{3}, b = 4$

2. (a) 5   (b) 2   (c) 7   (d) 16

3. (a) $(4, -4)$ (b) $(3, -\frac{3}{2})$ (c) $(-7\frac{1}{2}, -6)$ (d) $(5, -4\frac{1}{2})$

4. (a) b   (b) b   (c) m   (d) a   (e) m   (f) m

5. (a), (b)

6. (a) 7   (b) 13   (c) 5   (d) -1 (e) 5   (f) -5
   (g) -6 (h) -10

7. (a) 5   (b) 11   (c) 4   (d) 59   (e) 9   (f) 0
   (g) -19 (h) -16 (i) 2   (j) -2 (k) $2a + 1$ (l) $3b - 1$

8. (a) -1 (b) $-\frac{1}{3}$ (c) $-\frac{1}{2}$ (d) 6   (e) -6 (f) -5

9. (a) $7x - y - 22 = 0$ (b) $x + y + 8 = 0$ (c) $2x + y + 2 = 0$
   (d) $x - 2y - 17 = 0$ (e) $1.4x + y + 5.6 = 0$ (f) $0.2x + y + 0.52 = 0$

10. (a) $2x + y + 13 = 0$ (b) $x = -4$ (c) $y = -5$

11. (a) $5x - 2y - 7 = 0$ (b) $4x - 9y - 38 = 0$ (c) $12x + 5y - 1 = 0$ (d) $x + 2y = 0$

12. (a) $y = -2x + 3$ (b) $y = 3x - 7$ (c) $y = -\frac{1}{2}x + 2$ (d) $y = \frac{3}{4}x - 3$

    (e) $y = 3x + 4$ (f) $y = \frac{1}{2}x - \frac{5}{2}$ (g) $y = 4x + 31$ (h) $y = -\frac{3}{2}x + \frac{5}{2}$

13. $2x - y - 17 = 0$ 14. $x - 2y - 5 = 0$

15. (a) $3\sqrt{10}$ (b) $3\sqrt{2}$ (c) $\sqrt{261}$ (d) $2\sqrt{5}$

16. $AC = \sqrt{269}, BD = \sqrt{194}$

17. (a) $y = b$ (b) $y = m(x - 7) - 2$ (c) $y = mx + 5$ (d) $y = 4x + b$

19. (a) $(1, 1)$ (b) $(3, 0)$ (c) $(5.5, -2)$ (d) $(-3, 1.5)$ (e) $(3, 1)$ (f) $(\frac{1}{2}, 1)$

20. (a) -14 (b) 16   (c) 2   (d) 12   (e) 5   (f) 28

21. (a) $C = 5x + 1000$ (c) cost/book   (d) \$2500   (e) \$2000
    (f) 500   (g) $(0, 1000)$

4.17 CHAPTER 4 TEST

1. (a) -2 (b) $\frac{3}{4}$ (c) 0   (d) $\frac{1}{2}$ (e) -2 (f) 2

2. (a) $y = 2x - 1$ (b) $y = x + 4$ (c) $y = -x + 4$ (d) $x = 2$ (e) $y = 3x - 13$

3. 13   4. $(-4, 5)$ 6. (a) $y = mx + 7$ (b) $y = m(x - 3) - 2$

7. (a) A family of horizontal lines.   (b) A family of lines having y-intercept 3.

8. (b) $\ell = 3m + 7$ (c) 13 cm
   (d) 6 kg   (e) 7
   (f) The initial length of the spring is 7 cm.

4.18 CUMULATIVE REVIEW FOR CHAPTERS 1 TO 4

1. (a) 0.875; 0; 0   (b) $0.\overline{428571}$; 428571; 6
   (c) $0.\overline{2}$; 2; 1   (d) 0.08; 0; 0
2. (a) $\frac{1}{25}$ (b) $\frac{4}{9}$ (c) $\frac{13}{99}$ 4. Answers vary
5. (a) $3\sqrt{2}$ (b) $9\sqrt{2}$ (c) $5\sqrt{3}$ (d) $6\sqrt{2}$
6. (a) $\sqrt{20}$ (b) $\sqrt{175}$ (c) $\sqrt{48}$ (d) $\sqrt{8}$
7. (a) $6\sqrt{35}$ (b) 36   (c) $24\sqrt{3}$ (d) $6\sqrt{6} - 15\sqrt{2}$
   (e) 32   (f) 216   (g) $2\sqrt{2}$ (h) 1
8. (a) $5\sqrt{5} + 4\sqrt{2}$ (b) $4\sqrt{2}$ (c) $14\sqrt{3}$ (d) $18\sqrt{2}$ (e) $6\sqrt{3}$
9. (a) 8.1   (b) 8.7
10. (a) $6a^3b^5$ (b) $-6x^5y^3$ (c) $\frac{2a^2}{3b}$ (d) $3a$ (e) $\frac{4y^2}{9x^2}$ (f) $\frac{3ab^2}{2c}$
11. (a) 1   (b) $\frac{25}{9}$ (c) $\frac{5}{6}$ (d) -1
12. (a) $3x^2 - 4x + 1$ (b) $a - 3b + 10$ (c) $8x + 13y$ (d) $4x^3 - x^2 - 9x$
13. (a) $4b(3ac - a + 2c)$ (b) $2ax(a + 2 - 4a^2x)$ (c) $(3x + 5)(3x - 5)$ (d) $(x + 5)(x - 2)$
14. (a) $\frac{1}{2 + 3x}$, $x \neq -\frac{2}{3}, 0$ (b) $\frac{1}{x - 4}$, $x \neq -4, 4$ (c) $\frac{x + 2}{x + 3}$, $x \neq -3$ (d) $1, x \neq -2, 2$
15. (a) $\frac{22x}{15}$ (b) $\frac{19a - 5}{10}$
16. (a) $x = -8$ (b) $x = \frac{1}{3}$ (c) $x = 8$ 17. (a) $x < 1$ (b) $x \leq -8$
18. (a) {(1, 40), (2, 80), (3, 120), (4, 160)}
    (b) Domain: {1, 2, 3, 4}   (c) Range: {40, 80, 120, 160}
21. (a) $0.11   (b) $C = 0.60t + 0.11$ (c) $6.11
22. (a) $k = 0.3$ (b) 7.5 kg   (c) 42
23. (a) 3   (b) $\frac{2}{3}$ (c) 0   (d) 2   (e) $\frac{3}{2}$ (f) -2
24. (a) $y = 3x - 11$ (b) $y = x + 1$ (c) $y = -2x + 5$
    (d) $x = 3$ (e) $y = -2x + 4$
25. (a) $y = mx + 3$ (b) $y = m(x + 1) + 2$

REVIEW AND PREVIEW TO CHAPTER 5

EQUATIONS IN ONE VARIABLE

1. (a) 15   (b) 4   (c) 5   (d) 12   (e) 7   (f) 8
   (g) 15   (h) 7   (i) 5
2. (a) 5   (b) -8 (c) 0   (d) -1 (e) 2   (f) -4
3. (a) -5 (b) 4   (c) 4   (d) 4   (e) 1   (f) -3
4. (a) 9   (b) -12 (c) -3 (d) 3   (e) 5   (f) 2
5. (a) $\frac{3}{2}$ (b) 19   (c) $\frac{9}{4}$ (d) -8 (e) 5   (f) 7
   (g) 26   (h) 7
6. (a) $\frac{c - b}{a}$ (b) $ab - c$ (c) $a - bc$ (d) $a(b + c)$ (e) $\frac{abd + ac}{cd}$ (f) $b(a - c)$
7. (a) $\frac{c}{a - b}$ (b) 1   (c) $a + b$ (d) $\frac{a^2}{b - a}$
   (e) $\frac{abc}{bc - ac - ab}$ (f) $\frac{bc}{c - a}$

SIMPLIFICATION

1. (a) $x^2 - 23x$ (b) $x^2 + x - 12$ (c) $x^2 + 14x + 49$ (d) $2x^2 + 11x$
   (e) $4x^2 - 25$ (f) $9x^2 + 6x + 4$ (g) $22x$
2. (a) $3x^2 + 6x$ (b) $3x^2 - 2x$ (c) $-10x - 6$ (d) $-12x^2 - 17x$
   (e) $-3x^2 - 13x - 10$

FACTORING

1. (a) $(a + b)(a - b)$ (b) $(a - b)^2$ (c) $(a + 3)(a - 4)$ (d) $(a + 5)(a - 4)$
   (e) $a(a - b)$ (f) $(a - 2b)(a - 3b)$ (g) $(a - 4b)(a + 2b)$
2. (a) $a(a + b)(a - b)$ (b) $ab(a - b)$ (c) $b(a + b)(a - b)$ (d) $a(a + b)^2$

INTERSECTION AND UNION OF SETS

1. (a) $\{2, 4\}$ (b) $\{1, 2, 3, 4, 5, 6, 8\}$ (c) $\{2, 4, 5\}$ (d) $\{2, 4, 5\}$

TABLES OF VALUES

1. (a) $y = -8$ (b) $y = 0$ (c) $y = -3$ (d) $y = 24$
     $y = -2$ $y = -1$ $y = 11$ $y = -6$
     $y = 4$ $y = 0$ $y = 9$ $y = 24$

EXERCISE 5.1

1. (a) $(2, 12), (0, 14), (20, -6)$ (b) $(1, 11), (7, -1), (10, -7)$
   (c) $(9, 1), (2, -6), (-6, -14), (3, -5)$ (d) $(4, 6), (-3, -1), (-2, 0)$
2. (a) $(4, 5), (8, 1), (-3, 12), (14, -5), (12, -3)$ (b) $(9, 3), (8, 2), (5, -1), (3, -3), (-8, -14)$
   (c) $(1, 13), (5, 5), (7, 1), (6, 3), (10, -5)$
3. (a) $(3, 1)$ (b) $(4, 3)$ (c) $(2, 3)$
4. (a) 6 (b) 4 (c) $7, 3$ (d) $7, 1$

EXERCISE 5.2

1. (a) $(0, 3), (1, 4), (2, 5)$ (b) $(0, -1), (1, 1), (2, 3)$
   (c) $(0, 1), (1, 4), (2, 7)$ (d) $(0, 2), (1, 1), (2, 0)$
   (e) $(0, 4), (1, 3), (2, 2)$ (f) $(0, -1), (1, -3), (2, -5)$
   (g) $(0, 2), (1, 6), (2, 10)$ (h) $(0, 0), (1, 3), (2, 6)$
   (i) $(0, 0), (1, -1), (2, -2)$ (j) Answers vary
2. (a) $(0, 2), (3, 0)$ (b) $(0, 4), (5, 0)$
   (c) $(0, 4), (8, 0)$ (d) $(0, 9), (3, 0)$
   (e) $(0, -5), (3, 0)$ (f) $(0, 3), (-4, 0)$
   (g) $(0, 7), (7, 0)$ (h) $(0, -4), (4, 0)$
   (i) $(0, 3), (-3, 0)$ (j) $(\frac{7}{3}, 0), (0, -\frac{7}{2})$
3. (a) $(1, 1)$ (b) $(3, 2)$ (c) $(2, 1)$
4. (a) $(1, 3)$ (b) $(3, 5)$ (c) $(-2, 5)$ (d) $(-2, 6)$ (e) $(1, 1)$ (f) $(1, 7)$
5. (a) $(-2, 2)$ (b) $(2, -3)$ (c) $(6, 0)$ (d) $(2, 0)$
6. (a) none   (b) infinite   (c) none   (d) infinite

EXERCISE 5.3

1. (a) $(2, 2)$ (b) $(1, -1)$ (c) $(-1, 1)$ (d) $(2, -1)$
   (e) $(2, -\frac{1}{2})$ (f) $(1, 0)$ (g) $(1, \frac{1}{3})$ (h) $(3, \frac{1}{2})$
2. (a) $(2, \frac{3}{4})$ (b) $(1, 0)$ (c) $(13, -4)$ (d) $(-1\frac{1}{2}, 2)$
   (e) $(2, \frac{1}{2})$ (f) $(2, 3)$ (g) $(\frac{2}{5}, -\frac{3}{4})$ (h) $(6, 2)$

EXERCISE 5.4

1. (a) $y = -3x + 7$ (b) $x = -2y + 4$ (c) $y = \dfrac{-2x + 2}{3}$ (d) $x = \dfrac{-2y + 4}{3}$

   (e) $y = \dfrac{-5x + 20}{2}$ (f) $x = \dfrac{-2y + 20}{5}$ (g) $x = \dfrac{2y + 12}{3}$ (h) $y = \dfrac{4x + 11}{3}$

(i) $y = 5x - 7$ (j) $x = 2y - 4$ (k) $a = \dfrac{-3b - 4}{2}$ (l) $b = \dfrac{5a - 2}{3}$

(m) $y = \dfrac{2x - 4}{3}$ (n) $x = \dfrac{2y - 3}{3}$ (o) $a = \dfrac{3b - 6}{5}$ (p) $n = \dfrac{3m - 4}{7}$

2. (a) (2, 8)   (b) (1, −1)   (c) (2, −1)   (d) (−3, −6)
  (e) (−11, −7)   (f) (−5, 2)   (g) (−26, −11)   (h) (1, 1)
3. (a) (2, 2)   (b) (2, −2)   (c) (2, 1)   (d) (1, 2)
4. (a) (0, 2)   (b) (1, 0)   (c) (2, −1)   (d) $(2, -\tfrac{1}{4})$

  (e) $(2, -\tfrac{1}{4})$ (f) (−2, 0)   (g) (−1, 4)   (h) $(2, \tfrac{1}{3})$

  (i) $(3, -\tfrac{2}{3})$ (j) $(-1, \tfrac{2}{3})$

EXERCISE 5.5

1. (a) (5, 1)   (b) (5, 2)   (c) (3, 5)   (d) (1, 7)   (e) (1, 3)
  (f) (0, 2)   (g) (2, 0)   (h) $(1, -\tfrac{1}{2})$ (i) (1, 2)   (j) (3, 0)
2. (a) (4, 2)   (b) (3, 3)   (c) (4, 2)   (d) (7, 2)   (e) (2, 3)   (f) (2, 1)
3. (a) (3, 2)   (b) (−1, −2)   (c) (−2, 1)   (d) (−2, 5)
  (e) (−2, −3)   (f) (−1, 5)   (g) (−1, −2)   (h) (6, 2)
4. (a) $(-\tfrac{1}{2}, -\tfrac{2}{3})$ (b) $(\tfrac{5}{2}, -\tfrac{7}{3})$ (c) $(-\tfrac{7}{4}, 0)$ (d) (−6, 4)

  (e) (−5, −4)   (f) $(-\tfrac{1}{2}, -\tfrac{1}{3})$ (g) $(\tfrac{1}{2}, \tfrac{1}{4})$ (h) $(-\tfrac{2}{3}, -\tfrac{5}{2})$

EXERCISE 5.7

1. (a) (3, 4)   (b) (6, −4)   (c) (3, −3)   (d) (−6, −8)   (e) (−4, −2)   (f) (1, −1)
2. (a) (4, 3)   (b) (3, 4)   (c) (−1, −3)   (d) (0.1 −0.2)
  (e) (−0.5, 0.3)   (f) (−0.7, −0.3)   (g) (−0.4, −1.1)   (h) (1.2, −0.8)
3. (a) (1, 6)   (b) (−1, −5)   (c) (4, 5)   (d) (−3, −7)
  (e) (5, −3)   (f) (−3, −4)   (g) (20, 10)   (h) (0, 0)
4. (a) (5, 4)   (b) (−4, 7)   (c) (8, −6)   (d) (8, 6)   (e) (6, 9)   (f) (7, 6)

EXERCISE 5.8

1. (a) $\dfrac{b}{a}$ (b) $\dfrac{n}{m}$ (c) $\dfrac{a + b}{n}$ (d) $\dfrac{a + b}{m + n}$ (e) ab (f) $-mn$

  (g) $\dfrac{4}{a + b}$ (h) $\dfrac{-2y}{m - n}$ (i) $\dfrac{6}{a + b}$ (j) $\dfrac{t}{c - d}$ (k) $\dfrac{c + d}{g - h}$ (l) $\dfrac{t - s}{b - a}$

  (m) $\dfrac{m}{2a + b}$ (n) $\dfrac{b - a}{4c - 3t}$

2. (a) $\dfrac{m}{3 - b}$ (b) $\dfrac{11}{b - 5}$ (c) $\dfrac{8ab}{6a - b}$ (d) $\dfrac{c}{b - a}$ (e) $\dfrac{3(1 - a)}{5b - 2}$

3. (a) $(a, -b)$ (b) $(3a, -b)$ (c) $(-\tfrac{3}{2}n, m)$

  (d) $(5b, -3a)$ (e) $\left(\dfrac{23b}{13}, -\dfrac{a}{13}\right)$ (f) $\left(\dfrac{2a}{3}, -\dfrac{(a + 3b)}{3}\right)$

4. (a) $\left(\dfrac{m + n}{2a + b}, \dfrac{bm - 2an}{2a + b}\right)$ (b) $\left(\dfrac{3b - 2}{ab - 1}, \dfrac{3 - 2a}{1 - ab}\right)$ (c) $\left(\dfrac{8 - 6a}{6 - a^2}, \dfrac{4a - 18}{a^2 - 6}\right)$

  (d) $\left(\dfrac{6}{a + b}, \dfrac{2b - 4a}{a + b}\right)$ (e) $\left(\dfrac{eg - hn}{en - dn}, \dfrac{dg - hm}{dn - em}\right)$ (f) $\left(\dfrac{ce - bf}{ae - bd}, \dfrac{dc - af}{ae - bd}\right)$

EXERCISE 5.9

1. (a) consistent   (b) dependent   (c) inconsistent   (d) inconsistent   (e) consistent
   (f) dependent   (g) inconsistent   (h) consistent   (i) dependent   (j) dependent
2. (a) inconsistent, $\emptyset$ (b) dependent, $\{(x, y)|x + y = 4, x, y \in R\}$
   (c) consistent, (1, 1)   (d) consistent, (2, 3)
   (e) inconsistent, $\emptyset$ (f) consistent, $(-1, 1)$
3. (a) consistent   (b) inconsistent

EXERCISE 5.10

1. (a) $a = 2, b = 3, c = 2$ (b) $x = 4, y = 2, t = 5$
   (c) $a = 3, b = -2, c = -3$ (d) $x = -2, y = -3, m = -4$
   (e) $a = -1, b = 0, c = 1$ (f) $x = 2, y = -2, d = -\frac{1}{2}$
   (g) $a = 2, b = 3, c = -1, d = -2$ (h) $x = -2, y = -3, m = 4$

EXERCISE 5.12

1. (a) first   (b) second   (c) first, second, fourth   (d) fourth
   (e) second, third, fourth   (f) third   (g) first, second, third

EXERCISE 5.13

1. (a) (i) maximum of 27 at A, minimum of -6 at C   (b) (i) maximum of 6 at C, minimum of -21 at B
       (ii) maximum of 12 at C, minimum of -14 at B   (ii) maximum of 30 at A, minimum of -14 at C
       (iii) maximum of 24 at A, minimum of -13 at C   (iii) maximum of 2 at C, minimum of -8 at B
   (c) (i) maximum of 18 at D, minimum of -21 at B   (d) (i) maximum of 30 at E, minimum of -36 at B
       (ii) maximum of 32 at A, minimum of -18 at C   (ii) maximum of 27 at B, minimum of -19 at E
       (iii) maximum of 25 at A, minimum of -12 at C   (iii) maximum of 25 at D, minimum of -25 at A
   (e) (i) maximum of 14 at A, minimum of -36 at D   (f) (i) maximum of 44 at C, minimum of 0 at (0, 0)
       (ii) maximum of 49 at C, minimum of 0 at (0, 0)   (ii) maximum of 25 at B, minimum of -10 at D
       (iii) maximum of 7 at A, minimum of -9 at D   (iii) maximum of 16 at C, minimum of -8 at A
2. (a) maximum of 20 at (0, 5), minimum of 0 at (0, 0)
   (b) maximum of 62 at (4, 6), minimum of 0 at (0, 0)
   (c) maximum of 70 at (10, 0), minimum of 0 at (0, 0)
   (d) maximum of 14 at (1, 6), minimum of -42 at $(3, -10)$
   (e) maximum of 43 at (3, 7), minimum of 0 at (0, 0)
3. 80 Standard and 20 Championship   4. 15 bracelets and 12 necklaces
5. 10 portable and 12 table   6. 60 Super I and 30 Super II
7. 100 Standard and 100 Deluxe   8. 12 bears and 40 rabbits
9. 2 sailboats and 6 motorboats   10. 180 home computers and 5 portable computers

EXERCISE 5.14

1. Carl Rodgers hears the sound first, provided he sits within 36.4 m of his radio.
2. 11
4. Beginning at the top circle and working clockwise: 21, 23, 27, 29, 22, 24, 25, 26, 28
5. 1530 digits   6. B = 1, E = 9, H = 3, U = 6   7. 1, 17, 33, and 49
8. (a) 41   (b) Saturday   9. 72°   10. 130   11. 60 km/h   12. 301
13. $2 \times 2 \times 2 \times 3 \times 3 \times 17 \times 19$ 14. $\frac{8}{5}$ 15. $11.20   16. 18
17. 150 m by 300 m   18. $79.80   19. (b)

5.15 REVIEW EXERCISE

2. (a) (3, 0), (0, 4) (b) (3, 0), (0, 6) (c) (2, 0), (0, −3)
   (d) (2, 0), (0, −5) (e) (−3, 0), (0, 7) (f) (4, 0), (0, −4)
3. a, e, f

4. b, c, e, h

5. (a) $y = 4 - 2x$ (b) $x = 3y + 7$ (c) $y = \dfrac{5 - 3x}{2}$ (d) $a = \dfrac{4 - 3b}{2}$

   (e) $m = \dfrac{2n + 2}{3}$ (f) $e = \dfrac{4d - 7}{3}$ (g) $x = \dfrac{3y}{4}$ (h) $y = \dfrac{4 - 2x}{3}$

6. (a) Yes (b) Yes (c) No (d) Yes
   (e) No (f) Yes (g) Yes (h) No
7. (a) (−1, 2) (b) (5, 2) (c) (3, 5) (d) (−4, 2)
8. (a) (−1, 2) (b) (3, 4) (c) (−1, 2) (d) $(-\frac{1}{2}, 3)$

   (e) (−3, −4) (f) (1, 3) (g) $(\frac{1}{2}, \frac{1}{3})$ (h) (6, −3)

   (i) $(-\frac{2}{3}, -\frac{1}{5})$ (j) $(-\frac{3}{7}, \frac{1}{2})$

9. (a) (3, 4) (b) (4, 6) (c) (−10, 6) (d) (3, 3)
   (e) (−0.1, −0.5) (f) (3, −4) (g) (−0.3, 0.5) (h) (3, −4)
10. (a) inconsistent (b) dependent (c) consistent (d) inconsistent
    (e) consistent (f) dependent

11. (a) (3b, a) (b) $(-\frac{9}{2}b, -8a)$

    (c) (2b, 0) (d) $\left(\dfrac{cn + bd}{an + bm}, \dfrac{cm - ad}{bm + am} \right)$

14. (a) minimum −15, 0; maximum 16, 30 (b) minimum −20, 0; maximum 20, 42
    (c) minimum 0, 0; maximum 24, 43 (d) minimum −22, −20; maximum 20, 23
15. maximum 40, minimum 0 16. maximum 9, minimum −10
17. (a) a = 2, b = 3, c = −2 (b) a = −3, b = −4, c = 0
    (c) a = 5, b = −6, c = 4 (d) a = 2, b = −2, c = 3, d = −1
18. 40 bikinis and 60 trunks 19. 80 Super Dupers, 60 Supers

5.16 CHAPTER 5 TEST

1. (a) Yes (b) No (c) Yes (d) Yes
2. (a) (1, 5) (b) (3, 1) 3. (a) (1, 5) (b) (2, −2) (c) (11, 4) (d) (4, 9)
5. maximum 30, minimum −9 6. maximum 32, minimum 0

REVIEW AND PREVIEW TO CHAPTER 6

PERCENT IN PRACTICAL PROBLEMS

1. $162.64 2. $5938.50 3. $135.00 4. $377.50 5. $9360.00 6. $3.25
7. $1567.50 8. $3.21 9. $2700.00 10. $38.52 11. $165.85 12. $132.00
13. $82.39 14. $1.32 15. $625.95 16. $15 707.60
17. $312.50 18. $1360.00 19. $1908.00 20. $35.31

USING MATHEMATICAL SYMBOLS

1. (a) $2 + 3$ (b) 6×2 (c) $7 - 5$ (d) $\sqrt{7}$ (e) 5^2 (f) $8 - 4$
   (g) $2 + 5$ (h) 3×5 (i) $10 + 6$ (j) $\pi \in R$ (k) $16 - 5$ (l) $12 + 7$
   (m) $24 - 8$ (n) 16^2 (o) $4^2 + 3^2$ (p) $(4 + 3)^2$ (q) $2 \times 3 + 4$ (r) $2 \times 4 - 3$
   (s) $2 \times 5 + 2$

EQUATIONS IN ONE VARIABLE

1. (a) 2 (b) 4 (c) −5 (d) 4 (e) 4
   (f) 3 (g) −4 (h) $-\frac{1}{2}$ (i) 7 (j) 10

EQUATIONS IN TWO VARIABLES

1. (a) (1, 2) (b) (−3, −2) (c) (0, −4)

EXERCISE 6.2

1. (a) 3x
   (b) x + 4
   (c) x − 3
   (d) x + 5
   (e) x − 2
   (f) x + 5
   (g) 2x + 3
   (h) $\frac{1}{2}$x
   (i) x − 8
   (j) 3x − 20
   (k) 25x
   (l) $\frac{1}{2}$(x − 6)
   (m) $\frac{1}{3}$(x + 10)
   (n) 6x − 2
   (o) 4x
   (p) 10y
   (q) 0.09x
   (r) 0.12x
   (s) 0.1x
   (t) 0.12x

2. (a) x + 35 = 82
   (b) 5x = 185
   (c) 4x − 47 = 293
   (d) 9x + 57 = 795
   (e) 6x − 87 = 999
   (f) x − 5 = 17
   (g) x + 13 = 27
   (h) 3(x − 5) = 48
   (i) 5x + 13 = 163
   (j) 2x + 4 = 26
   (k) 3x − 7 = 92
   (l) $\frac{1}{2}$x + 11 = 43
   (m) 2x + 31 = 165
   (n) 400 ÷ 8 = s
   (o) 60 × 7.5 = d
   (p) 490 ÷ 35 = t
   (q) 0.05x = 30
   (r) 0.07x = 1.40
   (s) 0.25x = 17.75

3. (a) ℓ + w
   (b) 2ℓ + 3w
   (c) 3ℓ − w
   (d) x + 3y
   (e) 5x + 10y
   (f) 5x + 25y
   (g) 2x + 5y
   (h) 5x − 4y
   (i) 2ℓ + 3 + 4w

4. (a) x + y = 50
   (b) x − y = 40
   (c) b + g = 35
   (d) c − t = 8
   (e) h + p = 170
   (f) 2x + 3y = 48
   (g) 4d − 2q = 33
   (h) s + b = 35
   (i) 8t + (h − 2) = 251
   (j) ℓ + 3w = 48
   (k) 7ℓ − 5w = 38
   (l) 12ℓ − 5w = 487
   (m) 10d + 25q = 180
   (n) 10x + 5y = 765

EXERCISE 6.3

1. 147, 108
2. 821, 763
3. 747, 464
4. excavator, 14.6T, tractor 7.3T
5. 156, 93
6. 12, 6
7. 16, 14
8. 12, 10
9. baseball 148, basketball 608
10. 21, 20
11. 173, 81
12. Rome — London 715 km, London — Quebec City 3550 km
13. 147, 41
14. 224, 101
15. 576, 358
16. 25, 21
17. 15
18. 14
19. 13
20. 30
21. The dog is six years old.
22. 27
23. 74
24. 84
25. 27

EXERCISE 6.4

1. 14
2. 18
3. 17
4. 21
5. 13
6. 26
7. 31 dimes, 69 quarters
8. 13
9. 121 students, 242 adults
10. 210
11. 60
12. 13
13. 350

EXERCISE 6.5

1. (a) $200
   (b) $27
   (c) $360
   (d) $0.07x
2. $600 at 8%, $400 at 9%
3. $6000 at 9%, $2000 at 10%
4. $3000 at 7.5%, $3000 at 8.5%

EXERCISE 6.6

1. (a) 30
   (b) 200
   (c) 100
   (d) 0.3x
   (e) 0.35y
   (f) 0.09m
2. 60 kg of 30%, 140 kg of 40%
3. 200 kg of 40%, 300 kg of 20%
4. 40 kg of 40%, 60 kg of 30%
5. 200 kg of 9%, 300 kg of 12%
6. 100 kg of 35%, 400 kg of 45%

EXERCISE 6.7

1. (a) $20   (b) $15   (c) $60   (d) $3.10x   (e) $4.50y   (f) $3.07m
2. 350 kg
3. 400 kg of $7.20/kg, 800 kg of $5.60/kg
4. 60 kg at $3.30/kg, 40 kg at $3.60/kg
5. 240 kg of cashews, 160 kg of pecans
6. 120 kg at $6.60/kg, 80 kg at $7.20/kg
7. 90 kg at $7.50/kg, 110 kg at $9.50/kg
8. 200 mL of 25%, 800 mL of 50%
9. 14 kg at $0.80/kg, 6 kg at $1.50/kg
10. 60 L of 48%, 40 L of 40%
11. 4.5 kg at $4.50/kg, 2.5 kg at $6.50/kg

EXERCISE 6.8

1. (a) 240   (b) 12   (c) 50   (d) 40x
   (e) $\frac{y}{50}$ (f) 8 m   (g) $\frac{n}{30}$
2. 400 km   3. 5 h   4. 1.5 h   5. 3 h   6. 3.5 h   7. 60 km
8. 250 km   9. 30 km/h   10. 1.5 km/h   11. 25 km/h   12. 240 km   13. 100 km

6.9 REVIEW EXERCISE

1. 242, 135   2. 530, 248   3. 427, 385   4. 31, 28
5. 56, 24   6. 29, 28   7. 56   8. 183
9. 161 m by 142 m   10. 17   11. 71   12. 65 m by 23 m
13. 142   14. $3000   15. 180 kg   16. $1500   17. 3 h
18. 20 kg at $7.20/kg, 80 kg at $9.20/kg   19. $1800
20. 300 kg   21. 80 kg at $2.30/kg, 70 kg at $3.20/kg
22. 400 km   23. $1800 at 8%, $1200 at 7%
24. $3840 at 8%, $2560 at 6%   25. 26

6.10 CHAPTER 6 TEST

1. 51, 33   2. 15, 11   3. 15   4. 62   5. 150 kg
6. 60 kg of 20%, 40 kg of 40%   7. 150 km

REVIEW AND PREVIEW TO CHAPTER 7

USING TABLES

1. (a) 361   (b) 3.317   (c) 1728   (d) 4.359
   (e) 0.0833   (f) 14   (g) 17   (h) 0.1429
2. (a) (i) 1000   (ii) 1900   (iii) 1650   (b) 100   (c) 250
3. (a) Sept. 20 — 132, Oct. 8 — 254, Oct. 15 — 238, Oct. 23 — 181, Nov. 8 — 521
   (b) Adams — 118, Barclay — 134, Carlson — 152, Fleming — 115, Hong — 141, Lepage — 138, Murray — 100, Rossi — 122, Spina — 162, VanDusen — 144
   (c) 10%

EXERCISE 7.1

1. (a) 2×3 (b) 2×2 (c) 3×2 (d) 1×4
2. (a) $-3, 4, 1$ (b) $-2, 0, 4$ (c) 1, 0, 6   (d) -2 (e) 6   (f) 3×3
3. (a) $x = 7, y = 0$ (b) $x = -3$ (c) $x = -1, y = -4$

4. $\begin{pmatrix} 50 & 8 & 10 \\ 27 & 27 & 13 \\ 26 & 28 & 13 \\ 19 & 36 & 13 \\ 16 & 41 & 8 \end{pmatrix}$ 5. (a) 2680 (b) 4730 (c) $\begin{pmatrix} 4950 \\ 0 \\ 1273 \\ 4177 \\ 422 \\ 1821 \\ 3606 \\ 6003 \end{pmatrix}$

(d) (4600 422 933 3837 0 1482 3266 5664)
(e) (2688 7212 4666 1142 6532 4216 0 4794)

(f) $\begin{pmatrix} 0 \\ 9900 \\ 7354 \\ 1600 \\ 9200 \\ 6902 \\ 2688 \\ 2710 \end{pmatrix}$

EXERCISE 7.3

1. (a) (i) $\begin{pmatrix} -2 & -3 & 5 \\ -7 & 1 & -6 \end{pmatrix}$ (ii) $\begin{pmatrix} -5 & 4 \\ 3 & -2 \end{pmatrix}$ (iii) $\begin{pmatrix} -3 & -7 \\ 2 & 1 \\ 4 & -3 \end{pmatrix}$ (iv) $(-8 \quad 9 \quad 10 \quad -2)$

(v) $\begin{pmatrix} -1 \\ 4 \\ -5 \end{pmatrix}$ (vi) (-6) (vii) $\begin{pmatrix} -3 & -5 & 7 \\ -4 & 2 & -6 \\ -9 & 3 & 5 \end{pmatrix}$ (viii) $\begin{pmatrix} -6 \\ 2 \end{pmatrix}$

(b) (i) 2×3 (ii) 2×2 (iii) 3×2 (iv) 1×4 (v) 3×1 (vi) 1×1 (vii) 3×3
(viii) 2×1

2. (a) $\begin{pmatrix} 7 & 11 \\ 8 & 9 \end{pmatrix}$ (b) $\begin{pmatrix} 7 \\ -1 \\ 5 \end{pmatrix}$ (c) $\begin{pmatrix} -3 & 1 \\ -3 & 3 \\ 5 & 6 \end{pmatrix}$ (e) $\begin{pmatrix} 6 & 12 \\ 1 & -1 \end{pmatrix}$

3. (a) $\begin{pmatrix} -1 & 5 \\ 3 & 8 \end{pmatrix}$ (b) $\begin{pmatrix} 0 & 4 \\ 0 & 0 \end{pmatrix}$ (c) $\begin{pmatrix} 2 & 0 \\ 6 & 8 \end{pmatrix}$ (d) $\begin{pmatrix} -2 & 0 \\ -6 & -8 \end{pmatrix}$

(e) $\begin{pmatrix} -2 & 7 \\ 0 & 4 \end{pmatrix}$ (f) $\begin{pmatrix} -2 & 7 \\ 0 & 4 \end{pmatrix}$ (g) $\begin{pmatrix} 2 & -4 \\ 6 & 8 \end{pmatrix}$

4. (a) (i) $\begin{pmatrix} 84 & 44 \\ 63 & 66 \end{pmatrix}, \begin{pmatrix} 81 & 47 \\ 62 & 65 \end{pmatrix}$ (ii) $\begin{pmatrix} 165 & 91 \\ 125 & 131 \end{pmatrix}$

(b) (i) $\begin{pmatrix} 79 & 39 \\ 59 & 61 \end{pmatrix}, \begin{pmatrix} 74 & 45 \\ 56 & 61 \end{pmatrix}$ (ii) $\begin{pmatrix} 153 & 84 \\ 115 & 122 \end{pmatrix}$ (iii) $\begin{pmatrix} 12 & 7 \\ 10 & 9 \end{pmatrix}$

EXERCISE 7.4

1. (a) $\begin{pmatrix} 12 & 0 \\ 3 & 15 \end{pmatrix}$ (b) $\begin{pmatrix} 0 \\ 2 \\ -12 \end{pmatrix}$ (c) $(-20 \quad 8 \quad 12)$

(d) $\begin{pmatrix} 4 & 3 \\ 2 & -5 \end{pmatrix}$ (e) $\begin{pmatrix} 15a & 10b \\ -25a & 15b \end{pmatrix}$ (f) $\begin{pmatrix} -10 & 14 \\ 6 & 2 \end{pmatrix}$

2. (a) $\begin{pmatrix} 23 & 6 \\ 8 & -1 \end{pmatrix}$ (b) $\begin{pmatrix} 1 & -7 \\ 15 & 15 \\ 11 & 8 \end{pmatrix}$ (c) $\begin{pmatrix} 21 & -5 \\ 14 & -5 \end{pmatrix}$

(d) $\begin{pmatrix} 21 & -8 & -6 \\ -1 & 2 & -7 \end{pmatrix}$ (e) $\begin{pmatrix} -5 & -8 \\ 5 & 6 \end{pmatrix}$

3. (a) $\begin{pmatrix} 6 & -9 \\ 12 & 0 \end{pmatrix}$ (b) $\begin{pmatrix} -2 & 4 \\ -6 & 10 \end{pmatrix}$ (c) $\begin{pmatrix} 3 & -5 \\ 7 & -5 \end{pmatrix}$ (d) $\begin{pmatrix} 4 & -5 \\ 6 & 10 \end{pmatrix}$

(e) $\begin{pmatrix} 7 & -12 \\ 17 & -15 \end{pmatrix}$ (f) $\begin{pmatrix} -10 & 16 \\ -22 & 10 \end{pmatrix}$ (g) $\begin{pmatrix} 6 & -10 \\ 14 & -10 \end{pmatrix}$ (h) $\begin{pmatrix} -9 & 15 \\ -21 & 15 \end{pmatrix}$

4. (a) $\begin{pmatrix} 2 & -4 \\ 3 & -5 \end{pmatrix}$ (b) $\begin{pmatrix} 3 \\ -2 \\ -4 \end{pmatrix}$ (c) $\begin{pmatrix} 2 & 2 \\ 1 & 4 \end{pmatrix}$ (d) $\begin{pmatrix} -5 & 6 \\ 2 & -1 \end{pmatrix}$ (e) $\begin{pmatrix} 8 & 1 \\ 11 & -12 \end{pmatrix}$

(f) $\begin{pmatrix} 2 & -6 \\ 4 & -4 \end{pmatrix}$ (g) $\frac{1}{3}\begin{pmatrix} 13 & -6 \\ 5 & 6 \end{pmatrix}$

5. (a) $\begin{pmatrix} 8500 & 6000 \\ 8200 & 5600 \\ 4000 & 2500 \end{pmatrix}$ (b) $\begin{pmatrix} 8925 & 6300 \\ 8610 & 5880 \\ 4200 & 2625 \end{pmatrix}$

EXERCISE 7.5

1. (a) $\begin{pmatrix} 9 & 3 & 1 \\ 16 & 2 & 4 \end{pmatrix}$ (b) $\begin{pmatrix} 18 & 23 \\ 6 & -1 \end{pmatrix}$ (d) (-12) (e) $\begin{pmatrix} 19 & 8 & 19 \\ -23 & -5 & -23 \\ 37 & 19 & 37 \end{pmatrix}$

(f) $\begin{pmatrix} 9 \\ -8 \\ 11 \end{pmatrix}$ (g) $\begin{pmatrix} 20 & -10 \\ 8 & -4 \\ -4 & 2 \\ 12 & -6 \end{pmatrix}$ (j) $\begin{pmatrix} 3 & -2 & 4 \\ 5 & 1 & 6 \\ 5 & 2 & -3 \end{pmatrix}$ (k) $\begin{pmatrix} -3 & 5 \\ 6 & 4 \end{pmatrix}$

(l) $\begin{pmatrix} -5 & -2 \\ 3 & -7 \end{pmatrix}$ (m) $\begin{pmatrix} -29 \\ -18 \\ -14 \\ -3 \end{pmatrix}$ (n) $\begin{pmatrix} -10 & 9 \\ 16 & 14 \\ 4 & 9 \end{pmatrix}$

2. (a) $\begin{pmatrix} 2 & -5 \\ 4 & -9 \end{pmatrix}, \begin{pmatrix} -3 & -2 \\ -5 & -4 \end{pmatrix}$ (b) $\begin{pmatrix} 1 & 2 \\ 5 & 10 \end{pmatrix}, \begin{pmatrix} 4 & -7 \\ -4 & 7 \end{pmatrix}$

(c) $\begin{pmatrix} 3 & -3 \\ 5 & -7 \end{pmatrix}, \begin{pmatrix} 3 & -3 \\ 5 & -7 \end{pmatrix}$ (d) $\begin{pmatrix} 1 & -7 \\ 3 & -11 \end{pmatrix}, \begin{pmatrix} 1 & -7 \\ 3 & -11 \end{pmatrix}$

(e) $\begin{pmatrix} 7 & 14 \\ 13 & 26 \end{pmatrix}, \begin{pmatrix} 7 & 14 \\ 13 & 26 \end{pmatrix}$ (f) $\begin{pmatrix} 14 & -2 \\ 27 & -5 \end{pmatrix}, \begin{pmatrix} 9 & 1 \\ 18 & 0 \end{pmatrix}$

(g) $\begin{pmatrix} 6 & 14 \\ 7 & 27 \end{pmatrix}, \begin{pmatrix} 1 & 17 \\ -2 & 32 \end{pmatrix}$ (h) $\begin{pmatrix} 4 & 0 \\ 5 & 1 \end{pmatrix}, \begin{pmatrix} 9 & -3 \\ 14 & -4 \end{pmatrix}$

EXERCISE 7.6

1. a, b, d, f

2. (a) $\begin{pmatrix} 1 & -1 \\ -2 & 3 \end{pmatrix}$ (b) $\begin{pmatrix} \frac{1}{2} & -\frac{3}{2} \\ -\frac{1}{2} & \frac{5}{2} \end{pmatrix}$ (c) $\begin{pmatrix} -\frac{1}{2} & -\frac{3}{2} \\ \frac{1}{2} & 1 \end{pmatrix}$ (d) $\begin{pmatrix} \frac{1}{5} & 0 \\ -\frac{1}{10} & \frac{1}{2} \end{pmatrix}$ (f) $\begin{pmatrix} -3 & -2 \\ 1 & \frac{1}{2} \end{pmatrix}$

3. (a) $\begin{pmatrix} 3 & -2 \\ -1 & 1 \end{pmatrix}$ (b) $\begin{pmatrix} 3 & -1 \\ -5 & 2 \end{pmatrix}$ (c) $\begin{pmatrix} 10 & -7 \\ -17 & 12 \end{pmatrix}$

(d) $\begin{pmatrix} 12 & 7 \\ 17 & 10 \end{pmatrix}$ (e) $\begin{pmatrix} 10 & -7 \\ -17 & 12 \end{pmatrix}$ (f) $(AB)^{-1} = B^{-1}A^{-1}$

EXERCISE 7.7

1. (a) $(3, 2)$ (b) $(4, 1)$ (c) $(3, -2)$ (d) $(5, 3)$ (e) $(\frac{1}{2}, -3)$

(f) $(1, 6)$ (g) $(-3, -2)$ (h) $(3, -4)$ (i) $(-3, 4)$ (j) $(-4, 2)$

EXERCISE 7.9

1. (c) Churchill — $970, Vanier — $1280, Central — $1610, High Park — $1580, Parkside — $1600
   (d) $3000   (e) $4040   (f) $7040
2. (c) 1 — $1000, 2 — $670, 3 — $1480, 4 — $1720   (d) $4870
3. (c) January — $4810, February — $4880, March — $4060   (d) $13 750
4. (c) 1 — $4600, 2 — $6850, 3 — $5100, 4 — $6700, 5 — $7000   (d) $16 500   (e) $30 250
5. (c) I — $670, II — $969, III — $944, IV — $682, V — $730   (d) $3995
6. 43 34 32 26 41 58 41 33 41 58 33 29 56 25   7. SENDSHIPSNOW
8. GETOUTSOON   9. 78 133 48 84 37 62 46 78 23 45 57 100 59 103

EXERCISE 7.10

1. 210   2. 2 h 40 min
4. $1^3 + 12^3$; $9^3 + 10^3$ 5. 12.5%
6. Weigh any two groups of eggs. If they balance, then the third group must contain the lighter egg (otherwise one of the first two groups is lighter than the other, and so contains the lighter egg). Having found the group with the lighter egg, weigh any two eggs from this group and proceed as before.
9. (b) 4   10. 2 h   11. 38
12. At the South Pole and anywhere 1 km south of the circle centred at the North Pole with a circumference of 1 km.
13. 80°   14. 40 L   15. 72.5 cm   16. 09:22   17. $\frac{1}{8}$ 18. $\frac{27}{64}$
19. 78   20. (a) 45 m²   (b) 125%   21. (a)

7.11 REVIEW EXERCISE

1. (a) (i) 2 × 3   (ii) 3 × 2   (iii) 1 × 1   (iv) 2 × 2   (v) 3 × 1   (vi) 1 × 4

   (b) (i) $\begin{pmatrix} -3 & -5 & -2 \\ -4 & 0 & 6 \end{pmatrix}$ (ii) $\begin{pmatrix} -1 & -4 \\ 6 & -5 \\ 3 & 0 \end{pmatrix}$ (iii) (-7) (iv) $\begin{pmatrix} -2 & -3 \\ 1 & -6 \end{pmatrix}$ (v) $\begin{pmatrix} -3 \\ -1 \\ -2 \end{pmatrix}$

   (vi) $(-5 \ -6 \ -8 \ 4)$
2. (a) x = 4, y = −1, z = 4   (b) x = 2, y = 3, z = −1   (c) x = 1, y = 5, z = 2

3. (a) $\begin{pmatrix} 8 & 3 \\ 6 & 0 \end{pmatrix}$ (b) $\begin{pmatrix} 3 & 4 \\ 4 & 5 \end{pmatrix}$ (c) $\begin{pmatrix} 8 & -10 \\ -1 & 4 \\ -4 & 1 \end{pmatrix}$

   (d) $\begin{pmatrix} -12 & -6 & 15 \\ -3 & 9 & 0 \end{pmatrix}$ (e) $\begin{pmatrix} 1 & -2 \\ 4 & -5 \end{pmatrix}$ (f) $\begin{pmatrix} 6 & 10 \\ -4 & 8 \end{pmatrix}$
4. a, b, d
5. (a) $\begin{pmatrix} -2 & 6 \\ -6 & 13 \end{pmatrix}$ (b) $\begin{pmatrix} 8 & 1 \\ -6 & -8 \end{pmatrix}$ (c) $\begin{pmatrix} 10 & 9 \\ 14 & -22 \end{pmatrix}$

   (d) $\begin{pmatrix} 1 & -2 \\ 9 & -9 \\ 2 & 4 \end{pmatrix}$ (e) $\begin{pmatrix} 5 & 9 & -2 \\ -5 & -1 & 4 \end{pmatrix}$
6. (a) $\begin{pmatrix} 4 & 2 \\ 0 & 6 \end{pmatrix}$ (b) $\begin{pmatrix} -6 & 0 \\ 3 & 6 \end{pmatrix}$ (c) $\begin{pmatrix} 3 & -1 \\ -1 & 3 \end{pmatrix}$ (d) $\begin{pmatrix} 3 & 3 \\ 0 & 1 \end{pmatrix}$

   (e) $\begin{pmatrix} 5 & 9 & -2 \\ -5 & -1 & 4 \end{pmatrix}$ (f) $\begin{pmatrix} 0 & 3 \\ 3 & 15 \end{pmatrix}$ (g) $\begin{pmatrix} 3 & -2 \\ -3 & -6 \end{pmatrix}$ (h) $\begin{pmatrix} 4 & 2 \\ -2 & -7 \end{pmatrix}$

7. (a) $\begin{pmatrix} 13 & 13 \\ 21 & 11 \end{pmatrix}$ (d) (9) (e) $\begin{pmatrix} 3 & 4 & 1 \\ -2 & 4 & 2 \\ 3 & -1 & 5 \end{pmatrix}$
8. (a) x = −2, y = 0, z = 1   (b) x = 3, y = 2   (c) x = 1, y = 2
   (d) x = 3, y = 2   (e) x = 1, y = −2, z = 4
9. (a) (1, 2)   (b) (3, 1)   (c) (5, −1)   (d) (−2, −3)

10. (a) $\begin{pmatrix} 20 & 25 & 16 \\ 15 & 14 & 18 \\ 22 & 30 & 10 \\ 14 & 16 & 12 \end{pmatrix}$ (b) $\begin{pmatrix} 50 \\ 60 \\ 65 \end{pmatrix}$

(c) Westview — $3540, East — $2760, St. Mary's — $3550, Glendale — $2440   (d) $12 290

11. (a) $\begin{pmatrix} 7 & 10 & 5 \\ 6 & 10 & 10 \\ 7 & 5 & 7 \\ 5 & 15 & 9 \end{pmatrix}$ (b) $\begin{pmatrix} 70 \\ 75 \\ 55 \end{pmatrix}$

(c) Restaurant A — $1515, Restaurant B — $1720, Restaurant C — $1250, Restaurant D — $1970
(d) $6455
12. Store 1 — $2100, Store 2 — $3100, Store 3 — $1600, Store 4 — $1300   Total income $8100.
13. 69 51 32 23 129 91 70 48 54 40 83 57 102 73 77 53

7.12 CHAPTER 7 TEST

1. (a) 3×2 (b) $\begin{pmatrix} -1 & 3 \\ -2 & 0 \\ 1 & -4 \end{pmatrix}$

2. $x = 2, y = -1, z = 2$ 3. (a) $\begin{pmatrix} 7 & 9 \\ 5 & 14 \end{pmatrix}$ (b) $\begin{pmatrix} -15 \\ 16 \\ -21 \end{pmatrix}$

4. (a) $\begin{pmatrix} 6 & -2 \\ 3 & 4 \end{pmatrix}$ (b) $\begin{pmatrix} 7 & -4 & -10 \\ 10 & -7 & -17 \end{pmatrix}$ 5. (a) $(-1, 2)$ (b) $(1, 1)$

6. (a) $\begin{pmatrix} 5 & 2 & 3 \\ 3 & 3 & 4 \\ 6 & 2 & 0 \end{pmatrix}$ (b) $\begin{pmatrix} 5 \\ 3 \\ 1 \end{pmatrix}$

(c) Midget — 34, Junior — 28, Senior — 36   (d) 98

REVIEW AND PREVIEW TO CHAPTER 8

BASIC TERMS IN GEOMETRY

1. (i) (a) △ADC, △ACB   (b) PQ ∥ RS
   (c) $\overrightarrow{AQ}$, $\overrightarrow{CR}$ (d) ∠PAB, ∠RDC
   (e) ∠ADR   (f) ∠DAC is adjacent to ∠CAB
   (g) ∠RDA, ∠ACS
   (ii) (a) △EFG, △EHI   (b) TU ∥ WV
   (c) $\overrightarrow{GU}$, $\overrightarrow{HV}$ (d) ∠EFI, ∠EGH
   (e) ∠EFU   (f) ∠EFG is adjacent to ∠GFI
   (g) ∠TFI, ∠EHW
   (iii) (a) △JNK, △MNL   (b) WX ∥ YZ
   (c) $\overrightarrow{JW}$, $\overrightarrow{MZ}$ (d) ∠WJK, ∠MLZ
   (e) ∠NJW   (f) ∠YMN is adjacent to ∠NML
   (g) ∠WJN, ∠YMK

CLASSIFICATION OF TRIANGLES

1. (i) (a) scalene   (b) acute   (ii) (a) isosceles   (b) right
   (iii) (a) scalene   (b) obtuse   (iv) (a) equilateral   (b) acute

USING A PROTRACTOR

1. (a) 40°   (b) 70°   (c) 50°   (d) 130°   (e) 110°   (f) 140°
2. (a) 40°   (b) 80°   (c) 10°   (d) 50°
   (e) 130°   (f) 100°   (g) 140°   (h) 180°

EXERCISE 8.4

1. (a) ∠BAC = 73°   (b) ∠AED = 99°, ∠DEB = 81°   (c) ∠ABC = ∠ACB = 70°

(d) $\angle PQR = \angle QRP = \angle RPQ = 60°$ (e) $\angle ACD = 108°$ (f) $\angle BEC = 70°$
2. (a) $x = 30°$ (b) $x = 9°$ (c) $x = 39°$ (d) $x = 16°$ (e) $x = 10°$ (f) $x = 41°$

EXERCISE 8.6

1. (a) Proof by Authority   (b) Proof by Inspection   (c) Proof by Analogy
   (d) Proof by Induction   (e) Proof by Deduction
4. (a) $S = 180(n - 2)$ (b) Proof by Induction

EXERCISE 8.7

1. (a) $\angle DEF \to \angle RST$ (b) $\angle DFE \to \angle RTS$ (c) $\angle EDF \to \angle SRT$
   (d) $EF \to ST$ (e) $DE \to RS$ (f) $DF \to RT$
2. (a) $PQ = ST$ (b) $SU = PR$ (c) $QR = TU$
   (d) $\angle PQR = \angle STU$ (e) $\angle RPQ = \angle UST$ (e) $\angle QRP = \angle TUS$
3. (a) $AB = AC$, $BD = CD$, $AD = AD$, $\angle ABD = \angle ACD$, $\angle ADB = \angle ADC$, $\angle BAD = \angle CAD$
   (b) $AB = AC$, $AC = AB$, $BC = CB$, $\angle ABC = \angle ACB$, $\angle BCA = \angle CBA$, $\angle BAC = \angle CAB$
   (c) $TQ = PR$, $QS = RS$, $ST = SP$, $\angle TQS = \angle PRS$, $\angle QST = \angle RSP$, $\angle STQ = \angle SPR$
   (d) $AB = CD$, $BD = DB$, $AD = CB$, $\angle ABD = \angle CDB$, $\angle BDA = \angle DBC$, $\angle DAB = \angle BCD$
4. (b) Yes   (c) Yes
5. $\angle PRQ = 110°$, $ED = 25$ cm, $FD = 45$ cm, $RQ = 30$ cm

EXERCISE 8.8

1. $\triangle ABC \cong \triangle WVX$, $\angle BCA = \angle VXW$, $\angle BAC = \angle VWX$, $\angle ABC = \angle WVX$
   $\triangle DEF \cong \triangle RPQ$, $\angle DEF = \angle RPQ$, $\angle DFE = \angle RQP$, $\angle EDF = \angle PRQ$
   $\triangle GHI \cong \triangle UTS$, $\angle GHI = \angle UTS$, $\angle GIH = \angle UST$, $\angle IGH = \angle SUT$
   $\triangle JKL \cong \triangle MON$, $\angle JKL = \angle MON$, $\angle JLK = \angle MNO$, $\angle KJL = \angle OMN$
2. (a) $CO = AO$, $BO = DO$, $CB = AD$ (b) $AB = AC$, $BD = CD$, $AD = AD$
   (c) $AD = CB$, $AB = CD$, $BD = DB$ (d) $AB = AD$, $BC = DC$, $CA = CA$
   (e) $AB = CB$, $AD = CD$, $BD = BD$ (f) $AD = CB$, $AB = CD$, $BD = DB$

EXERCISE 8.9

1. $\triangle ABC \cong \triangle FED$, $\triangle GHI \cong \triangle VWX$, $\triangle JKL \cong \triangle UST$, $\triangle MNO \cong \triangle QPR$
2. (a) $AO = BO$, $\angle AOD = \angle COB$, $DO = CO$ (b) $AC = EC$, $\angle ACB = \angle ECD$, $BC = DC$
   (c) $AB = CD$, $\angle ABD = \angle CDB$, $DB = BD$ (d) $BD = CD$, $\angle BDA = \angle CDA$, $AD = AD$
   (e) $AD = CD$, $\angle DAB = \angle DCB$, $DB = DB$ (f) $BA = DA$, $\angle BAC = \angle DAC$, $AC = AC$

EXERCISE 8.10

1. $\triangle ABC \cong \triangle RPQ$, $\triangle DEF \cong \triangle OMN$, $\triangle HGI \cong \triangle XVW$, $\triangle JKL \cong \triangle SUT$
2. (a) $\angle BAC = \angle EDC$, $AC = DC$, $\angle ACB = \angle DCE$ (b) $\angle ABD = \angle CDB$, $BD = DB$, $\angle ADB = \angle CBD$
   (c) $\angle ABD = \angle ACD$, $BD = CD$, $\angle ADB = \angle ADC$ (d) $\angle AOD = \angle COB$, $OD = OB$, $\angle ADO = \angle CBO$
   (e) $\angle BAC = \angle DEC$, $AC = EC$, $\angle ACB = \angle ECD$ (f) $\angle ABD = \angle CBD$, $BD = BD$, $\angle ADB = \angle CDB$

EXERCISE 8.12

1. (a) alternate: c and d, b and e; corresponding: a and e, b and f; interior: b and d, c and e.
   (b) alternate: a and d, e and f; corresponding: a and b, d and f, a and e; interior: c and d, c and e.
2. (a) $a = 110°$, $b = c = 70°$ (b) $a = 60°$, $b = 60°$, $c = 120°$
   (c) $a = c = 65°$, $b = 115°$ (d) $a = 30°$, $b = 80°$, $c = 70°$
   (e) $a = 45°$, $b = 25°$, $c = 110°$ (f) $a = b = 60°$, $c = 120°$
3. (a) $x = 50°$, $y = 55°$, $z = 75°$ (b) $a = 65°$, $b = 75°$, $c = 40°$

(c) x = 50°, y = 70°, z = 60°   (d) x = 70°, y = 50°, z = 70°
(e) x = 35°, y = 80°, z = 65°   (f) x = 80°, y = 60°, z = 40°

EXERCISE 8.13

1. (a) x = 5   (b) y = 13   (c) b = 17   (d) c = 25
   (e) m = 30   (f) a = 12   (g) r = 11   (h) v = 18, w = 7
2. (a) 10 cm   (b) 13 m   (c) 17 m   (d) 50 cm   (e) 50 cm   (f) 26 cm
3. 5.39 cm   4. 283 mm   5. 323 m   6. 2.3 m   7. 3 m
8. a = $\sqrt{2}$, b = $\sqrt{3}$, c = 2, d = $\sqrt{5}$ 9. 21 cm by 21 cm
10. 220 cm   11. (a) 9.9   (b) 8.3   (c) 25   12. 195 cm

EXERCISE 8.15

1. (a) Yes   (b) No   (c) Yes   (d) No
2. (a) No   (b) Yes   (c) Yes   (d) Yes   (e) Yes   (f) Yes
3. (a) 6   (b) 30   (c) 60   (d) 84   (e) 24   (f) 7.5

EXERCISE 8.16

1. (a) 73°   (b) 8089 km
2. (a) 180°   (b) (i) 20 000 km   (ii) 13 000 km   (c) 7000 km
3. 81   4. 1.9 m and 2.1 m   5. −2, −1, and 0   6. 7 and 67
7. 8 cm long, 5 cm wide   8. 80 cm   9. $1.25   10. 2400
11. Roy Tovar received 3462 votes, Terry Harrison received 3326 votes
12. Yellow trail — $14\frac{5}{7}$ km, Blue trail — $5\frac{6}{7}$ km, Red trail — $19\frac{3}{7}$ km
13. 4.5 km   14. No   15. 2000 km   16. 120 cm long, 80 cm wide
17. 5 cm   18. 16 km   19. 2 h 24 min   20. 15 h

8.17 REVIEW EXERCISE

1. (a) 32°   (b) 83°   (c) 40°   (d) 26°
   (e) 20°   (f) 25°   (g) 65°   (h) 50°
   (i) a = 108°, b = 72°, c = 108°   (j) a = 62°, b = 43°, c = 75°
   (k) a = 38°, b = 103°, c = 65°   (l) a = 45°, b = 100°, c = 35°
   (m) a = 52°, b = 78°, c = 50°   (n) a = 78°, b = 60°, c = 42°
2. (a) 50   (b) 20   (c) 8   (d) $\sqrt{7}$ (e) $\sqrt{14}$ (f) $\sqrt{30}$
4. (a) Yes   (b) Yes   (c) No   (d) No   (e) No   (f) Yes

8.18 CHAPTER 8 TEST

1. (a) ∠x = 63°, ∠y = 55°   (b) ∠x = 65°, ∠y = 69°, ∠z = 46°   (c) ∠x = 23°, ∠y = 32°
2. (a) 39   (b) 16

8.19 CUMULATIVE REVIEW FOR CHAPTERS 5 TO 8

2. (a) (1, 1)   (b) (1, 1)   (d) (1, 2)
3. (a) dependent   (b) consistent   (c) inconsistent   (d) consistent
4. (a) (−1, 2)   (b) (−1, −5)   (c) (3, 7)   (d) (2, −2)   (e) $\left(\frac{b}{a}, \frac{a}{b}\right)$ (f) (1, 0)
7. 74, 16   8. 56, 37   9. 15, 13   10. $3.20   11. 26 h, 19 h
12. $3600, $7200   13. 7 km/h, 23 km/h

14. (a) $\begin{pmatrix} 7 & 2 \\ 1 & 4 \end{pmatrix}$ **(b)** $\begin{pmatrix} 9 & 3 \\ 2 & 8 \end{pmatrix}$ **(c)** $\begin{pmatrix} -3 & -2 \\ -2 & -2 \\ -1 & 1 \end{pmatrix}$ **(d)** $\begin{pmatrix} 7 & -7 \\ -7 & 7 \\ -3 & 0 \end{pmatrix}$

15. (a) $\begin{pmatrix} 32 & 33 \\ 16 & 15 \end{pmatrix}$ **(d)** $\begin{pmatrix} 20 \\ 2 \end{pmatrix}$ **(e)** $\begin{pmatrix} 36 & -16 \\ -2 & -26 \end{pmatrix}$

16. (a) $\begin{pmatrix} 6 & 9 \\ 3 & 12 \end{pmatrix}$ **(b)** $\begin{pmatrix} 10 & -30 \\ -15 & 10 \end{pmatrix}$ **(c)** $\begin{pmatrix} 0 & 9 \\ 4 & 2 \end{pmatrix}$ **(d)** $\begin{pmatrix} -4 & 3 \\ 2 & -6 \end{pmatrix}$ **(e)** $\begin{pmatrix} 12 & -9 \\ -6 & 18 \end{pmatrix}$ **(f)** $\begin{pmatrix} 5 & 6 \\ 10 & -2 \end{pmatrix}$

17. (a) 4, 5, -2 **(b)** 6, -2 **(c)** 2, 1, -2

18. (a) $\begin{pmatrix} 4 & 3 & 6 \\ 5 & 2 & 8 \\ 9 & 5 & 2 \end{pmatrix}$ $(5 \ \ 4 \ \ 3)$ **(b)** 173

REVIEW AND PREVIEW TO CHAPTER 9

PERIMETER

1. (a) 21 cm   (b) 16 cm   (c) 36 cm   (d) 14 cm
   (e) 19.1 cm   (f) 32 cm   (g) 42 cm   (h) 15 cm
2. (a) 44.0 m   (b) 37.7 m   (c) 45.7 cm   (d) 357.1 m   (e) 62.8 cm   (f) 13.7 cm

AREA

1. (a) 10.2 m²   (b) 21.9 m²   (c) 19.6 cm²   (d) 17.3 m²   (e) 36.5 cm²   (f) 15.0 cm²
   (g) 34.8 cm²   (h) 37.0 cm²   (i) 84.8 m²   (j) 12.7 cm²   (k) 235.6 cm²   (l) 77.7 cm²
   (m) 9.4 cm²

EXERCISE 9.1

1. (a) 72 cm²   (b) 150 cm²   (c) 304 cm²   (d) 340 cm²
2. (a) 88 cm³   (b) 1008 cm³   (c) 1200 cm³   (d) 213.3 cm³
3. (a) A = 760 cm², V = 1400 cm³   (b) A = 2336 cm², V = 7424 cm³
4. (a) 360 cm²   (b) 15 cm   5. 36 cm

EXERCISE 9.2

1. (a) 352 cm²   (b) 1011 cm²   (c) 283 cm²   (d) 352 cm²   (e) 36 cm²   (f) 54 cm²
2. 790 m²   3. r + h : r + 2h   4. 2(2r + h) : r + h
5. (c) 117.8 cm²   6. (a) 471 cm²   (b) 49 cm²
7. $2550   8. 377 cm²   9. 757 cm²

EXERCISE 9.3

1. (a) 352 cm³   (b) 1005 cm³   (c) 4019 cm³   (d) 3215 cm³   (e) 5102 cm³   (f) 9420 cm³
2. 942 m³   3. 2176 kg   4. 11.3 cm   5. 13 932 cm³

EXERCISE 9.4

1. (a) 75 cm²   (b) 283 cm²   (c) 628 cm²   (d) 301 cm²   (e) 283 cm²
   (f) 628 cm²   (g) 1884 cm²   (h) 1206 cm²   (i) 1413 cm²
2. 156 m²   3. 113 cm²   4. 4580 cm²   5. 3 : 2   6. 1016 cm²

EXERCISE 9.5

1. (a) 209 m³   (b) 513 m³   (c) 314 cm³   (d) 104 cm³   (e) 314 m³
   (f) 3215 m³   (g) 2010 m³   (h) 314 m³   (i) 2826 cm³
2. 471 m³   3. 16.9 mm³   4. 1225 cm³   5. 5191 cm³

EXERCISE 9.6

1. (a) 2123 cm²   (b) 7235 cm²   (c) 4069 cm²   (d) 1256 cm²
2. (a) 7235 cm³   (b) 4187 cm³   (c) 11 488 cm³   (d) 91 906 cm³
3. (a) A = 7850 cm², V = 65 417 cm³   (b) A = 31 400 cm², V = 523 333 cm³
   (c) A = 15 386 cm², V = 179 503 cm³   (d) A = 125 600 cm², V = 4 186 667 cm³
4. 12 661 cm³   5. (a) 91.9 cm³   (b) 275.7 cm³   (c) 91.9 cm³
6. 3 : 2   7. 9 : 8

EXERCISE 9.7

1. 864 cm²   2. 237.5 cm²   3. 3.1 m³
4. 25 cm by 25 cm by 15 cm, A = 2750 cm²
5. (a) x by 10 − 2x by 10 − 2x   (b) $4x^3 - 40x^2 + 100x$
6. (a) 1620.7 cm³   (b) 19 488 cm³   (c) 24 774 cm³   (d) 5326 cm³   (e) 5476 cm²
7. (a) 705 m³   (b) 17

EXERCISE 9.8

1. (a) 6   (b) 3   2. (a) infinite   (b) infinite
3. (a) 6   (b) 4   (c) 3   4. (d) 4
5. (a) rotational and reflectional   (b) rotational and reflectional
   (c) rotational and reflectional   (d) rotational and reflectional

EXERCISE 9.9

1. 90   2. Mr. White — brown, Ms. Brown — black, Mr. Black — white
3. 90°   4. 424.3 cm   5. 16   6. 25 min   7. 16, 18, 20
8. $\boxed{5}\ \boxed{\tfrac{1}{x}}\ \boxed{+}\ \boxed{4}\ \boxed{=}\ \boxed{\tfrac{1}{x}}\ \boxed{+}\ \boxed{3}\ \boxed{=}\ \boxed{\tfrac{1}{x}}\ \boxed{+}\ \boxed{2}\ \boxed{=}\ \boxed{\tfrac{1}{x}}\ \boxed{+}\ \boxed{1}\ \boxed{=}$
9. 6 km/h   10. 33
11. 18 monochrome monitors, 6 colour monitors   12. 1, 4, 10; 2, 5, 8
13. 75 mL   14. 12 h   15. 12 min
16. frontage — 1000 m, depth — 500 m   17. (a)

9.10 REVIEW EXERCISE

1. (a) 360 cm²   (b) 1005 cm²   (c) 324 cm²   (d) 628 cm²   (e) 2123 cm²   (f) 382 cm²
2. (a) 1570 cm³   (b) 301 cm³   (c) 3200 cm³   (d) 27 000 cm³   (e) 12 266 cm³   (f) 17 149 cm³
3. 1 to 4   4. 50 240 cm³   5. 4.9 cm
6. (a) 1809 cm²   (b) 452 cm²   (c) 10 205 cm²   (d) 224 cm²
7. 26.5 cm³   8. 188.4 cm³   9. 2.6 m²   10. 20.0 cm   11. 9.2 cm

9.11 CHAPTER 9 TEST

1. (a) 1570 cm²   (b) 1512 cm²   (c) 1809 cm²   (d) 825 cm²   (e) 7536 cm²   (f) 105 cm²
2. (a) 300 cm³   (b) 65 417 cm³   (c) 98 cm³   (d) 262 cm³   (e) 400 cm³   (f) 603 cm³
3. 785 cm³   4. 800 cm³

REVIEW AND PREVIEW TO CHAPTER 10

LENGTH OF A LINE SEGMENT

1. (a) 5   (b) 13   (c) 13   (d) 10   (e) $11\sqrt{2}$

SLOPE OF A LINE

1. (a) $\frac{2}{3}$ (b) 1   (c) 1   (d) $\frac{6}{5}$

    (e) 0   (f) $-\frac{3}{4}$ (g) -4 (h) $-\frac{7}{2}$

EQUATION OF A LINE

1. (a) $4x - y - 10 = 0$ (b) $2x - y - 3 = 0$ (c) $3x + y + 13 = 0$
   (d) $x + y + 5 = 0$ (e) $3x - y + 14 = 0$ (f) $6x + y - 22 = 0$
   (g) $x - 2y + 10 = 0$ (h) $x + 3y - 12 = 0$ (i) $2x + 4y + 7 = 0$
   (j) $20x - 30y - 11 = 0$ (k) $0.1x - y + 0.58 = 0$ (l) $1.2x + y + 0.24 = 0$
   (m) $6.1x - y - 24 = 0$ (n) $4.6x - y + 15.06 = 0$
2. (a) $2x - y - 1 = 0$ (b) $3x - y + 1 = 0$ (c) $5x + y + 10 = 0$
   (d) $2x + y + 8 = 0$ (e) $4x + y + 4 = 0$ (f) $x - 2y = 0$
   (g) $x - 3y + 11 = 0$ (h) $y - 4 = 0$ (i) $x - 3 = 0$
   (j) $9x + 2y - 19 = 0$ (k) $4x - y - 3 = 0$ (l) $3x - 2y + 1.8 = 0$
   (m) $3x + 2y - 4.2 = 0$ (n) $5x + 2y + 18 = 0$

SIMILAR TRIANGLES

1. (a) $x = 6.7$ (b) $x = 4.7, y = 5.2$ (c) $x = 3.2, y = 7.5$
   (d) $x = 15.6, y = 17.5$ (e) $x = 7.8, y = 7.7$

EXERCISE 10.1

1. (a) $(2, 10)$ (b) $(-2, 2)$ (c) $(-5, 3)$ (d) $(0, 0)$
   (e) $(-2, 8)$ (f) $(-3, -4)$ (g) $(-8, -2)$ (h) $(-5, -2)$
2. (a) $(7, 2)$ (b) $(-1, 1)$ (c) $(0, -3)$ (d) $(6, -5)$
   (e) $(1, 3)$ (f) $(5, 5)$ (g) $(4, -4)$ (h) $(1, -5)$
3. (a) $a = 4, b = 3$ (b) $a = 10, b = 8$ (c) $a = 5, b = -1$ (d) $a = 7, b = 9$
   (e) $a = 3, b = 9$ (f) $a = 2, b = -6$ (g) $a = 5, b = 6$ (h) $a = 4, b = 0$
   (i) $a = -3, b = \frac{1}{2}$

4. (a) $A' = (0, 2), B' = (-4, 3)$; length $= \sqrt{17}; m = -\frac{1}{4}$
   (b) $A' = (-4, -5), B' = (-5, -1)$; length $= \sqrt{17}; m = -4$
   (c) $A' = (-2, 5), B' = (1, 2)$; length $= 3\sqrt{2}; m = -1$
   (d) $A' = (0, 8), B' = (2, 7)$; length $= \sqrt{5}; m = \frac{1}{2}$

5. (b) $A'(6, 3), B'(5, 8), C'(7, 7)$ (d) $\sqrt{26}, \sqrt{5}, \sqrt{17}, \sqrt{26}, \sqrt{5}, \sqrt{17}$ (f) $-5, -\frac{1}{2}, 4, -5, -\frac{1}{2}, 4$

6. (a) $y = \frac{3}{2}x - \frac{1}{2}, y = \frac{3}{2}x + 9$ 9. $2x + y = 6$

EXERCISE 10.2

1. (a) 4 m away   (b) left   (c) right
2. (a) $(4, -7)$ (b) $(-2, -9)$ (c) $(6, 0)$ (d) $(0, 5)$
   (e) $(-1, 1)$ (f) $(6, 3)$ (g) $(8, -1)$ (h) $(0, 0)$
3. (a) $(-2, 5)$ (b) $(-4, 3)$ (c) $(8, 6)$ (d) $(1, 2)$
   (e) $(-7, 11)$ (f) $(0, -4)$ (g) $(-6, 0)$ (h) $(1, -1)$
4. (a) $(7, 3)$ (b) $(2, -3)$ (c) $(-6, 8)$ (d) $(-2, -1)$
   (e) $(11, 7)$ (f) $(4, 4)$ (g) $(0, -1)$ (h) $(-7, 0)$
5. (a) $(-6, -7)$ (b) $(-3, 0)$ (c) $(4, 3)$ (d) $(-9, 1)$
   (e) $(3, 3)$ (f) $(0, -7)$ (g) $(5, -7)$ (h) $(-7, -7)$

EXERCISE 10.3

2. (a) $P'(3, 6)$, $Q'(-1, 0)$; $|P'Q'| = 2\sqrt{13}$
   (b) $P'(2, 0)$, $Q'(-2, 1)$; $|P'Q'| = \sqrt{17}$
   (c) $P'(-1, 3)$, $Q'(0, 0)$; $|P'Q'| = \sqrt{10}$

3. (b)

	$|PQ|$	$|P'Q'|$	M_{PQ}	$M_{P'Q'}$
(i)	5	5	$\frac{4}{3}$	$-\frac{4}{3}$
(ii)	5	5	$\frac{4}{3}$	$\frac{3}{4}$
(iii)	5	5	$\frac{4}{3}$	$\frac{3}{4}$

4. (b) $A'(-1, -1)$, $B'(5, -2)$, $C'(3, -4)$
   (d) $|AB| = \sqrt{37}$; $|BC| = 2\sqrt{2}$; $|CA| = 5$; $|A'B'| = \sqrt{37}$; $|B'C'| = 2\sqrt{2}$; $|C'A'| = 5$;
   (f) $A'(1, 1)$, $B'(-5, 2)$, $C'(-3, 4)$; $|AB| = \sqrt{37}$; $|BC| = 2\sqrt{2}$; $|CA| = 5$; $|A'B'| = \sqrt{37}$; $|B'C'| = 2\sqrt{2}$; $|C'A'| = 5$

5. (a) $A'(-1, 1)$, $B'(6, 1)$, $C'(6, -5)$ (b) Both areas are 21 square units.

6. (a) $A'(2, -1)$, $B'(7, 3)$ (b) $y = \frac{2}{5}x + \frac{1}{5}$, $y = -\frac{2}{5}x - \frac{1}{5}$

7. (a) $(1, 2)$ (b) $(7, 6)$ 8. (a) $(2, 7)$ (b) $(-2, -7)$ 9. (b, a)

EXERCISE 10.4

1. (a) $180°$, $-180°$ (b) $140°$, $-220°$ (c) $90°$, $-270°$
2. (a) $-300°$ (b) $-350°$ (c) $330°$ (d) $90°$ (e) $40°$ (f) $-260°$
3. The centre of rotation.
4. (a) $180°$ (b) $90°$ (c) any angle   (d) $120°$ (e) $180°$ (f) $60°$
5. $P'(2, -4)$; $P(x, y) \rightarrow P'(y, -x)$

6.

	Angle of Rotation			
Point	$90°$	$180°$	$270°$	$-90°$
$A(1, 0)$	$(0, 1)$	$(-1, 0)$	$(0, -1)$	$(0, -1)$
$B(2, 1)$	$(-1, 2)$	$(-2, -1)$	$(1, -2)$	$(1, -2)$
$C(3, 4)$	$(-4, 3)$	$(-3, -4)$	$(4, -3)$	$(4, -3)$
$D(-1, 3)$	$(-3, -1)$	$(1, -3)$	$(3, 1)$	$(3, 1)$
$P(x, y)$	$(-y, x)$	$(-x, -y)$	$(y, -x)$	$(y, -x)$

7. (a) $(-y, x)$ (b) $(-x, -y)$ (c) $(y, -x)$ (d) $(y, -x)$ (e) $(-x, -y)$ (f) $(-y, x)$

EXERCISE 10.5

1. (a) $A'(-2, 7)$, $B'(1, 0)$ (b) $|AB| = |A'B'| = \sqrt{58}$ (c) $m_{AB} = m_{A'B'} = -\frac{7}{3}$

2. (a) $P'(-3, 1)$, $Q'(-7, 4)$ (b) $|PQ| = |P'Q'| = 5$; $m_{PQ} = \frac{4}{3}$, $m_{P'Q'} = -\frac{3}{4}$

3. (a) $D'(0, -1)$, $C'(-1, 3)$ (b) $|DC| = |D'C'| = \sqrt{17}$; $m_{DC} = \frac{1}{4}$, $m_{D'C'} = -4$

4. $|PQ| = |P'Q'| = 2\sqrt{10}$; $m_{PQ} = \frac{1}{3}$, $m_{P'Q'} = -3$ 5. $|ST| = |S'T'| = \sqrt{34}$; $m_{ST} = \frac{5}{3}$, $m_{S'T'} = -\frac{3}{5}$

6. (a) $|xy| = |x'y'| = 3\sqrt{5}$; $m_{xy} = 2$, $m_{x'y'} = 2$

9. (a) $A'(-6, -1)$, $B'(2, 0)$ (b) $y = -8x - 2$, $y = \frac{1}{8}x - \frac{1}{4}$

10. $y = \frac{5}{3}x - \frac{2}{3}$, $y = -\frac{3}{5}x + \frac{2}{5}$

EXERCISE 10.6

1. (a) 4, 4   (b) 2, 2   (c) 0, 1   (d) 2, 2   (e) 0, 2   (f) 1, 1
   (g) 0, 1   (h) 5, 5   (i) 6, 6   (j) 8, 8   (k) infinite   (l) 2, 2
   (m) 0, 1   (n) 3, 3   (o) 0, 3
2. (a) A H I M O T U V W X Y   (b) B C D E H I K O X
   (c) H I X   (d) H I N O X S Z

EXERCISE 10.7

1. (a) $(3, 3)$ (b) $(9, -3)$ (c) $(0, 6)$ (d) $(-15, -6)$ (e) $(-3, 1)$ (f) $(3a, 3b)$
2. (a) $(3, 1)$ (b) $(-1, 0)$ (c) $(-4, -2)$ (d) $(\frac{1}{2}, \frac{9}{2})$ (e) $(1, -\frac{3}{2})$ (f) $(\frac{1}{2}a, \frac{1}{2}b)$
3. (a) $(-5, -5)$ (b) $(0, -30)$ (c) $(10, -45)$ (d) $(-30, -4)$ (e) $(35, 5)$ (f) $(-5a, -5b)$
4. The centre of dilatation. Any line through the centre of dilatation. (If K = 1, all points and lines are unchanged.)
6. (a) greater   (b) same   (c) smaller   (d) smaller   (e) same   (f) greater
7. (a) $\frac{1}{3}$ (b) 3   (c) $\frac{4}{3}$
9. (a) $P'(3, 12)$, $Q'(18, 3)$ (b) $y = -\frac{3}{5}x + \frac{23}{5}$, $y = -\frac{3}{5}x + \frac{69}{5}$
10. (a) $A'(-2, -2)$, $B'(0, 2)$, $C'(6, 4)$
    (c) $AB = \sqrt{5}$, $BC = \sqrt{10}$, $CA = 5$, $A'B' = 2\sqrt{2}$, $B'C' = 2\sqrt{10}$, $C'A' = 10$
11. (a) $A'(3, 3)$, $B'(18, 3)$, $C'(18, 15)$
    (b) $AB = 5$; $(AB, 5)$, $(BC, 4)$, $(AC, \sqrt{41})$, $(A'B', 15)$, $(B'C', 12)$, $(A'C', 3\sqrt{41})$
    The lengths are increased by a factor of 3.
    (c) area of $\triangle ABC$ is 10; area of $\triangle A'B'C'$ is 90
    (d) 9

EXERCISE 10.8

1. (a) $\begin{pmatrix} -1 & 0 \\ 0 & 1 \end{pmatrix}$ (b) $\begin{pmatrix} 0 & 1 \\ 1 & 0 \end{pmatrix}$ (c) $\begin{pmatrix} 0 & -1 \\ -1 & 0 \end{pmatrix}$ (d) $\begin{pmatrix} -1 & 0 \\ 0 & -1 \end{pmatrix}$ (e) $\begin{pmatrix} 0 & 1 \\ -1 & 0 \end{pmatrix}$

2. (a) $P'\begin{pmatrix} 0 \\ -4 \end{pmatrix}$ $Q'\begin{pmatrix} -1 \\ -2 \end{pmatrix}$; $P'\begin{pmatrix} 0 \\ 4 \end{pmatrix}$ $Q'\begin{pmatrix} 1 \\ 2 \end{pmatrix}$; $P'\begin{pmatrix} 4 \\ 0 \end{pmatrix}$ $Q'\begin{pmatrix} 2 \\ -1 \end{pmatrix}$; $P'\begin{pmatrix} -4 \\ 0 \end{pmatrix}$ $Q'\begin{pmatrix} -2 \\ 1 \end{pmatrix}$

   (b) $P'\begin{pmatrix} 1 \\ -3 \end{pmatrix}$ $Q'\begin{pmatrix} -3 \\ 4 \end{pmatrix}$; $P'\begin{pmatrix} -1 \\ 3 \end{pmatrix}$ $Q'\begin{pmatrix} 3 \\ -4 \end{pmatrix}$; $P'\begin{pmatrix} 3 \\ 1 \end{pmatrix}$ $Q'\begin{pmatrix} -4 \\ -3 \end{pmatrix}$; $P'\begin{pmatrix} -3 \\ -1 \end{pmatrix}$ $Q'\begin{pmatrix} 4 \\ 3 \end{pmatrix}$

   (c) $P'\begin{pmatrix} 8 \\ -9 \end{pmatrix}$ $Q'\begin{pmatrix} 12 \\ -35 \end{pmatrix}$; $P'\begin{pmatrix} -8 \\ 9 \end{pmatrix}$ $Q'\begin{pmatrix} -12 \\ 35 \end{pmatrix}$; $P'\begin{pmatrix} 9 \\ 8 \end{pmatrix}$ $Q'\begin{pmatrix} 35 \\ 12 \end{pmatrix}$; $P'\begin{pmatrix} -9 \\ -8 \end{pmatrix}$ $Q'\begin{pmatrix} -35 \\ -12 \end{pmatrix}$

   (d) $P'\begin{pmatrix} -3 \\ 7 \end{pmatrix}$ $Q'\begin{pmatrix} -6 \\ 3 \end{pmatrix}$; $P'\begin{pmatrix} 3 \\ -7 \end{pmatrix}$ $Q'\begin{pmatrix} 6 \\ -3 \end{pmatrix}$; $P'\begin{pmatrix} -7 \\ -3 \end{pmatrix}$ $Q'\begin{pmatrix} -3 \\ -6 \end{pmatrix}$; $P'\begin{pmatrix} 7 \\ 3 \end{pmatrix}$ $Q'\begin{pmatrix} 3 \\ 6 \end{pmatrix}$

   (e) $P'\begin{pmatrix} 0 \\ 0 \end{pmatrix}$ $Q'\begin{pmatrix} -1 \\ 1 \end{pmatrix}$; $P'\begin{pmatrix} 0 \\ 0 \end{pmatrix}$ $Q'\begin{pmatrix} 1 \\ -1 \end{pmatrix}$; $P'\begin{pmatrix} 0 \\ 0 \end{pmatrix}$ $Q'\begin{pmatrix} -1 \\ -1 \end{pmatrix}$; $P'\begin{pmatrix} 0 \\ 0 \end{pmatrix}$ $Q'\begin{pmatrix} 1 \\ 1 \end{pmatrix}$

   (f) $P'\begin{pmatrix} 1 \\ 1 \end{pmatrix}$ $Q'\begin{pmatrix} -1 \\ 0 \end{pmatrix}$; $P'\begin{pmatrix} -1 \\ -1 \end{pmatrix}$ $Q'\begin{pmatrix} 1 \\ 0 \end{pmatrix}$; $P'\begin{pmatrix} -1 \\ 1 \end{pmatrix}$ $Q'\begin{pmatrix} 0 \\ -1 \end{pmatrix}$; $P'\begin{pmatrix} 1 \\ -1 \end{pmatrix}$ $Q'\begin{pmatrix} 0 \\ 1 \end{pmatrix}$

3. (a) $P'\begin{pmatrix} -4 \\ 1 \end{pmatrix}$ $Q'\begin{pmatrix} 3 \\ 2 \end{pmatrix}$; $P'\begin{pmatrix} -1 \\ -4 \end{pmatrix}$ $Q'\begin{pmatrix} -2 \\ 3 \end{pmatrix}$; $P'\begin{pmatrix} 4 \\ -1 \end{pmatrix}$ $Q'\begin{pmatrix} -3 \\ -2 \end{pmatrix}$

   (b) $P'\begin{pmatrix} 0 \\ 1 \end{pmatrix}$ $Q'\begin{pmatrix} 6 \\ -4 \end{pmatrix}$; $P'\begin{pmatrix} -1 \\ 0 \end{pmatrix}$ $Q'\begin{pmatrix} 4 \\ 6 \end{pmatrix}$; $P'\begin{pmatrix} 0 \\ -1 \end{pmatrix}$ $Q'\begin{pmatrix} -6 \\ 4 \end{pmatrix}$

   (c) $P'\begin{pmatrix} -2 \\ 7 \end{pmatrix}$ $Q'\begin{pmatrix} -35 \\ 10 \end{pmatrix}$; $P'\begin{pmatrix} -7 \\ -2 \end{pmatrix}$ $Q'\begin{pmatrix} -10 \\ -35 \end{pmatrix}$; $P'\begin{pmatrix} 2 \\ -7 \end{pmatrix}$ $Q'\begin{pmatrix} 35 \\ -10 \end{pmatrix}$

   (d) $P'\begin{pmatrix} 2 \\ -3 \end{pmatrix}$ $Q'\begin{pmatrix} 1 \\ -9 \end{pmatrix}$; $P'\begin{pmatrix} 3 \\ 2 \end{pmatrix}$ $Q'\begin{pmatrix} 9 \\ 1 \end{pmatrix}$; $P'\begin{pmatrix} -2 \\ 3 \end{pmatrix}$ $Q'\begin{pmatrix} -1 \\ 9 \end{pmatrix}$

   (e) $P'\begin{pmatrix} 0 \\ 0 \end{pmatrix}$ $Q'\begin{pmatrix} 1 \\ -1 \end{pmatrix}$; $P'\begin{pmatrix} 0 \\ 0 \end{pmatrix}$ $Q'\begin{pmatrix} 1 \\ 1 \end{pmatrix}$; $P'\begin{pmatrix} 0 \\ 0 \end{pmatrix}$ $Q'\begin{pmatrix} -1 \\ 1 \end{pmatrix}$

   (f) $P'\begin{pmatrix} 1 \\ 1 \end{pmatrix}$ $Q'\begin{pmatrix} 0 \\ -1 \end{pmatrix}$; $P'\begin{pmatrix} -1 \\ 1 \end{pmatrix}$ $Q'\begin{pmatrix} 1 \\ 0 \end{pmatrix}$; $P'\begin{pmatrix} -1 \\ -1 \end{pmatrix}$ $Q'\begin{pmatrix} 0 \\ 1 \end{pmatrix}$

4. $A'\begin{pmatrix} -3 \\ 4 \end{pmatrix} B'\begin{pmatrix} 0 \\ 1 \end{pmatrix} C'\begin{pmatrix} -2 \\ 7 \end{pmatrix}$

5. $A'\begin{pmatrix} -3 \\ 0 \end{pmatrix} B'\begin{pmatrix} 24 \\ 6 \end{pmatrix} C'\begin{pmatrix} -21 \\ -6 \end{pmatrix}$

6. A'(5, 0) B'(5, −5) C'(10, −5) D'(10, 0)

EXERCISE 10.9

1. 8 2. 8 3. 84 square units 4. 92.5%

5. Take a ball from the bag labelled RB and, according to the colour of the ball drawn, interchange labels with this bag and either the bag labelled RR or BB. The bag formerly labelled RB is now labelled correctly and if we now interchange the labels on the remaining two bags, then all three bags will be labelled correctly.

6. (a) 7.5 weeks (b) 1 a 33 weeks (c) 16 a (d) 171 233 a
7. 2250 cm³ 8. (a) Yes (b) Yes 9. 18 10. 22 m
11. loss of $1.26 12. 14 pigs, any number of chickens
13. after the fifth bounce 14. 42 km
15. (a) 22.5° (b) 1131 cm² (c) 76.9 cm (d) 18 568.7 cm² (e) 17 851.4 cm²
   (f) total area 18 096 cm², which is smaller than the circle in (d) and larger than the circle in (e)
16. 72.8% 17. (b), (c), and (d)

10.11 REVIEW EXERCISE

1. (a) (x + a, y + b) (b) (x, −y) (c) (−x, y) (d) (y, x) (e) (−y, −x)
   (f) (−y, x) (g) (−x, −y) (h) (y, −x) (i) (kx, ky)

2. (a) translation (b) reflection in x-axis (c) dilatation
   (d) translation (e) rotation (or dilatation) (f) reflection in y-axis

3. (a) (i) (0, 0) (ii) (3, −4) (iii) (−2, −1) (iv) (−6, 6)
      (v) (0, −5) (vi) (1, 1) (vii) (6, −$\frac{1}{2}$) (viii) (a, −b)
   (b) (i) (0, 0) (ii) (9, 12) (iii) (−6, 3) (iv) (−18, −18)
      (v) (0, 15) (vi) (3, −3) (vii) (18, $\frac{3}{2}$) (viii) (3a, 3b)
   (c) (i) (7, −3) (ii) (10, 1) (iii) (5, −2) (iv) (1, −9)
      (v) (7, 2) (vi) (8, −4) (vii) (13, −$\frac{5}{2}$) (viii) (a + 7, b − 3)
   (d) (i) (0, 0) (ii) (−3, 4) (iii) (2, 1) (iv) (6, −6)
      (v) (0, 5) (vi) (−1, −1) (vii) (−6, $\frac{1}{2}$) (viii) (−a, b)
   (e) (i) (0, 0) (ii) (−3, −4) (iii) (2, −1) (iv) (6, 6)
      (v) (0, −5) (vi) (−1, 1) (vii) (−6, −$\frac{1}{2}$) (viii) (−a, −b)

4.

	A(−2, −2)	B(4, 6)	C(2, 8)	P(x, y)
F	(−2, 2)	(4, −6)	(2, −8)	(x, −y)
R	(2, 2)	(−4, −6)	(−2, −8)	(−x, −y)
T	(0, −3)	(6, 5)	(4, 7)	(x + 2, y − 1)
D	(−1, −1)	(2, 3)	(1, 4)	($\frac{1}{2}$x, $\frac{1}{2}$y)

5. (ii) $\sqrt{26}, 2\sqrt{5}, \sqrt{10}$
   $\sqrt{26}, 2\sqrt{5}, \sqrt{10}$
   $\sqrt{26}, 2\sqrt{5}, \sqrt{10}$
   $3\sqrt{26}, 6\sqrt{5}, 3\sqrt{10}$

6. (a) 3, 3 (b) 4, 4

10.12 CHAPTER 10 TEST

1. (a) P'(4, 0) Q'(1, 1)
2. (a) A'(−2, −4) B'(3, −3)
   (d) A'(−4, 2) B'(−3, −3)
3. D'(−4, −2)
5. X'(8, 0) Y'(−12, −12)

(b) $\sqrt{10}$, $\sqrt{10}$
(b) A'(2, 4) B'(−3, 3)

(c) A'(4, −2) B'(3, 3)

4. (a) S'(2, −2) T'(−1, −3)

(b) $m_{ST} = -3$, $m_{S'T'} = \frac{1}{3}$

REVIEW AND PREVIEW TO CHAPTER 11

PARALLEL LINES AND INTERSECTING LINES

1. (a) a = 55°
   (e) f = 30°, g = 70°
   (i) l = 60°, m = 60°
   (m) q = 65°, r = 95°

(b) b = 145°
(f) h = 90°
(j) n = 30°, p = 30°
(n) s = 20°, t = 70°

(c) c = 130°, d = 130°
(g) j = 60°
(k) m = 50°, n = 70°

(d) e = 40°
(h) k = 65°
(l) p = 100°

CONGRUENT TRIANGLES

1. △ABC ≅ △RPQ (SAS)
   △GHI ≅ △TUS (SSS)
   △MON ≅ △VXW (ASA)
   △MON ≅ △KJL (ASA)
   △VXW ≅ △KJL (ASA)

TRANSFORMATIONS

1. (a) (i) (0, 0)
      (v) (0, 5)
   (b) (i) (0, 0)
      (v) (−20, 0)
   (c) (i) (1, −3)
      (v) (6, −3)
   (d) (i) (0, 0)
      (v) (0, −5)

(ii) (1, 0)
(vi) (1, −1)
(ii) (0, −4)
(vi) (4, −4)
(ii) (1, −2)
(vi) (0, −2)
(ii) (1, 0)
(vi) (1, 1)

(iii) (2, −3)
(vii) (4, 6)
(iii) (12, −8)
(vii) (−24, −16)
(iii) (−2, −1)
(vii) (7, 1)
(iii) (2, 3)
(vii) (4, −6)

(iv) (−5, −5)
(viii) (b, a)
(iv) (20, 20)
(viii) (−4a, −4b)
(iv) (−4, −8)
(viii) (a + 1, b − 3)
(iv) (−5, 5)
(viii) (b, −a)

3. (a) (x + 2, y + 7)   (b) A'(5, 7), B'(1, 8), O'(2, 7)

SYMMETRY

1. (a) 3, 3

(b) 4, 4

(c) 1, 1

EXERCISE 11.1

3. translation, reflection, rotation
4. (b) R'(−2, 1), S'(3, 2), T'(0, 5)
5. (b) A'(−1, −1), B'(5, −2), C'(3, −4)
   (f) A'(1, 1), B'(−5, 2), C'(−3, 4), $\sqrt{37}$, 2$\sqrt{2}$, 5
6. (a) A'(−1, 1), B'(6, 1), C'(6, −5)
8. O'(0, 0), P'(0, 2), Q'(−2, 2)

(d) $\sqrt{37}$, 2$\sqrt{2}$, 5, $\sqrt{37}$, 2$\sqrt{2}$, 5

(b) 21, 21

EXERCISE 11.2

4. (a) (i) (6, 7)   (ii) (3, 9)   (iii) (11, 10)   (iv) (x + 5, y + 6)
   (b) S ∘ T:(x, y) → (x + a + c, y + b + d)
5. (a) R_{90} (b) R_{115} (c) R_{u+u} (d) R_{90}

6.

	A(1, 2)	B(3, 0)	C(−2, 5)	P(x, y)
T ∘ T	(−3, 8)	(−1, 6)	(−6, 11)	(x − 4, y + 6)
R	(−1, −2)	(−3, 0)	(2, −5)	(−x, −y)
F ∘ G	(−1, −2)	(−3, 0)	(2, −5)	(−x, −y)
G ∘ F	(−1, −2)	(−3, 0)	(2, −5)	(−x, −y)
T ∘ R	(−3, 1)	(−5, 3)	(0, −2)	(−x − 2, y + 3)
R ∘ T	(1, −5)	(−1, −3)	(4, −8)	(−x + 2, −y − 3)
T ∘ F	(−1, 1)	(1, 3)	(−4, −2)	(x − 2, −y + 3)
F ∘ T	(−1, −5)	(1, −3)	(−4, −8)	(x − 2, −y − 3)

7. F ∘ G = G ∘ F = R
9. All

EXERCISE 11.3

4. (a) A″(6, 1) B″(9, −1) C″(11, 2) D″(9, 0)   (c) A‴(6, 9) B‴(9, 11) C‴(11, 8) D‴(9, 10)
(d) No

EXERCISE 11.4

1.

Isometry	Type of Transformation	Direct or Indirect	Coordinates of Image
T	translation	direct	(x + a, y + b)
S	reflection	indirect	(−x, y)
R	rotation	direct	(−y, x)
Q	reflection	indirect	(x, −y)
S ∘ Q	rotation	direct	(−x, −y)
Q ∘ S ∘ Q	reflection	indirect	(−x, y)

EXERCISE 11.5

1. (a) 9   (b) 90
2. 24
3. (a) 39 564 km   (b) 12.56 m
4. 6
5. (a) 3   (b) 2 m, 2$\sqrt{2}$ m, 2$\sqrt{3}$ m
6. 96 420; 87 531
7. The one that does not run.
8. 2025
9. 168 m³, 384 m²   10. 88
11. It will take 15 trips as follows: 2 children cross, 1 child returns, 1 adult crosses, 1 child returns, 2 children cross, 1 child returns, 1 adult crosses, 1 child returns, 2 children cross, 1 child returns, 1 adult crosses, 1 child returns, 2 children cross, 1 child returns, 2 children cross
12. 15 and 10   13. 130 m   14. 323 m   15. 11.3 L   16. 325
17. (a) 13, 18, 15   (b) 34, 55, 89   (c) 19, 31, 50
    (d) 14, 25, 39   (e) Answers vary   (f) Answers vary
18. 34.3 km/h   19. (a) 2018.4 m   (b) $17 828.64   21. (a) and (b)

11.7 REVIEW EXERCISE

1. (ii) $\sqrt{26}$, 2$\sqrt{5}$, $\sqrt{10}$
      $\sqrt{26}$, 2$\sqrt{5}$, $\sqrt{10}$
      $\sqrt{26}$, 2$\sqrt{5}$, $\sqrt{10}$
      3$\sqrt{26}$, 6$\sqrt{5}$, 3$\sqrt{10}$

3.

	A(−2, −2)	B(4, 6)	C(2, 8)	P(x, y)
F	(−2, 2)	(4, −6)	(2, −8)	(x, −y)
R	(2, 2)	(−4, −6)	(−2, −8)	(−x, −y)
T	(0, −3)	(6, 5)	(4, 7)	(x + 2, y − 1)
D	(−1, −1)	(2, 3)	(1, 4)	$(\frac{1}{2}x, \frac{1}{2}y)$
T ∘ D	(1, −2)	(4, 2)	(3, 3)	$(\frac{1}{2}x + 2, \frac{1}{2}y − 1)$
D ∘ T	$(0, −\frac{3}{2})$	$(3, \frac{5}{2})$	$(2, \frac{7}{2})$	$(\frac{1}{2}x + 1, \frac{1}{2}y − \frac{1}{2})$
F ∘ R	(2, −2)	(−4, 6)	(−2, 8)	(−x, y)
D ∘ F	(−1, 1)	(2, −3)	(1, −4)	$(\frac{1}{2}x, −\frac{1}{2}y)$
F ∘ D	(−1, 1)	(2, −3)	(1, −4)	$(\frac{1}{2}x, −\frac{1}{2}y)$
D ∘ D	$(−\frac{1}{2}, −\frac{1}{2})$	$(1, \frac{3}{2})$	$(\frac{1}{2}, 2)$	$(\frac{1}{4}x, \frac{1}{4}y)$
D ∘ R	(1, 1)	(−2, −3)	(−1, −4)	$(−\frac{1}{2}x, −\frac{1}{2}y)$
F ∘ T	(0, 3)	(6, −5)	(4, 7)	(x + 2, −y + 1)

4.

Isometry	Type of Transformation	Direct or Indirect
T	reflection	indirect
T ∘ U	rotation	direct
U ∘ T	rotation	direct
T ∘ R	translation	direct
R ∘ U	rotation	direct

11.8 CHAPTER 11 TEST

2. A′(−3, −5) B′(6, −2) C′(0, 2)
3. (a) P″(0, −5) Q″(5, 5) R″(5, 0) (b) rotation of 180°
4. L′(5, −2) M′(9, −6) N′(0, −7)
5. (a) (9, −8) (b) (9, −2) (c) (15, −1)
7. (a) direct (b) indirect (c) indirect (d) indirect

REVIEW AND PREVIEW TO CHAPTER 12

THE LENGTH OF A LINE SEGMENT

1. (a) HI — 4, GF — 0, OA — 4, BC — 4, DE — 8 (b) HI — 0, GF — 4, OA — 3, BC — 3, DE — −2
   (c) HI — 4, GF — 4, OA — 5, BC — 5, DE — 8.2
2. (a) 13 (b) 22 (c) 3 (d) 9

SCALE DRAWINGS — THE RULE OF THREE

1. (a) 4 m (b) 10 m (c) 5 m (d) 15 m
2. (a) 2 cm (b) 5.5 cm (c) 8.5 cm (d) 1.5 cm
3. (a) 9.5 cm (b) 7.0 cm (c) 6.0 cm

EXERCISE 12.1

1. b, e, f
2. (a) [4, 2]   (b) [6, −2]   (c) [−2, 3]   (d) [6, 0]
3. (a) (2, 5)   (b) (2, 11)   (c) (3, 3)   (d) (−1, 3)
4. (a) [−3, −2]   (b) [−1, 5]   (c) [5, 3]   (d) [0, −5]
6. (a) (6, 8)   (b) (0, 0)   (c) (4, 1)   (d) (7, 11)   (e) (−1, 1)
7. (b) and (c)
8. (a) [5, 9]   (b) [3, 7]   (c) [4, −1]   (d) [8, 6]
9. (a) 5   (b) 13   (c) 13   (d) 17
   (e) 25   (f) 17   (g) 10   (h) 5
10. (a) [4, 6]   (b) [−8, 4]   (c) [−6, −4]   (d) [2, −6]   (e) [−5, −2]
11. (a) [8, 7]   (b) [0, 9]   (c) [−1, −3]   (d) [9, 0]   (e) [2, 3]

EXERCISE 12.2

1. (a) [3, 4], [3, 5], [3, 4], [3, 5], [3, 5]   (b) $\overrightarrow{AB} = \overrightarrow{EF}$, $\overrightarrow{BC} = \overrightarrow{GH} = \overrightarrow{KL}$
3. $\overrightarrow{AB} = [5, −2]$, $\overrightarrow{BA} = [−5, 2]$, $\overrightarrow{BC} = [−10, −8]$, $\overrightarrow{CD} = [8, 5]$
   $\overrightarrow{DA} = [−3, 5]$, $\overrightarrow{AC} = [−5, −10]$, $\overrightarrow{DB} = [2, 3]$
4. (a) parallelogram   (b) $\overrightarrow{PQ} = [−2, 8]$, $\overrightarrow{QR} = [11, 6]$,
                               $\overrightarrow{SR} = [−2, −8]$, $\overrightarrow{PS} = [11, 6]$
5. D(6, 3)   6. (a) D(−1, −6)   (b) E(−1, −6)   7. (a) S(0, 14)   (d) No

8. (a)

[a, b]	$\sqrt{a^2 + b^2}$	$\dfrac{b}{a}$
[1, 2]	$\sqrt{5}$	2
[3, −4]	5	$-\dfrac{4}{3}$
[2, 4]	$2\sqrt{5}$	2
[3, −4]	5	$-\dfrac{4}{3}$
[1, 2]	$\sqrt{5}$	2
[1, 2]	$\sqrt{5}$	2
[3, −4]	5	$-\dfrac{4}{3}$
[−1, −2]	$\sqrt{5}$	2

(b) $\overrightarrow{CD} = \overrightarrow{GH} = \overrightarrow{MN}$
   $\overrightarrow{AB} = \overrightarrow{IJ} = \overrightarrow{KL}$

9. (a) a = 5, b = 3   (b) a = c, b = d
10. (a) same direction   (b) magnitude   (c) multiply the magnitude by $\frac{6}{5}$
11. (c) 447, N63°W
12. (b) 13 kn   13. (a) [0, 500]   (b) [100, 0]   (c) [−173, −100]
14. (b) east, 8.7 units   15. (b) 825 km/h   16. (b) 110 km   (c) 2.2 h

EXERCISE 12.3

1. (a) [7, 10]   (b) [1, 7]   (c) [3, −1]   (d) [7, −3]   (e) [−5, −7]
   (f) [7, 13]   (g) [0, 0]   (h) [0, 0]   (i) [3, 6]   (j) [0, 9]
2. (a) [−2, 5]   (b) [0, 8]   (c) [0, 0]   (d) [2, 10]   (e) [−1, −1]   (f) [2, 5]
3. magnitudes   (a) 13 km   (b) 33.5 km   (c) 10.4 km   (d) 15.6 km
4. (a) [7, 5]   (b) [9, 4]   (c) [5, 2]   (d) [−1, 1]
   (e) [1, 0]   (f) [−6, 1]   (g) [1, 3]   (h) [3, 4]
5. (a) [2, 3], a vector   (b) [a + c, b + d], a vector   (c) Yes, closure
6. (a) =   (b) =   (c) =   (d) =
7. (a) (i) [3, 2]   (ii) [−2, −6]   (iii) [−4, 3]   (iv) [−2, −4]

(c) (i) [0, 0]   (ii) [0, 0]
8. (a) $[-3, -4]$ (b) $[-3, -11]$ (c) $[5, -3]$ (d) $[4, 7]$ (e) $[-a, -b]$ (f) $[-a, -b]$
9. (c) (i) same magnitude   (ii) opposite direction

EXERCISE 12.4

1. (a) $\vec{a} + \vec{b}$ (b) $\vec{a} + \vec{c}$ (c) $\vec{a} + \vec{b}$
2. (a) $\vec{c}$ (b) $\vec{e}$ (c) $\vec{d}$ (d) $\overrightarrow{DB}$ (e) $\overrightarrow{AD} = \overrightarrow{BC}$ (f) $\overrightarrow{CA}$
3. (a) $\overrightarrow{AC}$ (b) $\overrightarrow{BD}$ (c) $\overrightarrow{AD}$
5. $\overrightarrow{AB} + \overrightarrow{BC} = \overrightarrow{AC} = \overrightarrow{AD} + \overrightarrow{DC}$
6. (a) $\overrightarrow{AE}$ (B) $\overrightarrow{CA}$ (c) $\overrightarrow{CA}$ (d) $\overrightarrow{EC}$ (e) $\overrightarrow{AC}$ (f) $\overrightarrow{CB}$
7. (a) $\overrightarrow{AC}$ (b) $\overrightarrow{AD}$ (c) $\overrightarrow{CE}$ (d) $\overrightarrow{BE}$ (e) $\overrightarrow{AE}$

EXERCISE 12.5

1. (a) $\vec{b} = \vec{a}, \vec{c} = -\vec{a}, \vec{d} = 2\vec{a}$
   (b) $\vec{b} = -2\vec{a}, \vec{c} = 1.5\vec{a}, \vec{d} = 3\vec{a}$
   (c) $\vec{b} = -1.5\vec{a}, \vec{c} = -0.5\vec{a}, \vec{d} = 2\vec{a}, \vec{e} = -3.5\vec{a}$
2. (a) [6, 15]   (b) [18, −6]   (c) [2, 4]   (d) [6, 9]   (e) [−2, 4]
   (f) [0, 0]   (g) [0, −6]   (h) [−2, 8]   (i) [10, 20]
3. (a) [10, 9]   (b) [2, 7]   (c) [2, 7]   (d) [1, 4]
   (e) [−10, −7]   (f) [18, 3]   (g) [20, 5]   (h) [0, −20]
4. (a) [14x, 8y]   (b) [9x, 7y]   (c) [20x, 4y]   (d) [24x, −3y]
6. (1, 3) (1, −1) (4, −2)   7. [3.5, 9.4]

EXERCISE 12.6

1. (a) [1, 2]   (b) [9, −1]   (c) [2, 2]   (d) [12, 18]
   (e) [0, 0]   (f) [−4, 7]   (g) [2x, b]   (h) [2a, −4b]
   (i) [−3a, 6b]   (j) [p − m, q − n]
2. (a) $\vec{c}$ (b) $\vec{c}$ (c) $-\vec{c}$ (d) $\vec{c}$ (e) $-\vec{c}$ (f) $\vec{d}$
3. (a) $\vec{a} = \vec{b} - \vec{c}, \vec{b} = \vec{a} + \vec{c}, \vec{c} = \vec{a} - \vec{b}$ (b) $\vec{a} = -(\vec{b} + \vec{c}), \vec{b} = -(\vec{a} + \vec{c}), \vec{c} = -(\vec{a} + \vec{b})$
4. (a) [8, 1]   (b) [14, −20]   (c) [−2, 0]   (d) [−21, 5]
   (e) [−11, 8]   (f) [−40, 40]   (g) [6, −18]   (h) [6, 21]
5. [0, 0]
6. (a) [3, 3]   (b) [−5, 19]   (c) [10, −31]   (d) [5, 20]   (e) [5, −5]
   (f) [3, −15]   (g) [21, −21]   (h) [8, −4]   (i) [13, 36]   (j) [−21, 14]
7. (a) $\overrightarrow{DB}$ (b) $\overrightarrow{EB}$ (c) $\overrightarrow{BE}$ (d) $\overrightarrow{AD}$ (e) $\overrightarrow{O}$ (f) $\overrightarrow{BD}$
8. (a) $\overrightarrow{AC}$ (b) $\overrightarrow{BD}$ (c) $\overrightarrow{AD}$ (d) $\overrightarrow{DA}$

EXERCISE 12.7

1. (a) $\overrightarrow{BA} = \overrightarrow{BC} + \overrightarrow{CA}, \overrightarrow{BC} = \overrightarrow{BA} - \overrightarrow{CA}, \overrightarrow{CA} = \overrightarrow{BA} - \overrightarrow{BC}$
   (b) $\overrightarrow{AB} = -\overrightarrow{CA} - \overrightarrow{BC}, \overrightarrow{BC} = -\overrightarrow{AB} - \overrightarrow{CA}, \overrightarrow{CA} = -\overrightarrow{AB} - \overrightarrow{BC}$
   (c) $\vec{w} = \vec{v} + \vec{u}, \vec{u} = \vec{w} - \vec{v}, \vec{v} = \vec{w} - \vec{u}$
2. (a) $\vec{x}$ (b) $\vec{y}$ (c) $-\vec{x}$ (d) $\vec{z}$ (e) $-\vec{x}$
   (f) $\vec{y} - \vec{x}$ (g) $\vec{x} - \vec{y}$ (h) $\vec{z}$ (i) $\frac{1}{2}\vec{z}$ (j) $\vec{z}$
   (k) $\vec{y} - \vec{x}$ (l) $\frac{1}{2}(\vec{y} - \vec{x})$ (m) $\frac{1}{2}(\vec{y} - \vec{x})$ (n) $\frac{1}{2}(\vec{x} - \vec{y})$
3. $\overrightarrow{AD} = \overrightarrow{AB} + \frac{1}{2}\overrightarrow{BC}$

EXERCISE 12.8

1. (a) (60°, 100)   (b) (210°, 200)   (c) (315°, 50)   (d) (135°, 30)
2. (a) 4 cm   (b) 6 cm   (c) 3 cm   (d) 5 cm   (e) 1.6 cm   (f) 3.6 cm
4. (59°, 583)   5. (293°, 1300)   6. (104°, 20.6)   7. (354°, 402)
8. (7°, 605)   9. (101°, 25.5)   10. (276°, 403)   11. (236°, 361)
12. (190°, 304)   13. (275°, 402)   14. (8°, 350), 346   15. (100°, 300), 296

EXERCISE 12.9

1. (a) [2, 0, 5]   (b) [7, 3, 0]   (c) [6, 5, 4]   (d) [0, 3, 9]
2. (a) 3.7   (b) 25.0   (c) 13.0   (d) 9.5   (e) 3.7
3. 5.2 m   4. 8.8 m   5. Yes

EXERCISE 12.10

2. 30 cm by 15 cm by 12 cm   4. 1, 2, 3, 4, 5; 6, 9; 7, 8
5. 2 arrows landed in the ring worth 16 and 4 landed in the ring worth 17.
6. 194 cm²   7. 9629.3 m³   9. 2401 m²   10. 44
11. 5   12. dime   13. 21
14. Beginning in the top-left corner move across the rows placing the digits as follows: 3, 5, 7, 1, 8, 2, 4, 6
15. 126 604.8 cm   16. 41.4%   17. 28 cm

12.11 REVIEW EXERCISE

1. (a) (7, −1)   (b) (4, −6)   (c) (2, −3)   (d) (−1, −1)
2. (a) [12, 13]   (b) [4, −9]   (c) [1, −6]   (d) [−14, 9]
3. (a) 5   (b) 5   (c) 13   (d) 17   (e) 13.0
   (f) 8.6   (g) 17   (h) $\sqrt{m^2 + n^2}$ (i) 10.5   (j) 17
   (k) 29   (l) 9.1   (m) $\sqrt{p^2 + q^2 + r^2}$ (n) 13
4. (a) (90°, 200)   (b) (180°, 100)   (c) (270°, 150)   (d) (0°, 200)
   (e) (45°, 10√2)   (f) (135°, 5√2)   (g) (225°, 3√3)   (h) 315°, 7√2)
5. $\overrightarrow{AE} = \overrightarrow{EC}$, $\overrightarrow{BE} = \overrightarrow{ED}$, $\overrightarrow{AD} = \overrightarrow{BC}$, $\overrightarrow{BA} = \overrightarrow{CD}$
6. (a) $\overrightarrow{x}$ (b) $\overrightarrow{y}$ (c) $\overrightarrow{a}$
7. (a) [12, 6]   (b) [8, −1]   (c) [13, 23]   (d) [5, −3]
   (e) 2√5   (f) √58   (g) 2√5 + √26   (h) [−6, −19]
8. (a) [2, 10]   (b) [12, 15]   (c) [6, 4]   (d) [6, −2]
   (e) √65 + 2√10 + 3   (f) 2√26
9. (b) $\overrightarrow{OA}$ = [4, 2], $\overrightarrow{AB}$ = [3, 3], $\overrightarrow{BC}$ = [−5, −5], $\overrightarrow{CD}$ = [−8, 1], $\overrightarrow{OD}$ = [−6, 1]
10. (b) P(2, 6), Q(6, 8)
    R(13, 13), S(15, 13)
11. $\overrightarrow{AB} = \overrightarrow{CD}$
12. (a) 6.2 m   (b) 7.8 m   (c) 14.0 m   13. (16°, 25.7)
14. (a) (6, 0)   (b) [2, 5], [8, 2], [8, 2], [2, 5]   (c) parallelogram
15. (b) [2, −1]   16. (a) (81°, 253)   (b) (99°, 253)   17. (b) parallelogram
19. 27.1 m

12.12 CHAPTER 12 TEST

1. (a) (0, 2)   (b) (−5, 3)   2. (a) 13   (b) 3   (c) 13
3. (a) $-2\overrightarrow{d}$ (b) $2\overrightarrow{c}$ (c) $\overrightarrow{a}$
4. (a) [6, −4]   (b) [−1, −5]   (c) [7, 1]   (d) [13, −3]   (e) [11, 4]   (f) [−2, 2]
5. (a) (0°, 3)   (b) (270°, 2)   (c) (45°, 2√2)   (d) (135°, √2)
6. (a) 6.6 m   (b) 10.8 m   7. (b) 47.2 kn/h
8. (a) 24 m   (b) 16.3 m   (c) 122°

REVIEW AND PREVIEW TO CHAPTER 13

PERCENT

1. (i) (a) $\frac{1}{4}$ (b) 0.25   (ii) (a) $\frac{3}{4}$ (b) 0.75   (iii) (a) $\frac{1}{3}$ (b) $0.\overline{3}$

   (iv) (a) $\frac{1}{10}$ (b) 0.1   (v) (a) $\frac{13}{20}$ (b) 0.65   (vi) (a) $\frac{6}{5}$ (b) 1.2

   (vii) (a) $\frac{17}{20}$ (b) 0.85   (viii) (a) $\frac{9}{4}$ (b) 2.25   (ix) (a) $\frac{1}{20}$ (b) 0.05

   (x) (a) $\frac{3}{200}$ (b) 0.015   (xi) (a) $\frac{21}{200}$ (b) 0.105   (xii) (a) $\frac{2}{3}$ (b) $0.\overline{6}$

   (xiii) (a) $\frac{1}{8}$ (b) 0.125   (xiv) (a) $\frac{3}{8}$ (b) 0.375   (xv) (a) $\frac{5}{8}$ (b) 0.625

   (xvi) (a) $1\frac{1}{8}$ (b) 1.125

2. (a) 40%   (b) 75%   (c) 70%   (d) 15%
   (e) 6%   (f) 25%   (g) 175%   (h) 57.5%
   (i) 34.5%   (j) 202.5%   (k) 62.5%   (l) 12.5%
   (m) 37.5%   (n) 125%   (o) 387.5%   (p) 162.5%

3. (a) 1   (b) 4.32   (c) 7.38   (d) 750
   (e) 1.44   (f) 0.1875   (g) 8   (h) 55.5
   (i) 14   (j) 630   (k) 3.6   (l) 1.1
   (m) 117   (n) 1100   (o) 325   (p) 12.5

4. 116   5. $6826.75   6. $1948.24   7. $337.50

8. (a) 37.5%   (b) 17.14%   (c) $133\frac{1}{3}$%   (d) $33\frac{1}{3}$%   (e) 20%   (f) $166\frac{2}{3}$%

9. 215

FRACTIONS

1. (a) $\frac{11}{8}$ (b) $1\frac{1}{6}$ (c) $1\frac{1}{9}$ (d) $1\frac{3}{56}$ (e) $1\frac{1}{33}$ (f) $1\frac{6}{35}$

   (g) $\frac{23}{24}$ (h) $\frac{38}{45}$ (i) $\frac{7}{8}$ (j) $1\frac{13}{28}$ (k) $\frac{11}{24}$ (l) $1\frac{2}{39}$

2. (a) $\frac{2}{15}$ (b) $\frac{35}{72}$ (c) $\frac{5}{48}$ (d) $\frac{2}{3}$ (e) $\frac{3}{25}$ (f) $\frac{3}{11}$

   (g) $\frac{4}{15}$ (h) $\frac{5}{22}$ (i) $\frac{32}{65}$ (j) $\frac{3}{8}$ (k) $\frac{5}{24}$ (l) $\frac{1}{5}$

3. (a) $\frac{3}{7}$ (b) $\frac{9}{11}$ (c) $1\frac{1}{4}$ (d) $\frac{5}{6}$ (e) $1\frac{2}{3}$ (f) $\frac{1}{3}$

   (g) $\frac{1}{3}$ (h) $1\frac{5}{14}$ (i) $\frac{5}{8}$ (j) $\frac{23}{24}$ (k) $2\frac{2}{3}$ (l) $\frac{11}{20}$

WORKING WITH TABLES

1. (a) 109.1   (b) 88.6   (c) 111.7   (d) 112.4

EXERCISE 13.1

1. (a) Bullets are consumed when tested.   (b) Testing all the ore results in actual mining.
   (c) Time and expense requires sampling only.   (d) Wine is consumed when tested.
   (e) Impossible to tag all geese.
2. automobile brakes, television sets, water craft
3. (a) biased, inaccurate   (b) expensive   (c) biased
7. 90 boys, 110 girls

EXERCISE 13.3

1. (a) 60   (b) 140   2. 1000   3. (a) 195   (b) 1
4. 1 — 1125, 2 — 1935, 3 — 1440, 4 — 1530, 5 — 1395, 6 — 1575

EXERCISE 13.6

1. (a) median   (b) mode   (c) mean   (d) mean
   (e) median   (f) mode   (g) mean
2. (a) 26; 53; 49.3   (b) 20; 12; 12.1   (c) 5; 4.5; 4.4   (d) 8; 8.5; 10.4   (e) 3 and 4; 4; 4.3
3. 17; 17; 17.4   4. (a) $31 000   (b) $31 000   (c) $31 029.41
5. (b) 51   (c) 62   (d) 63.6
6. (a) $55.75   (b) $56.75   (c) $56.66
7. (c) mean — 48.43; median — 49; modes — 1, 94;

EXERCISE 13.8

1. (a) 24   (b) 75   (c) 304   (d) 150   (e) 50
2. (a) 34%   (b) 82%   (c) 84%
3. (a) 16%   (b) 96%   (c) 16%
4. (a) 68%   (b) 98%   (c) 160   (d) 20
5. (a) 85%   (b) 1360   (c) 40   (d) 320
6. (a) 16%   (b) 80   (c) 420
7. (a) 16%   (b) 960   (c) 4920
8. range — 12; mean — 179; standard deviation — 3.35
9. range — 9; mean — 50; standard deviation — 2.51
10. (a) 82%   (b) 480   (c) 1500
11. (a) 12

(b)

x_i	$x_i - \bar{x}$	$(x_i - \bar{x})^2$	x_i^2
6	−6	36	36
7	−5	25	49
8	−4	16	64
8	−4	16	64
10	−2	4	100
11	−1	1	121
11	−1	1	121
11	−1	1	121
13	1	1	169
14	2	4	196
14	2	4	196
15	3	9	225
16	4	16	256
17	5	25	289
19	7	49	361
Total 180	—	208	2368

(c) 3.72   (d) 3.72

EXERCISE 13.9

1. (a) $\frac{3}{5}$ (b) $\frac{1}{1\,000\,000}$ (c) $\frac{3}{20}$ (d) $\frac{1}{2}$ (e) $\frac{1}{10}$ (f) $\frac{1}{20}$
2. (a) {H, T}   (b) {1, 2, 3, 4, 5, 6}
   (c) {buttered side up, buttered side down}   (d) {William, Debbie, Craig, Nicole}
3. (a) $\frac{1}{6}$ (b) $\frac{1}{2}$ (c) $\frac{1}{3}$ (d) 0   (e) 1
4. (a) $\frac{1}{100}$ (b) $\frac{1}{2}$ (c) $\frac{1}{5}$

5. (a) $\frac{1}{1000}$ (b) $\frac{1}{100}$ (c) 0   (d) 1

6. (a) $\frac{1}{52}$ (b) $\frac{1}{4}$ (c) $\frac{1}{13}$ (d) $\frac{1}{2}$ (e) $\frac{4}{13}$

7. (a) 12   (b) 3   (c) $\frac{1}{4}$ (d) $\frac{1}{3}$ (e) $\frac{3}{4}$

8. (a) $\frac{3}{5}$ (b) $\frac{2}{5}$ 9. $\frac{3}{4}$ 10. (a) $\frac{1}{2}$

EXERCISE 13.11

1. (b) 4   (d) 4   6. 216   7. 104   8. (b) 16 384

EXERCISE 13.12

1. (a) $\frac{1}{4}$ (b) $\frac{1}{4}$ (c) $\frac{1}{2}$

2. (a) $\frac{1}{4}$ (b) $\frac{3}{4}$ (c) $\frac{1}{13}$ (d) $\frac{12}{13}$

  (e) $\frac{1}{2}$ (f) $\frac{1}{26}$ (g) $\frac{1}{52}$

3. (a) $\frac{1}{2}$ (b) $\frac{1}{10}$ (c) $\frac{1}{4}$

4. (b) {(1, 1), (1, 2), (1, 3), (1, 4), (1, 5), (1, 6), (2, 1), (2, 2), ..., (5, 4), (5, 5), (5, 6), (6, 1), (6, 2), (6, 3), (6, 4), (6, 5), (6, 6)}

  (c) 0, $\frac{1}{36}$, $\frac{1}{18}$, $\frac{1}{12}$, $\frac{1}{9}$, $\frac{5}{36}$, $\frac{1}{6}$, $\frac{5}{36}$, $\frac{1}{9}$, $\frac{1}{12}$, $\frac{1}{18}$, $\frac{1}{36}$

  (d) $\frac{5}{18}$ (e) $\frac{1}{4}$

5. (a) 0   (b) $\frac{1}{216}$ (c) $\frac{1}{36}$

6. (a) $\frac{1}{8}$ (b) $\frac{3}{8}$ (c) $\frac{7}{8}$

7. (a) $\frac{3}{8}$ (b) $\frac{1}{4}$ (c) $\frac{11}{16}$

8. (a) $\frac{1}{4}$ (b) $\frac{1}{4}$ (c) $\frac{1}{2}$ (d) $\frac{1}{16}$ (e) $\frac{1}{2704}$ (f) $\frac{1}{52}$

9. (a) $\frac{9}{10\,000}$ (b) $\frac{81}{10^8}$ (c) $\frac{729}{10^{12}}$ 10. (a) 97%   (b) $\frac{9409}{10\,000}$

11. (a) (i) $\frac{2}{5}$ (ii) $\frac{3}{5}$ (iii) $\frac{3}{5}$ (iv) $\frac{6}{25}$ (v) $\frac{4}{25}$ (vi) $\frac{9}{25}$ (b) C

EXERCISE 13.13

2. $\frac{1}{3}$ 5. 19 m   6. 77   7. 204

8. 23, 29, 31, 37, 53, 59, 71, 73, 79

9. (a) 4.5 min   (b) 1.2 km   (c) They jog at a constant speed.

11. (a) 1, 1.5, 2, 2.5   (b) 9   (c) $\frac{n-1}{2}$

13.15 REVIEW EXERCISE

1. (b) 6   (d) 136   (f) 135.5   (g) 1.45

2. (a) $\frac{1}{4}$ (b) $\frac{3}{4}$ (c) $\frac{3}{10}$ (d) $\frac{7}{10}$ (e) $\frac{9}{20}$ (f) $\frac{11}{20}$

3. (a) $\frac{1}{6}$ (b) $\frac{2}{9}$ (c) $\frac{1}{2}$

4. (a) $\frac{1}{4}$ (b) $\frac{1}{52}$ (c) $\frac{3}{4}$ (d) $\frac{12}{13}$ (e) $\frac{3}{13}$ (f) $\frac{2}{13}$

5. (a) $\frac{1}{1296}$ (b) $\frac{5}{1296}$ (c) $\frac{1291}{1296}$ (d) $\frac{1}{1296}$

6. (a) 82%   (b) 2%   (c) 1600   (d) 1600

7. (a) 84%   (b) 840   (c) 480

13.16 CHAPTER 13 TEST

1. (b) (i) $\frac{1}{4}$ (ii) $\frac{1}{2}$ (iii) $\frac{3}{4}$

2. (a) $\frac{1}{2}$ (b) $\frac{1}{4}$ (c) $\frac{1}{13}$ (d) $\frac{1}{52}$

3. (a) $\frac{3}{5}$ (b) $\frac{1}{3}$ (c) $\frac{4}{15}$ (d) $\frac{1}{5}$

4. 40

6. (d) mean — 162.3, median — 161

5. (c) mean — 1.15; median — 1; mode — 0 and 1
   (e) standard deviation — 7.968

13.17 CUMULATIVE REVIEW FOR CHAPTERS 9 TO 13

1. (a) 636 cm² (b) 980 cm² (c) 80 384 cm² (d) 3768 cm² (e) 3300 cm² (f) 198 cm²

2. (a) 1485 cm³ (b) 113 040 cm³ (c) 4924 cm³ (d) 3253 cm³

3. (a) S'(3, −4), T'(−2, −1) (b) S'(2, 1), T'(−3, 4)
   (c) S'(4, 3), T'(1, −2) (d) S'(−4, −3), T'(−1, 2)

4. (a) P'(6, 2), Q'(4, −2) (b) Both have length $2\sqrt{5}$.

5. (3, −5) 6. A'(15, 21), B'(−9, −12)

7. (a) 4 (b) 1 (c) 1 (d) 0

8. R'(−1, 3), S'(4, 2), T'(−5, 6) 9. A'(−5, −1), B'(−2, −6), C'(−4, 3)

10. (a) (6, −6) (b) (4, 1) (c) (4, −9) 11. (a) (−3, 7) (b) (−9, −1)

12. (a) $2\overrightarrow{b} = [-10, -2]$ (b) $\overrightarrow{a} + \overrightarrow{b} = [-3, -4]$ (c) $\overrightarrow{a} - \overrightarrow{b} = [7, 4]$

13. (a) 304 km/h, 280° (b) W 10° S

14. (b) 9 (d) 73 (e) 73.54 15. 6, 32, 1.9

16. (a) $\frac{7}{18}$ (b) $\frac{11}{18}$ (c) $\frac{5}{18}$ (d) $\frac{13}{18}$ (e) $\frac{2}{3}$ (f) 0

GLOSSARY

acute angle An angle whose measure is between 0° and 90°.

acute triangle A triangle with all angles acute.

additive inverse The additive inverse of a real number, a, is (−a), such that

$$a + (-a) = -a + a$$
$$= 0$$

adjacent angles Two angles with a common vertex, a common side, and no interior points in common.

alternate angles Two angles between two lines on opposite sides of a transversal.

altitude of a triangle A line from a vertex, perpendicular to the opposite side.

angle A figure formed by two rays with a common endpoint called the vertex.

angle bisector A ray that divides an angle into two angles having the same measure.

area The number of unit squares contained in a region.

average The average of n numbers is the sum of the numbers divided by n.

axiom A statement that is assumed to be true. Also called a postulate.

axis A number line used for reference in locating points on a coordinate plane.

axis of symmetry A line that is invariant under a reflection.

bar graph A graph using bars to represent data.

BASIC Beginner's All-purpose Symbolic Instruction Code is a computer language.

biconditional statement A statement that can be written in "if and only if" form.

binomial A polynomial consisting of two terms.

broken line graph A graph using line segments to represent data.

central angle of a circle An angle subtended by an arc of a circle with the vertex at the centre.

centroid The point of intersection of the three medians of a triangle.

chord of a circle A line segment having its endpoints on the circumference.

circle The set of all points in the plane that are equidistant from a fixed point called the centre.

circle graph A graph using sectors of a circle to represent data.

circumcentre The centre of the circle, which passes through the three vertices of a triangle.

circumference The perimeter of a circle.

circumscribed circle A circle is circumscribed about a polygon if all the vertices of the polygon lie on the circle.

collinear points Points that lie in the same straight line.

complementary angles Two angles whose sum is 90°.

concentric circles Circles having the same centre.

conditional statement A statement that can be written in "if — then" form.

congruent angles Angles with the same measure.

congruent figures Figures having the same size and shape.

consecutive numbers Numbers obtained by counting by ones from any given number.

consistent equations Equations in a system that has at least one solution.

construction The process of drawing a geometric figure using only a ruler and a compass.

contrapositive The statement formed by interchanging the hypothesis and the conclusion in a biconditional statement and then negating both.

converse A statement obtained by interchanging the hypothesis and conclusion in an "if — then" statement.

coordinate A real number paired with a point on a number line.

coordinate plane A one-to-one pairing of all ordered pairs of real numbers with all points of a plane. Also called the Cartesian coordinate plane.

corollary A theorem that follows directly from the proof of another theorem.

coterminal angles Angles that have the same initial and terminal rays (arms).

cubic equation A polynomial equation of degree three.

cubic polynomial   A polynomial of the form $ax^3 + bx^2 + cx + d$, where $a \neq 0$.

degree   A unit of angle measure equal to $\frac{1}{360}$ of a rotation.

degree of a monomial   The sum of the exponents of the variables.

degree of a polynomial   The greatest of the degrees of a polynomial's terms after it has been simplified.

dependent equations   Equations in a system that has infinitely many solutions.

diagonal   A line segment with endpoints on two non-adjacent vertices of a polygon.

diameter of a circle   A chord that contains the centre of the circle. The largest chord.

dilatation   A transformation that maps each point of a figure to an image point so that for a centre C and a point P, $CP' = k(CP)$, where k is the scale factor.

direct variation   A function defined by an equation of the form $y = kx$.

distance from a point to a line   The length of the perpendicular segment drawn from the point to the line.

domain of a function   The set of numbers for which the function is defined. The set of all first coordinates of the ordered pairs in the function.

domain of a variable   The set of numbers that can serve as replacements for a variable.

END statement   The last statement in a computer program.

equation   An open sentence formed by two expressions separated by an equal sign.

equilateral triangle   A triangle with all sides equal.

equivalent equations   Equations that have the same solution over a given domain.

event   Any possible outcome of an experiment in probability.

exponent   The number of times the base occurs in a power.

exterior angle of a polygon   An angle formed by extending one side of a polygon and the other side of the same vertex.

factor   Number that is multiplied by another number to give a product.

factorial notation   Notation used to indicate the product of consecutive integers beginning with 1.

$$n! = 1 \times 2 \times 3 \times \ldots \times (n - 1) \times n$$

factoring   Finding the factors of a number or expression over a given set.

FOR – NEXT statement   Used to loop through the same set of statements several times on a computer.

formula   An equation that states the relationship among quantities that can be represented by variables.

frequency of an event   The number of times an event has taken place.

function   A rule that assigns to each element in the domain a single element in the range.

glide reflection   The composition of a translation and a line reflection.

greatest common factor   The greatest integer that is a factor of two or more integers.

greatest monomial factor   The factor of two or more monomials that has the greatest coefficient and the greatest degree.

histogram   A bar graph used to summarize and display a large set of data.

hypotenuse   The side opposite the right angle in a right triangle.

identity   An equation whose sides are equivalent expressions. The equation is true for every value of the variable.

identity elements   The identity element for addition is 0, since $a + 0 = a$. The identity element for multiplication is 1, since $a \times 1 = a$.

image   The image of A is A' following a transformation.

inconsistent equations   The equations in a system that has no solutions.

indirect reasoning   Assuming the opposite of what is to be proved and showing that this leads to a contradiction.

inequality   Two expressions separated by an inequality symbol.

inscribed angle   An angle subtended by an arc of a circle with its vertex on the circumference.

inscribed polygon   A polygon with its vertices on the circle.

integer A member of the set $\{\ldots, -3, -2, -1, 0, 1, 2, 3, \ldots\}$.

intersection The elements that two sets have in common.

inverse variation A function defined by an equation of the form $xy = k$, $(k \neq 0)$.

irrational number A real number that cannot be expressed in the form $\frac{a}{b}$, where a, b ϵ I, and b $\neq$ 0.

isometry A transformation that preserves lengths and angles.

isosceles triangle A triangle with two sides equal.

lateral area The sum of the areas of the faces of a polyhedron other than the base.

least common multiple The monomial with the smallest positive coefficient and smallest degree that is a multiple of several monomials.

LET statement Assigns a value or an expression to a variable.

line segment Two points on a line and the points between them.

line symmetry A figure has line symmetry if there is a line such that the figure coincides with its reflection image over the line.

linear equation An equation in which each term is either a constant or has degree 1.

linear function A function of the form $f(x) = mx + b$.

locus A set of points that satisfy a given condition.

mapping A mapping illustrates how each element in the domain of a function is paired with each element in the range. A correspondence of points between an object and its image.

mass The amount of matter in an object. The base unit for measuring mass is the kilogram.

matrix An array of numbers or other elements arranged in rows and columns.

mean The sum of the values divided by the number of values.

median When a set of numbers is arranged in order from smallest to largest or largest to smallest, the median is the middle number.

midpoint The point that divides a line segment into two equal parts.

mixed number A number that is part whole number and part fraction.

mode The number that occurs most often in a set of numbers.

monomial A number, a variable, or a product of numbers and variables.

multiplicative identity The number 1 is the multiplicative identity. The product of any number and 1 is identical to the original number.

multiplicative inverses If the product of two numbers is 1, they are called multiplicative inverses or reciprocals of each other.

mutually exclusive events Events that cannot both occur at the same time.

natural numbers The set of numbers $\{1, 2, 3, 4, 5, 6, \ldots\}$.

net A pattern for constructing a polyhedron.

NEW statement A command that clears a computer program from memory.

nonagon A polygon with nine sides.

number line A pictorial representation of a set of numbers.

numeral A symbol that represents a number.

obtuse angle An angle whose measure is greater than $90°$ but less than $180°$.

obtuse triangle A triangle with one obtuse angle.

octagon A polygon with eight sides.

octahedron A polyhedron with eight faces.

order of operations The rules to be followed when simplifying expressions. These rules are sometimes referred to as BODMAS or BEDMAS.

ordered pair A pair of numbers used to name a point on a graph.

origin The intersection of the horizontal axis and the vertical axis on a graph. It is described by the ordered pair (0,0).

orthocentre The point where the altitudes of a triangle intersect.

outcome The result of an experiment or a trial.

palindrome A number such as 232 that reads the same forwards as backwards.

parallel lines Two lines in the same plane that never meet.

parallelogram A quadrilateral with opposite sides parallel.

parameter An arbitrary constant.

partial variation A relation between two variables that involves a fixed amount plus a variable amount such as C = nd + 15.

pentagon A polygon with five sides.

percent A fraction (or ratio) in which the denominator is 100.

perimeter The distance around a polygon.

perpendicular bisector The line that cuts a line segment into two equal parts at right angles.

perpendicular lines Lines that intersect at right angles.

pi (π) The quotient that results when the circumference of a circle is divided by the diameter.

pictograph A graph using pictures to represent data.

polygon A closed figure formed by line segments.

polyhedron A three-dimensional object having polygons as faces.

polynomial A monomial or the sum of monomials.

population The entire set of items from which data is taken.

postulate A statement that is accepted without proof.

power A product obtained by using a base as a factor one or more times.

prime number A number with exactly two factors — itself and 1.

principal square root The positive square root.

prism A polyhedron with two parallel and congruent bases in the shape of polygons.

probability The probability of events occurring is the ratio of the number of favourable outcomes to the number of possible outcomes.

proportion An equation that states that two ratios are equal.

pyramid A polyhedron with three or more triangular faces and the base in the shape of a polygon.

Pythagorean theorem The area of the square drawn on the hypotenuse of a right-angled triangle is equal to the sum of the areas of the squares drawn on the other two sides.

quadrant One of the four regions formed by the intersection of the x-axis and y-axis.

quadratic equation A polynomial equation of degree two.

quadrilateral A polygon with four sides.

quotient The result of a division.

radian If an angle that is the central angle of a circle cuts off an arc whose length is equal to the length of the radius of the circle, then the measure of the central angle is 1 radian.

radical sign The symbol $\sqrt{}$.

radius The length of the line segment that joins the centre and a point on the circumference of a circle.

random sample A sample in which each member of the population has the same chance of being selected.

range The set of all second coordinates of the ordered pairs of a relation. The set of all values of a function f(x).

rate A ratio of two measurements having different units.

ratio A comparison of two numbers.

rational function A function of the form $\frac{P}{Q}$, where P and Q are polynomials.

rational number A number that can be expressed as the ratio of two integers.

ray Part of a line extending in one direction without end.

real numbers The set of all the rational and irrational numbers.

reciprocals Two numbers that have a product of 1.

rectangle A parallelogram with four right angles.

reflection A transformation that maps an object into an image by a reflection in a line.

reflex angle An angle whose measure is greater than 180° and less than 360°.

regular polygon A polygon in which all sides and angles are equal.

relation A set of ordered pairs.

repeating decimal A decimal in which one or more digits repeat without end.

rhombus A parallelogram in which all sides are equal.

right angle An angle whose measure is 90°.

right cone A cone in which the axis is perpendicular to the base.

right cylinder A cylinder in which the sides are perpendicular to the bases.

right prism A prism in which the lateral edges are perpendicular to the bases.

right triangle A triangle with one right angle.

root of an equation   A solution of the equation.

rotation   A transformation that maps an object onto its image by a rotation about a point.

rotational symmetry   A figure has rotational symmetry if it maps onto itself after a turn.

rounding   A process of replacing a number by an approximate number.

scalar   A term used for real numbers when working with vectors.

scale drawing   A drawing in which distances are reductions or enlargements of actual distances.

scale factor   The multiplication factor used in dilatations (enlargements and reductions).

scalene triangle   A triangle with no two sides equal.

scientific notation   Numbers written with one digit (not zero) to the left of the decimal place and a power of ten.

$$2700 = 2.7 \times 10^3$$

sector angle   An angle with vertex at the centre of a circle and subtended by an arc of the circle.

sector of a circle   A region bounded by two radii and an arc.

segment of a circle   A region bounded by a chord and an arc.

set   A collection of objects.

shell   A three-dimensional object whose interior is empty.

similar figures   Figures having corresponding angles equal and corresponding sides proportional.

skeleton   A representation of the edges of a polyhedron.

slope of a line   For a non-vertical line containing two distinct points (x_1, y_1) and (x_2, y_2), the slope is

$$m = \frac{y_2 - y_1}{x_2 - x_1}$$

solid   A three-dimensional object whose interior is completely filled.

solution set   A replacement for a variable that results in a true sentence.

sphere   The set of all points in space that are a given distance from a given point.

square   A quadrilateral with four congruent sides and four right angles.

square matrix   A matrix in which the number of rows is the same as the number of columns.

square root   The square root of a number is the number that multiplies itself to give the number.

standard form of a linear equation   A linear equation written in the form $Ax + By + C = 0$.

statistics   The science of collecting and analysing numerical information.

stem and leaf plot   A graph using digits of numbers to display data.

straight angle   An angle whose measure is $180°$.

supplementary angles   Two angles whose sum is $180°$.

surface area   The sum of all the areas of all faces of a polyhedron.

tangent to a circle   A line in the plane of a circle that intersects the circle in exactly one point.

term of a polynomial   The product of one or more numerical factors and variable factors.

terminating decimal   A decimal whose digits terminate.

tessellation   A repeated pattern of geometric figures that will completely cover a surface.

tetrahedron   A polyhedron with four triangular faces.

theorem   A mathematical statement that can be proved.

transformation   A mapping that maps the points of a plane onto the points of the same plane.

translation   A transformation that maps an object onto its image so that each point in the object is moved the same distance and direction.

transversal   A line that intersects two lines in the same plane in two distinct points.

trapezoid   A quadrilateral with one pair of parallel sides.

tree diagram   A diagram illustrating the possible outcomes of consecutive events.

triangle   A polygon with three sides.

trinomial   A polynomial with three terms.

union of sets   The set of all elements that belong to at least one of the sets.

value of a function   For every given element of the domain of a function there is a corresponding element in the range, called the value of the function.

variable   A letter or symbol used to represent a number.

vector   A directed line segment.

vertex of an angle   The common endpoint of two rays.

vertex of a polygon   The point where two adjacent sides meet in a polygon.

vertical line test   A test for determining whether a given graph is the graph of a function.

volume   The number of cubic units contained in a solid.

whole numbers   Numbers in the set $\{0, 1, 2, 3, 4, 5, \ldots\}$.

x-axis   The horizontal line used as a scale for the independent variable in the Cartesian coordinate system.

x-intercept   The x-coordinate of the point where a curve crosses the x-axis.

y-axis   The vertical line used as a scale for the dependent variable in the Cartesian coordinate system.

y-intercept   The y-coordinate of the point where a curve crosses the y-axis.

zero matrix   A matrix with all entries zero.

zero of a function   Any number x for which the value of the function is zero.

zero-product property   If $ab = 0$, then $a = 0$ or $b = 0$.

INDEX

NOTES AND PHOTOGRAPH CREDITS